Giant Fields of the Decade 2000–2010

Memoir 113

Edited by

R. K. Merrill and C. A. Sternbach

Published by

The American Association of Petroleum Geologists

Dear Sanford,

Thank you for your support and interest in the Giant Fields series – continuing Halbouty's Legacy!

Charles A. Sternbach

AAPG Editor: Barry J. Katz
AAPG Technical Publications Managing Editor: Beverly K. Molyneux

On The Cover:

Front cover—Core samples from Edvard Grieg, Johan Sverdrup, and Luno 2 in the Giant Johan Sverdrup Field (see Chapter 12 by Rønnevik et al., this Memoir, for more information; Map showing prospective regions of the Marcellus play compared with prospective area of the Barnett Shale in Texas (see Chapter 5 by Zagorski et al., this Memoir, for more information); Map of the Johan Sverdrup and Edvard Greig fields (see Chapter 12 by Rønnevik et al., this Memoir, for more information); Cross section showing the Edvard Grieg and Johan Sverdrup fields (see Chapter 12 by Rønnevik et al., this Memoir, for more information).

Back cover—Giant fields global map.

This publication is available in hardcopy from:

The AAPG Bookstore
P.O. Box 979
Tulsa, OK 74101-0979, U.S.A.
Phone: +1-918-584-2555
E-mail: bookstore@aapg.org
www.aapg.org
store.aapg.org

Geological Society Publishing House
Unit 7, Brassmill Enterprise Centre
Brassmill Lane, Bath BA13JN
United Kingdom
Phone: +44-1225-445046
E-mail: sales@geolsoc.org.uk
www.geolsoc.org.uk

The American Association of Petroleum Geologists

The American Association of Petroleum Geologists Books Refereeing Procedures

The Association makes every effort to ensure that the scientific and production quality of its books matches that of its journals. Since 1937, all book proposals have been refereed by specialist reviewers as well as by the Association's Books Editorial Board. If the referees identify weaknesses in the proposal, these must be addressed before the proposal is accepted.

Once the book is accepted, the Association Books Editorial Board ensures that the volume editors follow strict guidelines on refereeing and quality control. We insist that individual book papers can only be accepted after satisfactory review by two independent referees. The questions on the review forms are similar to those for the AAPG *Bulletin* journal. The referees' forms and comments must be available to the Association's Books Editorial Board upon request.

Although many of the books result from meetings, the volume editors are expected to commission papers that were not presented at the meeting to ensure that the book provides a balanced coverage of the subject. Being accepted for presentation at the meeting does not guarantee inclusion in the book.

More information about submitting a book proposal and editing a book for The American Association of Petroleum Geologists can be found on its web site: http://www.aapg.org/publications/submit/proposal.

Table of Contents

Acknowledgments

The authors would like to acknowledge the efforts of the late Myron K. "Mike" Horn for his dedication to documenting giant fields over the previous decades. Mike helped us identify prospective fields from his cumulative giant fields' database for this volume and assisted as a reviewer.

Financial Acknowledgments

AAPG wishes to thank the following for their generous contributions to
Giant Fields of the Decade, 2000–2010

AAPG Memoir 113

Lundin Norway AS

Contributions are applied toward the production cost of the publication,
thus directly reducing the book's purchase price and making the volume
available to a larger readership.

About the Editors

Dr. Robert Merrill has more than forty years of oil and gas industry experience in domestic and international exploration and staff positions for a range of companies, including American Stratigraphic Company, Cities Service Company, Occidental, Unocal, and Samson. In these positions he explored a variety of onshore and offshore basins around the world, including extensional basins, fold and thrust belts, and foreland basins both from a regional context as well as prospect generation. Countries in which he has exploration and acquisition experience outside North America include Australia, Argentina, Brazil, and Colombia in South America; Thailand, Malaysia, and Indonesia in Southeast Asia; Russia, Kazakhstan, and Azerbaijan in Central Asia; the North Sea; and central Europe. In 2005 Dr. Merrill formed Catheart Energy Inc., an independent exploration and consulting company, to actively pursue conventional and unconventional oil and gas opportunities. He also maintains a consulting practice focused on evaluating exploration portfolios. Dr. Merrill has his Ph.D. and M.S. from Arizona State University and his B.A. in Geology from Colby College.

Dr. Merrill has experience generating and evaluating prospects in both conventional and unconventional clastic reservoirs, including fractured reservoirs, tight gas sands, and carbonates. He utilizes probabilistic methods for prospect evaluation and reserves estimation and uses this information for comprehensive portfolio management. He has published papers covering a diverse range of subjects, including risk analysis in oil and gas, deep-overpressured gas in the Green River Basin and origin and migration of oils, the Wyoming/Utah/Idaho Overthrust belt and geothermal exploration and development.

He has volunteered with the International YMCA building schools in Vietnam and is a co-author of "Hydrology and Human Health: An Intersection for Nutrition Research in Bangladesh," which explores the health consequences of iron in the groundwater in the Gaibanda Area, Bangladesh. He currently serves on the Society of Exploration Geophysicists Geoscientists Without Borders Committee.

Dr. Merrill is a Fellow of the Geological Society of America, is a Chartered Geologist with the Geological Society, and has served on committees for the American Geological Institute and on the board of the Houston Geological Society. He served as both Secretary and President of the American Institute of Professional Geologists and is active in the American Association of Petroleum Geologists where he co-edited the *Giant Fields of the Decade, 1990–2000* Memoir and edited *Source and Migration Processes and Techniques for Evaluation* Memoir in 1991.

Charles A. Sternbach has explored for and discovered energy resources in the U.S. and around the globe for 35 years. He was Staff Geologist for Shell Oil Company, Exploration Manager for Tom Jordan (Jordan Oil and Gas), and President of First Place Energy (international frontier exploration) and is currently President of Star Creek Energy. Charles has a Ph.D. (and M.S.) in Geology from Rensselaer Polytechnic Institute and a B.A. in Geology from Columbia University.

Charles has focused his efforts on exploration creativity. He has studied how explorers and their teams find giant fields and new exploration and production resources. He created and leads popular AAPG Discovery Thinking Forums that have been standing room only events at annual AAPG conventions in North America (ACE) and around the world (ICE). Charles also created the AAPG Playmaker Forums. These are one-day forums on exploration creativity.

These programs integrate geology, geophysics, and engineering into case studies of business success. There have been 15 Discovery Thinking Forums since 2008 with about 8000 attendees. There have been 8 Playmaker Forums in the U.S., Canada, and Europe since 2012 with about 1000 attendees. About 100 speakers from both programs have posted their talks on the AAPG Search and Discovery web site with 40,000 viewings. More of these high-impact programs are planned for the future.

Charles is honored to be a co-editor with Dr. Robert Merrill on this fifth installment of the AAPG Memoir series *Giant Fields of the Decade, 2000–2010*. Along with his mentor, Michel T. Halbouty, Charles believes it is important to "think big." That is why we study giant fields like those in this and previous AAPG Memoirs. Thanks to all who strive to find oil and gas. They are a special breed contributing to the prosperity of society. Rare among this breed are the giant field finders. Their success represents the pinnacle of our profession, which rests on the broad base of those who came before. Thank you to all who leave our heritage better than they found it, like the authors in this book.

Charles resides in Houston, Texas. His wife Linda is a distinguished geophysical advisor. Charles is a leader in the global geological community. He will be president of AAPG 2017–2018 at the dawn of AAPG's second century. He is an Honorary Member of AAPG, the Houston Geological Society, and AAPG's Division of Professional Affairs.

1

Merrill, Robert K., and Charles A. Sternbach, 2017, Concepts, technology, price, and access drive Giant field discoveries, *in* R. K. Merrill and C. A. Sternbach, eds., Giant fields of the decade 2000–2010: AAPG Memoir 113, p. 1–8.

Concepts, Technology, Price, and Access Drive Giant Field Discoveries

Robert K. Merrill
Catheart Energy, Sugar Land, Texas, U.S.A. (e-mail: rmerrill@catheart.com)

Charles A. Sternbach
Star Creek Energy, Houston, Texas, U.S.A. (e-mail: carbodude@gmail.com)

This Memoir continues the AAPG Giant Oil and Gas Fields of the Decade series (Figure 1) initiated by Michel Halbouty in 1970 with AAPG Memoir 14, *Geology of Giant Petroleum Fields*. He continued the series in 1980 with Memoir 30, *Giant Oil and Gas Fields of the Decade, 1968–1978*; in 1992 with Memoir 54, *Giant Oil and Gas Fields of the Decade, 1978–1988*; and in 2003 with Memoir 78, *Giant Oil and Gas Fields of the Decade, 1990–1999*. A giant oil field is generally estimated to contain in excess of 500 million barrels of oil equivalent (MMBOE) estimated ultimate recovery. In this current volume, we are attempting to describe some of the more significant and representative fields discovered in the decade 2000 through 2010, all of which contain over 500 MMBOE estimated ultimate recovery (Figure 2). The decade of 2000 through 2010 is characterized by the rise of the "unconventional" plays. These are dominated by large regional accumulations in small microscopic pore throats. In addition to the unconventional accumulations, deep-water accumulations continue to have increasing importance in the global hydrocarbon budget.

This Memoir begins by looking at the global characteristics of the giant fields discovered in the decade 2000 through 2010. We then take a look at discovery trends and predictions from the current and previous decades and project those trends into the decade 2010 through 2020. In the field summaries, our objective is to document the type of trap for each field, followed by a discussion of trap formation; the age of the reservoir rocks; and the source, generation, and migration of the hydrocarbons. Additionally, we look to the factor(s) that drove the final investment decision and how "Discovery Thinking" contributed to a field's discovery. Finally, we look to understand why a field is important to oil and gas exploration; for instance, is a particular discovery the opening of a new play or a useful concept?

Looking at the discovery rate of giant fields since the late nineteenth century, at least four factors seem to control the frequency of discovery of giant oil and gas fields. These include concepts (e.g., geological models), technology, price, and access to drilling locations.

Many authors have discussed the importance of creativity in the exploration process. To paraphrase Halbouty (1970, p. 5) in Memoir 14, "Discovery Thinking" is a key to exploration that he succinctly described in the following language:

> "As we make it a point to learn how these giant fields formed, we should study the modes of occurrence of the accumulations, the types of trap, how each trap formed and how it was found, the age of the reservoir and the age, or ages, of the sediments in which the petroleum generated and from which it was expelled and migrated to the trap. We should ask ourselves: first, what is usual about each

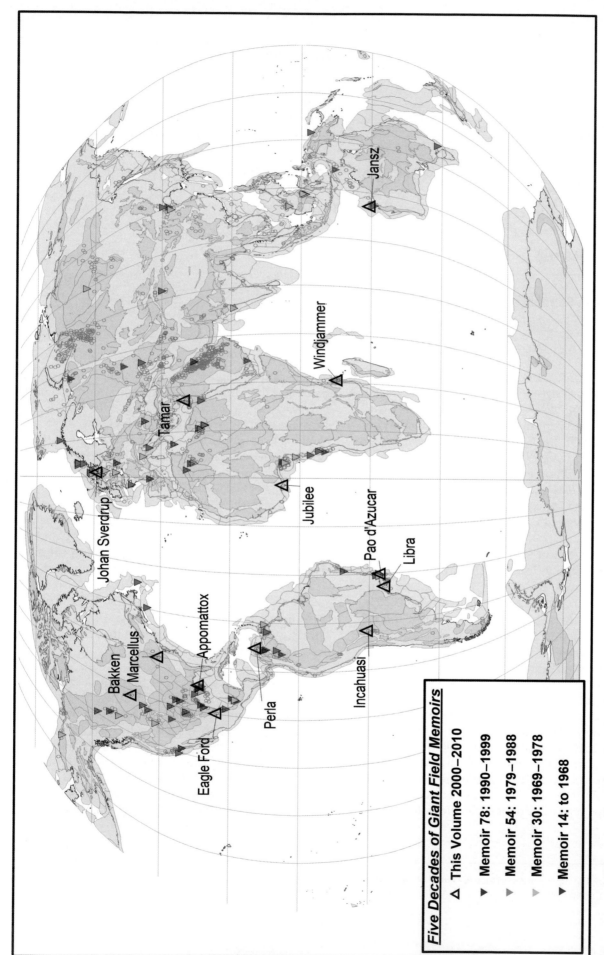

Figure 1. Five decades of Giant Field Memoirs. Open triangles indicating fields included in this volume.

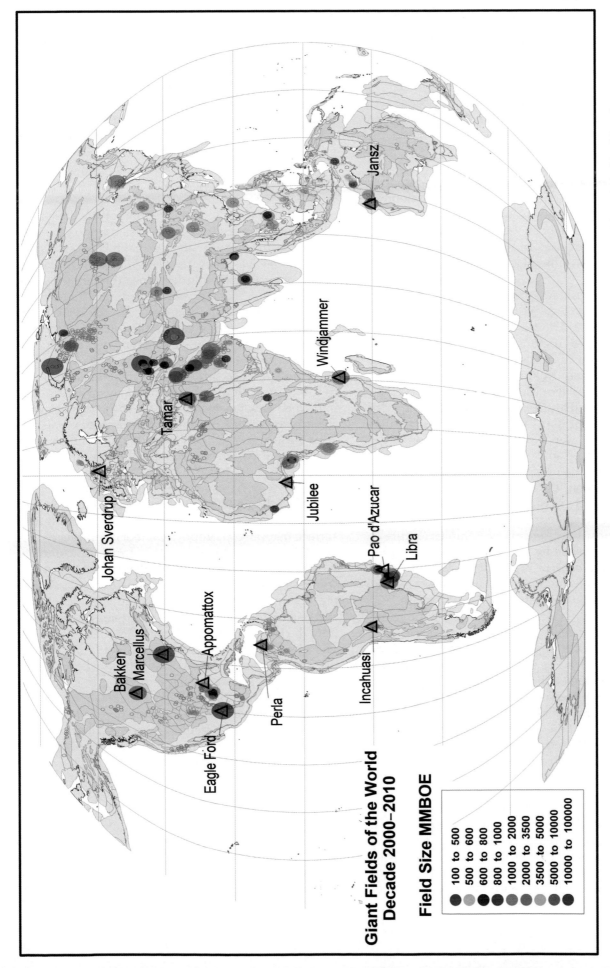

Figure 2. Giant Fields of the Decade discovered between 2000 and 2010 and currently estimated field size. Open triangles indicating fields included in this volume.

of these accumulations? And second, what is unusual? Then we must concentrate on the unusual, for commonly it is that unusual aspect which is the key to accumulation. Prejudiced ideas should be discarded, for it is these old, ingrained, hard-nosed prejudices which also stifle exploration; old prejudices must not be tolerated in our thinking of the future."

Figure 3 highlights the giant fields by the decade in which they were discovered. In general, the number of giant field discoveries was greatest in North and South America until about the middle of the twentieth century. Discoveries in the Middle East picked up in the 1920s with the discovery of Kirkuk. In the 1950s, the number of discoveries picked up in Russia and the Middle East, and the largest fields continued to be in the Middle East. In the decade 2000 through 2010, unconventional development in North America dominated the size of giant field discoveries. Other important discoveries in this decade included offshore subsalt development in Brazil and new gas fields in Tanzania and the eastern Mediterranean.

Figure 4 shows that the relationship between price and the number of giant field discoveries was not particularly correlated until the Organization of Petroleum Exporting Countries (OPEC) embargo in the 1970s. Following the price peak around 1981 and the following recession, the discovery rate declined by over 50% until early in the decade 2000 through 2010 when the price began to increase, leading to more discoveries. Interestingly, discovery volumes (Figure 5) decreased on a decade-by-decade basis between 1970 and 1990. The most dramatic increases were 1890 through 1900 with the discovery of Midway-Sunset and Kern River in California and 1920 through 1930 when Kirkuk (Iraq), Gachsaran (Iran), and Tia Juana (Venezuela) were discovered.

The evolution of geologic concepts that control the accumulation of oil and gas has evolved from the later decades of the nineteenth century when exploration was focused on oil seeps, beginning in 1868 with the discovery of La Brea Field in the Talara Basin, Peru, then Azerbaijan and the United States (i.e., California and Pennsylvania). Recognition of the importance of anticlines dominated the first half of the twentieth century, so surface mapping was recognized as a critical exploration tool.

Petrophysical tools began to be developed in 1927 with the first multielectrode electrical survey in a wellbore; shortly thereafter came the first resistivity log in 1929. Logging tools to detect hydrocarbons continued to develop until the decades 1940 through 1950 and 1950 through 1960 with the development of the petrophysical tools commonly used today (sonic logs, density logs) and development of reservoir characterization beginning with Archie's law in 1941. Our understanding of reservoirs truly began to increase with magnetic tape recording and processing of logs from tape. The first digitized log tape was on location about 1965, but it took until 1977 for a logging truck to be equipped with a computer. The 1970s also saw the first desktop computer–aided log analysis system introduced and the beginning of remote sensing using space imagery.

The use of seismic as an exploration tool began in 1914 when seismic tomography was used to delineate salt domes in Germany, and the first reflection seismograph survey was shot 1921, near Ardmore, Oklahoma. Seismic sources and tools developed through the 1950s and 1960s, and digital seismic recording began around 1963. Processing advances followed in the 1970s when seismic data were presented in color, seismic attributes were introduced, seismic inversion was introduced, seismic stratigraphic interpretation was developed, and bright spot technology was developed at Shell. In the 1970s, color presentation of seismic data was implemented, and seismic stratigraphy together with seismic attributes became common tools. Seismic attribute analysis matured in the 1990s, and the implementation of pattern recognition and neural network analysis was introduced in the 1990s.

By the year 2000, geological tools were available, including the anticlinal theory of accumulation and fracture systems; geochemistry of source rocks; subsurface mapping; petrophysical tools; and seismic acquisition, processing, and interpretation. To complete the story, it is important to note that the first reservoir stimulation was done using gunpowder in 1865, and the first hydraulic fracturing technique was developed and patented in 1949. Drilling technology progressed from the twin-cone roller bit to the tri-cone bit in 1935. The diamond bit was introduced in 1941. Offshore production began in 1897 in Summerfield Field, California, followed by barge drilling in Louisiana in 1911 with the Gulf #1 Ferry Lake. In 1948, the Kermac #16 was drilled 10 miles offshore in Louisiana. Measurement-while-drilling was described around 1964 and was first used in an offshore well in 1980. Horizontal drilling began to be utilized extensively in the 1980s. Finally, coiled tubing drilling began around 1991, and the first hybrid coiled tubing drill rig was developed in 1997.

The decade 2000 through 2010 can be thought of as the beginning of the unconventional revolution. The integration of rock mechanics using geology, geophysics, and engineering in this decade led to new workflows for geologists, geophysicists, and engineers

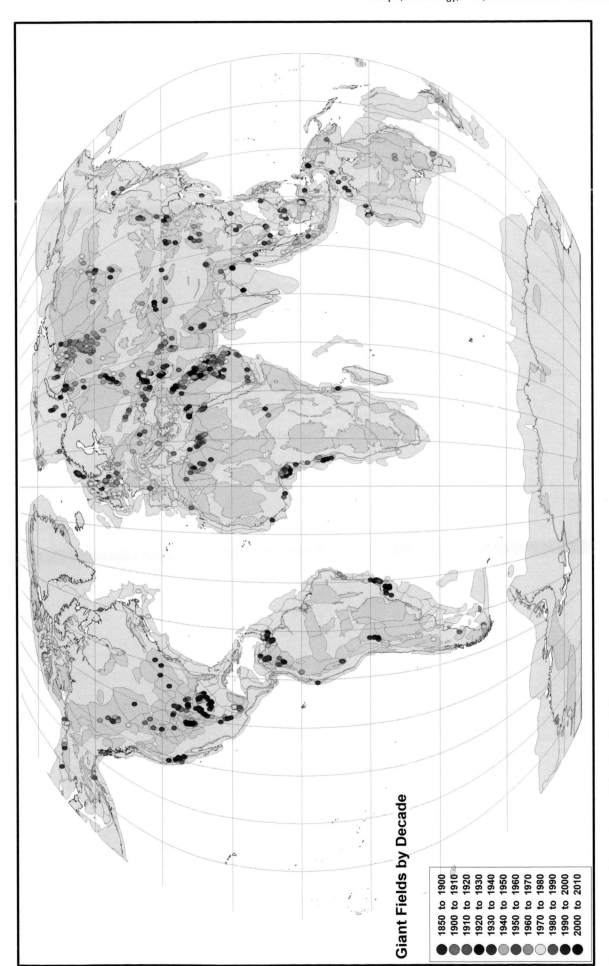

Giant Fields by Decade

1850 to 1900
1900 to 1910
1910 to 1920
1920 to 1930
1930 to 1940
1940 to 1950
1950 to 1960
1960 to 1970
1970 to 1980
1980 to 1990
1990 to 2000
2000 to 2010

Figure 3. Giant Fields of the world by decade of discovery.

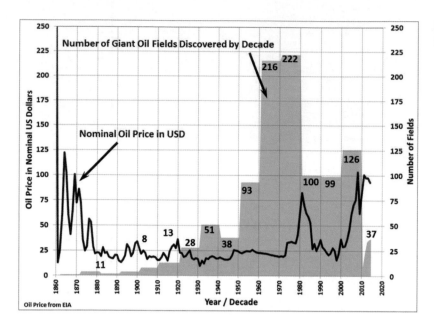

Figure 4. Number of giant oil fields discovered by decade and nominal oil price in US dollars.

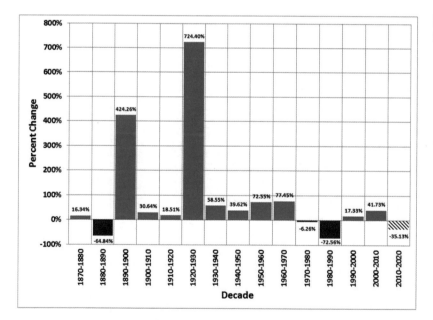

Figure 5. Percent change by decade of giant fields discovery.

to complete wells in reservoirs previously considered too tight for economic production. This integration brought together intensive core analysis and new sample imaging techniques to characterize the pores in low-permeability rocks. As discussed by Carmalt and Moscariello in this volume, these basin-scale accumulations are recognized as giant accumulations, but statistically, these accumulations are a separate population from conventional accumulations.

In summary, all giant accumulations have common attributes of a petroleum system, including reservoir, trap, seal, source rock, and generation and migration of hydrocarbons. Reservoir porosity and permeability extend from systems that will give up hydrocarbons without stimulation to those requiring significant hydraulic fracture stimulation. Traps and seals can be regional in the case of continuous hydrocarbon deposits (unconventional), or they can be confined to smaller areas by structural and stratigraphic conditions (conventional). All petroleum systems require that an organic-rich source rock be mature, but in the case of unconventional accumulations, the hydrocarbons have not migrated out of the source rock, so the source rock is also the reservoir.

Traditional roles in discovering giant fields over previous decades included the "rockers" (geologists well versed in reservoirs), the "trappers" (geophysicists mapping the geometry of accumulations), and the "sealers and the sourcers" (explorers following source rock and seals). More than ever, successful giant field discovery in the decade 2000 through 2010 was led by the "integrators." "If you know how to hammer, every problem is a nail. Modern explorers need to diversify their tool kit" (Steven Getz, 2015, personal communication). Basin analysis, geochemistry, cutting-edge seismic imaging, and rock mechanics have become important additions to the explorer's skill set. The ingenuity of combined disciplines continues to meet the demands of an energy-hungry world.

REFERENCES CITED

Halbouty, M. T., 1970, Geology of giant petroleum fields: AAPG Memoir 14, 575 p.

Halbouty, M. T., 1980, Giant oil and gas fields of the decade, 1968–1978: AAPG Memoir 30, 596 p.

Halbouty, M. T., 1992, Giant oil and gas fields of the decade, 1978–1988: AAPG Memoir 54, 526 p.

Halbouty, M. T., 2003, Giant oil and gas fields of the decade, 1990–1999: AAPG Memoir 79, 340 p.

Carmalt S. W., and Andrea Moscariello, 2017, What is a giant field?, *in* R. K. Merrill and C. A. Sternbach, eds., Giant fields of the decade 2000–2010: AAPG Memoir 113, p. 9–14.

2

What Is a Giant Field?

S. W. Carmalt and Andrea Moscariello

Department of Earth Sciences, University of Geneva, Geneva, 13 rue des Maraîchers, 1205, Switzerland (e-mails: scarmalt@swconsult.ch, andrea.moscariello@unige.ch)

ABSTRACT

Study of giant oil and gas fields is useful not only to understand oil and gas habitat but also because statistical analysis of these data sheds light on future energy supplies. In such statistical studies, the definitions of both "giant" and "field" are important. The development of giant accumulations that are not fields increases the resource supply but can simultaneously decrease the accuracy of resource estimates and production forecasts unless care is taken with definitional issues.

BACKGROUND

This volume is the fifth in a series of AAPG Memoirs that focus on the giant oil and gas fields.[1] As Michel Halbouty correctly observed in his introduction to the first volume in 1970, the giants play a disproportionate role with respect to both hydrocarbon reserves and hydrocarbon production. And as Grunau (1983) observed, the giant fields frequently provide the best data available on what has been discovered. Because oil plus natural gas account for over half of the global energy supply (IEA, 2014), their contribution to the global economy is a subject of interest and commentary far beyond the science of geology. Inclusion of the unconventional reserves and production from Canadian oil sands, and the continuous Bakken oil play and Marcellus gas play, have been cited for a range of opinions far removed from the science of geology.

Over the past two centuries, fossil fuels have become critical to the functioning of the economy. Oil's role has been particularly important, with much of the world's economic progress over the past century being ascribed to readily available oil (e.g., Hall and Klitgaard, 2012). The economic well-being of society is closely aligned with its energy supply (e.g., Tverberg, 2011), as shown in Figure 1.

Particularly when oil prices are high, discussion turns to how much oil resource remains on this finite planet. Such a peaking of interest occurred in the 1970s (e.g., Haun, 1975), and there has been renewed interest in the subject over the past decade of high prices. The issue of remaining resources is complex, involving not only raw material availability, but also questions of economics, technology, population, and ecology, to name but some areas of interaction. Political policy decisions are inevitably made and as scientists we can only strive to make our inputs into such discussions as objective as possible.

The giant oil and gas fields are especially important because of their disproportionate contribution to the total oil and natural gas resource. Different

---

[1] *The AAPG Memoirs are Memoir 14 (Halbouty, ed., 1970); Memoir 30 (Halbouty, ed., 1980); Memoir 54 (Halbouty, ed., 1992); Memoir 78 (Halbouty, ed., 2003); and this volume.*

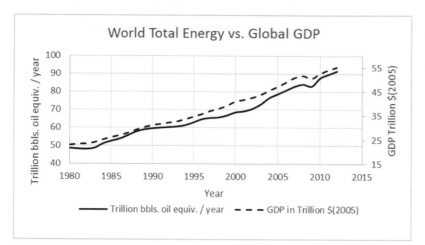

Figure 1. Relationship between global GDP and world energy (sources: BP, 2014; World Bank, 2015).

approaches to using the data that the giant fields provide can result in different outlooks on the question of the remaining resource. But unless the definition of a giant field is explicit, each contribution is unique and cannot be compared with other studies. They thus fall short of the objective standard to which we aspire.

For example, Horn (2007) uses the giant field data to predict that giant fields eventually will account for only about 40% of the total amount of oil and gas recovered, whereas Nehring (2010) argues that reserve growth from existing giants will make them a more, rather than a less, important source of oil over coming decades. Deffeyes (2001) suggests that a major increase in reserves will require discovery of at least one field larger than Ghawar. Despite the current importance of oil sand deposits and the continuous deposits such as the Bakken and Marcellus in production statistics, the objective question is whether these should be included in the statistical data for giant fields or whether they represent fundamentally different types of hydrocarbon accumulation. Distinguishing between such different types of deposit is common in studies of other economic resources[2]; for example, hydrothermal gold veins are clearly different from placer gold deposits.

CURRENT GIANT FIELD DEFINITION

The more recent compilations of giant fields by Horn (2003; this volume) include a definition for a giant field from Carmalt and St. John (1986): "…a giant oil or gas field is considered to be one for which the estimate of ultimately recoverable oil is 500 million bbl of oil or gas equivalent. Gas is converted to oil at a ratio of 6,000 cu ft/bbl.

Some fields are, therefore, giants only because their combined amounts of oil- and gas-equivalent total at least 500 million bbl, and not because either resource is that great by itself." Carmalt and St. John were aware of the more precise definitions suggested by Halbouty et al. (1970) and Nehring (1978) but faced the problem that detailed information is not always known about reservoir characteristics. Thus it is difficult to write a precise and consistent definition to indicate when separate subsurface pools can be combined into a single field and when they cannot. Instead, while Carmalt and St. John were precise about the giant part of the definition—equal to or greater than 500 million barrels (or oil equivalent) of ultimately recoverable oil and natural gas—they left the field part of the definition to common understanding. To paraphrase Stewart (1964), "…it is difficult to define, but I know one when I see one." And it was left at that. Statistical use of giant field data coupled with the significant technical advances that allow for exploitation of oil sands and continuous resources requires that the field part of the definition be made more precise. We suggest that compilations including both field and nonfield hydrocarbon resources be relabeled giant accumulations to indicate that some entries are not fields and that individual entries include an appropriate indication of the type of accumulation.

In Halbouty's introduction to Memoir 14, there is an explanation for using a compromise size for the giant part of the definition. Suggestions that the size be variable depending on access to markets, or other economic or operational details, were considered. But in the final paper of the volume, which established the public inventory of giants, the 500 million barrel figure was used, with a 3.5 trillion cubic feet cutoff for gas fields, which were listed separately. All subsequent compilations have used the 500 million barrel figure. However, the 3.5 trillion cubic feet of gas was changed to 3.0 trillion cubic feet (Nehring, 1978), presumably to allow a single

---

[2]*The analogy between types of hydrocarbon deposits and types of ore deposits was suggested by Professor Stephen Kesler of the University of Michigan (2015, personal communication).*

listing of giant hydrocarbon fields. Having a single list allows for combination giants of both oil and gas.

The second part of the definition of a giant field, namely what constitutes a field, was discussed in Memoir 14's final paper, which contained the listing of giants. The basic concept of a field was, and remains, a volume of the subsurface into which a hydrocarbon fluid has flowed. The devil is in the three-dimensional details of this subsurface volume. The original definition includes phrases such as "uninterrupted by permeability barriers" and "separate structural closures [with] a single, or common oil/water contact" and concludes with "There are other factors which also may be used to define an area as a single field." But then exceptions were allowed for geographically close groups of small fields with the same geologic setting. These were distinguished by names that included words such as complex, group, trend, or greater. Sometimes, the names of several smaller fields are simply combined in the list with hyphens, e.g., the Kelly-Snyder-Diamond M field. In short, an oil geologist's concept of a field was already proving difficult in definition, if not in concept.

Nehring (1978) made an attempt to make the Halbouty (1970) definition more exact. Nehring's specification started with the single accumulation—noting that a single accumulation "is synonymous with a pool or reservoir"—but then narrowly expanded this definition to include "a set of closely related accumulations." The expansion had to meet one of two standards: "multiple pools trapped by a common geologic feature" or "laterally distinct pools within a common formation and trapped by the same type of geologic feature where the lateral separation...does not exceed one-half mile" (0.8 km). In practice, both Halbouty (1970) and Nehring (1978) tended to group accumulations of pools into a single field rather than to use their definitions to separate a single field into two or more smaller fields on grounds of a precise definition. In arriving at a field definition, the model in people's minds was the exploration trilogy of source + reservoir + trap, a schema that implies fluid movement or migration in the subsurface. The overall consensus was that a field should be contiguous (or nearly so) on a map; that it should relate to a common source + reservoir + trap habitat; and furthermore should, if possible, not be dependent on nongeological factors such as political or operational criteria.

PROBLEMS WITH THE CURRENT DEFINITION

Following the comprehensive lists Halbouty (1970) and Nehring (1978) provided, additional compilations were published by St. John (1980), Carmalt and St. John (1986), and Horn (2003). The Bakken and Marcellus plays, which are discussed in this volume, do not fit the traditional concept of field and should therefore not be included in statistical compilations of field data. We are not suggesting that these important accumulations not be discussed and understood; indeed, some argue that they represent the future of our industry. It is only that we should not include them in field statistics; they deserve their own compiled list.

The importance of what should be considered a giant field is underscored by Nehring's (2010) observation that recovery growth from already discovered giant fields over the coming decades will double the contribution of unconventional oil to the oil and gas resource base. In using this language, Nehring is clearly distinguishing giant fields from continuous accumulations. That this is a reasonable prediction is underscored by Klett and Schmoker (2003), who show that between 1981 and 1996, the existing giant fields accounted for an increase of 160 billion barrels of new reserves. While some of these may have been reserves reported for political reasons (Aleklett, 2012), reserve increases are also documented over this period in the United States where political factors were not an issue.

An illustration of the confusion that can result from inconsistent definitions can be seen in the reserve figures for Canada and Venezuela, which clearly show the addition of extra-heavy oil and bitumen-derived oil to the oil reserve statistics. The reserves themselves were not discovered in the years of increase; rather, people have known about them for decades, which makes this statistical reporting difficult to interpret. When making statistical projections, it is more useful to be able to identify both reserve and production contributions from fields, especially giant fields, as opposed to the contributions made by other types of accumulations. At present, more and more unconventional reserves are being added to the resource base, again raising the question of whether these resources are found in oil fields.

On the other hand, the unconventional resources of Arctic areas and deep-water marine areas currently being explored will, in all likelihood, result in the discovery of fields as we intuitively think of them. To justify the high operational costs, the drilling targets almost certainly are what we geologists normally consider giant fields.

We avoid the term unconventional to describe hydrocarbon accumulations. The term's current use indicates that it has significantly different meanings to different people. These meanings vary, but as Berman (2015) has pointed out, they basically translate to mean "expensive." While the term unconventional may therefore contribute to economics, we don't think it contributes to geologic understanding. Furthermore, some unconventional accumulations fit the intuitive sense of a field, whereas others do not.

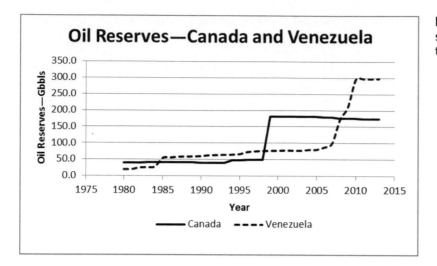

Figure 2. Oil reserves of Canada and Venezuela, showing an increase based on changed definitions (source: BP Statistical Review, 2014)

A REVISED GIANT FIELD DEFINITION

So what should the definition of giant field be? The giant part of the definition is sufficiently precise with respect to quantity: 500 million barrels of oil equivalent. Indeed, giant can refer to both fields and other types of accumulations. Natural gas is converted to oil equivalent at the ratio of 6000 cubic feet of gas equaling one barrel of oil. Using a single recognizably approximate conversion is preferable to a more accurate figure that might vary from field to field. But referring to the amount as ultimate recoverable oil creates confusion with the "ultimately recoverable resources" (McGlade, 2012) terminology used in resource evaluations; the latter contains amounts that are both as yet undiscovered or that, while discovered, are contingent on a better economic or technologic environment. For fields, we believe a better description would be current estimate of final size" which can be shortened to size estimate, which is to say the sum of historic production and the 2P (proved plus probable) reserves as defined in the Petroleum Resources Management System (PRMS) (SPE, 2011). In practice, this is what prior compilations seem to have used and meant. The contingent and undiscovered sections of the PRMS approach should be added to the estimated size only when the resource can be considered a 2P reserve.

Our concept of field follows the pattern established by Halbouty and Nehring in the 1970s but is made more explicit with differentiations to distinguish fields from nonfield accumulations. Our field definition thus has three components: (1) fluid composition, (2) geologic setting, and (3) geographic proximity. Accumulations that don't meet all criteria can be important parts of the hydrocarbon resource but should be distinguished as nonfield accumulations. Because the subsurface is heterogeneous, there will be some uncertainty on the precise limits in individual cases. Nevertheless, we believe

that the definition will, in most cases, unambiguously distinguish a specific accumulation as either a field or a different type of hydrocarbon accumulation. An accumulation that falls outside our definition but that has always been considered a single field should continue to be considered a single field. We stress that to the extent possible, the definitions should rely on physical parameters and not on economic or operational criteria.

Fluid Composition

The complete gradation in nature from light oils to bitumen needs an arbitrary dividing line to separate fields from nonfield deposits. We take 10° API as the point at which the fluid is so viscous that it should be considered a nonfield accumulation rather than a field. This is a commonly used dividing line, with higher API gravities considered heavy oil and those with lower gravity being termed extra-heavy oil (Meyer and Attanasi, 2013; McGlade, 2012; SPE, 2011). The existing field compilations have frequently adopted an operational definition—if the oil is produced by techniques used in oil fields producing lighter API gravity, then the accumulation is a field; if not, it is not. For this reason, the exclusion of extra-heavy oil from giant field compilations is imperfect. From a statistical viewpoint, it is best to leave existing fields alone, but use the 10° API dividing line when considering whether to call a new giant extra-heavy oil addition a field.

Geologic Setting

The geologic setting for oil and gas accumulations is the primary focus for most petroleum geologists. The oil or gas that constitutes a hydrocarbon accumulation occurs within the pore spaces of a rock, which we call a reservoir. But a reservoir is not always a field. To be a field, the oil or gas also must be confined in the reservoir by one or more geologic features that are different from the reservoir itself. This is the aspect of our definition that distinguishes giant accumulations such as the Bakken area and the Marcellus formation from fields. The different geologic feature may be a structure such as an anticline, one or more faults, a stratigraphic change, or a hydrodynamic regime; the critical thing is that there is something more than only the geologic character of the reservoir rock itself that is creating the accumulation. The implication is that the oil or gas would flow out of the reservoir if not for this, or these, different geologic features. Frequently, there are several different geologic features that act in concert to create the field. The classic case is a structure such as an anticline with stratigraphy that has a very low permeability formation overlying the reservoir. Implicit in such a system is that over geologic time the oil or gas has flowed, which is part of the implicit understanding of a field.

Geographic Proximity

Our final requirement for a field is that it be a contiguous (or nearly contiguous) geographic entity. There are at least two difficulties with this part of the concept. The first is how far apart the different segments can be when they are discrete segments. For example, a number of the North Sea oil fields are composed of fault blocks that have separated the subsurface pools from each other, a situation that also characterizes many Niger delta fields. The source, reservoir formation, and trapping mechanism is identical from fault block to fault block, so it is entirely the separation in plan view that determines whether the pools constitute one or more fields. An operational factor may intrude here, as we don't advocate having a single offshore platform producing from two separate fields simply because the map view of their separation is over some arbitrary line. Such separations can also result from differing depositional characteristics such as those found in reservoirs deposited in deltaic and fluvial environments. But the greater the geographic distance separating two pools, the more justification there needs to be for considering the accumulation as a single field. We believe that one kilometer is a reasonable distance beyond which significant justification is required to consider separate pools as a single field.

A second problem with lateral separations is that of two separate accumulations that overlap in plan view. Aquino et al. (2003) suggest this for the Sihil Field in the Cantarell area; Campbell (2013) describes two vertically superimposed hydrocarbon systems in Saudi Arabia, with gas accumulations that are below the known oil accumulations and which are generated by different source rocks. We suggest that in these cases, the likely congruence of trapping structures leads to accumulations being considered a single field, at least intuitively. So while two giants being superimposed in plan view is not impossible, we suggest that an overlap creates the very strong preference for considering all horizons as a single field.

CONCLUSION

Following these ideas, we propose that the definition for a giant field in Carmalt and St. John (1986) be modified to read, "A giant oil or gas field is an accumulation of oil, natural gas, or a combination of these that has an estimated final recovery of 500 million barrels of oil and/or natural gas hydrocarbons of no less than 10° API gravity and that are trapped in the subsurface in a single or similar geological manner and that are a contiguous (or nearly contiguous) feature in map view, with gas being converted to oil equivalent at a ratio of 1 barrel = 6000 cubic feet."

The inevitable rough edges to this definition are not important; rather, for resource estimations and resulting policy decisions, what is important is recognizing the giant fields as a specific subset of giant hydrocarbon accumulations. At present, nonfield types of giant accumulation are playing a major role in changing the oil and gas industry.

As we have already noted, unconventional Arctic and deep-water marine exploration programs are searching for structures that, when discovered, probably will fit our definition of field. On the other hand, we do not consider as fields the accumulations of extra-heavy oil or bitumen. What such accumulations should be called is open for discussion. At present, there are not so many non-field giant accumulations that it is a major issue. Our preferred terms are continuous accumulation for the Bakken and the Marcellus types where the extraction is directly from an impermeable source rock; degraded accumulations for the oil sands; and potential resources for oil shales. At least some of these are already being exploited and are making important contributions to the economy. They are giant accumulations, just not giant fields.

We are mindful of comments by McGlade (2013) about uncertainty in resource evaluations. The new types of hydrocarbon resources presently and potentially being developed are certainly giant in their potential. But not distinguishing them from fields runs the risk of devaluing the resource projections upon which policy decisions are made.

ACKNOWLEDGMENTS

We thank the late M. K. Horn for his work in maintaining the tabulation of giant fields over the years. We are grateful both to him and to Robert Merrill for their encouragement in preparing this paper. We also thank our many colleagues who have shared and discussed "the elephants" with us over the years.

REFERENCES CITED

Aleklett, K., 2012, Peeking at peak oil: New York, Springer, 325 p.

Aquino, J. A. L., J. M. Ruiz, A. F. F. Marcos, and J. H. García, 2003, The Sihil Field: Another giant below Cantarell, offshore Campeche, Mexico, in M. T. Halbouty, ed., Giant oil and gas fields of the decade, 1990–1999: AAPG Memoir 78, p. 141–150.

Berman, A., 2015, Years not decades: Proven reserves and the shale revolution: Presentation to the Houston Geological Society, Houston, Texas, 23 February 2015, accessed May 11, 2015, https://www.youtube.com/watch?v=5Ae1fg44l7E.

BP, 2014, Statistical review of world energy, 2014: BP, accessed July 7, 2015, http://www.bp.com/content/dam/bp-country/de_de/PDFs/brochures/BP-statistical-review-of-world-energy-2014-full-report.pdf.

Campbell, C. J., 2013, Campbell's atlas of oil and gas depletion: New York, Springer 411 p.

Carmalt, S. W., and B. St. John, 1986, Giant oil and gas fields, in M. T. Halbouty, ed., Future petroleum provinces of the world: AAPG Memoir 40, p. 11–53.

Deffeyes, K. S., 2001, Hubbert's Peak : The impending world oil shortage: Princeton, New Jersey, Princeton University Press, 190 p.

Grunau, H. R., 1983, Natural gas in major basins worldwide attributed to source rock type, thermal history and bacterial origin, in Proceedings of the Eleventh World Petroleum Congress: London, John Wiley & Sons, p. 293–302.

Halbouty, M. T. , ed., 1970, Geology of giant petroleum fields: A symposium of papers on giant fields of the world including those presented at the 53rd Annual Meeting of the AAPG in Oklahoma City, Oklahoma, April 23–25, 1968: AAPG Memoir 14, 575 p.

Halbouty, M. T., ed., 1980, Giant oil and gas fields of the decade, 1968–1978: AAPG Memoir 30, 596 p.

Halbouty, M. T., ed., 1992, Giant oil and gas fields of the decade, 1978–1988: Proceedings of the conference held in Stavanger, Norway, September 9–12, 1990: AAPG Memoir 54, 526 p.

Halbouty, M. T., ed., 2003, Giant oil and gas fields of the decade, 1990–1999: AAPG Memoir 78, 331 p.

Halbouty, M. T., A. A. Meyerhoff, R. E. King, R. H. Dott Sr., H. D. Klemme, and T. Shabad, 1970, World's giant oil and gas fields: Geologic factors affecting their formation, and basin classification. Part I, in M. T. Halbouty, ed., Geology of giant petroleum fields: AAPG Memoir 14, p. 502–528.

Hall, C. A. S., and K. A. Klitgaard, 2012, Energy and the wealth of nations : Understanding the biophysical economy: New York, Springer, 402 p.

Haun, J. D., ed., 1975, Methods of estimating the volume of undiscovered oil and gas resources: AAPG Studies in Geology 1, 195 p.

Horn, M. K., 2003, Giant fields, 1868–2003, in M. T. Halbouty, ed., Giant oil and gas fields of the decade 1990–1999: AAPG Memoir 78, CD-ROM Data.

Horn, M. K., 2007, Giant field trends 2: Giant fields likely to supply 40%+ of world's oil and gas: Oil & Gas Journal, v. 104, no. 14, accessed August 29, 2016, http://www.ogj.com/articles/print/volume-105/issue-14/exploration-development/giant-field-trends-2-giant-fields-likely-to-supply-40-of-worldrsquos-oil-and-gas.html.

International Energy Agency (IEA), 2014, World energy outlook: Report 1026–1141: Paris, Organisation for Economic Co-operation and Development, 748 p.

Klett, T. R., and J. W. Schmoker, 2003, Reserve growth of the world's giant oil fields, in Giant oil and gas fields of the decade, 1990–1999: AAPG Memoir 78, p. 107–122.

McGlade, C. E., 2012, A review of the uncertainties in estimates of global oil resources: Energy, v. 47, no. 1, p. 262–270, DOI:10.1016/j.energy.2012.07.048.

McGlade, C. E., 2013, Uncertainties in the outlook for oil and gas: London, University College London, 329 p.

Meyer, R. F., and E. D. Attanasi, 2013, Heavy oil and natural bitumen: Strategic petroleum resources, USGS Fact Sheet 70-03: Reston, Virginia, U. S. Geological Survey, 2 p.

Nehring, R., 1978, Giant oil fields and world oil resources, Report R2284.pdf, R-2284-CIA: Santa Monica, California, Rand Corporation, 188 p.

Nehring, R., 2010, AAPG Foundation 2010SPK: AAPG Foundation Presentation, Greensboro, Georgia, accessed April 24, 2015, http://www.nehringdatabase.com/images/pdfs/AAPG%20Foundation%202010SPK.pdf.

SPE, 2011, PRMS Guidelines, Standard: Richardson, Texas, SPE, accessed October 21, 2014, http://www.spe.org/industry/docs/PRMS_Guidelines_Nov2011.pdf, 222 p.

Stewart, P., 1964, Jacobellis v. Ohio: 378 US 184, U.S. Supreme Court Reports.

St. John, B., 1980, Sedimentary basins of the world and giant hydrocarbon accumulations (a short text to accompany the map: Sedimentary basins of the world): Tulsa, Oklahoma, AAPG, 23 p.

Tverberg, G., 2011, Is it really possible to decouple GDP growth from energy growth?: Our Finite World, accessed April 28, 2015, http://ourfiniteworld.com/2011/11/15/is-it-really-possible-to-decouple-gdp-growth-from-energy-growth/.

World Bank, 2015, GDP (constant 2005 US$) data table: World Bank, accessed May 13, 2015, http://data.worldbank.org/indicator/NY.GDP.MKTP.KD/countries?display=default.

3

Stark, Philip (Pete), and Leta K. Smith, 2017, Giant oil and gas fields of the 2000s:
A new century ushers in deeper water, unconventionals, and more gas,
in R. K. Merrill and C. A. Sternbach, eds., Giant fields of the decade 2000–2010:
AAPG Memoir 113, p. 15–28.

Giant Oil and Gas Fields of the 2000s: A New Century Ushers in Deeper Water, Unconventionals, and More Gas

Philip (Pete) Stark

IHS, 15 Inverness Way East, Englewood, Colorado 80112, U.S.A. (e-mail: pete.stark@ihsmarkit.com)

Leta K. Smith

Houston, Texas 77056, U.S.A. (e-mail: letaksmith@me.com)

ABSTRACT

Estimated recoverable oil and gas from giant field discoveries from 2000 through 2009 was 383 billion barrels of oil equivalent (BBOE)—a 92% increase from the prior decade and the largest addition from giant fields since the 1970s. This dramatic increase in giant field resources was driven by the emergence of shale gas and tight oil discoveries in North America. These so-called unconventional or continuous resource plays added almost 177 BBOE of new resources—mostly from super-giant plays like the Marcellus, Bakken-Three Forks, Eagle Ford, and Montney formations. In harmony with recent trends, giant natural gas discovery volumes greatly exceeded those of oil and contributed about 260 BBOE (1558 trillion cubic feet) of new resources. Traditional conventional giant discoveries added 198 BBOE of new resource—slightly less than in the prior decade and almost 55% of the total. Super-giant fields such as Galyknysh (Yoloten) with 67 BBOE gas and condensate in Turkmenistan, Kashagan in Kazakhstan; Lula in Brazil; and Kish 2 in Iran accounted for almost 60% of the giant conventional resources. The share of deepwater discoveries increased and contributed 23% of the conventional giant field volumes. The Santos Basin mega presalt and the Levantine Basin were the most important deepwater play openers.

INTRODUCTION

Breakthroughs in liberating commercial production from unconventional shale gas and tight oil reservoirs in North America boosted estimated recoverable resources from giant fields in this decade to 383 billion barrels of oil equivalent (BBOE)—a 92% increase over the prior decade. This is the largest volume of resource additions from giant fields since the 1970s. The number of giant fields increased by 38% during this decade. However, the discovery of 14 super-giants (greater than 5 BBOE), including

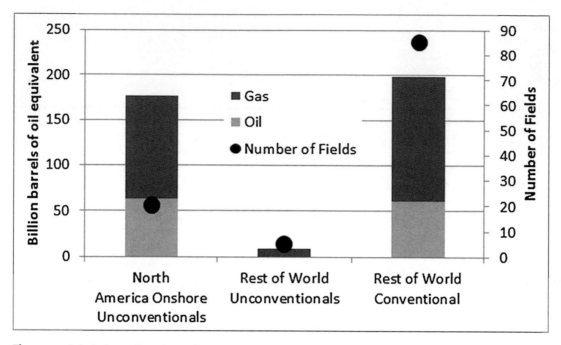

Figure 1. Global giant oil and gas discoveries, 2000–2009 (source: IHS Markit IRIS21 database).

10 super-giant unconventional plays, boosted the average discovery size to almost 3.5 BBOE and drove this huge increase in resource additions. Importantly, giant oil discoveries contributed 123.6 billion barrels of recoverable liquids—essentially double that of the prior decade (Figure 1). Continuing recent trends, giant gas discovery volumes greatly exceeded those of oil. They added an enormous 260 BBOE (1558 trillion cubic feet [tcf]) of new recoverable gas resource—an 88% increase from the prior decade. Conventional oil and gas giant discoveries contributed 198 BBOE of new resource—about 51% of the total resource added from all conventional fields during the decade. The share of deepwater discovery volumes increased and contributed 23% of the conventional giant field volumes even though the onshore super-giant 400 tcf (67 BBOE) Galkynysh (Yoloten) gas condensate field dwarfed the other conventional discoveries.

The emergence of giant North American unconventional discoveries was a game changer for resource additions during this decade. The relative impact of the North American giants in context with conventional giants in the rest of the world is evident in the discovery map (Figure 2). But industry will be challenged to repeat this performance. The number and average size of conventional giant fields and of North American unconventional plays discovered since 2009 have decreased substantially. Moreover, it may be difficult to

replicate the North American unconventional renaissance in other parts of the world.

CONVENTIONAL DISCOVERIES

Globally

Between 2000 and 2009, there were 85 conventional oil and gas discoveries made that were larger than 500 million barrels of oil equivalent (MMBOE).[1] The total resource these giants contributed was 198 BBOE (Table 1). Compared to the previous decade, this represents four more giant fields but 4 BBOE fewer reserves were found (Figure 3).[2]

Among these giants, more than twice as much gas was found than oil. Gas volumes discovered totaled 138 BBOE, whereas oil volumes (including condensate) totaled 60 billion barrels (bbl). This is in large part due to a single super-giant (>5 BBOE) field. The 400 tcf (67 BBOE) Galkynysh (Yoloten) gas condensate field was discovered in Turkmenistan in 2004. It is the largest discovery of the decade and more than three times larger than Kashagan (Kazakhstan, 19.7 BBOE),

---

[1]*Proven plus probable (2P) reserves.*
[2]*According to data in the IHS Markit IRIS21 database. This differs from that reported by Halbouty (2003), who used different data sources.*

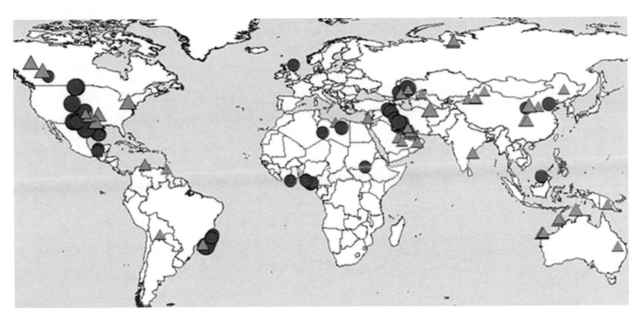

Figure 2. Global giant oil and gas discoveries, 2000–2010. Giant oil and gas discoveries with recoverable barrels of oil equivalent represented by graduated symbols—circles for oil, triangles for gas. The map includes five giants discovered in 2010 (not just the 2000–2009 discussed in this paper) as a reference for the giant and strategically important fields discovered that year (according to IHS) that are included in this book (source: IHS Markit IRIS21 database).

which is the second largest discovery of the decade and also a super-giant. If not for this one Galkynysh (Yoloten), the discoveries of the decade would have totaled only 131 BBOE—significantly less than the previous decade.

There were two other super-giant conventional discoveries in the decade. These were Lula in Brazil (9.1 BBOE) and Kish in Iran (8.8 BBOE). Together, these four super-giants total 104.7 BBOE, making up more than half of the volume in all of the giants.

Giants and super-giants contributed 57% of the total volume of oil and gas found in all conventional discoveries in the decade. The discoveries made in fields smaller than 500 MMBOE hold 147.4 BBOE, and there are over 5000 of these smaller discoveries, many of which are unlikely ever to be developed due to their small size.

Increasingly, the conventional giants are being found in deeper water, as evidenced by the discoveries in the presalt of Brazil (Table 2). Deepwater giants made up 23% of the volume found in all conventional giants in the 2000–2009 decade, and if the onshore Galkynysh (Yoloten) were excluded because of its anomalous size, deep water would have accounted for 35% of the total conventional volumes found. That number was only 15% in the previous decade. This follows the global trend for conventional discoveries of all sizes. For oil fields, more than 50% of volumes

found have been in deep water since 2002 and for gas fields since 2005 (IHS, 2015).

The emergence of the presalt in Brazil and the eastern Mediterranean gas play garnered a great deal of attention, as new plays always do. But it is also notable that giants are still being found in older plays, in some cases, a decade or more after the last giant was found. New giants found in mature provinces occurred in South Sudan, Kazakhstan, Russia, the United Kingdom, and Trinidad and Tobago.

By Region

At a regional level, the giant gas fields of the decade were dominated by the Commonwealth of Independent States (CIS) with 76 BBOE liquids and gas (Table 3). Asia-Pacific was second with 20 BBOE. The Middle East and Latin America tied for third for gas giants with 5 BBOE each.

Not surprisingly, oil giants were dominated by Latin America with 24 BBOE liquids and associated gas being found, mostly in Brazil's Santos Basin presalt play (Table 4). Interestingly, there was as much associated gas found in giant Latin American oil fields as there was nonassociated gas found there in gas giants.

Table 1. Giant oil and gas fields found between 2000 and 2009[a] (source: IHS Markit IRIS21 database).

Region	Country	Field Name	Basin	Situation	Discovery Year	Oil or Gas Field	Total Hydrocarbons (MMBOE)
Africa	Libya	Gialo North (059-6J)	Sirte	Onshore	2002	Oil	1200
Africa	South Sudan	Palogue	Melut	Onshore	2002	Oil	960
Africa	Libya	Arous El Bahar (054/01-A-001)	Sirte	Deep water	2009	Gas	930
Africa	Nigeria	Bonga Southwest 1	Niger Delta	Deep water	2001	Oil	920
Africa	Nigeria	Akpo	Niger Delta	Deep water	2000	Gas	880
Africa	Ghana	Jubilee	Cote d'Ivoire	Deep water	2007	Oil	840
Africa	Nigeria	Usan	Niger Delta	Deep water	2002	Oil	700
Africa	Nigeria	Egina	Niger Delta	Deep water	2003	Oil	630
Africa	Nigeria	Bonga North 1	Niger Delta	Deep water	2004	Oil	610
Africa	Libya	NC186-I/NC115-R	Murzuq	Onshore	2005	Oil	540
Asia-Pacific	Indonesia	Abadi	Bonaparte	Deep water	2000	Gas	3480
Asia-Pacific	Australia	Jansz	North Carnarvon	Deep water	2000	Gas	3470
Asia-Pacific	China	Puguang	Sichuan	Onshore	2003	Gas	2090
Asia-Pacific	China	Nanpu	Bohai Gulf	Shallow water	2005	Oil	1750
Asia-Pacific	India	Deen Dayal	Krishna-Godavari	Shallow water	2005	Gas	1430
Asia-Pacific	China	Longgang	Sichuan	Onshore	2006	Gas	1420
Asia-Pacific	Papua New Guinea	Elk-Antelope	Papuan	Onshore	2006	Gas	960
Asia-Pacific	China	Dina	Tarim	Onshore	2001	Gas	920
Asia-Pacific	Australia	Wheatstone	North Carnarvon	Shallow water	2004	Gas	870
Asia-Pacific	Australia	Pluto	North Carnarvon	Deep water	2005	Gas	820
Asia-Pacific	China	Xushen	Songliao	Onshore	2002	Gas	800
Asia-Pacific	Australia	Calliance	Browse	Deep water	2000	Gas	750
Asia-Pacific	China	Lungu East	Tarim	Onshore	2004	Gas	630
Asia-Pacific	Australia	Poseidon 1	Browse	Deep water	2009	Gas	590
Asia-Pacific	Australia	Clio 1	North Carnarvon	Deep water	2006	Gas	550
Asia-Pacific	Malaysia	Gumusut-Kakap	Baram Delta	Deep water	2003	Oil	550
Asia-Pacific	China	Jiyuan	Ordos	Onshore	2001	Oil	530
Asia-Pacific	China	Yilake	Tarim	Onshore	2003	Gas	530
Asia-Pacific	China	Kelameili	Junggar	Onshore	2006	Gas	520
Asia-Pacific	Malaysia	Kikeh	Baram Delta	Deep water	2002	Oil	520
Asia-Pacific	Australia	Prelude	Browse	Shallow water	2007	Gas	510
CIS	Turkmenistan	Galkynysh (Yoloten)	Amu-Darya	Onshore	2004	Gas	67,100
CIS	Kazakhstan	Kashagan	Precaspian	Shallow water	2000	Oil	19,700
CIS	Russia	Kamennomysskoye-More	West Siberian	Shallow water	2000	Gas	3170
CIS	Russia	Kamennomysskoye Severnoye	West Siberian	Shallow water	2000	Gas	2330
CIS	Russia	Vladimir Filanovsky	North Caucasus Platform	Shallow water	2005	Oil	1360
CIS	Russia	Khvalynskoye	Mangyshlak-Central Caspian	Shallow water	2000	Gas	1020
CIS	Kazakhstan	Aktote	Precaspian	Shallow water	2003	Gas	940
CIS	Kazakhstan	Kairan	Precaspian	Shallow water	2003	Oil	740
CIS	Uzbekistan	Surgil	North Ustyurt	Onshore	2002	Gas	685
CIS	Russia	Kuvykin	Mangyshlak-Central Caspian	Shallow water	2003	Gas	560
Europe	United Kingdom	Buzzard	Moray Firth Province	Shallow water	2001	Oil	800

18

Region	Country	Field	Basin/Province	Location	Year	Type	Reserves
Latin America	Brazil	Lula	Santos	Deep water	2006	Oil	9110
Latin America	Brazil	Iara	Santos	Deep water	2008	Oil	4430
Latin America	Brazil	Jupiter	Santos	Deep water	2008	Oil	2050
Latin America	Venezuela	Perla	Upper Guajira	Shallow water	2009	Gas	1960
Latin America	Brazil	Sapinhoa	Santos	Deep water	2008	Oil	1830
Latin America	Brazil	Jubarte	Campos	Deep water	2001	Oil	1810
Latin America	Brazil	Mexilhao	Santos	Deep water	2001	Gas	1550
Latin America	Brazil	Lapa	Santos	Deep water	2007	Oil	1270
Latin America	Brazil	Golfinho	Espirito Santo	Deep water	2003	Oil	940
Latin America	Mexico	Tsimin	Sureste	Shallow water	2008	Oil	710
Latin America	Brazil	Baleia Azul	Campos	Deep water	2003	Oil	640
Latin America	Trinidad and Tobago	Mango	Trinidad	Shallow water	2000	Gas	590
Latin America	Mexico	Ayatsil 1 (Ku-Maloob-Zaap Complex)	Sureste	Shallow water	2007	Oil	570
Latin America	Bolivia	Incahuasi	Chaco	Onshore	2004	Gas	560
Latin America	Brazil	Xerelete	Campos	Deep water	2001	Oil	530
Latin America	Brazil	Cachalote	Campos	Deep water	2002	Oil	500
Middle East	Iran	Kish 2	Rub' Al Khali Province	Onshore	2005	Gas	8830
Middle East	Iran	Yadavaran	Central Arabian Province	Onshore	2001	Oil	4050
Middle East	Iran	Sefid Zakhur	Zagros Province	Onshore	2007	Gas	2290
Middle East	Kuwait	Umm Niqa	Central Arabian Province	Onshore	2006	Gas	2120
Middle East	Israel	Tamar	Levantine	Deep water	2009	Gas	1680
Middle East	Iran	Halegan	Zagros Province	Onshore	2009	Gas	1580
Middle East	Iraq	Bina Bawi 1	Zagros Province	Onshore	2007	Oil	1260
Middle East	Iran	Lavan	Rub' Al Khali Province	Onshore	2003	Gas	1190
Middle East	Kuwait	Ruhaya 2	Central Arabian Province	Onshore	2004	Oil	1160
Middle East	Saudi Arabia	Ghazal	Central Arabian Province	Onshore	2000	Gas	1150
Middle East	Iraq	Shaikan	Zagros Province	Onshore	2009	Oil	1100
Middle East	Saudi Arabia	Arabiyah	Central Arabian Province	Shallow water	2008	Gas	1080
Middle East	Kuwait	Noura 1	Central Arabian Province	Onshore	2000	Gas	1000
Middle East	Iraq	Kurdamir 1	Zagros Province	Onshore	2009	Oil	920
Middle East	Iraq	Tawke	Zagros Province	Onshore	2005	Oil	870
Middle East	Iran	Sefid Baghun	Zagros Province	Onshore	2009	Gas	870
Middle East	Iran	Homa	Zagros Province	Onshore	2000	Gas	850
Middle East	Saudi Arabia	Tukhman 2	Rub' Al Khali Province	Onshore	2002	Gas	690
Middle East	Iran	Day	Zagros Province	Onshore	2001	Gas	650
Middle East	Iran	Paranj	Zagros Province	Onshore	2007	Oil	650
Middle East	Iran	Azar	Zagros Province	Onshore	2005	Oil	590
Middle East	Iraq	Miran West	Zagros Province	Onshore	2009	Gas	580
Middle East	Iran	Band-E-Karkheh	Zagros Province	Onshore	2005	Oil	560
North America	United States	Kaskida	Deep Water Gulf of Mexico	Deep water	2006	Oil	1390
North America	United States	Tiber	Deep Water Gulf of Mexico	Deep water	2009	Oil	650
North America	United States	Hadrian North	Deep Water Gulf of Mexico	Deep water	2005	Oil	610
North America	United States	Julia	Deep Water Gulf of Mexico	Deep water	2007	Oil	520

aSome of the giants presented elsewhere in this volume do not appear on this list, or this list may contain different information about a field. This list is based solely on IHS data.

CIS - Commonwealth of Independent States.

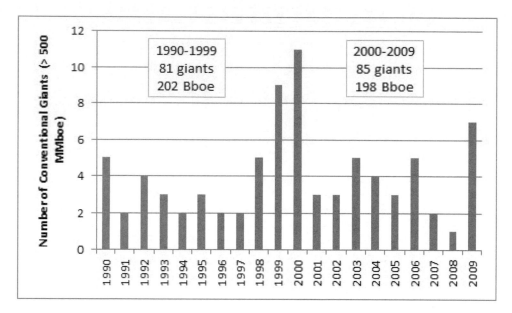

Figure 3. Number of conventional giant fields found annually, 1990–2009 (source: IHS Markit IRIS21 database).

Table 2. Number and total volume of oil and gas found in giant fields by geographic situation (source: IHS Markit IRIS21 database).

Situation	Number of Discoveries	Oil (Bbbl)	Gas (BBOE)
Onshore	36	16	96
Shallow water (<1000 ft)	18	16	24
Deep water (1000 to 5000 ft)	20	9	13
Ultradeep water (>5000 ft)	11	18	55

Table 3. Gas giants: number and total volume of liquids and gas (source: IHS Markit IRIS21 database).

Region	Number of Giants	Liquids (Bbbl)	Gas (BBOE)	Total Hydrocarbon (BBOE)
CIS	7	0.8	75	76
Middle East	14	4	21	5
Asia-Pacific	17	1	19	20
Latin America	4	0.6	4	5
Africa	2	0.7	11	2

CIS - Commonwealth of Independent States.

Africa: Africa had 10 giant conventional discoveries during the decade, with half of them in Nigeria. However, the largest—Gialo North (059-6J)—was in Libya (Figure 4). It ranks number 28 among the global list of

Table 4. Oil giants: number and total volume of liquids and associated gas found by region (source: IHS Markit IRIS21 database).

Region	Number of Giants	Liquids (Bbbl)	Associated Gas (BBOE)	Total Hydrocarbon (BBOE)
Latin America	12	20	4	24
CIS	3	13	9	22
Middle East	9	9	2	11
Africa	8	5	1	6
Asia-Pacific	4	2	1	3
North America	4	3	0.2	3
Europe	1	0.8	0.3	1

CIS - Commonwealth of Independent States.

giants. Although not the largest, arguably the Jubilee field discovered in Ghana in 2007 was more significant for proving up the potential of the transform margin play. Onshore, the Palogue field in South Sudan (Sudan before the country split), discovered in 2002, is the largest giant found during the decade. It is also the largest field in the country. This is significant because it was discovered after nearly 40 other smaller fields had been found.

African giants represented by papers in this volume include Jubilee (Ghana) and Windjammer (Mozambique), which is not included in Table 1 because it was discovered in 2010.

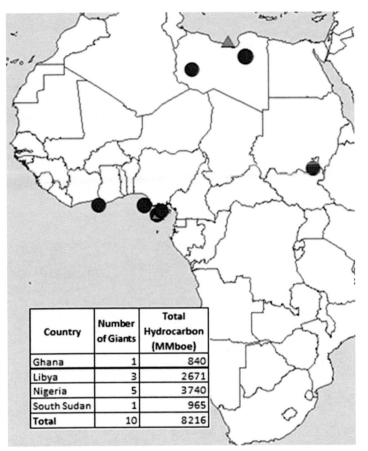

Figure 4. Giants fields found in Africa during 2000–2009. Oil fields in circles. Gas fields in triangles (source: IHS Markit IRIS21 database).

Country	Number of Giants	Total Hydrocarbon (MMboe)
Ghana	1	840
Libya	3	2671
Nigeria	5	3740
South Sudan	1	965
Total	10	8216

Asia-Pacific: The Asia-Pacific region had 21 giant conventional discoveries during the decade, with China and Australia having the majority (Figure 5). All but four of the regional giant discoveries are gas. The exceptions are two in China and two in Malaysia. Although China and Australia had the most giant discoveries, Indonesia and Australia share the distinction of having the largest discoveries in the region. Both had 3.5 BBOE gas discoveries, Indonesia's Abadi field being in the Bonaparte Basin and Australia's Jansz field being in the North Carnarvon Basin, essentially both being on the Northwest Shelf area. These fields rank seventh and eighth among global conventional giants.

Four fields from the Asia-Pacific region are discussed elsewhere in this volume: Jansz (Australia), Gaoshiti-Moxi and Sulige (China), and Mangala (India). Jansz is the eighth largest giant field globally.

CIS: Giants in the CIS region make up nearly half of the oil and gas volumes in all giants of the decade, with the two largest discoveries globally (Galkynysh in Turkmenistan and Kashagan in Kazakhstan) being in the region (Figure 6). The region also has two other fields (Kamennomysskoye-More and Kamennomysskoye Severnoye) that are in the top 10 globally. The Kashagan discovery was one of only two oil giants in the region; the other one was Vladimir Filanovsky in the Russia Caspian sector. Kashagan was significant not only for its size but also for being another giant in the same play as Tengiz and Karachagnak, two significant giants that had been found nearly three decades earlier (Lisovsky et al., 1994). Half of the 10 giants are in Russia in West Siberia and in the Caspian region. For Russia, this is two more giants than were discovered in the previous decade and 50% more volume. Turkmenistan had not had a giant discovery since 1990, and Uzbekistan had not had one since 1985.

The two largest discoveries in Russia—Kamennomysskoye-More and Kamennomysskoye Severnoye—were in the South Kara-Yamal province of the West Siberia basin. The last discovery of any size made in the same play (Marresalinskaya Dolganskaya) was 12 years earlier, and yet these two giants are the third and fourth largest CIS discoveries of the decade.

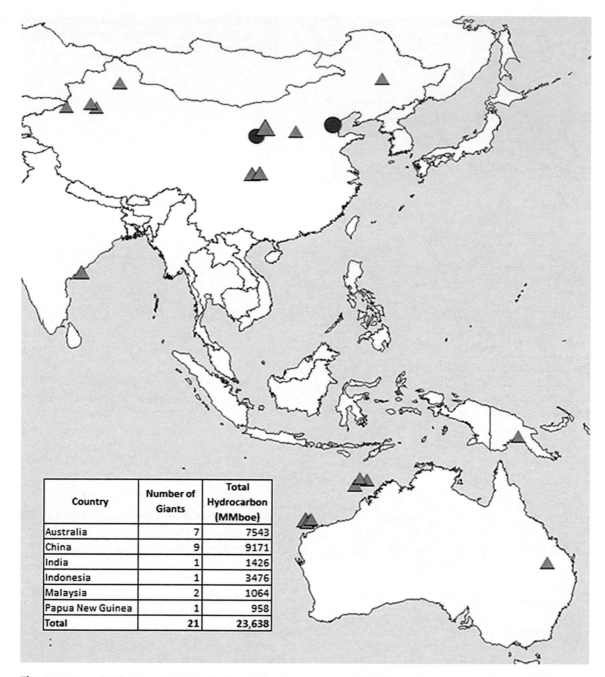

Country	Number of Giants	Total Hydrocarbon (MMboe)
Australia	7	7543
China	9	9171
India	1	1426
Indonesia	1	3476
Malaysia	2	1064
Papua New Guinea	1	958
Total	21	23,638

Figure 5. Giant fields found in Asia-Pacific during 2000–2009. Oil fields in circles. Gas fields in triangles (source: IHS Markit IRIS21 database).

Europe: Europe had only one giant discovery, the 800 MMBOE Buzzard field discovered in the Moray Firth province in 2007 (Figure 7). This is the fifth giant that has been discovered in this province. The last giant (Britannia) was found nearly a decade earlier in 1998. Adding another giant to the list after so many years is significant because it indicates the province still has remaining potential.

The European giant field Johan Sverdrup, discovered in 2010 in the Horda Platform of Norway, is discussed elsewhere in this volume.

Latin America: The 16 Latin American giants are dominated by Brazil, with 11 of the giant discoveries (Figure 8). The six Brazilian presalt giants in the Santos Basin were the opening of the mega-presalt

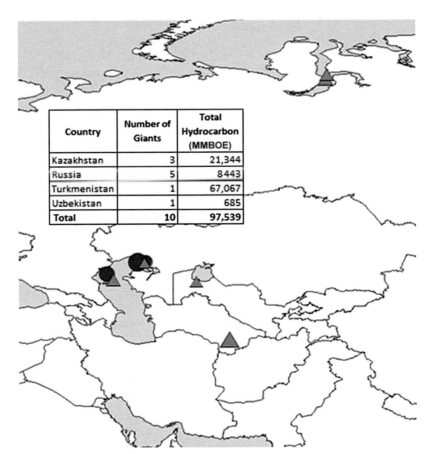

Figure 6. Giants fields found in the CIS during 2000–2009. Oil fields in circles. Gas fields in triangles (source: IHS Markit IRIS21 database).

Country	Number of Giants	Total Hydrocarbon (MMBOE)
Kazakhstan	3	21,344
Russia	5	8443
Turkmenistan	1	67,067
Uzbekistan	1	685
Total	10	97,539

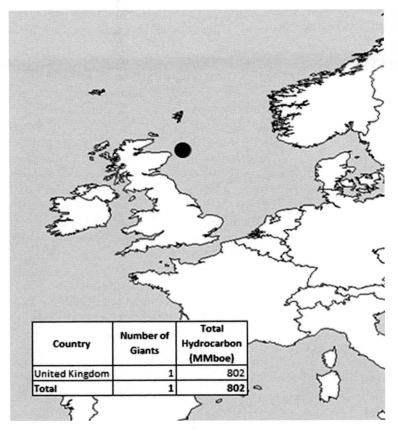

Figure 7. Giants fields found in Europe during 2000–2009. Oil fields in circles. Gas fields in triangles (source: IHS Markit IRIS21 database).

Country	Number of Giants	Total Hydrocarbon (MMboe)
United Kingdom	1	802
Total	1	802

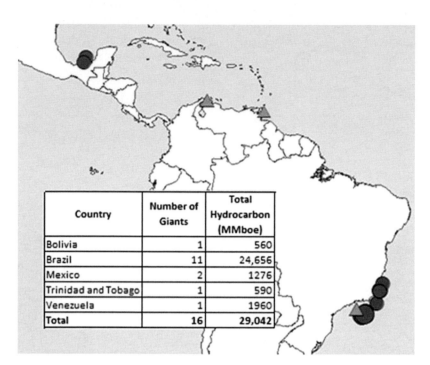

Figure 8. Giants fields found in Latin America during 2000–2009. Oil fields in circles. Gas fields in triangles (source: IHS Markit IRIS21 database).

Country	Number of Giants	Total Hydrocarbon (MMboe)
Bolivia	1	560
Brazil	11	24,656
Mexico	2	1276
Trinidad and Tobago	1	590
Venezuela	1	1960
Total	16	29,042

play, which arguably is the most important conventional new play opening of the decade globally. The Lula discovery is the third largest globally, and the Iara discovery is the fifth. Although a more mature province, the Campos Basin continued to be important, with four giants found there in the earliest part of the decade.

Other giants in Latin America were significant for different reasons. The Mango field in Trinidad and Tobago was significant because it was the first giant found in the Palmiste-Erin shelf play since 1968. In Venezuela, the Perla gas condensate discovery in the Upper Guajira Basin was significant because of Venezuela's need for more gas. Similar to the giant in Trinidad and Tobago, the two giants discovered in the Sureste Basin of Mexico were important because the last previous giant found in this mature province was in 1993. Finally, the Bolivian gas discovery Incahuasi (discovered 2004, 300 tcf [50 BBOE]) was the first giant found in the Bolivian side of the Chaco Basin since 1999, with nothing larger than 360 billion cubic feet (BCF) being found in the intervening years. This field, along with the Brazilian giants Libra and Pao d'Azucar, is covered elsewhere in this volume.

Middle East: The Middle East had the most giants found during the decade, with 14 gas giants and 9 oil giants (Figure 9). Iran, Iraq, Israel, Kuwait, and Saudi Arabia all had at least one giant gas discovery, but only Iran, Iraq, and Kuwait had giant oil discoveries.

Iran had nearly half of all the giant discoveries in the region and overwhelmingly dominated the total volumes with 6.2 BBOE of oil and 15.9 BBOE of gas. The 8.8 BBOE Kish gas condensate discovery was the largest in the region and the fourth largest globally. The Yadavaran discovery was the sixth largest globally.

All of the giants except one are in the traditional producing provinces of Central Arabia, Rub' Al Khali, and Zagros, although the Kurdamir discovery in the Zagros province of Iraq is a new play (Oligocene) in the province. The Tamar discovery in Israel opened an entirely new play (Miocene and Pliocene) in the deepwater portion of the Levantine Basin. Aside from Tamar and one shallow water giant in Saudi Arabia, all others are onshore. The offshore discovery in Saudi Arabia was the Arabiyah, which was Aramco's fifteenth in the shallow-water Persian Gulf and the first since 1979. All 15 of the discoveries offshore are giants, but this field is the first giant gas discovery.

North America: The only conventional new giants being found in North America are in the Deepwater Gulf of Mexico (Figure 10). Hadrian North is an Upper Miocene giant, whereas Tiber, Kaskida, and Julia are all Lower Tertiary discoveries. There are now 30 discoveries in the Lower Tertiary, with four of them being giants. The Appomattox discovery made in 2010, which proved the potential in the Jurassic play, is discussed elsewhere in this volume.

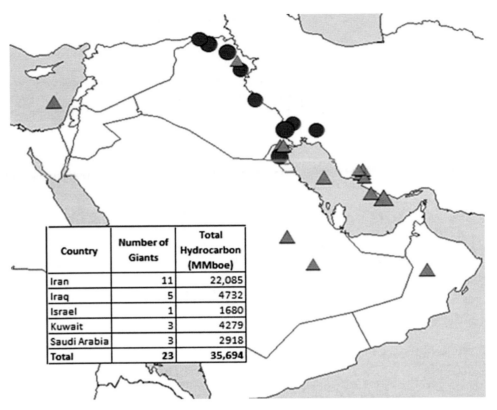

Figure 9. Giants fields found in the Middle East during 2000–2009. Oil fields in circles. Gas fields in triangles (source: IHS Markit IRIS21 database).

Country	Number of Giants	Total Hydrocarbon (MMboe)
Iran	11	22,085
Iraq	5	4732
Israel	1	1680
Kuwait	3	4279
Saudi Arabia	3	2918
Total	23	35,694

and tight rocks and ushered in the so-called unconventional revolution during the first decade of the new millennium. The unprecedented magnitude of the unconventional revolution has been a game changer for North American oil and gas resources and supplies and has impacted global oil and gas markets as well. The total estimated recoverable resource for 20 giant North American unconventional discoveries is 176 BBOE—an average of 8.8 BBOE per play (Figure 11). This compares to 198 BBOE from 85 conventional giant discoveries—an average of 2.3 BBOE from the conventional discoveries in the rest of the world (Figure 3). Including five giant international unconventional discoveries with 8.6 BBOE recoverable gas resource, the total global unconventional discoveries boosted global resources from giant fields during this decade by 93%.

The large areal extent of the tight reservoirs in these unconventional—or continuous—resource plays translates to very large recoverable resource estimates even though current recovery factors are much lower than those for conventional reservoirs. The areal extent of North American giant unconventional plays ranges from about 632 mi^2 (1637 km^2) for the Ardmore Woodford to more than 82,000 mi^2 (212,379 km^2) for the Marcellus in the Appalachian Basin. Correspondingly, 11 of the North American unconventional discoveries

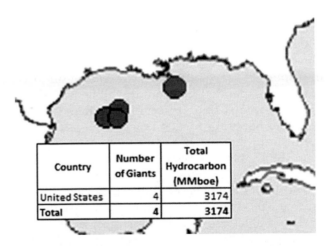

Country	Number of Giants	Total Hydrocarbon (MMboe)
United States	4	3174
Total	4	3174

Figure 10. Giant fields found in North America during 2000–2009. Oil fields in circles. Gas fields in triangles (source: IHS Markit database).

UNCONVENTIONAL DISCOVERIES

North America

The combination of horizontal boreholes and multistage hydraulic fracturing unlocked the ability to produce commercial quantities of gas and oil from shale

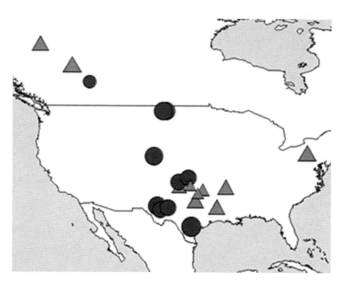

Figure 11. Unconventional giants found in North America during 2000–2009. Oil in circles. Gas in triangles (source: IHS Markit database).

are super-giants with more than 5 BBOE of recoverable resource combined. The Marcellus with 35.6 BBOE, and Horn River with 13 BBOE, lead the gas discoveries. The Eagle Ford with 25 BBOE and the Bakken with 15.9 BBOE lead the oil-dominated discoveries (Tables 5 and 6).

Shale Gas and Tight Gas: The breakthrough for shale gas is attributed to Mitchell Energy, which, in 2002, demonstrated commercial volumes of gas production from horizontal boreholes from the Mississippian Barnett Shale in the Ft. Worth Basin of North Central Texas. Surging gas production from the Barnett triggered widespread efforts to replicate this success in other shale gas source rocks (Martineau, 2007). An impressive series of seven giant shale and tight gas discoveries soon followed in the United States, including the Arkoma Basin Woodford Shale, the Fayetteville Shale in the eastern Arkoma Basin, the Granite Wash along the southwest flank of the Anadarko Basin, the

Haynesville Shale in north Louisiana, the Marcellus Shale in the Appalachian Basin, and the Woodford Shale in the Ardmore Basin and on the northeast flank of the Anadarko Basin (Figure 11). These eight giant shale and tight gas plays are estimated to have technically recoverable resources, including 388,451 tcf (64,742 BBOE) of gas and 2.23 billion barrels of oil (bbo) and condensate (Table 6).

Canadian operators also capitalized on the shale boom with the discovery of two giant shale gas plays—the Triassic Montney Shale in the Western Canadian Basin and the Devonian Muskwa (Horn River) Shale in the Horn River Basin. These two super-giant plays are estimated to have 137,088 tcf (22,848 BBOE) and 10.4 bbo of technically recoverable resource (Table 6).

Tight Oil: About the same time that George Mitchell demonstrated that horizontal wells could enhance gas production from shale, an independent, Richard Findley, convinced Lyco Energy Resources to test oil production from the tight Middle Bakken dolomite in Richland County, Montana. Drilling longer horizontal laterals finally demonstrated economic production, and the Bakken play took off in the Elm Coulee field during 2003. In this paper, the Elm Coulee field is included in the overall estimated Bakken recoverable resource of 15.9 BBOE (Table 6). But horizontal drilling did not flourish in tight oil reservoirs outside the Bakken play until natural gas prices collapsed during the 2008–2009 economic recession. In response to recovering post-recession oil prices, operators expanded horizontal well tests to similar tight calcareous shale reservoirs such as the Eagle Ford and Niobrara formations as well as to underperforming tight clastic reservoirs. Moving updip from shale gas fairways to test shallower oil-prone parts of the same shale reservoir led to the discovery of the liquids-rich Eagle Ford calcareous shale during 2009. The Eagle Ford, with almost 25 BBOE of recoverable resource, is the largest tight oil play. By the end of 2009, the unconventional tight oil renaissance was well underway, and 10 giant oil-prone discoveries with an estimated aggregate recoverable resource of 82.6 BBOE were under development in North America.

Five super-giants with 60 BBOE recoverable resource account for almost 73% of the total estimated tight oil resource in North America and amount to 84% of the total resources from 43 giant conventional oil discoveries made from 2000 through 2009 in the rest of the world (Figure 11). Giant North American tight oil discoveries made a huge impact on global oil resource additions from 2000 through 2009.

Table 5. Giant North American unconventional oil and gas resources discovered 2000–2009 (source: IHS Markit database).

Country	Giant Fields	Oil (MMBOE)	Gas (MMBOE)	Total (MMBOE)
Canada	3	11,121	23,161	34,282
United States	17	52,196	90,047	142,243
Total NAM	20	63,317	113,288	176,525

Table 6. North American giant shale gas and tight oil discoveries 2000–2009 (source: IHS Markit database).

Country	Play Name	Basin Name	Situation	Discovery Year	Oil or Gas	Total Hydrocarbons (BOE)
United States	Barnett	Fort Worth	Onshore	2002	Gas	8203
United States	Bakken	Williston	Onshore	2003	Oil	15,931
United States	Cleveland, Tonkawa, Marmaton	Anadarko	Onshore	2003	Oil	3572
United States	Arkoma Woodford	Arkoma	Onshore	2004	Gas	1550
United States	Fayetteville	Arkoma	Onshore	2005	Gas	6047
United States	Granite Wash	Anadarko	Onshore	2005	Gas	4587
United States	Three Forks	Williston	Onshore	2006	Oil	8651
United States	Haynesville	TX- LA Salt	Onshore	2006	Gas	8963
United States	Bone Spring	Delaware	Onshore	2006	Oil	5290
United States	Wolfberry	Midland	Onshore	2006	Oil	3449
United States	Marcellus	Appalachian	Onshore	2006	Gas	35,628
United States	Wolfcamp	Delaware	Onshore	2007	Oil	4276
United States	Woodford	Ardmore	Onshore	2007	Gas	997
United States	Cana Traditional	Anadarko	Onshore	2008	Gas	995
United States	Eagle Ford	Upper Gulf Coast	Onshore	2009	Oil	24,983
United States	Mississippian	Anadarko Shelf	Onshore	2009	Oil	3998
United States	Niobrara	Denver	Onshore	2009	Oil	5124
Canada	Horn River	Horn River	Onshore	2007	Gas	13,000
Canada	Montney	Western Canadian	Onshore	2001	Gas	20,294
Canada	Cardium	Western Canadian	Onshore	2008	Oil	988

Rest of World Unconventional

Success in North American unconventional reservoirs triggered efforts to establish commercial production from similar tight reservoirs in other parts of the world. Five giant unconventional gas fields/plays with aggregate 8.6 BBOE of gas were discovered from 2000 through 2009 outside of North America (Table 7 and Figure 2). Similar to the evolution of unconventional plays in North America, coal bed methane and tight sand plays were the first to be developed internationally. Internationally, IHS tracks unconventional discoveries by field rather than by play, so comparisons with North American unconventional giant discoveries are not yet totally aligned. For example, the 2009 Combabula field discovery with 503 MMBOE of gas in Australia's Walloon coal bed methane play was included for this report because it made the giant field cutoff. The overall Bowen-Surat Basin Walloon play, however, was discovered during 1996. The pre-2000 discovery date disqualifies the overall play from this report even though the 92 other fields in the play

Table 7. Giant international unconventional gas discoveries during the period 2000–2009 (source: IHS Markit IRIS21 database).

Country	Field Name	Play Name	Basin	Situation	Discovery Year	Oil or Gas	Total Hydrocarbons (MMBOE)
Australia	Combabula	Walloon CBM	Bowen-Surat	Onshore	2009	Gas (coal-bed)	503
Australia		Walloon CBM	Kumbarilla Ridge	Onshore	2001	Gas (coal-bed)	535
China	Sulige	Permian Stratigraphic	Ordos	Onshore	2000	Tight gas	5684
China	Shouyang (Qinshui)	Taiyuan CBM	Qinshui	Onshore	2007	Gas (coal-bed)	717
Oman	Khazzan	Barik Stratigraphic-Structural	Oman	Onshore	2001	Tight gas	1189

contain an estimated 2.7 BBOE. The Walloon coal bed methane play in the Kumbarilla Ridge province is included, on the other hand, because the first discovery was during 2001, and the nine fields in the play are estimated to have 535 MMBOE of recoverable coal bed gas.

China's unconventional exploration established two giant discoveries, the Shouyang field in the Taiyuan coal bed methane play with 717 MMBOE of gas and the super-giant Sulige tight gas field with 5.7 BBOE of gas. Oman also reported a giant tight gas discovery, the Khazzan field with 1.2 BBOE of gas.

These five giant discoveries with aggregate 8.6 BBOE of gas indicate the potential for future international unconventional discoveries. Shale gas and tight oil exploration has expanded internationally since 2009, but establishment of new giant supplies will be challenging in several regions due to multiple above-ground challenges.

CONCLUSIONS

For giant oil and gas discoveries, the new millennia introduced the first significant production from a new resource type—the unconventional oil and gas shale resource plays. While the viability of shale plays outside North America is challenged due to multiple above-ground factors, their importance to North America cannot be overstated. This volume is about the past decade, but as of publication, U.S. crude production had exceeded that of the 1980s, with IHS forecasting that it could exceed the previous highest levels ever (in 1970) during the period 2023–2029.

On the other hand, outside North America, the most important near-term source of new oil will be in deep water. New discoveries onshore and in shallow water are in overall decline, with only deepwater discoveries increasing in number and volume. Gas also is increasingly important. As global demand for gas rises due to its being a cleaner burning fuel than coal, so are commercialization options, especially for offshore finds.

The petroleum industry will be challenged to replicate the track record of giant field discoveries from 2000 to 2009. At the mid-point of the current decade, the number and size of giant conventional oil and gas giants have dropped substantially, and it appears that the cycle for new North American unconventional plays has passed its peak.

ACKNOWLEDGMENTS

The authors thank IHS colleagues James Verón, Bob Fryklund, and Aube Plop-Montero for comments, ideas, and assistance in preparing this manuscript. We also thank IHS Markit, Inc. for allowing us to publish this manuscript and the data contained herein.

REFERENCES CITED

Halbouty, M. T., 2003, Giant oil and gas fields of the 1990s: An introduction, *in* M. T. Halbouty, ed., Giant oil and gas fields of the decade, 1990–1999: AAPG Memoir 78, p. 1–13.

Lisovsky, N., G. Gogonenkov, and Y. Petzoukha, 1994, The Tengiz oil field in the Pre-Caspian basin of Kazakhstan (former USSR): Supergiant of the 1980s, *in* Michel. T. Halbouty, ed., Giant oil and gas fields of the decade, 1978–1988: AAPG Memoir 54, p. 101–122.

Martineau, D., 2007, History of Newark East Field and the Barnett Shale as a gas reservoir: AAPG Bulletin, v. 91, no. 4, p. 399–403.

Smith, L., S. Farrell, and R. Pocius, 2015, Conventional exploration and discovery trends: IHS Markit proprietary report, 41 p.

Godo, Ted, 2017, The Appomattox field: Norphlet Aeolian sand dune reservoirs in the deep-water Gulf of Mexico, in R. K. Merrill and C. A. Sternbach, eds., Giant fields of the decade 2000–2010: AAPG Memoir 113, p. 29–54.

4

The Appomattox Field: Norphlet Aeolian Sand Dune Reservoirs in the Deep-Water Gulf of Mexico

Ted Godo

Shell USA, Retired, 14938 Cindywood Drive, Houston, Texas, U.S.A. 77079 (e-mail: tjgodo@gmail.com)

ABSTRACT

Exploration for oil in the Norphlet reservoir in the deep-water Gulf of Mexico began in 2003 at prospect Shiloh (DC269). The well found oil but not an economic volume. The second prospect, Vicksburg (DC353), was drilled in 2007. This well found a larger in-place volume of oil, but with an immovable solid hydrocarbon component within pore spaces, there was great uncertainty as to the potential producible volumes. Two subsequent wells (Fredericksburg [DC486] and Antietam [DC268]) were dry and had a very small amount of oil, respectively. Finally, in late 2009, the fifth well (Appomattox [MC392]) was a significant discovery of high-quality oil in a thick aeolian Norphlet sandstone.

INTRODUCTION

The first oil discovery made in the Norphlet reservoir occurred in Mississippi in 1967. This discovery initiated exploration for the Norphlet reservoir that resulted to date with finding 32 small oil and gas discoveries (northeast Texas, 2; Mississippi, 15; Alabama, 14; and Florida, 2) (Figure 1). The fairway of Norphlet exploration extended southeast into the shallow Gulf of Mexico state waters of Mobile Bay. In 1979, a discovery in the bay was made whereupon further exploration continued there throughout the 1980s and 1990s. The first production in Mobile Bay occurred in 1989. Also during the 1980s, other exploration wells were drilled in federal waters of the Florida panhandle occurred with only small discoveries of oil and gas. None of these small discoveries in federal waters were ever produced.

Exploration of the Norphlet in the deep waters of the Gulf of Mexico deep-water Norphlet play segment began with lease acquisition in December 2001 (Figure 1). The first well drilled prospect Shiloh (DC269) and targeted three stacked Jurassic objectives (Cotton Valley [Tithonian] and Haynesville [Kimmeridgian] deltaic sandstones, and Norphlet [Callovian] aeolian sandstones) (Godo, 2006). At Shiloh, the only oil found was in the Norphlet sandstone, which was both sealed and charged by the overlying Smackover. The results at Shiloh prompted further exploration and drilling in the deep water for additional Norphlet prospects. Exploration drilling continued through 2009 with some oil found in the first Vicksburg well and a dry hole at Fredericksburg prospects, but no commercial success. The learnings from each well greatly helped to identify specific

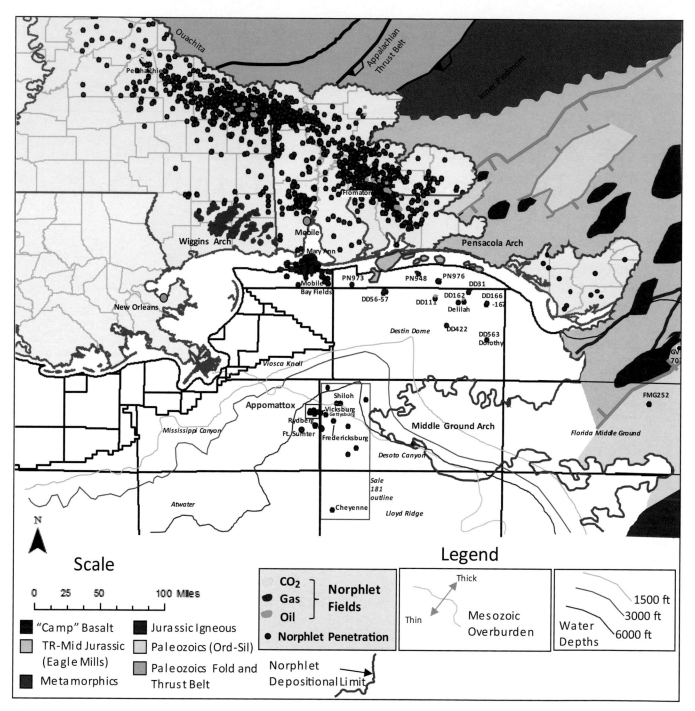

Figure 1. The Norphlet sandstone has been penetrated onshore in the Southern gulf coast states (brown circles). Offshore well locations are identified by the protraction abbreviation and the wells block number or their prospect name. Norphlet exploration since 2003 has been in water depths greater than 5000 ft (1524 m). The names of Shell's prospects were used from American Civil War battles.

critical risk factors to enhance the understanding of the key play elements. Finally, in late 2009, economic success was achieved with the discovery of the thick oil charged aeolian sands in the Appomattox field.

The Norphlet reservoirs discovered to date have shown that thick aeolian sand development (up to 900 ft [274 m] true vertical thickness) with high net-to-gross ratios are present in the current deep-water play environment. The oil has excellent qualities and low viscosity. At Appomattox, the Norphlet reservoir should average a peak production estimated to reach approximately 175,000 barrels of oil equivalent (BOE) per day and includes the development of approximately 650 million BOE resources from the Appomattox and adjacent Vicksburg fields. Additional new nearby discoveries by Shell at prospects Fort Sumter and Rydberg could easily bring the total resource volume to over 800 million BOE.

This chapter is intended to review the historical aspects of the Norphlet play as well as to summarize and integrate much of the excellent industry work that led to the discovery of the Appomattox field in 2009.

REGIONAL STRATIGRAPHY AND STRUCTURAL SETTING

Synrift Phase: Deposition of the Eagle Mills

The Gulf of Mexico began to form after the initial rift stage that separated North and South America. The earliest opening began along the Atlantic margin, with successive rifting beginning from the north and progressively younger age rifting to the south. The rift basins along the present-day Atlantic coast are filled with continent-derived fluvial and lacustrine red beds referred to as the Newark Supergroup (Olsen, 1997). Sediments in the Newark Supergroup consist of a dryland red bed sequence of alluvial and fluvial conglomerates, sandstone, and siltstone with occasional lacustrine mudrocks. All of these sediments are intruded by Jurassic diabase sills, dikes, and extrusive flow deposits. Basalt intrusions and flows occurred over a 10 million km^2 (4 million mi^2) area of central Pangaea, dated at approximately 200 Ma (also known as CAMP—Central Atlantic Magmatic Province) (Manspeizer et al., 1988; Olsen, 1997; Marzoli et al., 1999; Hames et al., 2000; McHone, 2000). In the onshore trend of rift basins, diabase igneous rocks in dikes have been radiometrically dated at 180 to 200 Ma (Scott et al., 1961; Baldwin and Adams, 1971; Ash, 1980; Chowns and Williams, 1983; Arthur, 1988).

In the southeastern United States, synrift deposition occurred from the Late Triassic into the lower Jurassic (Cornet and Olsen, 1985) (Figure 2). The South Georgia rift trend—the southern continuation

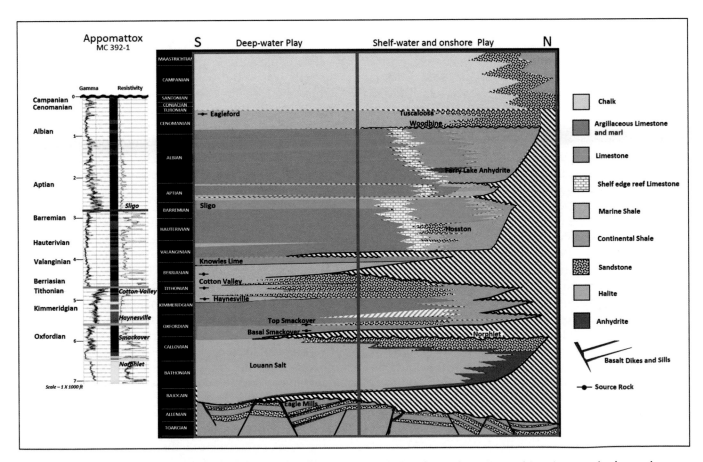

Figure 2. This stratigraphic column illustrates the lateral changes from shelf to basinal positions. This column only shows the Mesozoic stratigraphy of the eastern Gulf of Mexico highlighting general lithologies. Note the stratigraphic location of the Norphlet sandstone deposited directly on evaporites. The Norphlet clastic wedge represents the ephemeral fluvial wash and aeolian sands deposited around the rim edge of the forming Gulf of Mexico. The Appomattox well left of the column illustrates the typical gamma-ray and resistivity response of the stratigraphic column.

of the Atlantic rift margin—cuts across South Carolina and southern Georgia into northern Florida. The offshore extension of this trend into the northeast Gulf of Mexico covers portions of the Gainesville, Destin Dome, and Desoto Canyon protraction areas (Scott et al., 1961; Gohn et al., 1978; Mitchell-Tapping, 1982; Chowns and Williams, 1983; Moy and Traverse, 1986; Thomas, 1988; Raymond, 1989; Salvador, 1991; Burch and Weidie, 1994; Macrae and Watkins, 1995; Wood and Benson, 2000; Heffner, 2013; Parker, 2014). The Eagle Mills Formation was deposited within the rift grabens and then spilled across a wider initially sagging basin. The environment of deposition for Eagle Mills sediment was a dryland environment (Mitchell-Tapping, 1982; Harrelson and Ingram, 2000). These sediments consist of conglomerates from alluvial fans, varicolored mudstones, siltstones, and sandstones from ephemeral fluvial deposition and aeolian sandstones (Dawson and Callender, 1992).

The Eagle Mills Formation is known only from the subsurface and is named from the Amerada Eagle Mills No. 1 well located in Ouachita County, Arkansas (Weeks, 1938). The maximum thickness estimated for the Eagle Mills is approximately 7000 ft (2134 m), and it was deposited adjacent to the Ouachita Tectonic trend from Texas eastward into Arkansas and Mississippi (Gawloski, 1983). Mickus et al. (2009) define this rift trend area based on an analysis of its gravity and magnetic signature. In northeast Texas, Eagle Mills well penetrations are described as a succession of red siltstones, sandstones, and shales. These sediments have also been intruded by diabase dikes and sills, and often covered by lava flows. An erosional unconformity surface on these rocks is then transgressed by the Smackover (Green, 1989). Minor oil production from the Eagle Mills was discovered by Murphy Oil and occurs in two fields in east Texas (Green, 1989; Reed, 1991). In these fields, oil is sourced from the overlying Smackover source rock charging downward into the Eagle Mills. The fields lie up-dip from Louann Salt deposition. In the east Texas basin, deep well control below the Louann Salt, White et al. (1999) reported salt older than Louann salt he called the Rosewood formation and interpreted it to be a part of the Eagle Mills sequence. White proposed that deposition occurred continuously from the Late Triassic through the Upper Jurassic and limited to the deeper rift basins. The deep well that penetrated this older sequence is the Exxon-Fina Ray-1 well. This well drilled 4800 ft (1463 m) of subsalt sediments interpreted to range in age Lower to Middle Jurassic (White et al., 1999).

In southern Arkansas, estimates of Eagle Mills's thickness range up to 2 km (1.2 mi) of red beds (Scott et al., 1961; Vernon, 1971; Woods and Addington, 1973). The formation is not only confined to rift basin geometry but also fills and spills over the grabens with continued deposition marking the transition between rift and sag phases (Hutchinson and Klitgord, 1988; Green, 1989; Hurbert et al., 1992; Schlische, 1993; Withjack et al., 1998, 2012; White et al., 1999). In southwest Arkansas, fossil algae and leaf impressions from an Eagle Mills core indicate a Late Triassic age (Scott et al., 1961; Traverse, 1987; Wood and Benson, 1991). Based upon reported leaf impressions and other work, Rainwater (1968) proposed the possible existence of lacustrine facies deposited in rift valley lakes.

In the Gulf of Mexico, there are several undrilled, but seismically well-defined, rift-formed half grabens likely filled by continental red beds (Macrae and Watkins, 1995; Dobson and Buffler, 1997). The Sohio-1, in Gainesville 707, drilled a seismically defined half graben and found 4775 ft (1455 m) of siltstones and volcaniclastics, all intruded by basalt dikes, with no lacustrine or marine shale described (Applegate and Lloyd, 1985) (Figure 1). One particularly large undrilled graben underlies the Delilah wells, and a smaller half graben is present under prospects Shiloh (DC269) and Antietam (DC268) (Figure 1).

The Eagle Mills continental facies not only filled the half graben but was also deposited more widely across the areas between the grabens. The overfilling and spreading out of this continental facies was likely deposited as a sag phase was beginning but before seas that deposited the Louann Salt transgressed this unconformity. The Fredericksburg well located in Desoto Canyon Block 486 penetrated a small amount of the Eagle Mills formation (Figure 1). At the bottom of this well, below a thin Louann Salt weld, are red shales and silt intruded by basalt. The thin salt was evacuated by early subsidence as the dominantly fluvial facies of Norphlet inverted after landing on the basement. The basalt appears to be weathered at an unconformity on a small buried hill, rather than in a graben. The hill was left as a small structural high that remained prior to Louann Salt deposition. Seismic interpretation at the well supported erosional relief on the basement surface. Fractures were observed in the igneous rocks during drilling operations. Four rotary sidewall cores were taken in the igneous interval. The cores are described as coarse-grained basalt or possibly dolerite/diabase with large (>1 mm) phenocrysts of plagioclase that are suspended in a groundmass composed of plagioclase laths, pyroxene (augite), and magnetite. The basalt shows some likely hydrothermal alteration of chlorite with corrensite as a replacement of olivine. Pebble-sized, rounded fragments of basalt can be seen in contact with laminated mica-rich silty mudstone, suggesting the well drilled into a paleo-topographic high. In addition, hematite content levels were relatively high at 6% for otherwise unweathered basalt. The age of this basalt is interpreted as having formed during either CAMP (200 Ma) or synrift/early breakup (190 to 165 Ma).

Regional Sag/Predrift Phase: Louann Salt–Norphlet Deposition

The Louann Salt was first penetrated in its strati-graphic position in the Lion Oil–A-9 Hays well located in Union County, Arkansas. The well was drilled in 1932 and penetrated nearly 1300 ft (396 m) of salt. From then until as late as 1960, workers suggested that the Louann Salt ranged from Permian to Jurassic in age (Andrews, 1960). A palynomorph assemblage of Middle or Late Jurassic age from the top of the Challenger Salt Dome in the Sigsbee Knolls area was reported by Kirkland and Gerhard (1971) and (Ladd et al., 1976). In addition, palynological data from several species were collected from diapiric salt domes in Texas and Louisiana. Jux (1961) assigned a Rhaetic-Liassic (Late Triassic to Early Jurassic) age to this salt. More recently, Stern et al. (2011) reported radiometric age dating from xenoliths of alkalic igneous sampled from salt domes in southern Louisiana. This age yielded a date of approximately 160 million years. Deeper older salt may be late Bathonian, and the uppermost part may extend into the early Oxfordian (Bishop, 1967; Salvador, 1991). Todd and Mitchum (1977) assigned the Louann Salt to a time interval from Aalenian to Bathonian (or Middle Jurassic). This is based on the Gulf of Mexico sediments lying between on trend with rift and early sag sediments in the Newark Supergroup (eastern coast of North America) and exposures in central Mexico (Salvador, 1991). General acceptance today for the youngest aged salt is mainly of Callovian age.

The Louann Salt was deposited as an aerially extensive and thick salt body during a sag phase of subsidence at the end of synrift sedimentation. Locally there were areas with time gap interruptions between the rift and sag phases (Figure 2). Examples of where Louann Salt was deposited in lower areas while erosion occurred on upthrown fault blocks can be found in the east Texas basin (Green, 1989; White et al., 1999). Other seismic examples, but not penetrated by wells, can be found in parts of the eastern Gulf of Mexico (EGOM) in Destin Dome, Desoto Canyon, and the deep basin of the Lloyd Ridge protraction area offshore.

The sag phase includes the initial subsidence phase that allows enough marine water to enter the basin to initiate salt deposition on top of the rift fill sequence. The first salt deposition begins to fill the remaining low topography of the rift, expanding regionally with more gulf subsidence. The sag phase plate reconstructions for Louann Salt deposition suggest that the most likely entry point for marine waters was from the Pacific. This inlet may have been through narrow opening(s) between land masses attached to Mexico at the same time and before the Yucatan began significant counterclockwise rotation (Marton and Buffler, 1994; Pindell, 1985, 1994; Pindell and Keenan, 2001, 2009; Bird et al., 2005). Separation between the Yucatan and the southern United States would provide wider potential access for water entering the Gulf of Mexico. Salvador (1991) suggested that water entry into the salt basin was probably intermittent during times of hurricanes or very high tides, whereas at other times, the Pacific waters would either close or become restricted to a few of the deeper channels that communicated with the Pacific. Padilla y Sanchez (2007, 2014) stated that the seawaters most likely began their advance toward the Proto–Gulf of Mexico from the Pacific through the central part of Mexico. This area today lies in the border area between the states of Zacatecas and San Luis Potosi.

An anhydrite facies of the Louann Salt is found along the updip margins of the salt basin where there occurred periodic flooding and drying. The thickest anhydrites are deposited on top of the periodically flooded paleo high blocks (e.g., Wiggin uplift) (Cagle and Kahn, 1983; Rhodes and Maxwell, 1993). Alternating wetting and drying at the salt basin margin produced gypsum, which converted to anhydrite with a thickness range of 10 to 40 ft (3 to 12 m). Oxley et al. (1967) first named the Pine Hill Anhydrite Member of the Louann Salt (Figure 2). Raymond (1989) designated the type well of the Pine Hill Anhydrite as the Brandon-Miller-1 well drilled near Pine Hill, Alabama. With the high density of the anhydrite, the Pine Hill can produce an excellent hard seismic event at the base of the Norphlet aeolian section. Thicker anhydrite, up to hundreds of feet, are found mainly in the depositionally updip areas, while in the more basinal position of Appomattox, the anhydrite is too thin or absent to map the base Norphlet. The Pine Hill anhydrite in the basinal positions of the onshore Mississippi salt basin is also not present (Mancini et al., 1999). Without the presence of anhydrite between the Louann halite and the Norphlet sands, water salinity within the Norphlet can spike extremely high with precipitation of halite cement (Hartman, 1968; Studlick et al., 1990; Schenk and Schmoker, 1993). In the literature, anhydrite that occurs at the base of the Louann Salt has also been given the lithostratigraphic name of the Werner anhydrite (Imlay, 1940; Hazzard et al., 1947; Oxley et al., 1967; Anderson, 1979; Tolson et al., 1983; Mink and Mancini, 1995; Raymond, 1989; Ericksen and Theiling, 1993). The Werner anhydrite has been reported in literature only from onshore well penetrations (Woods Addington, 1973; Salvador, 1991).

Deposited on top of the Louann halite/Pine Hill anhydrite is a dryland clastic sediment wedge. This wedge can be found along the marginal edges of the gulf basin and has been named the Norphlet formation (Figure 1). The name Norphlet was given to these dryland sediments first drilled in a well located near a small community in Arkansas of the same name. The name Norphlet, interestingly enough, is a misspelling of the original intended name for this community. In 1891, a request was made by a Mr. Nauphlet, a local resident of the community, asking that the new post office be located there and use his name. However, due to either poor penmanship by Mr. Nauphlet or a government oversight, the name was spelled Norphlet, and the post office and town names were established. This deep well drilled near the town now named Norphlet was called the number 49 Werner Saw Mill. This new lithologic formation drilled at the bottom of the well found 170 ft (52 m) of clastics. Imlay (1940) proposed these sediments be named the Norphlet tongue of the Eagle Mills formation, using the nearby town's name. Five years later, in 1945, these 170 ft of gravelly red beds below the Smackover limestone and above the salt were formally named the Norphlet formation (Hazzard et al., 1947).

The Norphlet formation is composed of clastic sediments deposited in an arid climate by gravity, wind, and rain water. The water likely ran across ephemerally flowing sheet floods dispersing a flow across the salt flat. These thin and poorly developed sands found in southern Arkansas were likely deposited in the manner (Imlay, 1940; Hazzard et al., 1947). Not only in southern Arkansas but also in Texas, and Louisiana, the Norphlet is generally thin, averaging 50 ft (15 m) of total thickness (15 to 70 ft [5 to 21 m]). It is mostly composed of red shale, silts, and some thin sands (Dickinson, 1969). Further east, however, into Mississippi, Alabama, and Florida, the Norphlet thickens to over 1200 ft (366 m) locally with mostly aeolian sandstone (Studlick et al., 1990). Across this three-state area, the gross Norphlet thickness commonly ranges between 200 and 400 ft (61 and 122 m) (see Marzano et al., 1988, their figure 4).

There are distinct regional Norphlet sediment source terrains where rock fragment types have been used to define sediment provenance (Ryan et al., 1987). Norphlet sandstones found in Florida, Alabama, and Mississippi reflect an influence of metamorphic and feldspathic-rich plutonic rocks of the Appalachian Piedmont province (Thomas, 1985; Ryan et al., 1987). Sandstones in east Texas, northern Louisiana, and southern Arkansas were derived from the feldspar-poor sedimentary and metasedimentary rocks of the Ouachita System (Ryan et al., 1987). Thomas (1985, see his figure 2) provides a pre-Mesozoic map of likely exposed highland present during Norphlet deposition, which supports the rock fragments found in these Norphlet sandstones drilled onshore.

Norphlet sandstones drilled offshore in the Gulf of Mexico have igneous rock fragments. The highland source for the Norphlet is located in the present day Florida peninsula and in the adjacent Gulf of Mexico. The highland is made up of a Lower Paleozoic Ordovician through Devonian section intruded by and overlain with an igneous rocks section (Applin, 1951; Bass, 1969; Barnett, 1975; Smith, 1982; Klitgord and Popenoe, 1984). These Ordovician–Devonian age clastics in north to central peninsular Florida now subcrop beneath the Cretaceous and younger sediments (Pojeta et al., 1976). The basement terrain of southern Peninsular Florida is made up of Lower Cambrian to Precambrian granite and Lower Jurassic volcanics (Barnett, 1975; Smith, 1993). In offshore waters west of Florida, several wells have penetrated below the Upper Jurassic unconformity and found igneous rocks. For example, Shell penetrated some 550 ft (168 m) of weathered and solid granite in the PB7 number-one well. Texaco drilled a well in PB100 and drilled over 1000 ft (305 m) of diabase and rhyolite. Mobil also drilled a well and found over 700 ft (213 m) of Paleozoic metaquartzite intruded with diabase sills in EL915.

The Paleozoic rocks in Florida are an inherited remnant of the African continent (Klitgord and Popenoe, 1984; Christenson, 1990). Florida Paleozoic rocks have similar lithologic age counterparts on its conjugate margin located in the Bove basin of Guinea (Kilgord and Popenoe, 1984; Christenson, 1990; Villeneuve and Komara, 1991; McHone, 2000). Lovell and Weislogel (2010) have shown, from zircon ages taken from Norphlet sands drilled offshore and onshore but near the present coastline, that the offshore sands have their sediment source area as the Panhandle-African terrain seen in Florida Paleozoic rocks. Offshore in the Gulf of Mexico west of Florida are Ordovician clastics cored at the bottom of the Texaco 1 (Florida Middle Ground Bock 252) (Christenson, 1990). This well was drilled on a feature called the Middle Ground Arch. The Middle Ground Arch highland was exposed in part from at least Callovian until Late Kimmeridgian when the crest was finally buried by marine waters.

The aerial extent of the arch during Norphlet deposition as originally defined by Martin (1978) is very large and covered some 5000 mi^2 (12,950 km^2). This is nearly two thirds of the Desoto Canyon protraction area (Figure 1). This arch separated two salt embayments on the north and southern flanks. The Desoto salt basin lies off the north flank, and the West Florida basin is off the south flank (Martin, 1978; Dobson and Buffler, 1997; Pilcher et al., 2014). In addition to being a highland sediment source for the Norphlet, its geomorphic shape may have also acted as a wind barrier to focus wind out into the basin. The Norphlet depositional environment adjacent to this highland was dominated by alluvial fans, which built a sediment wedge thinning downdip. This sediment wedge along the north and west flanks of the arch is interpreted to range in thickness from 450 ft (137 m) to its facies pinchout. Norphlet alluvial fan facies are found in onshore wells drilled near the depositional highland front exposed during Norphlet deposition (Pepper, 1982). These fans consist of the coarser grain sandstone and conglomerate (see cross-sections by Tolsen et al., 1983; also Dinkins, 1968; Wilkerson, 1981; Pepper, 1982). Washing out beyond the toe of the alluvial fans are ephemeral deposits of sand, silt, and mud. Sediments washed outward of the fans were deposited by flooding basinward onto salt flats. The salt flats were likely either subaerially exposed or partially covered by the very shallow waters of the Louann Sea. This buildup of mud, silt, and sand out onto a flatland surface was an ideal location for winds to then redistribute these sediments across a dried fluvial outwash. Depending on wind direction and sediment supply, sands can be blown into sheet or dune sand morphologies, forming an aeolian sand sea (or erg) on top of the fluvial outwash deposits. Sediment supply and subsidence rates will determine whether sand sheets or dunes such as barchan, star, or longitudinal are formed. The common vertical stacking pattern of fluvial and aeolian facies are both present, then aeolian always overlays thinner fluvial sediments. Aeolian and fluvial facies that interfinger can happen nearer the foot of the alluvial or bajada fans.

Across the widespread dryland facies of the Norphlet that lay west and southwest of the Middle Ground Arch, small localized areas experienced very rapid subsidence rates. These areas were likely related to strike slip faulting occurring deeper and beneath the Louann salt. Being a more ductile body, the salt may have developed pull-apart basins where at the surface of the salt it became a gentle topographic low area. Rapid water runoff across the flat Norphlet plain would seek out these low areas and deposit the muds and silt. With more sediment concentrating deposition in these lows, subsidence rate increased only to continue collecting more water lain or water modified dryland sediments. These local areas received Norphlet sediments up to 1200 ft (365 m). Internally, the team referred to these

active sinkhole like basins as pothole basins. The size of these pothole basins were small compared to the greater Norphlet desert area and ranged in area between 5 and 8 mi^2 (8 to 13 km^2). The subsidence rate within potholes was so high during the Norphlet that total evacuation of underlying salt resulted in the Norphlet sediments structurally inverting or turtling even as the Smackover transgression was occurring. Prospects Fredericksburg (DC486), Petersburg (DC525), and Swordfish (DC843) are examples of these drilled turtles.

Formation of dune and interdune architectures depend on the relationship of four variables (dune size, interdune size, dune migration rate, and dune aggradation rate) (Mountney, 2012). While increased sediment supply can produce a closely spaced dune complex, other variables such as wind velocity, and direction and rate of dune subsidence below the paleo water table, strongly control whether dry or wet dunes will be dominate. In Appomattox field, both wet (water table-influenced) and dry dune facies exist and are oil filled. Dry dune facies have the best reservoir properties mainly because the build topographically higher than wet dune. This added height will produce longer and steeper grainfall or avalanche bedforms deposited on the lee side of the dune. Steep angles of climb also enable larger proportions of the original bedforms to be preserved (Mountney and Howell, 2000). Several studies in literature show much better porosity and permeability in the grainfall facies (Schenk, 1981; Marzano et al., 1988; Dixon et al., 1989; Ajdukiewicz et al., 2010) as well as in all whole cores and calibrate image logs taken in Appomattox and surrounding discovery wells (Douglas, 2010; Godo, 2011). Better poro-perms in this bedform are primarily because it has the coarsest grain size and with later formation of diagenetic clay coats, pore throat size will be larger.

Conditions in the Norphlet dryland system were not conducive for preservation of paleontological data that could help age-date the formation. In the current deep-water play around Appomattox, wells have found only sparse material. The age dates that have been found give a wide age range from Upper Triassic (Carnian) to Middle to Upper Jurassic and consist of dinocysts, pollen, and spores such as found in the Fredericksburg well (DC486). Of course, some of these palynological dates likely represent dates from reworking of sediments exposed in the sediment source terrane. At Appomattox, for example, acritarchs of Devonian age were found in the Norphlet, which likely came from eroded Silurian or Devonian rocks in Florida.

Drift Phase: The Smackover Formation: Plate reconstructions in the Gulf of Mexico have been addressed by numerous publications. A favored timing and reconstruction described by Kneller and Johnson (2011) suggests seafloor spreading began at 163 Ma (Callovian). The first reliable and oldest age date from microfossils are found at the top of the Smackover Formation that represent the first carbonates on top of the Louann salt. The basal Smackover carbonate that represents the initial transgression of the sea is completely devoid of any life other than algae deposited in the highly saline waters. Above this basal Smackover carbonate is a period where salinity lessens as the underlying salt was completely buried and more seawater began to circulate. In the upper Smackover Formation, wave energy began to be high enough to develop some carbonate grainstones and it is in sediment deposited around this time that the Oxfordian age call from microfossils can be made.

The Smackover Formation was first penetrated near the town of Smackover Arkansas by the deepening of a well beneath the shallow Cretaceous reservoirs in the Smackover field. Bingham (1937) named this new 700-ft-thick limestone formation using its type locality as found in the Lion Oil Hayes No. 9-A well. The Smackover Formation in the Arkansas–Louisiana–east Texas area is divisible into three units, or members (Dickinson, 1968). Dickinson described the lower member as a dense and laminated limestone, the middle member as a sandy limestone, and the upper member as an oolitic limestone. Referring to the Mississippi salt basin, Oxley et al. (1967) described lower and upper Smackover facies. Oxley described and named the upper portion of the lower member as the "Brown Dense" limestone, which is described as dense to finely nonporous crystalline with a dark brown to dark gray color. Oxley further described the base of the brown dense limestone as grading into a dark gray to black, dense, argillaceous, thinly laminated, pyritic limestone.

More recently, Mancini et al. (1992) defined the Smackover in the greater Alabama area as consisting of three members defined as lower, middle, and upper (also in Moore, 1984; Benson, 1988). Benson (1988) described the lower member as a lime mudstone that contains stromatolites, intraclasts, and peloidal–oncoidal wackestone to packstone. The middle member was described as laminated mudstone with some peloidal and skeletal wackestone to packstones (Mancini and Benson, 1980; Benson, 1985). The upper member consists of subtidal to intertidal and supratidal fenestral mudstones and anhydrites (Mancini and Benson, 1980; Benson, 1988; Mann, 1988). Prather (1992, his figures 11 and 12), also working in the Alabama area, characterized the time-stratigraphic framework of the Smackover Formation. Prather recognized that the formation had an initial transgressive systems tract (TST) followed by a highstand systems tract (HST). A maximum flooding surface (MFS) marked the boundary at the top of the TST. At this maximum flooding surface are laminated mudstones that define a condensed zone. The maximum flooding surface contains the richest source rocks in the Smackover. The (upper) Smackover (HST) has a mud-supported facies of pellet wackestone that is overlain by a grain-supported facies of pellet packstone, oolite-pellet-intraclast lime grainstone and/or dolograinstone, and a mixed lithologic facies of dolomudstone, intraclastic grainstone, caliche-pisolite, and calcrete (Prather, 1992).

Offshore, in Desoto Canyon and Mississippi Canyon protraction areas, the Smackover has the same stratigraphic framework described by Prather (1992). Particularly evident is the seismically defined clinoform geometry in the central and southern portion of the Desoto Canyon area. Clinoforms demonstrate the progradational nature of the highstand systems tract. The clinoforms enter from the updip central portion of the Desoto embayment prograde southwestward subparallel with the northern margin of the Middle Ground Arch. The clinoforms are composed of shale, silts and some thin carbonates (e.g., at Dorothy DD563) (Figure 1). At more outboard well locations, such as at prospect Shiloh (DC268) and Antietam (DC269), the silty-shale clinoform sets are at a very low angle to the basal Smackover event, yet sands and silts are still present in this interval. The silts and sands in Shiloh are a mixture of upper fine-grained to coarse silt-sized detrital grains composed mostly of quartz, plagioclase, muscovite, and altered argillaceous rock fragments. The matrix is a mixture of detrital and authigenic clays derived from the alteration of lithic grains and carbonate grains with some cement present in small amounts. Carbonate grains are mostly ooids. Virtually all visible porosity has been eliminated in this sandstone due to quartz cementation, pore-filling clay, and extensive compaction. The basal Smackover (also called the brown dense member [Oxley et al., 1967]) lies directly on top of either the Norphlet or Louann Salt provided Norphlet was not deposited (e.g., wells DD166, DD167, and PN973) (Figure 1). The Smackover source rock in the Destin Dome area is less rich than in wells drilled further offshore. Possible source rock dilution due to clastic dilution by the sediments entering the basin shown by the progradational clinoforms may limit source rock richness in this area.

At Appomattox, the three members of the Smackover can be easily distinguished on well logs (Figure 3). The lower member represents the initial transgression (TST) and has three sub-members. The three sub-members are made up of red shale, a high-density pyrite zone, and a basal carbonate with intervals of algal laminated source rocks (brown dense of Oxley et al., 1967). The middle member represents the distal

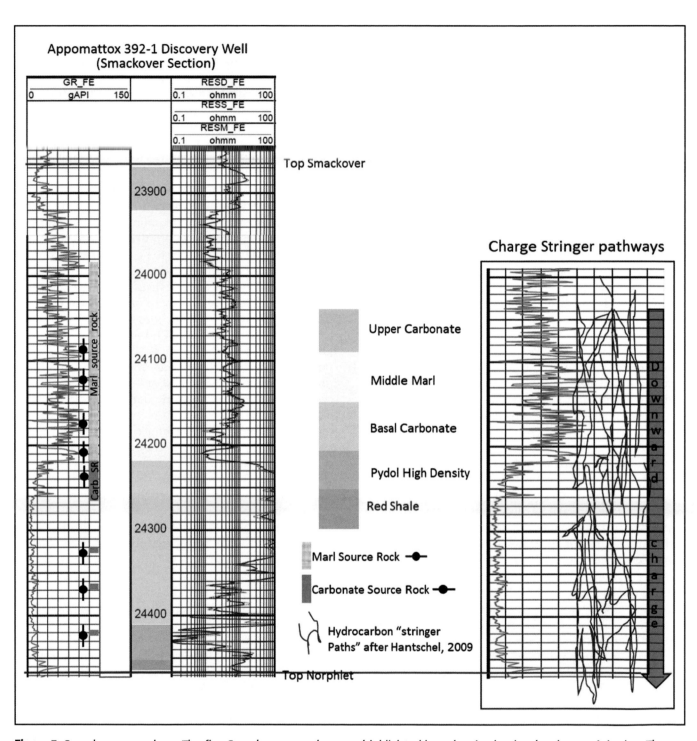

Figure 3. Smackover members. The five Smackover members are highlighted by colors in the depth column of the log. The members are: 1) thin red shale; 2) the high-density member locally referred to as the pydol section (pyrite-dolomite); 3) basal carbonate; 4) middle marl; and 5) upper carbonate. The Smackover has two source-rock types: 1) middle marl source rock and 2) MLZ carbonate source rock. The downward migration path shown conceptually by red lines are conceptualized and modeled after the stringer concept and illustration in Hantschel and Kauerauf (2009).

toesets of the clinoform package. The upper member is a limestone that represents facies deposited in a higher-wave energy environment (e.g., oolites, pellets, and some skeletal fractions) associated with the topset portion of the clinoform package. It is usually at this interval or slightly younger that the first paleontological faunae are present to interpret a top Oxfordian age.

Source rock intervals in the Smackover consistently show the two types of source rocks in two of the members. These two members are the basal carbonate limestone and the middle marl member. No whole cores have been taken in the Smackover in any of the deep-water wells. However, a significant amount of rotary core samples were taken systematically with overlapping section in each of the Smackover members from all Shell operated wells.

Basal Red Shale: The initial flooding at the base of the Smackover is represented by a variable thickness of red-colored shales and siltstones. The shale interval located on top of aeolian dunes is the thinnest and made up of a very distinctive red claystone shale. This red shale on top of the topographically high dunes can approach 10 ft (3 m) at a maximum. It is compositionally very different from the more typical red shales found in areas with no sand dunes. This red shale has compositional descriptions as extremely iron-rich and described as argillaceous ironstones, hematite claystones, and/or pyrite hematite ironstones. Hematite as measured with X-ray diffraction is upward of 50% hematite. At top of the dunes, only this thin iron rich claystone or shale is found before carbonate deposition occurs with the associated heavy mineral assemblage. In areas where there are no sand dunes to build the topographic relief, the depositional area was flat and received sediments by ephemerally flowing rainwater emptying into the encroaching seawater of the Smackover transgression. The silty shale and thin siltstones deposited in this interval thicken to four times (up to 40 ft [12 m]) due to the absence of the dune topographic relief. The red-brown silty shale deposited in this interval has less iron than the iron-rich claystone but more silt content and occasionally interbedded with thin siltstones. Only at the very top of this interval lies the thin iron claystone that underlies the first carbonate bed. The topographically low areas away from the dune fields filled first with red-brown silty shale and siltstone. Rising seawater during Smackover transgression expanded across the fringing Norphlet dryland red-clastic system. Gradually, the slow water rise entombed and preserved the Norphlet sand dunes that rose above the desert plain. The very shallow quiet waters that transgressed the Norphlet desert did not have conditions sufficient for the carbonate factory to go into production. The water column incorporated red clays of the transgressed desert redistributing and concentrating them into a layer. Carbonate precipitation lagged behind an initial drowning until the water became sufficiently deep (Ginsberg, 1971).

High-Density Zone: The matrix rock of the high-density zone is carbonate that was the first deposited overlying the very red iron rich claystone. The highdensity values cause the log signature to express a very characteristic spike in the density and on the resistivity and conductivity logs. This same zone is also known informally as the pydol zone by geologists working the Norphlet fields in Mobile Bay of the Alabama coast. The name pydol is a consolidation of the words pyrite and dolomite that together that dominate this zone in areas both in shallow and deep waters of the Gulf of Mexico. At Appomattox and the surrounding area, the high-density zone has been extensively sampled with rotary cores. The thickness of this zone averages around 35 ft (11 m), but in areas of thicker red shale, pyrite zone thickness can be up to 50 ft (15 m). Pyrite makes up to 50% of some rotary core samples based on point count and X-ray analysis data. The matrix rock is dolomitized micrite with remnant organic layers thought to be algal concentrations and anhydrite. Dolomitization renders any primary depositional forms as indistinguishable except for peloidal mud texture and these organic laminae. Also present in the lower pyrite zones are nodules of finely crystalline bassanite ($CaSO_4 \bullet \frac{1}{2}H_2O$). The nodules were deposited as gypsum as seawater evaporated within a sabkha setting. Bassanite is a transitional phase between gypsum and anhydrite. As the water column deepened, it became density stratified with a strong brine base overlain by more normal seawater. In the lower euxinic water column, organic material was effectively trapped at the redox boundary to promote localized sulfate reduction (Hurtgen et al. 1999). Under anoxic conditions, seawater sulfate is reduced to H_2S, which reacts with detrital iron minerals and ultimately forms pyrite (Goldhaber and Kaplan, 1974; Berner, 1984; Raiswell et al., 1988). Studies have shown that bacterial sulfate reduction with the formation of pyrite takes place within the uppermost centimeters of burial (Berner, 1970; Raiswell et al., 1988). Based on isotope work, it has been shown that pyrite in the Smackover is there due to bacterial sulfate reduction.

Basal Carbonate: Overlying the pyrite mineralized zone is a very clean, nearly clay-free (< 5% based on X-ray diffraction carbonate. Thicknesses vary from 125 to over 400 ft (38 to over 122 m). The basal carbonate is characterized on the gamma ray log by having the lowest count levels compared to all other lithologies. Depositional features are not diagnostic but rare mud pellets or ooids may be found in some intervals. Algal layers are present in mainly laminations but some are wavy and may represent some stromatolite or microbiolite growth structure. Other features found in this member are organic filled stylolites and patchy anhydrite concentrations with early dolomitization of lime mudstones. Micropores within the dolomitized units are usually oil filled. The limestone color is tan to light brown with intervals colored by zones of algal laminations. This more laminated zone is commonly referred to in industry as the MLZ, or microlaminated zone (Shew and Garner, 1990; Mancini et al., 1999). Algal microlaminations are randomly distributed in the lower member but are concentrated in the uppermost portion of the basal carbonate. The concentration of MLZs causes serrations on the otherwise consistently low gamma count. More argillaceous material is deposited with the algal material, which increases the gamma ray spikes.

Algal microlaminations were deposited in a quiet body of water during the initial transgression of the Smackover. Algal blooms could have occurred during the periodic rainfall providing fresh water runoff into the saline waters allowing the algae to proliferate on the top of the saline water. Hypopycnal flow of fresh water running across the top of the higher-density (hypersaline) water column would have been the mechanism to create this condition. Algae would instantly grow and thrive on this relatively still freshwater body. Gradually, through evaporation, the fresh water would become more saline, causing the algae to die and sink into the anaerobic body of standing water to accumulate and preserve in thin laminations. Clay particles also settle out of suspension through the process of flocculation (the clumping of clay particles together due to a positive–negative charge relationship created by the seawater). Settling together algae and clays created the laminations. These intervals are the source rocks that generate the early asphaltine products that make up the solid hydrocarbon residues found in the underlying Norphlet reservoir (Godo et al., 2011). The actual total organic content (TOC) of the microlaminations can be very rich. However, because the laminations or stylolites are thin, measuring the TOC of a thicker interval using a bulk rock analysis will have much lower apparent richness value. This is due to the dilution effect of the non-source matrix rock.

In summary, the Smackover transgression had no surf zone or beach environment for the Norphlet. The transgressive systems tract began with a gentle flooding of the Norphlet desert with minimal reworking of the sand dune topography. The water column was clay-rich water that deposited the characteristic red shale. As the water deepened, the column became stratified under anoxic conditions and highly saline waters near the water bottom. The source rock was deposited as algal blooms flourished and died.

Middle Member: The basal contact of this middle member with the underlying lower member is transitional from limestone to increasing interbeds upward of marl. This increased interbedded argillaceous amount is expressed through a serrations of the gamma ray curve that increases upward into the middle member (Figure 3). The middle member has more argillaceous material, but still has significant calcium carbonate content. A more accurate description and quantifiable lithology would be a marlstone. Here the clay content varies between 30 and 65% based upon X-ray diffraction results from rotary cores taken in all of the Smackover penetrations. Pettijohn (1957) defines a marlstone as containing 35 to 65% clay and 65 to 35% carbonate. Bedding in the marl is massive with no fissility. Within the middle marl member, the richest source rocks are present in the beds with the most argillaceous content as shown with the highest gamma ray log spikes. The richness has the highest levels of TOC, S2, and HI values. Onshore, the Smackover mudstones are also the main source rock facies in the North Louisiana salt basin, the Mississippi Interior salt basin, and the Manila and Conecuh subbasins (Oehler, 1984; Sassen et al., 1987; Sassen and Moore, 1988; Claypool and Mancini, 1989; Mancini et al., 2003).

Upper Member: The upper member of the Smackover Formation commonly has more high-energy facies, such as ooid grainstones, but they have very low porosity due to extensive cementation. The most outboard location of the seismically defined clinoform geometry is between Shiloh and the Mississippi Canyon protraction area. In this most outboard area around Appomattox, the upper Smackover is composed of more micritic limestone rather than the packstone to grainstone facies. The paleontologic pick for the top Oxfordian is generally found 200 to 300 ft (61 to 91 m) above this carbonate section, which is correlated as the top Smackover. No source rock material is present in this member.

THE NORPHLET PETROLEUM SYSTEM

The Norphlet petroleum system is fundamentally different from all other plays in the Gulf of Mexico. The Norphlet lies at the base of the sedimentary package above the salt. Therefore, in the Norphlet play, there is only one chance for charge by the overlying source rock, since all of the other source rocks of the Tithonian or younger age are not structurally positioned to provide charge. Only the source rocks in the overlying Smackover are in a position to provide oil charge for the Norphlet sandstone. Norphlet oil at Appomattox has been typed to the Smackover source rocks. As a result of stratigraphic juxtapositioning, the source rock and the reservoir rock experience the same heating necessary to generate and expel hydrocarbons. This means the reservoir has to withstand porosity and permeability degradation and destruction by both grain crushing and cementation. Cementation due to high temperatures is the primary cause of porosity and permeability loss in the Norphlet sandstones.

Porosity in the Norphlet is mostly primary intergranular porosity. Initial coarser grain sizes are more favorable to withstand later compaction and cementation resulting in the most permeable facies today. Waterlain sandstone facies in the Norphlet that were deposited by ephemeral fluvial outwash and have the lowest porosity and most importantly very low permeability. Permeability in the facies is low that there is no relative underpressuring of this interval to create a pressure relief point for the downward charge. As such only Norphlet aeolian facies receive and laterally move the hydrocarbon charge. Sand dunes have the coarsest grain size, particularly if found as avalanche facies deposited on the lee side of the dune face (Lupe and Ahlbrandt, 1979; Schenk, 1981; Fryberger et al., 1983; Lindquist, 1983; Marzano et al., 1988; Dixon et al., 1989; Net, 2003; Worden and Morad, 2003; Ajdukiewicz et al., 2010; Douglas, 2010). Cementation is inhibited from occurring in the sandstone by the thin chlorite that grew from the initial clay rims that coated the grains during and after deposition (Crone, 1975; Walker, 1979; Matlack et al., 1989; Turner et al., 1993; Shammari et al., 2011). This chlorite effectively insulates the detrital quartz grains from encountering silica-rich pore waters that precipitate out quartz cement by nucleation onto the detrital quartz grains. Transforming clay coats to chlorite is due in large part to the igneous detrital grain component derived from the sediment sources in the Florida highlands. Igneous sand grain components dissolved quickly after burial and supplied the clay elements needed to grow additional chlorite on the more stable quartz sand grains. In the Norphlet reservoir, it has been shown that the sand grains need to have at least 98% of the grain surface coated by chlorite to prevent extensive quartz cementation and thus preserve the permeability (Taylor et al., 2004). Significant quartz cementation that begins with temperatures over 200° Fahrenheit will cement and close smaller pore throats around the sand grains that are lacking clay coats. Potential Norphlet reservoirs must survive burial temperatures up to and over 350° Fahrenheit (Mobil Bay).

To charge the Norphlet sandstones with oil, downward charge occurs from the adjacent overlying source rocks in the Smackover Formation. Source rock intervals in the Smackover consistently show the two types of source rocks in two of the members. These two members are the basal carbonate limestone and the middle marl member (Figure 3). The middle marl member has the higher argillaceous content, with up to 85% in some beds, but does not exhibit bedding fissility. These intervals are the richest source rocks and display the highest gamma ray counts. Interbedded in this interval are some marls with lower argillaceous content. The generally high argillaceous percentages in the entire middle member would classify these rocks as argillaceous to calcareous mudstones (Pettijohn, 1957). The basal carbonate member has very little argillaceous content and is mostly all calcium carbonate (clean limestone) with some intervals of magnesium carbonate (dolomite). The source rock material in this unit is very different compared to the kerogen in the middle member. In the basal carbonate, the kerogen is found as thin algal microlaminations. When the laminations are concentrated enough to stack vertically, the gamma ray log will show a more serrated pattern. These serrations marked by algal laminations also contain a bit more argillaceous content that were deposited as the algal material sank to the seafloor. Laminations can be scattered throughout the basal carbonate but are always found near the top of this unit as it transitions into the overlying middle marl section. The Smackover source rock richness values are fairly consistent regardless of either lateral position or thickness changes. Greater thickness would equate to more of the same source rock rather than a change in the richness value.

Source rock maturation in the Smackover begins as all source rocks do, by initially filling all of the micro and macro porosity in the source rock. The organic richness of the source rock will control how much oil volume can first saturate the source rock pores before exiting. Kerogen in a source rock matrix is grouped as individual kerogen masses within the rock matrix. Both kerogen richness and its distribution (or fabric) within the rock matrix will affect how much heat will be required to initiate hydrocarbon expulsion. A lower heat will be required to expel hydrocarbons if the source rock has a higher kerogen richness and a fabric of interconnected kerogen masses (Pepper, 1991; Hantschel and Kauerauf, 2009). Conversely, for leaner source rocks with less connectivity, a higher heat is required for expulsion of hydrocarbons. Standard vitrinite reflectance charts, for example, may indicate hydrocarbon expulsion begins at a level of 0.65 to 0.75 VR. This is generally true for an average source rock richness with average kerogen connectivity. The Smackover source rocks require a higher threshold of heating than these standard values. If the kerogen is distributed in a more continuous network, the diffusion of hydrocarbons can occur much faster with the same amount of heat (Stainforth and Reinders, 1990; Thomas and Clause, 1990).

Overpressure has been widely accepted as the driving mechanism of petroleum expulsion (England and Fleet, 1991). The direction of expulsion is controlled by the relative impermeability of the overlying versus the underlying strata. If the underlying strata have significantly more permeability and a lower capillary entry pressure, the resulting pressure gradient will force a downward migration of petroleum into the permeable carrier beds (England et al., 1987; Sylta, 2004). Essentially, a permeable Norphlet reservoir acts as an underpressured sink for oil to enter. Microfracturing in the source rock, caused by overpressure due to source rock maturation, has also been cited as a method for adding pathways for primary hydrocarbon migration. Pepper and Corvi (1995a) suggested that microfracturing is formed through the amalgamation of desorbed molecules within a collapsing kerogen network and the weight of the overhead lithostatic load. The pathway to microfracturing is thought to first begin by the joining of oil molecules transformed from the kerogen masses within the matrix rock. The pathway of oil movement is by "stringers" that evolve from an expulsion point and move along a stringer pathway (Hantschel and Kauerauf, 2009) (Figure 3). In the Norphlet petroleum system, the permeable aeolian sand is the exit point for all of the stringer paths. Once created, pathways are filled by a continuous oil phase under pressure, and the pressure is relieved as oil enters the permeable Norphlet sand. From there, lateral permeability allows the fluid to move updip to an even less pressured area. The aeolian dune facies is the only permeable Norphlet sandstone. If present, this aeolian sand is both the first carrier bed out of the source rock and is also the objective reservoir to accumulate oil in the trap. The Smackover source rocks can be described as fair when comparing these source rocks with, for example, the much richer Tithonian source rock. The benefit in exploring for the Norphlet reservoir is its juxtaposition with the source rock to limit migration losses.

NORPHLET AREA EXPLORATION HISTORY

Pre-2001: Norphlet Onshore and on the Shelf

Although the Norphlet formation was first penetrated in 1935 and later given its formation name in 1947, another 20 years would pass before hydrocarbons were found in the formation (Figure 1). The Smackover was already a productive reservoir in 1967 when Shell made the Norphlet a primary objective at prospect Pelahatchie in Mississippi. The industry was quite surprised when a high-pressure oil discovery in the Norphlet formation was reported (Oxley et al., 1967; Karges, 1968; Hartman, 1968; Cockrell, 2005). With the results at Pelahatchie, the Norphlet became a new primary objective for exploration wells. Between 1967 and 1979, nearly every year saw between one and three Norphlet field discoveries made in Mississippi, Alabama, and Florida.

Alabama reported its first Norphlet discovery at Flomaton one year later. During development drilling at Flomaton, it was determined that the tight Smackover was actually not the top seal for the Norphlet. With offset drilling, Smackover porosity was found, and the team then realized that the actual top seal was stratigraphically higher in the Haynesville anhydrites. After final appraisal, the bulk of the hydrocarbons were determined to be in the Smackover reservoir facies. Today, the Smackover in this trend has the local field names of Flomaton, Jay, and Blackshear, all on this anticline. Jay field has cumulatively produced over 400 million barrels of oil from the Smackover reservoir (Ottman et al., 1973; Sigsby, 1976; Mancini et al., 1985a; Melas and Friedman, 1992), while Flomaton is the lone Norphlet field on the structure.

In total, 33 Norphlet fields have been discovered onshore in Texas (2), Mississippi (15), Alabama (14), and Florida (2) (Figure 1). Norphlet hydrocarbon traps are structural and involve salt anticlines, basement paleotopography, and normal (extensional) faults (Jackson and Harris, 1982; Mancini et al., 1985a). All of the discoveries were made before 1996. Seventeen of the fields were found between 1967 and 1980, with 10 fields found in the 1980s and 6 fields in the 1990s. The discoveries are dominantly oil, with five gas discoveries and six CO_2 accumulations (Studlick et al., 1990). The largest Norphlet oil field onshore is Flomaton field, where cumulative production was 10 million bbl of oil and 135 BCF as reported in 1984 with production in decline. All of the other Norphlet oil fields have ultimate recoveries that range from less than one million barrels with a few fields at 5 million barrels (Mancini et al., 1985a; Marzano et al., 1988; Champlin, 1996). The carbon dioxide (CO_2) production from the Norphlet in these fields represents the deepest commercial CO_2 gas fields in the world (Zhou et al., 2012). The CO_2 concentration and atomic makeup indicate a strong mantle signature rather than CO_2 derived from thermal decomposition of carbonate (Stevens et al., 2004; Zhou et al., 2012). The Jackson Dome intrusion, which is dated to about 70 million years ago, is the most likely source (Studlick et al., 1990).

Onshore, there are more Smackover fields than Norphlet fields. This is partly due to the fact that the Norphlet sandstone has a more limited areal extent than the porosity in the Smackover limestone. But the primary reason there are fewer Norphlet fields onshore is that the Smackover is a poor top seal and the closest seal is stratigraphically younger in the Kimmeridgian (Buckner anhydrites). Onshore, the structure in the Jurassic are generally lower relief compared to the offshore fields. In the lower relief fields, with the oldest topseal in the Kimmeridgian, the column heights required to force the hydrocarbons down in to the Norphlet larger than what the structures can accommodate. Where rarer Norphlet fields do occur onshore, it requires that local Smackover variations produce a Smackover top seal, and the hydrocarbon column can then fill the Norphlet. Smackover topseal formation is typically found in more basinal positions (closer to the present coastline and offshore) where the Smackover water depths were deep enough to become stratified forming tight limestone potential topseals. Basinal Smackover topseal development is found in the state waters of Mobile Bay and in the current deep-water play area of the Appomattox field.

Offshore, the Norphlet play began in 1969, when Mobil Oil Company leased offshore tracts in the state waters of lower Mobile Bay off the Alabama coast (Figure 1). Prospect Mary Ann was to be the first Norphlet exploration prospect. However, delays due to numerous legal and environmental issues had to be endured before Mobil was allowed to begin drilling (Wade et al., 1999; Frost, 2010). It was not until 1979 that Mary Ann finally completed drilling and was announced as a major gas discovery. The announcement was a needed boost for the Norphlet play. This boost was needed largely because during the 10-year wait to drill, the exploration drilling in the adjacent federal waters had no found any commercial success. The offshore drilling during this ten year time span began in 1973 lease sale. In this sale successful bidders acquired leases in the Destin Dome (DD) and Pensacola (PEN) protraction areas, which subsequently saw several wells drilled down to the Norphlet. Sun Oil leased DD block 166 and drilled the first well into the Louann Salt for a Smackover objective on a simple structure downthrown on the basin rimming fault (DD166). The well found shows in the Smackover, but the formation lay directly on salt without any deposited Norphlet section. Exxon had a different play in mind when it spent over $600 million for six contiguous blocks over Destin Dome in the 1973 federal waters lease sale. Their play was to test the upper Cretaceous Woodbine and Tuscaloosa sand pinchout traps on a flank of the Destin anticline. After drilling six wells on their blocks

with no success, a seventh well was drilled deep to the Louann Salt. This well (DD162 #3) found over 300 ft (91 m) of aeolian sand (20 to 23% porosity) with 56 ft (17 m) of fluvial sediments below before reaching total depth in the Louann Salt. The top 100 ft (30 m) of the Norphlet whole core was oil stained, indicating a small residual oil column. The Exxon well is located less than 8 mi (13 km) south of the Sun well (DD166), where no Norphlet section was deposited. In 1977, Amoco drilled a structure on the basin rimming fault zone similar to the Sun well. Amoco drilled the well in block DD31 down to the Louann Salt. The well found 330 ft (101 m) of sandstone above 146 ft (45 m) of fluvial shale and silt on top of a thin Pine Hill anhydrite and Louann Salt. The top 30 ft (9 m) of Norphlet showed dead oil staining and intervals with gas shows over 120 ft (37 m) in variable porosity of 14 to 18%. The last true exploration well was drilled in Destin Dome in 1989.

To summarize the results of the Norphlet exploration in the Desoto salt basin: There are a total of 12 prospects that were drilled to the Louann Salt. Some of the wells found that no Norphlet was deposited (Pen973, DD167-Chevron1, DD422), or only thin Norphlet composed of alluvial gravel, sand, and silt was present (DD563). Thick seismic pod-shaped dunes of porous aeolian sands are found on the west side of the Destin Dome anticline. These seismic pods are identical in form to those found in the Mobile Bay area. This pod-shaped dune area represents a small sand erg with some wells finding thick dunes in proximity with other wells finding thin or no sand in and around the erg margin. The thickest penetration of a sand dune pod is in the Shell Delilah prospect. In this well, just over 1000 ft (305 m) of porous sand (19 to 20% porosity) was found with 80 ft (24 m) of oil. Another targeted seismic pod was at prospect Delilah-DD160-1, where Shell found another small oil column in the thick sand. At prospect Robin-DD111-1, volume calculations indicate it is a 5- to 6-million-barrel discovery. There also have been gas discoveries made in the Norphlet by Sohio (Pen 948), Texaco (Pen996), and Chevron (DD56-57). The Chevron (DD56-57) discovery is the largest, with likely reserves in the range of a few hundred BCF of gas. In 1988, the first offshore production from the Norphlet began at Mary Ann. Today, in Mobile Bay, there is a complex set of Norphlet fields around the initial Mary Ann discovery. This complex has over 60 Norphlet producing wells that are in 15 fields located on adjacent longitudinal seif dune ridges (Story, 1998; Bagnold, 2005). By 2006, there was cumulative production of over 4 tcf of gas from these fields. Estimated original proved gas from Norphlet reservoirs in the Alabama coastal waters and adjacent federal waters is 7.462 tcf (Kugler and Mink, 1999).

2001–2010: The Shift to Deep Water and the Discovery of Appomattox

In 1998, Shell assembled a multidisciplinary team to study the regional Mesozoic play in the deep-water EGOM. The intent was to understand the play for the upcoming lease sale 181, which was scheduled for 3 years later in December 2001 (Figure 1). Sale 181 was the first in the EGOM in 13 years; the last lease sale had been in 1988. The new sale area contained 256 deep-water blocks (or 1.47 million acres) with most blocks in water depths greater than 8000 ft (2438 m). The Shell strategy for the area was to capture blocks that had large Mesozoic structures with primarily Jurassic objectives in closure. Assuming discoveries in the largest hub volume prospects, smaller volume prospects would provide attractive tiebacks to the larger fields.

The specific primary objectives in the deep-water portion of the play were Jurassic-aged sandstones in the Cotton Valley (Tithonian), Haynesville (Kimmeridgian), and Norphlet (Callovian). Geologically, the Cretaceous rocks in the sale area were all deposited basinward of its shelf margin and the closest shelf well control is found in Main Pass blocks 253 and 254 (Petty, 1999; Mancini et al., 2001). In the deep-water play, Cretaceous objectives were potential turbidites spilling across the shelf margin into the sale 181 deep-water area. To support this, thick occurrences of coeval shelf sandstones are present in Valanginian- to Hauterivian-aged (Hosston) and Albian-(Paluxy)aged sediments. In the Upper Jurassic, this new sale area was reconstructed to be a shallow dipping ramp shelf margin with deltaic sands expanding in growth fault wedges. Below the deltaics and above the Louann Salt were the dryland objective reservoirs of the Norphlet charged by the overlying Smackover. Above the Smackover lie the Upper Jurassic Cotton Valley and Haynesville sandstones. In the Kung Fu well (VK117), the Cotton Valley, and upper Haynesville sandstones are interpreted as shallow-water deltaic sands. Interbedded shales with this section have source rock potential. The gross thickness of this clastic interval expands or thickens within growth faults located at the deltaic fronts. Extending further down depositional dip in the current deep-water play area, the sands thin, and the shale becomes a richer source rock (Figure 2).

Shell was very successful in lease sale 181, winning acreage on all of its top tier prospects. Three wells would be planned as the minimum number to test the play if only marginal success was found. The plan was to drill a well in the north half of the sale area and a second well in the southern portion. These wells were designed to test the full range of stratigraphic and structural opportunities and maximize exposure across the play area. The third well would depend on the relative success and would allow for concept learnings from the first two wells to select the location. Choosing which prospect would be the first to drill was a relatively easy decision.

Prospect Shiloh (DC269) was chosen as the first exploration well and was drilled in 2003. This prospect enabled a single well to stratigraphically test the entire Mesozoic section, where all three Jurassic primary objectives were stacked vertically, and the petroleum systems could be fully tested (Godo, 2006). Volumetric analysis at Shiloh revealed that the three objectives had unequal volumes inherent in the downthrown growth structure given that the area of closure became smaller with depth. The horizon with the largest volume potential was the Haynesville sand objectives with over 17,000 acres at the maximum closure. The Haynesville sands required the underlying Smackover source rock for vertical charge. At the Cotton Valley and Norphlet levels, the closures were much smaller. At the Norphlet level, two smaller closures were present beneath the larger simple closure in the Haynesville. This well would penetrate only the eastern closure (called Shiloh), leaving the western closure (named Antietam) as a potential follow-up well. The Smackover source rock was required to vertically charge downward into the Norphlet. Downward charge was a well-accepted concept due to the experience onshore with the same Norphlet charge mechanism.

The results of Shiloh were both positive and negative. The Tithonian or Cotton Valley did not contain any significant sands. It did, however, show that the entire section was a marine source rock, which helped sustain later exploration efforts. The Cotton Valley had a small closure area, so there was still excitement as drilling began to penetrate the Hayesville large-volume potential objective. More significant disappointment came when the Haynesville was found to contain only calcareous mud sequences with no sandstones or porosity of any kind. Alternating carbonate percentages in the marls and shale of the Haynesville produced the necessary sonic and density differences needed to create Haynesville reflectivity. However, the pattern of seismic reflections did indicate a growth fault position. The Haynesville paleogeography around the Middle Ground Arch was similar to the present-day area between the Florida Keys and its mainland. This environment expanded into a fault system moving downdip in response to gravity loading on the Louann Salt adjacent to the Middle Ground Arch (also referred to as the southern platform [Dobson and Buffler, 1997] and the Desoto Arch [Christenson, 1990]). After penetrating the Haynesville and not finding any reservoirs, only the small closure area containing the Norphlet remained.

By this point, it was realized that no hub class volumes would be discovered at Shiloh no matter what the Norphlet might contain. As the Norphlet was about to be penetrated, some were already looking to the next well in the south (likely prospect Cheyenne) as the next hope. But drilling activity on Shiloh was not finished yet. Upon exiting the basal Smackover carbonate, the well took a 2 lb/gal inflow at the top of the Norphlet. The well circulated bottoms up, and the mudlog reported bright red shale cuttings and some sandstone. Drilling continued through sand with streaming oil cut florescence and a resistivity log that indicated a sharp oil water contact after only 170 ft (52 m). The well drilled only a total thickness of 250 ft (76 m) of Norphlet before encountering 20 ft (6 m) of Pine Hill above the Louann Salt. Recovering high-quality oil samples with low viscosity helped to justify a core to be taken in a bypass wellbore. This core would provide the information required for facies determination and more rock quality information. There was complete recovery of the bypass core, and the core displayed nothing but repeated cycles of high-angle aeolian cross-bedding. Petrographic analysis revealed chlorite coats around sand grains with oil-filled pores just like those found in the Destin Dome aeolian sands. With porosity values in the 15% range, the sharp oil–water contact was much too abrupt for rocks in this porosity range. There was no real transitional oil column with gradual decreasing saturations, nor was there pressure evidence of any water gradient. The presence of oil shows to the base of the formation also supported the interpretation that the present-day oil contact was in fact a residual contact. Shiloh was a small oil field with commerciality in question, but Shell had what was needed to develop an aeolian sand erg concept to further the Norphlet exploration play.

It was only 11 weeks after Shell had taken the core in Shiloh that a second deep-water sale, lease sale 189, was to be held. The area of the new lease sale was the same as the original lease sale 181 area. With the new information from Shiloh, the Norphlet play probability of success (PoS) in this area had been substantially upgraded. The Norphlet play was now potentially viable on its own and no longer required closures at other objective levels. New Norphlet prospects in sale 189 were named Vicksburg (DC353), Fredericksburg (DC486), and Gettysburg (DC398). It appeared that this new play was under the radar of Shell's competitors.

Three months after sale 189, yet another lease sale was held. This time the lease offering area was different, as it was in the central district of the Gulf of Mexico. This sale area was adjacent to the previous two lease sales. The new lease sale was numbered 190, and the prize was a Norphlet prospect called Appomattox.

The Appomattox lease blocks had been newly released by the previous operator who had held the lease for 10 years without drilling. Also in this sale was the western closure culmination of the just leased Vicksburg prospect. As bids were being prepared, there was a feeling that competition would be limited, given it appeared that the industry had not yet caught on to the Norphlet play. Sale 190 was held, and Shell bid a relatively low amount and narrowly lost the key Appomattox block to a competitor that was targeting shallow Tertiary bright spots.

During late 2003 and early 2004, a second well was planned to test the southernmost portion of the Mesozoic play, and it targeted prospect Cheyenne. The well reached its total depth in August 2004 and was a test of the lower Tertiary through uppermost Jurassic stratigraphy. There was a very strong Miocene bright spot amplitude that the well would test, but it was not Shell's primary objective. The primary objective of Cheyenne was thought to be Cotton Valley sands encased in mature source rock on a four-way simple dip closure. Actual results were different below the base Aptian, as an unconformity minimized the thickness of the Cotton Valley section. No moveable hydrocarbons were found in the Mesozoic section. There was some oil recovered from the Smackover via a Modular Formation Dynamics Tester. The final result at Cheyenne was that it had made a shallow Miocene-aged gas discovery. At that point, Shell's partner Anadarko took over operations on the block and tied the gas discovery into the Independence semisubmersible production hub facility. With a second Mesozoic well now finished but no oil volumes being found, there was much less enthusiasm for committing to a third well. A smaller team remained focused on Norphlet exploration, following up on the results of Shiloh. The question was asked of the team, would Norphlet fields all be just small accumulations like those found at Shiloh, Destin Dome and in all of the onshore fields?

In 2004, with the Cheyenne well dry in the Mesozoic, there was no rush to select the third well to be drilled, if in fact even would there be approval for one. Appomattox was still the team's favorite prospect to drill but Shell did not own the lease. Shell continued negotiations with the lease owner to acquire the Appomattox block. Meanwhile, the team matured prospect Vicksburg in the portfolio. Three years passed before approval and in 2007, when Vicksburg was about to be drilled, Shell finally received word that the Appomattox leases had been acquired through commercial trade negotiations. However, drilling Vicksburg had already begun. With planning and permitting processes accelerated, Appomattox could not be drilled before perhaps two more years.

The Vicksburg well was drilled in 2007 and was timed to allow for the results to impact the evaluation of additional Norphlet prospects in the upcoming lease sale area. The Vicksburg (DC353) exploration well at location B, penetrated a thrust-faulted nose in the Norphlet sandstone, with the oil–water contact found in the hanging wall. The oil-in-place discovery at Vicksburg was in the mid-range of the predrill volume estimate (Godo et al., 2011). Shell integrated the Vicksburg results into the existing conceptual model and acquired several leases over a dozen new Norphlet prospects.

With the discovery at Vicksburg, there was a large momentum to drill soon, even before Appomattox could be drilled. At that time, only a few prospects in the Norphlet portfolio had approved paperwork that were ready to be drilled. Prospect Fredericksburg was one of these prospects. The four-way simple structure at Fredericksburg had an outward attractiveness; however, the prospect itself lacked some of the analogous characteristics of the previous Norphlet discoveries. Fredericksburg was drilled several months after Vicksburg, and the well was a confirmed dry hole with no oil shows.

The dry hole at Fredericksburg seemed to sound the death knell for the play. However, a clever strategy emerged to give the Norphlet one last chance to either find big oil or exit the play. That strategy had Shell drilling two Norphlet prospects back to back, regardless of the results of the first well. The two prospects chosen for this program were Appomattox (finally drill-ready) and Antietam. After all, it was said that both prospects were just a syncline away from discovered oil (Antietam to Shiloh and Appomattox to Vicksburg). Antietam found a very thin oil column over a larger residual oil column. But given the two-well commitment to the area, Appomattox would still be drilled.

In 2009, the exploration well at Appomattox (MC392-1) found porous aeolian sand filled with oil pay to the base of the well (Figures 4 and 5). Obviously, the team was very excited. That excitement was nothing, however, compared to the excitement level after a downdip sidetrack (AppoOHst) again found oil-filled sand with pay to the base of the reservoir. The implication of finding oil this deep on the structure had a palpitating effect. The depth of this oil section was deeper than what was thought to be the predrill spill point. This predrill spill point was defined as a syncline located on the northeast flank of Appomattox. Finding oil this deep in the sidetrack well combined with the observation that there was no apparent crestal faulting to give access to the predrill spill point led imaginations to soar regarding potential trap size. The key question was, "How big is this thing?" In order to find the oil–water contact (OWC) with the rig in this position, a third well was designed to

go downdip and find the contact. The drillers designed an essentially horizontal well to stay within the Norphlet while drilling downdip on the structure in search of water. This second sidetrack ultimately penetrated the oil–water contact (OWC) in the most downdip sidetrack well (AppoOHbp) (see Figure 5) and proved up an oil column in excess of 2000 ft (610 m) in the south fault block. Appomattox appeared to be the hub class volume field the team had been in search of for nearly a decade.

Further Appomattox appraisal drilling was delayed by the Gulf of Mexico drilling moratorium that followed the Macondo incident in 2010. Despite the Gulf of Mexico drilling moratorium being lifted in October 2010, there were a series of new permitting issues to work through before appraisal of Appomattox could restart.

Appraisal operations resumed in July 2011, and the Appomattox Northeast Fault Block was successfully appraised by the MC348-1 well and an updip sidetrack in late 2011 and early 2012. The objective of this well was to penetrate a depth equivalent to the OWC contact found in the original hole in the Northeast Fault Block in order to test the mega case and potentially discriminate between a one- or two-hub development scenario. In addition, this well would test the connectivity of the structure and hold the MC348 lease.

The original Northeast appraisal well, designed to test the upside volume realization, was unsuccessful and found only thick, high-quality, wet Norphlet sand. However, the subsequent updip Northeast sidetrack confirmed the presence of a significant hydrocarbon accumulation in the Northeast Fault Block. Immediately after the Northeast Fault Block appraisal well was drilled, the western extension of the South Fault Block was successfully appraised, indicating hydraulic communication over geologic time in the southern half of the structure. In August 2012, this appraisal well was sidetracked to a target in the Northwest Fault Block with the aim of proving additional stock tank oil initially in place (STOIIP) and sizing the production system.

Appraisal continued through mid-2013 with the drilling of the nearby Vicksburg A pod in early 2013 followed by the eastern extension of the Appomattox field—Corinth, in early to mid-2013. Corinth was a dry hole; however, Vicksburg A added over 100 million BOE to the Appomattox resource.

APPOMATTOX FIELD DEVELOPMENT

Following the Appomattox and Vicksburg field discoveries and in parallel with appraisal, significant engineering studies have been completed that have led to the final selection of a development concept for

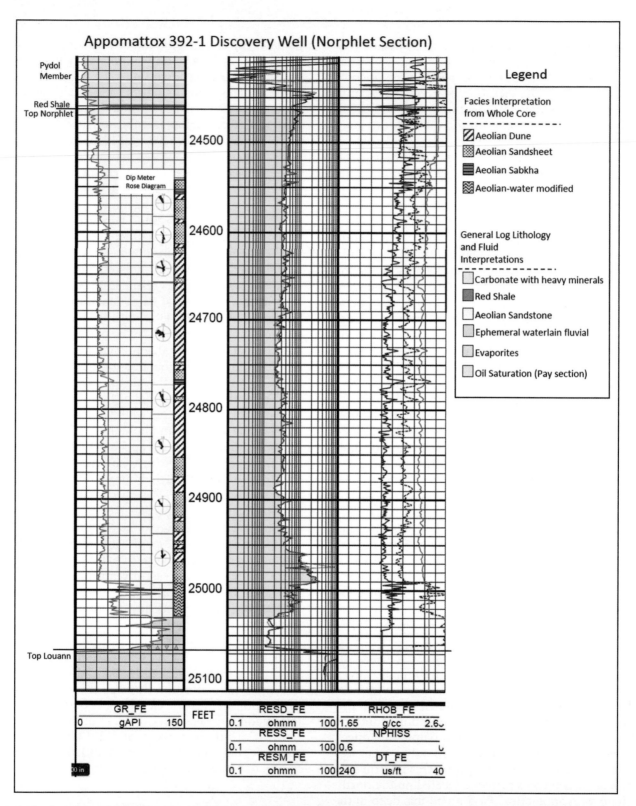

Figure 4. The log shown is the discovery well for the Appomattox field. Nearly 600 ft (183 m) of gross Norphlet section with most of it aeolian sandstone (colored yellow by the gamma ray curve). The green colored area under the resistivity curve illustrates the section of very high oil saturation. A continuous whole cored section describes in more detail the specific facies types: 1) Aeolian dune deposits have a dominance of avalanche strata relative to wind-ripple strata, together with the unimodal and consistent dip azimuth, they support a barchan/barchanoid dune morphology. Avalanche strata are typically interbedded with flat-lying wind-ripple strata, suggesting that successive dune deposits are separated by interdune facies. 2) Aeolian sandsheet deposits typically made up of decimeter to meter scale sets of flat-lying wind-ripple to low angle laminated sandstones. 3) Sabkha deposits are dominated by flat-lying, irregularly bedded sandstones with reworked anhydrite clasts, with preserved wind-ripples having a low mud content. 4) Sheet/streamflood deposits are characterized in core by sharp-based, occasionally erosive with rip up mud clasts. They are normally graded beds of massive and/or flat-lying laminated sandstones. These likely represent rapid deposition under an upperflow regime conditions likely in an unconfined, ephemeral sheetflood depositional setting.

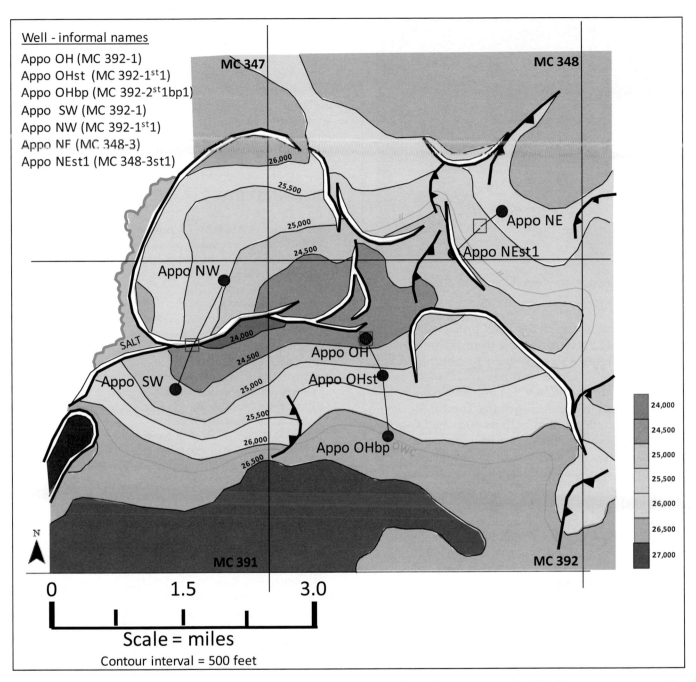

Figure 5. The four-way dip closure of the Appomattox oil field located in Mississippi Canyon (MC) blocks 391, 392, 347, and 348. The discovery well for this field is the MC292-1 well and was followed up with 2 downdip sidetrack wells drilled to the Louann salt. Three subsequent appraisal wells then tested the structural flanks of the discovery. The first appraisal well location was in the Northeast flank of the structure (MC348). The final two appraisal penetrations were in the southwest and northwest flanks of the structure (MV391). The square boxes represent the surface locations of the rigs for the discovery and appraisal programs.

the fields. Sanctioned in 2015, the Appomattox development host will consist of a semisubmersible, four-column production host platform, a subsea system featuring six drill centers, 15 producing wells, and five water injection wells (Figure 6). The upsized export pipeline will serve the Appomattox host for oil export

and will have preinstalled subsea connection points, which will allow for future interconnections.

The Appomattox development will initially produce from the Appomattox and Vicksburg fields, with average peak production estimated to reach approximately 175,000 BOE per day. This will be the

Figure 6. The Appomattox development concept.

largest output of any of the Shell projects in the Gulf of Mexico. The platform and the Appomattox and Vicksburg fields will be owned by Shell (79%) and Nexen Petroleum Offshore U.S.A. Inc. (21%), a wholly owned subsidiary of CNOOC Limited.

The sanctioned project includes capital for the development of 650 million BOE resources at Appomattox and Vicksburg, with start-up estimated around the end of this decade. Additional discovered opportunities in the area that could be tied back into the Appomattox hub would bring the total estimated discovered resources in the area to more than 800 million BOE. Shell continues exploration prospecting and drilling in the Norphlet area of the Gulf of Mexico.

ACKNOWLEDGMENTS

The author is honored to present this information on the giant Appomattox discovery as one of the oil fields selected for this AAPG Memoir.

The author wishes to thank and acknowledge both Shell and Nexen for permission to share this information. Thanks are also given for allowing the expansion of this paper to include a historical perspective of the play as well as provide a current perspective on the deep-water play segment, something that the authors feel is an important part of preserving this play-opening history in the Gulf of Mexico.

The support and tenacity shown by management through times of repeated exploratory challenges has been remarkable. Despite somewhat limited economic success over years of exploration in the play, it has demonstrated to be both a commercial success and an outstanding learning experience for the geoscientists involved.

Thankfully, this knowledge has paid off with success at Appomattox, Vicksburg, Rydberg, and Fort Sumter in the current deep-water play. Of course, all these learnings could not have happened without the rich history of former geoscientists working this play. Acknowledgment and gratitude are given to all of those individuals who span nearly 50 years of Norphlet work. Though there is not enough space to give proper credit to all of them, to all of them we extend our humble gratitude.

REFERENCES CITED

Ajdukiewicz, J. M., P. H. Nicholson, and W. L. Esch, 2010, Prediction of deep reservoir quality from early diagenetic process models in the Jurassic eolian Norphlet formation, Gulf of Mexico: AAPG Bulletin, v. 94, p. 1189–1227.

Anderson, E. G., 1979, Basic Mesozoic study in Louisiana, the northern coastal region, and the Gulf Province: Louisiana Geological Survey Folio Series no. 3, 58 p.

Andrews, D. I., 1960, The Louann Salt and its relationship to Gulf Coast salt domes: Gulf Coast Association of Geological Societies Transactions, v. 10, p. 215–240.

Applegate, A. V., and J. M. Lloyd, 1985, Summary of Florida petroleum production and exploration, onshore and offshore through 1984: Florida Geological Survey, Information Circular, no. 101, 69 p.

Applin, P. L., 1951, Preliminary report on buried pre-Mesozoic rocks in Florida and adjacent states: U.S. Geological Survey Circular, no. 91, 28 p.

Arthur, J. D., 1988, Petrogenesis of early Mesozoic tholeiite in the Florida basement and an overview of Florida basement geology: Florida Geological Survey Report of Investigations, no. 97, 38 p.

Ash, S. R., 1980, Upper Triassic floral zones of North America, *in* D. C. Dilcher and T. N. Taylor, eds., Biostratigraphy of fossil plants: Stroudsburg, Pennsylvania, Dowden, Hutchinson & Ross, Inc., p. 153–170.

Bagnold, R. A., 2005, The physics of blown sand and desert dunes: Mineola, New York, Dover Publications, Inc., 265 p.

Baldwin, O. D., and J. A. S. Adams, 1971, 40K/40Ar ages of the alkalic igneous rocks of the Balcones fault trend of Texas: Texas Journal of Science, v. 22, p. 223–231.

Barnett, R. S., 1975, Basement structure of Florida and its tectonic implications: Gulf Coast Association of Geological Societies Transactions, v. 25, p. 122–142.

Bass, M. N., 1969, Petrography and ages of crystalline basement rocks of Florida-some extrapolations: AAPG Memoir 11, p. 283–310.

Benson, D. J., 1985, Diagenetic controls on reservoir development and quality Smackover formation of southwest Alabama: Gulf Coast Association of Geological Societies Transactions, v. 35, p. 317–326.

Benson, D. J., 1988, Depositional history of the Smackover formation in southwest Alabama: Gulf Coast Association of Geological Societies Transactions, v. 38, p. 197–205.

Berner, R. A., 1970, Sedimentary pyrite formation: American Journal of Science, v. 268, p. 1–23.

Berner, R. A., 1984, Sedimentary pyrite formation: An update: Geochimica et Cosmochimica Acta, v. 48, p. 605–615.

Bingham, D.H., 1937, Developments in Arkansas-Louisiana-Texas Area, 1936–1937: American Association of Petroleum Geologists Bulletin, v. 21, no. 8, p. 1068–1073.

Bird, D. E., K. Burke, S. A. Hall, and J. F. Casey, 2005, Gulf of Mexico tectonic history: Hotspot tracks, crustal boundaries, and early salt distribution: AAPG Bulletin, v. 89, no. 3, p. 311–328.

Dishop, W. F., 1967, Age of Pre-Smackover formations, North Louisiana and South Arkansas: American Association of Petroleum Geologists Bulletin, v. 51, p. 244–250.

Burch, D. E., and A. E. Weidie, 1994, Petrology, stratigraphy, and depositional history of the upper Triassic–lower Jurassic Eagle Mills formation, Choctaw County, Alabama: Transactions of the Gulf Coast Associations of Geological Societies, v. 44, p. 117–118.

Cagle, J. W., and M. A. Khan, 1983, Smackover-Norphlet Stratigraphy, South Wiggins Arch, Mississippi and Alabama: Gulf Coast Association of Geological Societies Transactions, v. 33, p. 23–29.

Champlin, S. D., 1996, The petrophysical characteristics of Jurassic reservoirs of the Coastal Mississippi counties and adjacent state waters: Mississippi Office of Geology, Department of Environmental Quality, Open File Report 42, 80 p.

Christenson, G., 1990, The Florida Lineament: Gulf Coast Association of Geological Societies Transactions, v. 40, p. 99–115.

Chowns, T. M., and C. T. Williams, 1983, Pre-Cretaceous rocks beneath the Georgia Coastal Plain: Regional implications: U.S. Geological Survey Professional Paper 1313-L, p. L1–L42.

Claypool, G. E., and E. A. Mancini, 1989, Geochemical relationships of petroleum in Mesozoic reservoirs to carbonate source rocks of Jurassic Smackover formation, southwestern Alabama: AAPG Bulletin, v. 73, p. 904–924.

Cockrell, A., 2005, Drilling ahead: The quest for oil in the Deep South, 1945–2005: Jackson, University Press of Mississippi, 301 p.

Cornet, B., and P. E. Olsen, 1985, A summary of the biostratigraphy of the Newark Supergroup of eastern North America, with comments on early Mesozoic provinciality, in R. Weber, ed., 3rd Congresso Latinoamericano de Paleontologia, Mexico, Simposio Sohre Floras del Triasico Tardio, su Fitografia y Paleoecologia, Memoria: Mexico City, Universidad National Autonoma de Mexico, Instituto de Geologia, p. 67–81.

Crone, A. J., 1975, Laboratory and field studies of mechanically infiltrated matrix clay in arid fluvial sediments: Ph.D. thesis, University of Colorado, 162 p.

Dawson, W. C., and C. A. Callender, 1992, Diagenetic and sedimentologic aspects of Eagle Mills–Werner conglomerate sandstones (Triassic–Jurassic), northeast Texas: Gulf Coast Association of Geological Societies Transactions, v. 24, p. 449–457.

Dickinson, K. A., 1968, Upper Jurassic stratigraphy of some adjacent parts of Texas, Louisiana and Arkansas: USGS Professional Paper 594E, 25 p.

Dickinson, K. A., 1969, Upper Jurassic carbonate rocks in northeastern Texas and adjoining parts of Arkansas and Louisiana: Gulf Coast Association of Geological Societies Transactions, v. 19, p. 175–187.

Dinkins, T.H., Jr., 1968, Jurassic stratigraphy of central and southern Mississippi, in Jurassic stratigraphy of Mississippi: Mississippi Geol., Econ. and Topog. Survey Bull. 109, pp. 9-37

Dixon, S. A., D. M. Summers, and R. C. Surdam, 1989, Diagenesis and preservation of porosity in the Norphlet formation (Upper Jurassic), southern Alabama: AAPG Bulletin, v. 73, p. 707–728.

Dobson, L. M., and R. T. Buffler, 1997, Seismic stratigraphy and geologic history of Jurassic rocks, northeastern Gulf of Mexico: American Association of Petroleum Geologists Bulletin, v. 81, p. 100–120.

Douglas, S. W., 2010, The Jurassic Norphlet formation of the deep-water eastern Gulf of Mexico: A sedimentologic investigation of aeolian facies, their reservoir characteristics, and their depositional history; M.S. thesis, Waco, Texas, Baylor University, 59 p.

England, W. A., A. S. Mackenzie, D. M. Mann, and T. M. Quigley, 1987, The movement and entrapment of petroleum fluids in the subsurface: Journal of the Geological Society, v. 144, p. 327–347.

England, W. A., and A. J. Fleet, 1991, Introduction: Petroleum Migration, Geological Society of London, Special Publication no. 59, p. 1–6.

Ericksen, R. L., and S. C. Theiling, 1993, Regional Jurassic Geologic Framework and Petroleum Geology, Coastal Mississippi and Adjacent Onshore State and Federal Waters, Mississippi Department of Environmental Quality Office of Geology, Open File Report 22, 67 p.

Frost, W., 2010, The somewhat accidental discovery of the Mobile Bay Gas Field: A story of perseverance and good fortune: AAPG Search and Discovery Article no. 110133, 27 p.

Fryberger, S. G., A. M. Al-Sari, and T. J. Clisham, 1983, Eolian dune, interdune, sand sheet, and silica clastic sabkha sediments of an offshore prograding sand sea, Dhahran area, Saudi Arabia: American Association of Petroleum Geologists Bulletin, v. 67, p. 280–312.

Gawloski, T., 1983, Stratigraphy and environmental significance of the continental Triassic rocks of Texas: Baylor Geological Studies, v. 41, p. 48.

Ginsberg, R. N., 1971, Landward movement of carbonate mud: New model for regressive cycles in carbonates (abs.): AAPG Bulletin, v. 55, p. 340.

Godo, T., 2006, Norphlet aeolian Dunes in the deep water Gulf of Mexico (abs.): Houston Geological Society Bulletin, v. 49, no. 2, p. 11

Godo, T. J., E. Chuparova, and D. E. McKinney, 2011, Norphlet aeolian Sand Fairway established in the deep water Gulf of Mexico: AAPG Search and Discovery Article no. 90124, 2011 AAPG Annual Convention and Exhibition, April 10–13, 2011, Houston, Texas.

Gohn, G. S., D. Gottfried, M. A. Lanphere, and B. B. Higgins, 1978, Regional implications of Triassic or Jurassic age for basalt and sedimentary red beds in the South Carolina coastal plain: Science, v. 202, no. 4370, p. 887–890.

Goldhaber, M. B., and I. R. Kaplan, 1974, The sulfur cycle, *in* E. D. Goldberg, ed., The sea, v. 5: New York, Wiley-Interscience, p. 569–655.

Green, M., 1989, Eylau, Tophat and West Texarkana (Smackover, Eagle Mills) Field Complex, Bowie County, Texas: p. 54–60 *in* P. W. Shoemaker, eds, Occurrence of oil and gas in northeast Texas; East Texas Geological Society Publication Series: 1989 Edition, p. 5460.

Hames, W. E., P. R. Renne, and C. Ruppel, 2000, New evidence for geologically instantaneous emplacement of earliest Jurassic Central Atlantic magmatic province basalts on the North American margin: Geology, v. 28, p. 859–862.

Hantschel, T. A., and A. I. Kauerauf, 2009, Fundamentals of basin and petroleum systems modeling: Berlin and Heidelberg, Germany, Springer-Verlag, 476 p.

Harrelson, D. W., and S. L. Ingram, 2000, Geology of the Mississippi Valley Gas #1 Terry Bell, Washington County, Mississippi: Gulf Coast Association of Geological Societies Transactions, v. 50, p. 631–636.

Hartman, J. A., 1968, The Norphlet sandstone, Pelahatchie Field, Rankin County, Mississippi: Transactions of the Gulf Coast Association of Geological Societies, v. 18, p. 2–11.

Hazzard, R. T., W. C. Spooner, and B. W. Blanpied, 1947, Notes on the stratigraphy of the formations which underlie the Smackover Limestone in south Arkansas, northeast Texas and north Louisiana: Reference Report on Certain Oil and gas Fields of north Louisiana, south Arkansas, Mississippi and Alabama: Shreveport Geological Society Publication, v. 2, p. 483–503.

Heffner, D. M., 2013, Tectonics of the South Georgia rift, Ph.D. thesis, University of South Carolina, 178 p.

Hurbert, J. F., P. E. Feshbach-Meriney, and M. A. Smith, 1992, The Triassic–Jurassic Hartford rift basin, Connecticut and Massachusetts: Evolution, sandstone diagenesis, and hydrocarbon history: AAPG Bulletin, v. 76, no. 11, p. 1710–1754.

Hurtgen, M.T., T. W. Lyons, E. D. Ingall, and A. M. Cruse, 1999, Anomalous enrichment of iron monosulfide in euxinic marine sediments and the role of H_2S in iron sulfide transformations: American Journal of Science, v. 299, p. 556–588.

Hutchinson, D. R., and K. D. Klitgord, 1988, Evolution of rift basins on the continental margin off southern New England, *in* W. Manspeizer, ed., Triassic–Jurassic rifting: Continental breakup and the origin of the Atlantic Ocean and passive margins, part A: Amsterdam, Elsevier, p. 81–98.

Imlay, R. W., 1940, Lower Cretaceous and Jurassic formations of southern Arkansas, and their oil and gas possibilities: Arkansas Geologic Survey Informational Circular no. 12, 65 p.

Jackson, J. B., and P. M. Harris, 1982, Jurassic petroleum geology of Southwestern Clarke County, Mississippi: Transactions of the Gulf Coast Association of Geological Societies, v. 32, p. 45–57.

Jux, U., 1961, The palynologic age of diapiric and bedded salt in the Guli mast al province: Louisiana Geological Survey Bulletin, v. 38, p. 46.

Karges, H. K., 1968, Pelahatchie field: Mississippi giant? Transactions of the Gulf Coast Association of Geological Societies, v. 18, p. 264–274.

Kirkland, D. W., and J. E. Gerhard, 1971, Jurassic salt, central Gulf of Mexico, and its temporal relation to circum-Gulf evaporites: American Association of Petroleum Geologists Bulletin, v. 55, p. 680–686.

Klitgord, K. D., and P. Popenoe, 1984, Florida: A Jurassic transform plate boundary: Journal of Geophysical Research, v. 89, no. B9, p. 7753–7772.

Kneller, E. A., and C. A. Johnson, 2011, Plate kinematics of the Gulf of Mexico based on integrated observations from the Central and South Atlantic: Gulf Coast Association of Geological Societies Transactions, p. 283–299.

Kugler, R. L., and R. M. Mink, 1999, Depositional and diagenetic history and petroleum geology of the Jurassic Norphlet formation of the Alabama Coastal Waters Area and Adjacent Federal Waters Area: Marine Georesources and Geotechnology, v. 17, nos. 2–3, p. 215–232.

Ladd, J. W., R. T. Buffler, J. S. Watkins, J. L. Worzel, and A. Carranza, 1976, Deep seismic reflection results from the Gulf of Mexico: Geology, v. 4, p. 365–368.

Lindquist, S. J., 1983, Nugget formation reservoir characteristics affecting production in the overthrust belt of S.W. Wyoming: Journal of Petroleum Technology, v. 35, p. 1355–1365.

Lovell, T., and A. Weislogel, 2010, Detrital zircon U–Pb age constraints on the provenance of the Upper Jurassic Norphlet formation, eastern Gulf of Mexico: Implications for paleogeography: Gulf Coast Association of Geological Societies Transactions, v. 60, p. 443–460.

Lupe, R., and T. S. Ahlbrandt, 1979, Sediments of an ancient eolian environment: Reservoir inhomogeneity, *in* E. D. McKee, ed., A study of global sand seas: USGS Professional Paper no. 1052, p. 241–251.

Macrae, G., and J. S. Watkins, 1995, Early Mesozoic rift stage half graben beneath the Desoto Canyon salt basin, northeastern Gulf of Mexico: Journal of Geophysical Research, v. 100, no. B9, p. 17,795–17,812.

Mancini, E. A., and D. J. Benson, 1980, Regional stratigraphy of Upper Jurassic Smackover carbonates of southwest Alabama: Gulf Coast Association of Geological Societies Transactions, v. 30, p. 151–165.

Mancini, E. A., R. M. Mink, and B. L. Bearden, 1985a, Upper Jurassic Norphlet hydrocarbon potential along the regional peripheral fault trend in Mississippi, Alabama, and the Florida Panhandle: Transactions of the Gulf Coast Association of Geological Societies, v. 35, p. 225–232.

Mancini, E. A., B. H. Tew, and R. M. Mink, 1992, Hydrocarbon productivity characteristics of Upper Jurassic Smackover carbonates, Eastern Gulf Coastal Plain: Gulf Coast Association of Geological Societies, v. 42, p. 237–244.

Mancini, E. A., B. H. Tew, and R. M. Mink, 1993, Petroleum source rock potential of Mesozoic condensed section deposits of southwest Alabama, *in* B. J. Katz and L. M. Pratt, eds., Source rocks in a sequence stratigraphic framework: American Association of Petroleum Geologists Studies in Geology, v. 37, p. 147–162.

Mancini, E. A., M. Badali, T. M. Puckett, and W. C. Parcell, 2001, Mesozoic carbonate petroleum systems in the northeast Gulf of Mexico area, *in* GCSSEPM Foundation's

21st Annual Research Conference, Petroleum Systems of Deep-Water Basins, December 2–5, p. 423–451.

Mancini, E. A., R. M. Mink, B. L. Bearden, and R. R. Hamilton, 1987, Recoverable natural gas reserves from the Jurassic Norphlet formation, Alabama coastal waters area: Gulf Coast Association of Geological Societies Transactions, v. 37, p. 153–160.

Mancini, E. A., W. C. Parcell, T. M. Puckett, and D. J. Benson, 2003, Upper Jurassic (Oxfordian) Smackover carbonate petroleum system characterization and modelling, Mississippi Interior salt basin area, northeastern Gulf of Mexico, USA: Carbonates and Evaporites, v. 18, p. 125–150.

Mancini, E. A., T. M. Puckett, W. C. Parcell, and B. J. Panetta, 1999, Topical reports 1 and 2: Basin analysis of the Mississippi Interior salt basin and petroleum system modeling of the Jurassic Smackover formation, eastern Gulf Coastal Plain: U.S. Department of Energy, Technical Report, Project DE-FG22-96BC14946, 425 p.

Mann, S. D., 1988, Subaqueous Evaporites of the Buckner Member, Haynesville Formation, Northeast Mobile County, Alabama: GCAGS Transactions, v. 38, p. 187–196.

Manspeizer, W., 1988, Triassic–Jurassic rifting and opening of the Atlantic: An overview, in W. Manspeizer, ed., Triassic–Jurassic rifting, continental breakup and the origin of the Atlantic Ocean and passive margins: New York, New York, Elsevier, p. 41–79.

Manspeizer, W., and H. L. Cousminer, 1988, Late Triassic–early Jurassic synrift basins of the U.S. Atlantic margin, in R. E. Sheridan and J. A. Grow, eds., The Atlantic continental margin, the geology of North America, U.S.: Boulder, Colorado, Geological Society of America, v. 1–2, p. 197–216.

Martin, R. G., 1978, Northern and eastern Gulf of Mexico continental margin: Stratigraphic and structural framework; 1. The setting: Stratigraphic and structural framework, in A. H. Bouma, G. T. Moore, and J. M. Coleman, eds., Framework, facies, and oil trapping characteristics of the upper Continental Margin: Studies in Geology no. 7: Tulsa, Oklahoma, AAPG, p. 21–42.

Marton, G., and R. T. Buffler, 1994, Jurassic reconstruction of the Gulf of Mexico basin: International Geology Review, v. 36, p. 545–586.

Marzano, M. S., G. M. Pense, and P. Andronaco, 1988, A comparison of the Jurassic Norphlet formation in Mary Ann Field, Mobile Bay, Alabama to onshore regional Norphlet trends: Transactions Gulf Coast Association of Geological Societies, v. 38, p. 85–100.

Marzoli, A., P. R. Renne, E. M. Piccirillo, M. Ernesto, G. Bellieni, and A. De Min, 1999, Extensive 200 million-year-old continental flood basalts of the central Atlantic magmatic province: Science v. 284, p. 616–618.

Matlack, K. S., D. W. Houseknecht, and K. R. Applin, 1989, Emplacement of clay into sand by infiltration: Journal of Sedimentary Petrology, v. 59, p. 77–87.

McHone, J. G., 2000, Non-plume magmatism and rifting during the opening of the central Atlantic Ocean: Tectonophysics, v. 316, p. 287–296.

Melas, F. F., and G. M. Friedman, 1992, Petrophysical characteristics of the Jurassic Smackover formation, Jay Field,

Conecuh Embayment, Alabama and Florida: AAPG Bulletin, v. 76, no. 1, p. 81–100.

Mickus, K., R. J. Stern, G. R. Keller, and E. Y. Anthony, 2009, Potential field evidence for a volcanic rifted margin along the Texas Gulf Coast: Geology, v. 37, no. 5, p. 387–390.

Mink, R. M., and E. A. Mancini, 1995, Upper Jurassic and Lower Cretaceous Oil Reservoirs of the Updip Basement Structural Play, Southwest, Alabama: Gulf Coast Association of Geological Societies Transactions, v. 45, p. 441–448.

Mitchell-Tapping, H. J., 1982, Exploration analysis of the Jurassic Apalachicola Embayment of Florida: Transactions of Gulf Coast Association of Geological Societies, v. 32, p. 413–425.

Moore, C. H., 1984, The upper Smackover of the Gulf rim: Depositional systems, diagenesis, porosity evolution and hydrocarbon production, in W. P. S. Ventress, D. G. Bebout, B. F. Perkins, and C. H. Moore, eds., The Jurassic of the Gulf Rim: Proceedings of the Third Annual Research Conference, Gulf Coast Section Society of Economic Paleontologists and Mineralogists, p. 283–307.

Mountney, N. P., 2012, A stratigraphic model to account for complexity in aeolian dune and interdune successions: Sedimentology, v. 59, no. 3, p. 964–989.

Mountney, N.P., and J. A. Howell, 2000, Aeolian architecture, bedform climbing and preservation space in the Cretaceous Etjo formation, NW Namibia: Sedimentology, v. 47, p. 825–849.

Moy, C., and A. Traverse, 1986, Palynostratigraphy of the subsurface Eagle Mills formation (Triassic) from a well in east-central Texas: Palynology, v. 10, p. 225–234.

Net, L. I., 2003, Linking diagenetic styles to reservoir quality: The Eolian Nugget Sandstone (Jurassic), SW Wyoming; AAPG Search and Discovery Article no. 90013 at 2003 AAPG Annual Meeting, May 11–14, Salt Lake City, Utah, 3 p.

Oehler, J. H., 1984, Carbonate source rocks in the Jurassic Smackover trend of Mississippi, Alabama, and Florida, in J. G. Palacas, ed., Petroleum Geochemistry and Source Rock Potential of Carbonate Rocks, AAPG Studies in Geology, v. 18, p. 63–69.

Olsen, P. E., 1997, Stratigraphic record of the early Mesozoic breakup of Pangea in the Laurasia–Gondwana rift system: Annual Review of Earth and Planetary Sciences, v. 25, p. 337–401.

Ottman, R. D., P. L. Keys, and M. A. Ziegler, 1973, Jay field: A Jurassic stratigraphic trap: Gulf Coast Association of Geological Societies Transactions, v. 23, p. 146–157.

Oxley, M. L., E. Minihan, and J. M. Ridgway, 1967, A study of the Jurassic sediments in portions of Mississippi and Alabama: Transactions of the Gulf Coast Association of Geological Societies, v. 17, p. 24–48.

Padilla y Sanchez, R. J., 2007, Evolucion geologica del sureste mexicano desde el Mezosoico al presente en el contexto regional del Golfo de Mexico.:Boletin de la Sociedad Geologica Mexicana: Tomo LIX, Num. 1, Universidad Nacional Autonoma de Mexico,Facultad de Ingenieria, Division de Ciencias de la Tierra, p. 19–42.

Padilla y Sanchez, R. J., 2014, Tectonics of eastern Mexico–Gulf of Mexico and its hydrocarbon potential: AAPG Search and Discovery Article no. 10622, 54 p.

Parker, E. H., 2014, Crustal magnetism, tectonic inheritance, and continental rifting in the southeastern United States: GSA Today, v. 24, no. 4–5, p. 4–9.

Pepper, A. S., 1991, Estimating petroleum expulsion behavior of source rocks: A novel quantitative approach, *in* A. J. Fleet and W. H. England, eds., Petroleum migration: Special Publication of the Geological Society of London, no. 59, p. 9–31.

Pepper, A. S., and P. J. Corvi, 1995a, Simple kinetic models of petroleum formation: Part I. Oil and gas generation from kerogen: Marine and Petroleum Geology, v. 12, p. 291–319.

Pepper, F., 1982, Depositional environments of the Norphlet formation (Jurassic) in southwestern Alabama: Transactions of the Gulf Coast Association of Geological Societies, v. 32, p. 17–22.

Pettijohn, F. J., 1957, Sedimentary rocks (2nd ed.): New York, New York, Harper, 718 p.

Petty, A. J., 1999, Northeast gulf's James, Andrew exploration history outlined: Oil and Gas Journal, v. 97, no. 44, p. 440–450.

Pilcher, R. S., R. T. Murphy, and J. M. Ciosek, 2014, Jurassic raft tectonics in the northeastern Gulf of Mexico: SEG/AAPG Interpretation, v. 2, no. 4, p. SM39–SM55.

Pindell, J. L., 1985, Alleghenian reconstruction and subsequent evolution of the Gulf of Mexico, Bahamas and proto-Caribbean: Tectonics, v. 4, p. 1–39.

Pindell, J. L., 1994, Evolution of the Gulf of Mexico and the Caribbean, *in* S. K. Donovan and T. A. Jackson, eds., Caribbean geology: An introduction: Kingston, University of the West Indies Publishers Association, p. 13–39.

Pindell, J. L., and L. Kennan, 2001, Kinematic evolution of the Gulf of Mexico and Caribbean, *in* Transactions: Petroleum systems of deep-water basins; Global and Gulf of Mexico experience: GCSSEPM 21st Annual Research Conference, December 2–5, Houston, Texas, p. 193–220.

Pindell, J. L., and L. Kennan, 2009, Tectonic evolution of the Gulf of Mexico, Caribbean and northern South America in the mantle reference frame: An update, *in* K. James, M. A. Lorente, and J. Pindell, eds., Origin and evolution of the Caribbean Region: Geological Society of London, Special Publication, v. 328, p. 1–55.

Pojeta, J., J. Kriz, and J. E. Berdan, 1976, Silurian-Devonian Pelecypods and Paleozoic stratigraphy of subsurface rocks in Florida and Georgia and related Silurian Pelecypods from Bolivia and Turkey: U.S. Geological Survey Professional Paper no. 879, 32 p.

Prather, B. E., 1992, Evolution of a late Jurassic carbonate-evaporite platform in the Conecuh embayment, northeastern Gulf Coast, U.S.A.: AAPG Bulletin, v. 76, no. 2, p. 164–190.

Rainwater, E. H., 1968, Geological History and Oil and Gas Potential of the Central Gulf Coast: Gulf Coast Association of Geological Societies Transactions, v. 18, p. 124165.

Raiswell, R., F. Buckley, R. A. Berner, and T. F. Anderson, 1988, Degree of pyritization of iron as a paleoenvironmental indicator of bottom-water oxygenation: Journal of Sedimentary Petrology, v. 58, p. 812–819.

Raymond, D. E., 1989, Upper Cretaceous and Tertiary lithostratigraphy and biostratigraphy of west-central Alabama, *in* C. W. Copeland, ed., Guidebook 26th Annual Field Trip, October, p. 75–92.

Reed, C. H., 1991, Clarksville field, Red River County, Texas: Production and facies interpretation: Oil and Gas Journal, v. 89, no. 23, p. 49–54.

Rhodes, J. A., and G. B. Maxwell, 1993, Jurassic stratigraphy of the Wiggins Arch, Mississippi: Gulf Coast Association of Geological Societies Transactions, v. 43, p. 333–344.

Ryan, W. P., W. C. Ward, and R. L. Kugler, 1987, Provenance of the Norphlet sandstone, northern Gulf coast: Transactions, Gulf Coast Association of Geological Societies, v. 37, p. 457–468.

Salvador, A., 1991, Triassic–Jurassic, *in* A. Salvador, ed., The Geology of North America, v. J, The Gulf of Mexico basin: Geological Society of America, p. 131–180.

Sassen, R., and C. H. Moore, 1988, Framework of hydrocarbon generation and destruction in eastern Smackover trend: AAPG Bulletin, v. 72, p. 649–663.

Sassen, R., C. H. Moore, and F. C. Meendsen, 1987, Distribution of hydrocarbon source potential in the Jurassic Smackover formation: Organic Geochemistry, v. 11, p. 379–383.

Schenk, C. J., 1981, Porosity and textural characteristics of eolian stratification (abs.): AAPG Bulletin, v. 65, p. 986.

Schenk, C. J., and J. W. Schmoker, 1993, Role of halite in the evolution of sandstone porosity, Upper Jurassic Norphlet formation, Mississippi salt basin: Gulf Coast Association of Geological Societies Transactions, v. 43, p. 357–362.

Schlische, R. W., 1993, Anatomy and evolution of the Triassic–Jurassic continental rift system, eastern North America: Tectonics, v. 12, p. 1026–1042.

Scott, K. R., W. E. Hayes, and R. P. Fietz, 1961, Geology of the Eagle Mills Formation: Transactions of the Gulf Coast Association of Geological Societies, v. 11, p. 1–14.

Shammari, S., S. Franks, and O. Soliman, 2011, Depositional and facies controls on infiltrated/inherited clay coatings: Unayzah Sandstones, Saudi Arabia: AAPG Search and Discovery no. 50459, Houston, Texas, 26 p.

Shew, R.D., and Garner, M. M., 1990, Reservoir Characteristics of Nearshore and Shelf Sandstones in the Jurassic Smackover Formation, Thomasville Field, Mississippi, *in* J. H. Barwis, J. G. Mcpherson, and J. R. J. Studlick, eds., Sandstone Petroleum Reservoirs: Springer-Verlag, New York, p. 437–464.

Sigsby, R. J., 1976, Paleoenvironmental analysis of the Big Escambia Creek-Jay-Blackjack Creek field area: Gulf Coast Association of Geological Societies Transaction, v. 26, p. 258–270.

Smith, D. L., 1982, Review of the tectonic history of the Florida Basement: Tectonophysics, v. 88, p. 122.

Smith, D. L., 1993, Role of continental closure in the distribution of Florida basement features *in* J. L. Pindell, ed., Mesozoic and Early Cenozoic Development of the Gulf of Mexico and Caribbean Region: SEPM Gulf Coast Section, 13th Annual Research Conference Proceedings, p. 18.

Stainforth, J. G., and J. E. A. Reinders, 1990, Primary migration of hydrocarbons by diffusion through organic matter networks, and its effect on oil and gas generation, *in*

B. Durand and F. Behar, eds., Advances in organic geochemistry 1989: Organic Geochemistry, v. 16, p. 61–74.

Stern, R. J., E. Y. Anthony, M. Ren, B. E. Lock, I. Norton, J. Kimura, T. Miyazaki, T. Hanyu, Q. Chang, and Y. Hirahara, 2011, Southern Louisiana salt dome xenolith: First glimpse of Jurassic (ca. 160 Ma) Gulf of Mexico crust: Geology, v. 39, no. 4, p. 315–318.

Stevens, S. H., S. Tye, and S. H. Hyman, 2004, Natural analogs for geologic sequestration: Cap rock evidence for multi-million-year CO$_2$ storage, in Building on the current technology base to provide viable options to reduce carbon intensity: Carbon Capture and Sequestration Third Annual Conference, May 3–6, Alexandria, Virginia.

Story, C., 1998, 3-D seismic case histories from the Gulf Coast basin: Transactions of the Gulf Coast Association of Geological Societies Special Publication, June, p. 123–129.

Studlick, J. R. J., R. D. Shew, G. L. Basye, and J. R. Ray, 1990, A giant carbon dioxide accumulation in the Norphlet formation, Pisgah anticline, Mississippi, p. 181–203 in J. H. Barwis, J. G. Mcpherson, and J. R. J. Studlick, eds., Sandstone Petroleum Reservoirs: New York, Springer-Verlag.

Sylta, Ø., 2004, Hydrocarbon migration, entrapment and preservation: Processes and evaluation: Ph.D. thesis, Norwegian University of Science and Technology, Department of Geology and Mineral Resources Engineering, p. 1–16.

Taylor, T., R. Stancliffe, C. Macaulay, and L. Hathon, 2004, High temperature quartz cementation and the timing of hydrocarbon accumulation in the Jurassic Norphlet sandstone offshore Gulf of Mexico, USA, in J. M. Cubitt, W. A. England, and S. Larter, eds., Understanding petroleum reservoirs: Towards an integrated reservoir engineering and geochemical approach: London, Geological Society, Special Publication, v. 237, p. 257–278.

Thomas, M. M., and J. A. Clouse, 1990, Primary migration by diffusion through kerogen: II. Hydrocarbon diffusivities in kerogen: Geochimica et Cosmochimica Acta v. 54, p. 2781–2792.

Thomas, W. A., 1985, The Appalachian–Ouachita connection: Paleozoic Orogenic Belt at the southern margin of North America: Annual Review of Earth and Planetary Sciences, v. 13, p. 175–199.

Thomas, W. A., 1988, Early Mesozoic faults of the northern Gulf Coastal Plain in the context of opening of the Atlantic Ocean, in W. Manspeizer, ed., Triassic–Jurassic rifting: Amsterdam, Elsevier, p. 461–476.

Todd, R. G., and R. M. Mitchum Jr., 1977, Seismic stratigraphy and global changes of sea level: Part 8. Identification of upper Triassic, Jurassic and lower Cretaceous seismic sequences in Gulf of Mexico and offshore west Africa, in C. E. Payton, ed., Seismic stratigraphy: Applications to hydrocarbon exploration: AAPG Memoir 26, p. 145–163.

Tolson, J. S., C. W. Copeland, and B. L. Bearden, 1983, Stratigraphic profiles of Jurassic strata in the western part of the Alabama Coastal Plain: Alabama Geological Survey Bulletin 122, 425 p.

Traverse, A., 1987, Pollen and spores date origin of rift basins from Texas to Nova Scotia as early Late Triassic: Science, v. 236, p. 1469–1472.

Turner, P., M. Jones, D. J. Prosser, G. G. Williams, and A. Searl, 1993, Structural and sedimentological controls on diagenesis in the Ravenspurn North gas reservoir, UK Southern North Sea; Petroleum Geology Conference series, v. 4: London Geological Society, p. 771–785.

Vernon, R. C., 1971, Possible future potential of pre-Jurassic Western Gulf basin, in Future petroleum provinces of the United States—their geology and potential: AAPG Memoir 15, v. 2, p. 954–979.

Villeneuve, M., and S. Komara, 1991, Lower Paleozoic transgressions and regressions in the Bove basin (Guinea and Guinea-Bissau, Africa): Stratigraphic, sedimentologic and paleogeographic Data: Journal of African Earth Sciences, v. 12, no. 1–2, p. 67–77.

Wade, W. W., J. R. Plater, and J. Q. Kelley, 1999, History of coastal Alabama natural gas exploration and development, final report: New Orleans, Louisiana, Outer Continental Shelf Study MMS 99-0031, U.S. Department of the Interior, Minerals Management Service, Gulf of Mexico OCS Region, 189 p.

Walker, T. R., 1979, Red colour in eolian sand, in E.D., McKee, ed., A study of global sand seas: USGS Professional Paper 1052, p. 62–81.

Weeks, W. B., 1938, South Arkansas stratigraphy with emphasis on the older coastal plain beds: AAPG Bulletin, v. 22, no. 8, p. 953–983.

White, G. W., S. J. Blanke, and C. F. Clawson II, 1999, Evolutionary model of the Jurassic sequences of the east Texas basin: Implications for hydrocarbon exploration: Gulf Coast Association of Geological Societies Transactions, v. 49, p. 488–498.

Wilkerson, R. P., 1981, Depositional environments and regional stratigraphy of Jurassic Norphlet formation in South Alabama: Transactions of the Gulf Coast Association of Geological Societies, v. 31, p. 417–419.

Withjack, M. O., R. W. Schlische, M. L. Malinconico, and P. E. Olsen, 2012, Rift-basin development: Lessons from the Triassic–Jurassic Newark basin of eastern North America, in W. U. Mohriak, A. Danforth, P. J. Post, D. E. Brown, G. C. Tari, M. Nemcok, and S. J. Sinha, eds., Conjugate divergent margins: Geological Society, London, Special Publications 369, p. 301–321.

Withjack, M. O., R. W. Schlische, and P. E. Olsen, 1998, Diachronous rifting, drifting, and inversion on the passive margin of central eastern North America: An analog for other passive margins: AAPG Bulletin, v. 82, p. 817–835.

Wood, G. D., and D. G. Benson Jr., 1991, First report of the algal coenobium Plaesiodictyon from the North American Triassic: Paleoecologic and paleogeographic significance (abs.): Palynology, v. 15, p. 255.

Wood, G. D., and D. G. Benson Jr., 2000, The Algal Coenobium Plaesiodictyon 9: The North American occurrence of the algal coenobium Plaesiodictyon; Paleogeographic, paleoecologic, and biostratigraphic importance in the Triassic: Palynology, v. 24, p. 9–20.

Woods, R. D., and J. W. Addington, 1973, Pre-Jurassic geologic framework northern Gulf basin: Gulf Coast Association of Geological Societies Transactions, v. 23, p. 92–108.

Worden, R. H., and S. Morad, 2003, Clay minerals in sandstones: A review of the detrital and diagenetic sources and evolution during burial, p. 3–41, *in* R. H. Worden and S. Morad, eds., Clay cement in sandstones: International Association of Sedimentology Special Publication 34, Blackwell Publishing, Oxford, UK.

Zhou, Z., C. J., Ballentine, M. Schoell, and S. H. Stevens, 2012, Identifying and quantifying natural CO_2 sequestration processes over geological timescales: The Jackson Dome CO_2 Deposit, USA: Geochimica et Cosmochimica Acta, v. 86, p. 257–275.

5

Zagorski, William A., Martin Emery, and Jeffrey L. Ventura, 2017, The Marcellus
Shale Play: Its Discovery and Emergence as a Major Global Hydrocarbon
Accumulation, *in* R. K. Merrill and C. A. Sternbach, eds., Giant fields of the
decade 2000–2010: AAPG Memoir 113, p. 55–90.

The Marcellus Shale Play: Its Discovery and Emergence as a Major Global Hydrocarbon Accumulation

William A. Zagorski

*Range Resources Corporation, 3000 Town Center Boulevard, Canonsburg, Pennsylvania 15317, U.S.A.
(e-mail: bzagorski@rangeresources.com)*

Martin Emery

*Chisholm Energy Holdings, LLC., 801 Cherry Street, Suite 1222, Unit 20, Fort Worth, Texas 76102, U.S.A.
(e-mail: memery@chisholmenergy.com)*

Jeffrey L. Ventura

*Range Resources Corporation, 100 Throckmorton Street, Suite 1222, Fort Worth, Texas 76102, U.S.A.
(e-mail: jventura@rangeresources.com)*

ABSTRACT

The Middle Devonian Marcellus shale play has emerged as a major world-class hydrocarbon accumulation. It has rapidly evolved into a major shale gas target in North America and represents one of the largest and most prolific shale plays in the world with a prospective area of approximately 114,000 km^2 (44,000 mi^2). Two major core areas have emerged, each with a unique combination of controlling geologic factors. Production from the Marcellus play reached 16 billion cubic feet of gas equivalent per day (BCFepd) in 2015, and it has been recognized as the largest producing gas field in the United States since 2012.

The organic-rich black shales comprising the Marcellus shale were deposited in a foreland basin that roughly parallels the present-day Allegheny structural front. The Marcellus shale accumulated within an environment favorable to the production, deposition, and preservation of organic-rich sediments. The key geologic and technical factors that regionally define the Marcellus play core areas include organic richness, thermal maturity, degree of overpressure, pay thickness, porosity, permeability, gas in place, degree of natural fracturing, mineralogy, depth, structural style, lateral target selection, completion design, and important rock mechanics issues such as the ability to be fractured, rock brittleness versus ductility, and the ability to generate complex fractures. Structural setting and deformation styles are critical to address natural fracture trends, potential geologic hazards such as faulting and fracturing in structurally complex areas, and fracture stimulation containment issues.

Since the Marcellus shale unconventional shale gas reservoir discovery in 2004 until May 2015, more than 8600 horizontal Marcellus shale wells had been drilled in Pennsylvania, West Virginia, and limited portions of eastern Ohio. Many decades of future drilling potential remain due to the enormous extent of the Marcellus shale play. Horizontal Marcellus wells report initial production rates ranging from less than 1 MMCFe/day to over 47.6 MMCFe /day. Despite the large number of wells drilled and completed to date and production of 16 BCFepd in 2015, the play is still in its infancy due to its vast geographic extent and production potential.

The Marcellus shale represents a continuous-type gas accumulation and when fully developed will comprise a large continuous field or series of fields. Over its productive trend, the Marcellus shale play has significant additional reserve potential in the overlying organic shales in the Devonian Age Rhinestreet, Geneseo, and Burket units as well as deeper potential in the Ordovician Age Utica/Point Pleasant units. Estimates of recoverable reserves from the world's largest gas fields combine their reserve estimates for all key productive units in the field/play trend. Likewise, estimates of in-place gas resources for the Marcellus play range from 2322 tcf for the Marcellus (Hamilton Group) to over 3698 tcf for the combined Devonian Age Marcellus-Geneseo-Rhinestreet system. This represents the largest technically accessible in-place gas resources in the world.

INTRODUCTION

The Middle Devonian Marcellus shale in the Appalachian basin of the northeastern United States represents the premier unconventional natural gas resource of North America. The organic-rich sediments that comprise the Marcellus shale were deposited in a foreland basin setting. The Marcellus shale formation is positioned in the lower portion of the Hamilton group (Middle Devonian), which is bounded above by the Tully Limestone and below by the Onondaga Limestone. Immediately above the Marcellus and Tully intervals are the organic-rich and productive Rhinestreet, Geneseo, and Burkett shales, which are an important, yet largely untapped, part of the Marcellus play.

The Appalachian basin has been an important shale gas producing province since the early 1800s. Since 2004, the organic-rich Marcellus shale, a major source rock, became a major successful hydrocarbon reservoir target for drilling. The modern era of Marcellus shale production began in October 2004 when the Range Resources Renz Unit No. 1 well in Mount Pleasant Township of Washington County, Pennsylvania, was completed using a large Barnett shale–style slick-water fracture stimulation treatment. The play was successfully tested horizontally in 2007, resulting in the establishment of production rates that encouraged industry and generated public interest in the Marcellus shale. The play has attracted the attention of independents, major oil companies, and international partners as discoveries continue to expand the scope of the play and highlight the formation's reservoir characteristics and long-term economic potential. As of May 2015,

more than 70 companies had acquired lease positions and drilled over 8616 horizontal wells across a broad play area encompassing a prospective region of over 114,000 km^2 (44,000 mi^2) across Pennsylvania, West Virginia, New York, Maryland, and Ohio. Production from the Marcellus reached 16 BCFe/day in 2015 and is expected to exceed 20 BCFe/day by 2020.

Prospective limits of the Marcellus shale play are defined to the north, south, and east by the outcrop belt of the unit and to the west by insufficient thermal maturity combined with thinning of the Marcellus shale. Key geologic parameters controlling the productive capability of the Marcellus shale include thickness, total organic content, porosity, permeability, thermal maturity, degree of overpressure, depth, gas show characteristics, and rock mechanics. The wide area of prospective acreage, favorable geologic setting, and excellent production performance confirm the Marcellus shale play's enormous reserve potential.

There are enormous volumes of gas present within the Appalachian Basin Marcellus shale play. We estimate total in-place gas resources of 2322 tcf for the Marcellus and 3698 tcf for the combined upper Devonian shale and Marcellus system. Not yet calculated are the potential reserves underlying the Marcellus play in the deeper Ordovician Point Pleasant-Utica gas petroleum system. When compared to the gas-in-place (GIP) estimates for the top 15 gas fields in the world, the Marcellus gas play has nearly double the gas in place of the North Pars field.

In 2013, the Marcellus shale became the largest producing gas field in the United States. Production reached approximately 16 BCFe/day in 2015 and is expected to reach over 20 BCFe/day by 2020. Recoverable reserve estimates for the Marcellus shale range from 87 tcf and 3.5 billion bbl of natural gas liquids (Milici, 2005) to as high as 867 tcf (Engelder, 2009). Most recent estimates of the Marcellus generally fall within the range of 160 to 489 tcf (Engelder, 2009).

PETROLEUM DEVELOPMENT HISTORY OF THE APPALACHIAN BASIN: PRE-MARCELLUS SHALE ERA

The Appalachian basin represents an historically significant producing province recognized as the birthplace of the modern U.S. petroleum industry (Figure 1). In 1859, the Drake well discovery in Titusville, Pennsylvania, initiated a robust petroleum industry that grew to worldwide prominence. The Drake discovery and subsequent activity initially focused on the development of oil reservoirs from shallow upper

Devonian sandstone reservoirs that were deposited along a broad arcuate trend extending from western New York through large portions of Pennsylvania and West Virginia. Shallow oil and gas was developed from various Mississippian-age targets in eastern Ohio, western West Virginia, and Kentucky. Shallow oil and gas exploration continued until the early 1900s, when secondary recovery projects and methods became increasingly important. Significant exploration for natural gas was initiated in Pennsylvania and western West Virginia in the late 1800s, yielding significant natural discoveries that were critical starting points for our modern natural gas industry.

The giant Lima Indiana oil field was discovered in the Trenton Limestone in northwestern Ohio in 1884 and quickly expanded into adjacent Indiana and Illinois. Production from the Lima Indiana field is estimated at over 485 million barrels of oil and over 1 tcf associated gas. Another giant gas field, the Big

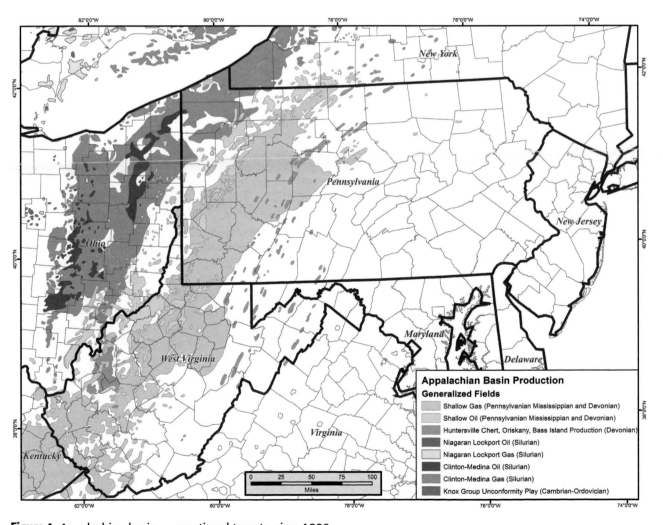

Figure 1. Appalachian basin conventional targets, circa 1990.

Sandy field, was discovered in Kentucky in 1921 and quickly expanded into West Virginia and Virginia. The Big Sandy field was one of the first significant commercial giant accumulations from upper Devonian source rocks. Production from the Big Sandy field is expected to exceed 3 tcf. From 1930 to 1980, industry focused on exploration for the lower Devonian–age Huntersville chert and Oriskany sandstone along several broad northeast to southwest trending anticlines that extend from New York southward into Pennsylvania and West Virginia. This phase of exploration yielded several major fields and many other smaller pools as well as some of the basin's most prolific individual gas wells. Most of the larger of these fields were later converted to active gas storage fields. Primary production from the lower Devonian–age Huntersville chert and Oriskany sandstone fields is estimated at over 1.4 tcf (Flaherty, 1992; Harper, 1992).

A major lower Silurian–age stratigraphic target, the Clinton Medina sandstone, was discovered in Ohio in 1887 and expanded from eastern Ohio into northwestern Pennsylvania and western New York from the 1940s well into the late 1990s. Significant Cambrian Ordovician production associated with the Knox unconformity production was established in the late 1960s in Ohio (Morrow County) and continues today. Prior to 2004 and the emergence of the Marcellus play, the last big conventional industry play in the Appalachian basin was a major resurgence of interest in the Ordovician Trenton Black River interval when several major gas discoveries were developed in central New York and to a lesser degree central West Virginia and Ohio.

Prior to the discovery and commercialization of the Marcellus, the estimated total cumulative and recoverable production from the Appalachian basin's key petroleum systems as defined by the USGS (Ryder et al., 2011) was 69.8 tcf and 3.5 bbl of oil. This study did not account for the full potential of the Marcellus shale or the deeper unconventional play in the Ordovician–age Utica Point Pleasant formations. These estimates are important benchmarks to compare the size and scope of historic conventional plays in the Appalachian basin to the potential now being developed from Marcellus shale.

HISTORY OF APPALACHIAN BASIN UNCONVENTIONAL SHALE DEVELOPMENT

The Appalachian basin has a unique history related to unconventional gas development (Figure 2). Shale gas development in the Appalachian basin began in the early 1800s. The discovery and commercial use of natural gas from upper Devonian shales was first reported in 1825 in Fredonia, New York, which

is widely recognized as the birthplace of the natural gas industry (Lash, 2014). This discovery and expansion of operations significantly predates the early North American oil discoveries in Ontario in 1858 and the Drake oil discovery in Titusville, Pennsylvania, in 1859. By 1860, there were several shallow shale gas fields established over a broad fairway along the Lake Erie shoreline extending from Fredonia, New York, southwest to Sandusky, Ohio (Harper, 2008). These fields produced from organic-rich black shale formations, including the upper Devonian Dunkirk, Rhinestreet, and Middlesex formations and, to a lesser extent, the middle Devonian Marcellus formation. Similar unconventional shale gas resources were developed in the middle Ordovician upper Trenton interval in north-central New York along the southern Lake Ontario shoreline between 1888 and 1940 (Robinson, 1985). In both plays, these relatively shallow wells were used mainly for domestic and light industrial purposes that were extensively developed until the mid-1900s. Initial reported gas volumes for these fields were low and are not considered commercial by modern standards. Nonetheless, these discoveries represent important milestones in the development of unconventional gas resources in North America.

North America's first giant unconventional shale discovery in the Appalachian basin, the Big Sandy field, was discovered in early 1920s in northeastern Kentucky (Hunter, 1935). The primary target is the upper Devonian Huron shale combined with contributions from the Cleveland shale, Rhinestreet shale, and Marcellus shale intervals at depths ranging from 609 m (2000 ft) to over 1829 m (6000 ft) in West Virginia and Virginia. Two key characteristics of the Big Sandy field are a low-pressure gradient combined with a well-established open natural fracture network. These characteristics significantly differentiate Big Sandy field from modern shale plays such as the Barnett, Fayetteville, Haynesville, and the Marcellus, which characteristically display higher pressure gradients combined with lower-density open natural fracture networks. More than 21,000 wells, mostly vertical, have been drilled in the Big Sandy field in eastern Kentucky, southern West Virginia, southern Ohio, and southwest Virginia. The Big Sandy field is considered a giant field with an estimated recovery exceeding 3 tcf.

The Big Sandy field was critically important in aiding understanding of production mechanisms and drivers from unconventional resources. This field was the subject of extensive joint government and industry research from the early 1970s through the early 1990s. These studies provided an excellent basin-wide framework for understanding the extent and various mechanisms governing known shale gas producing areas

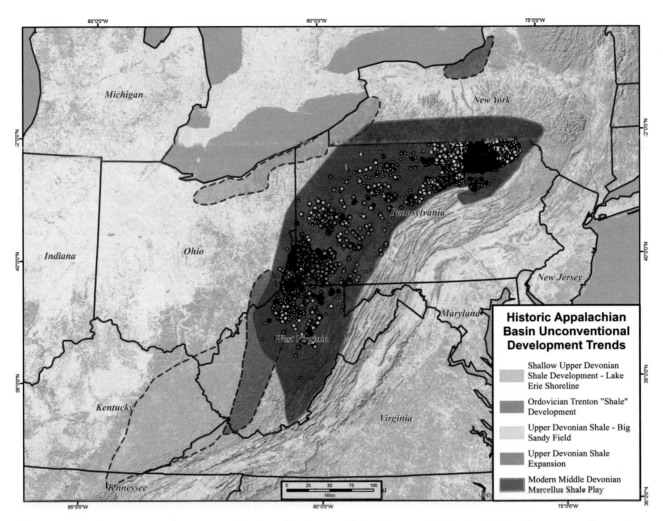

Figure 2. Map depicting major unconventional production trends in the Appalachian basin, key discovery wells, and Marcellus play activity (modified from Zagorski et al., 2012).

at that time and helped provide the path for new Devonian shale discoveries that expanded the Big Sandy field further eastward into central West Virginia. This research also identified the Antrim shale and New Albany shales as potential unconventional plays, both of which were successfully developed by industry prior to the discovery of the Barnett shale and the Marcellus.

COMMERCIAL DEVELOPMENT OF THE MARCELLUS SHALE

Prior to 2004, the Marcellus shale was considered a major Appalachian basin source rock with pervasive natural shows but only a minor exploration target. Earliest low-volume production from the Marcellus can be dated to around 1900 from very shallow depths in northern New York, which were suitable only for domestic purposes.

The Marcellus interval was sometimes completed as a secondary pay zone in the West Virginia portion of the Big Sandy field. From the 1930s through the 1960s in Pennsylvania and New York, there was early interest in the Marcellus during the drilling of early gas discoveries in the underlying Huntersville Chert and Oriskany sandstone. Often, these early Huntersville chert and Oriskany sandstone wells reported significant natural gas shows in the Marcellus shale. These initial shows, while reporting high flow rates, blew down very quickly, indicating limited wellbore connectivity to porosity, permeability, and natural fracturing. A few early Marcellus completions were attempted in northern and northeastern Pennsylvania, usually through natural completions or by explosive shot.

Identification of the Marcellus shale as a potential reservoir by the Eastern Gas Shale Project (EGSP) encouraged several operators to pursue testing of this interval in the late 1970s and early 1980s. Several completions of the Marcellus shale researched and even financed as a result of the U.S. Department of Energy (DOE)–funded Eastern Gas Shale Project (EGSP) were conducted across south-central New York and southwestern Pennsylvania from 1979 through 1982. These wells were extensively studied but achieved only marginal rates of production that were unsuited for large-scale development. These early Marcellus tests in New York were all completed using foam-based fracture treatments (Van Tyne, 1993).

In Pennsylvania, one of the earliest successful tests of the Marcellus shale was drilled and completed in 1979 in Allegheny County. In Washington County, Pennsylvania, three wells were drilled in 1982. In Allegheny and Washington Counties of Pennsylvania, two of these four early tests of the Marcellus were stimulated with carbon dioxide or nitrogen foam–based treatments and showed very poor test rates. Two of these early tests were completed with small-volume slick-water treatments, which yielded more measureable rates and pressures. While these early water based fracture treatments were clearly more effective than the foam treatments, these initial treatments were simply not large enough to establish the rates of production needed to achieve play commerciality on a broad scale. This initial testing phase failed to reach commercial play expectations because of technological limitations and a lack of understanding of how hydraulic fracturing technology can be effectively applied in areas where natural fracture networks were lacking and where significant over pressure was present.

There continued to be limited testing of the Marcellus shale in Pennsylvania, West Virginia, and New York after 2000 as interest in the Barnett grew. These tests also repeated either the foam-based treatments of the past or very-small-scale hydraulic fracture treatments, neither of which were comparable in size and scale to the standard completion treatments being applied to vertical wells in the emergent Barnett shale play in the Fort Worth basin in Texas since 1997.

2004: FIRST COMMERCIAL DEVELOPMENT OF THE MARCELLUS SHALE

The modern era of Marcellus shale gas development began in October 2004 with the successful vertical completion of the Marcellus interval by Range Resources Corporation in Washington County, Pennsylvania. Here, the company had previously drilled an unsuccessful deep exploration well, the Renz Unit 1 to test deeper Devonian and Silurian targets below the Marcellus on a seismic-defined structural closure associated with a left lateral strike-slip fault system. During the drilling of

the Renz Unit well in 2003, several large gas shows were observed in the Marcellus shale. In 2003, Range and other companies were initiating significant shifts in corporate strategy, transitioning from traditional, higher-risk exploration to identifying and testing large-scale and repeatable resource plays. By the end of 2003 and early 2004, horizontal drilling in the Barnett shale had successfully evolved. The Barnett shale quickly became the largest proven gas field in the United States, eventually ramping up to over 6.33 BCFe/day in November 2011 (Powell and Brackett, 2015).

The new exploration paradigm became where the next Barnett-type play/field could be found. Operators were looking throughout North America for new shale gas plays, including the Appalachian basin. The Marcellus shale play in the Appalachian basin and the Renz Unit wellbore then became the focus of an extensive technical analysis by Range Resources. The Barnett and Marcellus plays were compared in terms of geographic extent, depth, thermal maturity, thickness, pressure, reported gas shows, organic content, and gas in place. Range's technical team reviewed old well reports for the numerous well penetrations of the Marcellus in Pennsylvania and nearby areas that documented the distribution and intensity of gas shows in the Marcellus, particularly in southwestern Pennsylvania. A number of these gas shows were identified in some old wells offsetting Range's available Renz wellbore, some dating back to the 1940s. This initial research suggested that the Marcellus could contain significantly larger resource potential than the Barnett, as the Marcellus covers a much larger geographic area than the Barnett.

In early 2004, Range had an opportunity to test the Marcellus in the Renz Unit well combined with a substantial acreage position. Conventional wisdom then was to not test the Marcellus. Unsuccessful attempts to commercialize the play had been tried before in the 1940s and in the 1970s through 1997. Operators of these earlier, unsuccessful, attempts tried various stimulation treatments, usually foam-based treatments or very small gelled water fracture stimulations, in an attempt to unlock hydrocarbons from the Marcellus. These treatments were very small and mere fractions of the scale successfully applied to the Barnett. The explorationist's viewpoint countered that the Marcellus had great gas shows, and its broad prospective play was significantly larger than the Barnett, so it should be approached and tested using the same completion approach successfully applied to the Barnett shale.

On October 23, 2004, a large Barnett-style water frac consisting of 3,569,500 L (943,000 gal) of water and 167,800 kg (370,000 lbs) of sand was used to treat a 27 m (90 ft) gross interval of the Marcellus organic shale in the Renz Unit 1 well (Figure 3). The well was flow tested on October 24, 2004, at an initial rate of 0.300

Figure 3. Photo of Renz Unit 1 large-scale hydraulic fracturing treatment of the Marcellus shale on October 23, 2004 (modified from Ventura, 2013). Photo courtesy of Range Resources Corporation.

MMCFe/day. This rate favorably compared to Barnett vertical tests and marked the discovery of the modern Marcellus shale play. The Renz Unit 1 completion established the production rates needed to encourage both industry and public interest in the Marcellus shale. After a year shut-in period, the Renz Unit 1 was turned on line at an initial rate of 0.800 MMCFe/day. The Marcellus pressure build-up test showed a clearly overpressured gradient of 0.65 psi/ft, confirming the suspected analog to the Barnett shale play. With the establishment of commercial production rates, the modern era of the Marcellus gas play in Appalachian basin had started.

EARLY VERTICAL/HORIZONTAL DEVELOPMENT, 2005 THROUGH 2007

Development of the Marcellus play progressed slowly following the Renz Unit discovery. There was limited drilling and testing (both vertical and horizontal) within the play over the next couple of years. In 2005, Range drilled two successful vertical delineation wells offsetting the Renz Unit. In 2005 and 2006, Range drilled three operationally successful horizontal wells

in the Marcellus shale. However, the initial rates for these first three horizontal wells were not commercial compared to current Barnett horizontal wells. Compared to the successful vertical completions, these early Marcellus horizontal tests were expensive and problematic, largely due to a combination of lack of services and insufficient field experience drilling and completing the Marcellus as a horizontal play.

Activity in the Marcellus play slowly accelerated in 2006 as 28, mostly vertical, Marcellus wells were drilled along a wide fairway that encompassed north-central West Virginia, through most of Pennsylvania, and into southern New York. A landmark vertical Marcellus discovery well was drilled in 2006 in Susquehanna County, Pennsylvania, by Cabot Oil and Gas. The discovery well, the Cabot Oil and Gas Teel 5, was the first new oil and gas well to be drilled in Susquehanna County in 34 years and the fifth well ever drilled in that county. The Teel well initial unrestricted production test rate was reported to be 7 MMCFe/day (Cabot, 2009). A major challenge was there simply was no industry experience in drilling and completing horizontal wells in the Marcellus like there was in the Barnett and emergent Fayetteville plays. A major change was needed to advance the commercialization of the Marcellus into its next successful phase. The largest complicating factor facing all of the early Marcellus pioneers was the lack of services, equipment, and infrastructure and operational experience in the basin to perform multiple-stage slick-water hydraulic fracture treatments.

Drilling activity and success in the Marcellus play increased significantly in 2007. Key step-out and exploration wells were drilled across northeastern and southwestern Pennsylvania. Most significant were the first economically successful horizontal completions in Washington County, Pennsylvania, by Range Resources. In early 2007, while the technical challenges of drilling and completion were slowly being solved, production results lagged, with production rates not exceeding those from vertical wells. After drilling three disappointing horizontal wells in the Marcellus, Range Resources made changes in the lateral target selection and completion approach. The fourth horizontal well, the Gulla 9H, tested 3.2 MMCFe/day after fracture stimulation (Figure 4)

Figure 4. Photo of drilling operations on the Gulla 9H, the key 2007 Marcellus horizontal well located in Washington County, Pennsylvania (modified from Ventura, 2013). Photo courtesy of Range Resources Corporation.

and was the breakthrough horizontal well for the Marcellus shale play.

Later in 2007, Range drilled and completed three more successful horizontal wells, testing 3.7 MMCFe /day, then 4.3 MMCFe/day and 4.7 MMCFe/day. These successful horizontal completions provided the repeatability needed to advance the emerging Marcellus play. Range issued a press release on December 10, 2007, announcing the results of the successful Marcellus horizontal wells. Immediately afterward, investment analyst Ross Smith/ITG (now Warburg Pincus) released an exciting report to industry and the financial community about the horizontal breakthroughs in the Marcellus and the exciting potential of the play, comparing it to the Barnett Shale (RSEG, 2007). The gold rush phase of the play now moved into full gear as a lease acquisition boom started.

MARCELLUS BOOM: 2008 THROUGH 2010

The year 2008 was the breakout year for the Marcellus shale play. Over 130 horizontal completed Marcellus wells were reported, marking the major industry shift from vertical wells to predominantly horizontal development, which was a major milestone. In early 2008, Dr. Terry Engelder and Dr. Gary Lash gave their initial estimate of recoverable Marcellus reserves (50 tcf), which provided early tangible clues of how large a field it promised to be when compared to the world's largest gas fields. By late 2009, more than 70 companies had acquired significant lease positions and drilled numerous horizontal wells, establishing a broad play area for the Marcellus across Pennsylvania, West Virginia, New York, Maryland, and Ohio. By 2009, the industry recognized core productive areas of the Marcellus that consist of the original discovery area in southwestern and northeastern Pennsylvania. Over 2280 Marcellus horizontal tests were drilled between 2008 and 2010, and by year-end 2010, over 80 drilling rigs were reported as active in West Virginia and Pennsylvania.

2010 THROUGH PRESENT DAY

By 2010 and 2011, the Marcellus play had attracted the attention of major independents, major oil companies, and international partners. From 2010 onward, core producing areas had become increasingly delineated in northeastern and southwestern Pennsylvania as well as northern West Virginia. By year-end 2011, the Marcellus rig count peaked at over 100 horizontal rigs. By 2012, the Marcellus play was recognized as the

key reservoir element. Increased clay content is generally believed to marginalize reservoir potential and performance. Pyrite volume is high based on focused ion beam/scanning electron microscopy (FIB/SEM) data. Both the northeastern and southwestern core areas of the Marcellus have the highest volume of organic material and lower clay volumes. Calcite-filled fractures are common in the Marcellus, increasing in size and intensity from west to east. Barite nodules are common in core and outcrop. Fluid sensitivity studies indicate the Marcellus has low sensitivity to freshwater and saltwater. Using recycled production water in fracture treatments is now an industry standard practice in the Marcellus play. Understanding the variation in mineralogy and organic content within varying lithofacies in the Marcellus shale and the lithofacies stratigraphic distribution are critical to lateral placement in the Marcellus shale for optimal productivity. Target intervals, usually within the lower Union Springs member, contain high TOC and high organic

porosity. Understanding the mechanical properties of lithofacies with differing mineralogy and organic content is essential for effective hydraulic stimulation of the Marcellus.

EARLY STRATIGRAPHIC RESEARCH

Paleogeographic reconstruction by Ettensohn (1985b), Woodrow and Sevon (1985), and Blakey (2005) depict that the organic-rich deposition occurred in a large nearly enclosed three-sided embayment that likely would have served to enhance oceanic organic productivity. Figure 7 depicts the paleogeographic reconstruction by Blakey (2005) of the Appalachian area at about 385 Ma. The arid conditions that were believed present during deposition of the organic-rich facies led to probable sediment starvation, as evidenced by the decrease in noneolian siliciclastic deposition in the organic-rich facies, preventing dilution of the

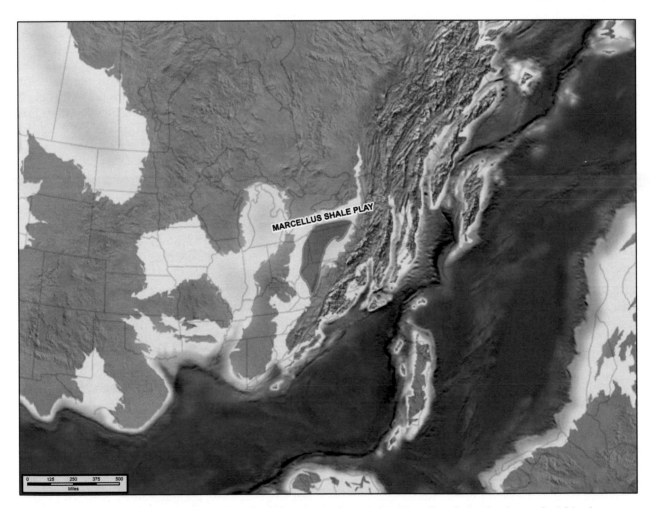

Figure 7. Middle Devonian paleogeography depicting the outline of the Marcellus shale play located within the restricted Marcellus shale depositional basin (modified from Blakey, 2005).

accumulating organic material. Ettensohn (1985a, b, 1992, 2004) assigned the period of deposition of the Marcellus shale to be the second of four tectonically related depositional phases associated with the Devonian Acadian Orogeny. Each of Ettensohn's four tectophases of the Acadian Orogeny represent regressive episodes that were further subdivided into four stages: (1) the beginning of tectonism and rapid subsidence leading to the accumulation of black shales, (2) deposition of gray shales and siltstones due to impending collision and regression, (3) collision causing widespread uplift and regional disconformities, and (4) widespread accumulation of limestone during a tectonically quiet transgressive period. During deposition of the Marcellus, the central Appalachian basin is interpreted to have been located between 15° and 30° south latitude (Ettensohn, 1992) with a dry tropical or savannah-like climate where rainfall was seasonal with extended dry conditions.

The creation, deposition, and preservation of the organic-rich Marcellus sediments was controlled by three primary factors: (1) primary photosynthetic production, (2) bacterial decomposition, and (3) bulk sedimentation rate (Sageman et al., 2003). The traditional interpretation of deposition of the organic-rich members of the Marcellus is a preservation model of organic enrichment where there is a permanently stratified water column with anoxic or euxinic (anoxic-sulfidic) bottom water conditions that allowed for the preservation of organic material (Demaison and Moore, 1980). This preservation model is best reflected in Ettensohn's proposed model of a nearly permanent pycnocline (Ettensohn, 1992).

Unconformity surfaces below and above the Marcellus are interpreted to become conformable to the southeast, into the deeper parts of the basin (Hamilton-Smith, 1993). A major Middle Devonian unconformity that lies above the Tully limestone (Hamilton-Smith, 1993) progressively removes stratigraphically older units from east to west. Westward toward the Cincinnati arch, this regional unconformity truncates the entire Tully, Hamilton and progressively older formations.

RECENT STRATIGRAPHIC RESEARCH

Recent stratigraphic and sedimentologic research is developing better and more detailed depositional models of the varying lithofacies within the Marcellus shale and other unconventional reservoir mudstones. The ongoing research allows better understanding and prediction of where the more organic-rich parts, which contain greater in-place hydrocarbons, are

positioned stratigraphically. Recent workers dispute the original theory of deep-water deposition with consistent anoxia. Werne et al. (2002) and Sageman et al. (2003) proposed that the Marcellus organic-rich members were deposited without a permanent pycnocline and with possible seasonal fluctuations. MacQuaker et al. (2009) investigated the Marcellus at bed scale levels and found sedimentary structures inconsistent with a continuous deep-water anoxic model, including rip-up clasts and ripple lamina. He proposed that the organic-rich mudstones were not deposited in waters that were persistently anoxic; rather, the seafloor was occasionally reworked, which would have led to destruction of a portion of the organics. Boyce and Carr (2010) proposed that possible small local microanoxic environments played a role in the deposition of the organic-rich members based on local variations in the black shale units and thin limestones. The lower part of the Union Springs member seems to have been deposited below wave base and has the highest TOC content. The upper Union Springs member oscillated between anoxic and dysoxic conditions based on decreasing concentrations of U and Mo and increasing concentration of Mn (Wendt et al., 2015). Elevated U and Mo concentrations and the lack of bioturbation in the lower Union Springs indicate euxinic to anoxic bottom water conditions (Wendt et al., 2015).

Lash (2008) interprets the Cherry Valley and the Purcell limestones to be stratigraphically equivalent, while other authors, including de Witt et al. (1993) and Werne et al. (2002), correlate Cherry Valley and Purcell as separate. Lash and Engelder (2009) assign two third-order transgressive-regressive sequences to the Marcellus formation. The lower sequence includes the upper part of the underlying Onondaga formation, Union Springs, and Cherry Valley Members. The upper sequence includes the upper part of the Cherry Valley member, the Oatka Creek member, and the Stafford limestone member of the Skaneateles formation. The sequence stratigraphic framework of Lash and Engelder (2009) allows prediction of the key reservoir organic-rich shale lithofacies of the condensed sections positioned around the maximum flooding surfaces. The Union Springs member is thin or absent to the west and northwest, where a ravinement surface at the base of the upper Marcellus sequence exists. Kohl et al. (2014) interpret a forced regression and falling stage systems tract in the upper part of the Union Springs member. Lash (2008) identifies several unconformities to be present within the Marcellus shale within distal areas of the Appalachian basin, including western New York and northwestern Pennsylvania. These include unconformities that are the upper sequence boundaries for the Union Springs and Oatka

Creek shales. Lash (2009) documents that the entire Union Spring shale has been removed by a regional disconformity in some of these areas.

STRUCTURAL SETTING

Regional structural features influencing the Marcellus shale hydrocarbon system include the position of the Rome trough and related basement faulting patterns, strike-slip faulting and lateral ramps in Allegheny thrust fault systems, the presence (or absence) of the underlying Silurian Salina salt and associated decollement surfaces, and regional fold development and amplitude, which influence the degree of natural fracturing in the Marcellus shale. The major structural features of the Appalachian basin and key shale production trends of the Appalachian basin are depicted

in Figures 8 and 9. Regional structural elements of the Appalachian basin from west to east include the Waverly arch and Cincinnati arch to the west, the Cambridge arch and Burning Springs anticline further eastward, the Rome trough, and the anticlinal fold belts in the Appalachian plateau and Valley and Ridge provinces.

The majority of Marcellus shale development lies in the Appalachian plateau physiographic province. This province is characterized by generally gentle structures and an overall lack of intense faulting toward the western portions of the province. Structural complexity increases to the east toward the structural front where high-amplitude detached, salt-cored anticlines trend northeast–southwest. The structural front represents the boundary between the plateau and the Valley and Ridge provinces, where the Devonian section rises quickly to the surface and crops out. The Valley

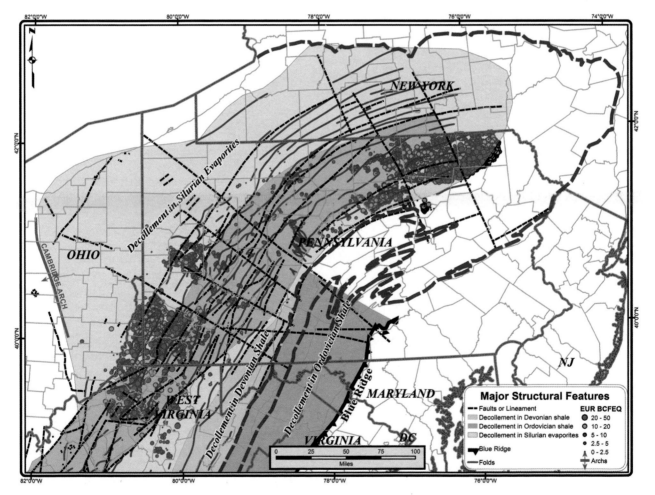

Figure 8. Map showing the primary structural features of the Appalachian basin that influence the Marcellus shale play. Key decollement trends from Colton (1970), Frey (1973), and Sanford (1993) are shown together with Marcellus well control (modified from Zagorski et al., 2012, and Schumaker, 1996). DC = District of Columbia; DE = Delaware; NJ = New Jersey.

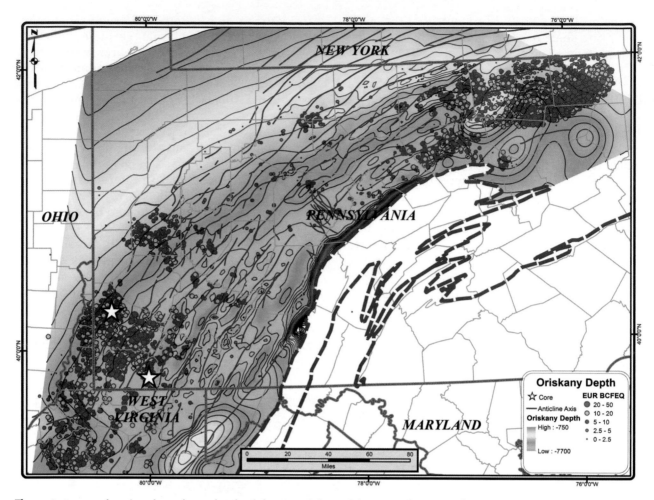

Figure 9. A map showing the subsea depth of the top of the Oriskany sandstone and major structural features. Core locations refer to Marcellus core examples referred to later in this text. (modified from Zagorski et al., 2013). DC = District of Columbia; DE = Delaware; NJ = New Jersey.

and Ridge provinces represent the most structurally challenging area in which the Marcellus shale is present. The area is structurally complex with high-amplitude detached folds, repeated and overturned beds, and multiple thrust faults detached in multiple decollement levels but mainly sourced in the highly ductile Salina salt beds.

IMPACT OF BASEMENT FAULTING

A key component of the Marcellus play is the strong influence basement faulting has on various key aspects of the play, including thickness, thermal maturity, reservoir quality, BTU content, organic content, clay content, and mechanical properties. Figure 8 depicts the basement structure of the Appalachian basin together with major interpreted basement-related faults, the projected position of the Rome trough, and

key Devonian shale and Marcellus shale production trends. Major basement faults fall into two classifications: (1) strike parallel to the basin and related to the Rome trough and (2) faults trending perpendicular to the strike of the basin and interpreted as transform faults or cross-strike discontinuities (CSDs) (Harper and Laughrey, 1987). These basement faults represent zones of weakness believed to have been reactivated several times during the Paleozoic period (Negus-DeWyss, 1979; Lee, 1980; Shumaker, 1993).

The Rome trough represents a major structural feature of the Appalachian basin and is comprised of a failed rift system that formed in the middle Cambrian period. The Rome trough has been extensively studied in West Virginia and eastern Kentucky and extends into Pennsylvania and New York (Shumaker, 1996; Harper and Laughrey, 1987; Scanlin and Engelder, 2003; Kulander and Ryder, 2005). Shumaker (1993) showed several areas where the Rome trough affected sedimentation of key Devonian organic shale members and where reactivation of basement faults provided for enhanced areas of natural fracturing. Within the Marcellus shale play, Kulander and Ryder (2005) defined the boundaries of the Rome trough in southwestern Pennsylvania through a series of regional cross-sections and regional two-dimensional reconnaissance seismic profiles. The Rome trough appears to delineate areas of maximum depositional thickness of key organic shale beds in the Marcellus shale as well as overlying beds such as the Tully. In addition, it is a critical feature related both to the burial and thermal maturity history of the Marcellus shale. The position of the Rome trough system is related closely to the highest observed pressure gradients in the Marcellus shale.

Offsetting the Rome trough strike-parallel basement faults are a series of cross-striking basement faults, which are likely transform faults created during rifting episodes in the Cambrian and Ordovician periods (Harper and Laughrey, 1987). These have been investigated based on lineament studies, remote sensing analysis, surface drainage patterns, aeromagnetic and gravity studies, and structural mapping. The surface expressions of these strike normal faults were called cross-strike structural discontinuities (CSDs) by Wheeler (1980). The two most significant include the Tyrone-Mt. Union lineament (Rodgers and Anderson, 1984; Canich and Gold, 1977) and the Pittsburgh-Washington lineament (Lavin et al., 1982). Rodgers and Anderson (1984) reported that an increase in natural fracturing and also enhanced hydrocarbon and fluid migration occurred along the Tyrone-Mt. Union lineament. Both of these features appear to be critical elements in the Marcellus play. Within the Appalachian basin, these cross-strike features often have a detrimental effect on oil and gas production from many reservoirs, with field terminations occurring at or near the cross-strike features. In some areas of the Marcellus play, the effect on the CSDs appears to be neutral or even additive, as is the case in southwestern Pennsylvania. Other areas of the Marcellus play, such as Clearfield County, observe a more negative association with Marcellus productivity. The CSDs probably allowed migration of mature source rock hydrocarbons to shallower reservoirs. Marcellus-sourced hydrocarbons could have had access to upper Devonian conventional reservoirs along the CSDs and the associated fracturing, and the Marcellus was depleted of hydrocarbons and pressure along the structural discontinuity. Lateral ramps in the Allegheny compressional system also could have allowed access of Marcellus hydrocarbons to younger reservoirs either through fault juxtaposition or migration along the lateral thrust fault.

ORGANIC CONTENT

The Marcellus shale is a world class source rock. The total organic carbon (TOC) content in the Marcellus shale ranges from less than 1% to over 18% (wt.%) based on review of regional core and log data. The macerals deposited in the Marcellus sediment are predominantly marine algal and prone to generate oil (type II). Minimum TOC threshold values for good source rocks and prospective shale gas plays are considered to be typically 2% (wt.%) or higher (Jarvie, 2005). The Marcellus shale has some of the highest TOC of modern thermogenic-style source rock plays. Studies by Reed (2008) suggest calculated original TOC contents in the Marcellus shale to be in the 4 to 20% (wt.%) range. One of the best indirect measurements of TOC content in the Marcellus shale is its gamma ray count. The spectral gamma ray log data show that most of the natural gamma radiation in the Marcellus shale is due to uranium, which is preserved only in sediments deposited in euxinic to anoxic environments where organic matter accumulates and is preserved. Schmoker (1981a, b) documented a direct correlation between the organic content of Appalachian shales and the wire-line log gamma ray intensity. Significantly high TOC content (5% or greater) can be identified with gamma ray counts of 200 API or greater. In southwestern Pennsylvania and northern West Virginia, peak gamma ray counts in excess of 300 to 400 API are not uncommon and reflect the higher uranium content and TOC in this portion of the play. Within the Marcellus shale play, TOC can be directly related to organic porosity, which results from the maturation and conversion of kerogen to hydrocarbons and the cracking of liquid hydrocarbons to pyrobitumen.

THERMAL MATURITY

Figure 10 is the thermal maturity map of the Marcellus shale compiled using a combination of publically available and proprietary measured vitrinite reflectance values and calculated R_o data. Thermal maturity patterns in the Marcellus generally increase in a southeasterly direction, ranging from 0.5% R_o equivalent in northwestern Pennsylvania to greater than 3.5% R_o equivalent in northeastern Pennsylvania. Recent Marcellus shale drilling activity and results indicate that most significant hydrocarbon potential and production occur approximately southeast of the 1.0% R_o equivalent maturity contour in the western portions of Pennsylvania, West Virginia, eastern Ohio, and southern New York. Based on the drilling results released to date, at

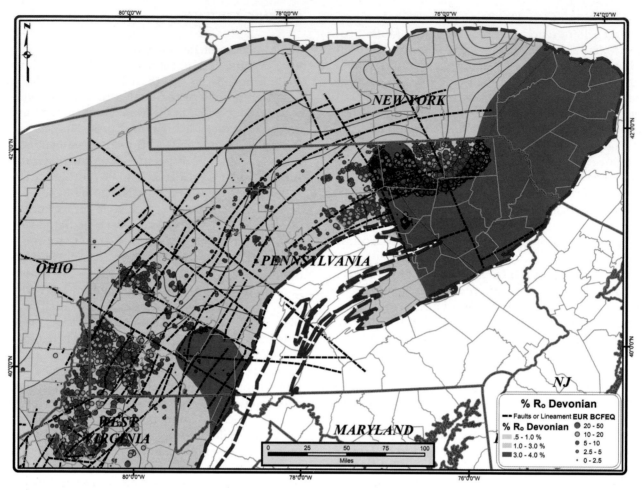

Figure 10. A map showing the thermal maturity trends for the Marcellus shale play and major basement faults (modified from Repetski, 2008, and Zagorski et al., 2013). DC = District of Columbia; DE = Delaware; NJ = New Jersey.

thermal maturity values of greater than 3.5% R_o equivalent, the productive potential of the Marcellus shale significantly decreases. Also shown on Figure 10 are major basement fault patterns and the Rome trough. Several major cross-striking basement faults appear to relate to discontinuities in the observed thermal maturity patterns. In addition, the Marcellus shale play in northeastern Pennsylvania appears to have been subjected to greater depths of burial as well as increased sedimentation and subsidence rates (Faill, 1985), which clearly influenced thermal maturity patterns.

Thermal maturity is a critical play element for the Marcellus shale. Thermal maturity studies for the Appalachian basin (Rowan, 2006) assume that the measured and estimated R_o values in the Marcellus shale require greater depths of burial and higher temperatures than those presently observed. The Rome trough and associated basement faults were critical to reaching the needed burial depths and pressures. The

northwestern boundary of the Rome trough likely represents a hinge zone where rapid burial of the Marcellus allowed it to reach the current observed thermal maturity levels.

The two emerging core areas developing in the Marcellus shale play have somewhat different thermal maturity characteristics. In the southwestern area, the established production to date from the Marcellus occurs in a thermal maturity range of 1.0 to 2.8% R_o, with commercial gas discoveries occurring both in a dry gas window to the east and a combination gas/gas condensate play to the west. Here, Btu contents in the Marcellus are around 1000 to the east and approach 1400 in the western areas near the 1.0% R_o contour. The established productive areas of the Marcellus shale in the northeastern part of the play have a higher thermal maturity profile, with most production occurring between R_o values of 2.0 to over 3.0%. Here, the Btu values are in the range of 1000 Btu to 1080 Btu.

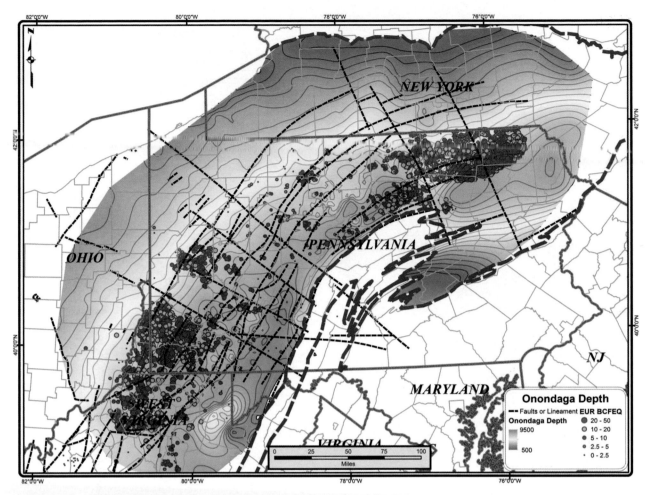

Figure 11. A map showing the drilling depths in TVD to the base of the Marcellus shale and major basement faults (modified from Zagorski et al., 2012). DC = District of Columbia; DE = Delaware; NJ = New Jersey.

DRILLING DEPTHS

Figure 11 shows the range of required drilling depths (TVD) to the base of the Marcellus across its main productive fairway. The map and distribution of depth data illustrate a key structural framework of the Appalachian basin that represents a strongly asymmetric trough. The majority of commercial production established to date from the Marcellus has been within a general depth fairway of 1375 to 2750 m (4500 to 9000 ft). The maximum drilling depths are encountered in synclines just basinward of the structural front. In general, increased depth results in higher gas-in-place values due to increases in both thermal maturity and overpressure. Encouraging horizontal production tests have been made in the Marcellus as shallow as 1158 m (3800 ft) TVD in northwestern Pennsylvania and as deep as 3048 m (10,000 ft) TVD in the Bedford syncline area. These both are in noncore areas but should be considered as future prospective play areas.

OVERPRESSURE

A key parameter influencing the Marcellus play is overpressure. A near-normal or overpressure gradient is essential for effective large-scale water fracs. Effective fracture stimulation is a critical play element needed to unlock hydrocarbons from the Marcellus, Utica, Eagleford, Haynesville and other modern shale plays in North America. Each displays overpressure gradients in its core areas. In the Marcellus shale play, pressure gradients range from 0.40 to over 0.80 psi/ft. The pressure generation mechanism is the conversion of liquid hydrocarbons to gas combined with uplift or unroofing. In general, the core productive areas have the highest pressure gradients. Marcellus pressure gradient trends are shown in Figure 12. Normal to overpressure gradients are observed across most of the Marcellus shale play in north-central West Virginia and northward into most of Pennsylvania and the southern tier of New York. Pressure gradients in

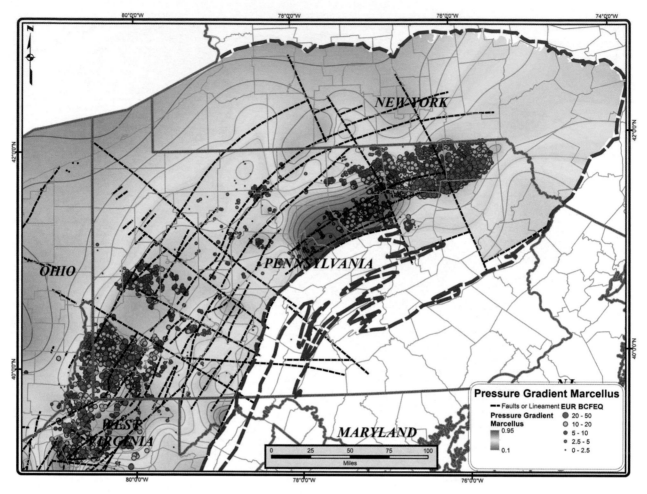

Figure 12. A map showing the pressure gradient trends for the Marcellus shale play and major basement faults (modified from Zagorski et al., 2011). DC = District of Columbia; DE = Delaware; NJ = New Jersey.

these areas are projected to range from approximately 0.43 to more than 0.80 psi/ft. The position of the Rome trough system is closely related to the areas of highest observed pressure gradients in the Marcellus shale.

In addition, the development of overpressure appears to be directly related to burial history and thermal maturity and can be seen to be clearly associated with areas where thermal maturity of greater than 0.9 to 1.0% equivalent R_o is observed. The overpressure mechanism is most likely conversion of liquid hydrocarbon to dry gas within a fixed pore space, which generated the observed high 0.6 to 0.8 psi/ft gradients. The original Marcellus pressure cell was then uplifted to its present depth without the full dissipation of the pressure cell due to the overall low permeability of the Marcellus and upper Devonian shale systems. The seal was not perfect and via migration through natural fractures, the Marcellus and overlying upper Devonian shale represent the likely source for the majority of shallower Devonian- and Mississippian-age conventional reservoirs. The coincidence of the Marcellus shale overpressure trends and

the Rome trough is striking, particularly with the onset of the gas window of the Marcellus.

The normal and overpressured Marcellus areas in the Appalachian basin have been largely retained over geologic time, which helped to preserve both natural gas volumes and the overpressured cell generated during thermal maturation and uplift. Interestingly, except for source rocks such as the Marcellus and Utica Point Pleasant shales, the majority of conventional reservoir zones in the Appalachians basin are modestly underpressured, especially in areas where the Silurian Salina beds are absent.

One possible theory proposed to explain the presence of overpressure in Pennsylvania as well as northern and southern West Virginia is the close association between the presence of the deeper Silurian Salina formation to the highest degree of overpressure in the Marcellus. The Marcellus is overpressured where the Salina formation is present and significantly underpressured where the Salina formation is absent. This relationship between the presence of the Salina formation and the overpressured portion of the Marcellus shale might be related to two factors. The first is that the evaporites of the Salina are the preferential structural detachment where the Salina is present. The thrust detachment jumped to the Marcellus and younger Devonian source-rock shales where the Salina formation is absent and probably compromised any pressure cells that had developed. The second factor may be that the thermal conductance of the salt in the Salina provided higher thermal stress to the Marcellus shale. The Marcellus is mostly in the gas window above Salina evaporites where the liquid hydrocarbons have been converted to gas and generated and overpressure cell. Here, during Alleghenian thrusting, much of the early and basinal accommodation was provided by the deformation of the Salina and then to a lesser extent the overlying Devonian shales. In the no-salt areas south of the Burning Springs feature and especially in southern West Virginia and Kentucky, the organic Devonian shale acted as the most ductile beds and hence experienced much more deformation and natural fracturing.

The presence of a regional decollement in the Salina group evaporites has been proposed (Gwinn, 1964; Shumaker, 1996; Milici and Swezey, 2006) for the area underlain by the thick Salina salt. This Salina decollement created an allochthonous block that was transported generally westward along low-angle detachment thrust faults. Shumaker (1996) also proposed that south of the Salina pinch-out, the basal detachment zone occurred within the Devonian shale (Rhinestreet, Huron, and Marcellus) interval. It is proposed that this detachment and extensive movement in the Devonian section led to severe compromise of seals within and above the Marcellus and subsequent loss of hydrocarbons and pressure.

MARCELLUS THICKNESS TRENDS

Most current industry drilling activity is associated with areas having greater than 15 m (50 ft) of gross Marcellus shale thickness. Figure 13 depicts the gross

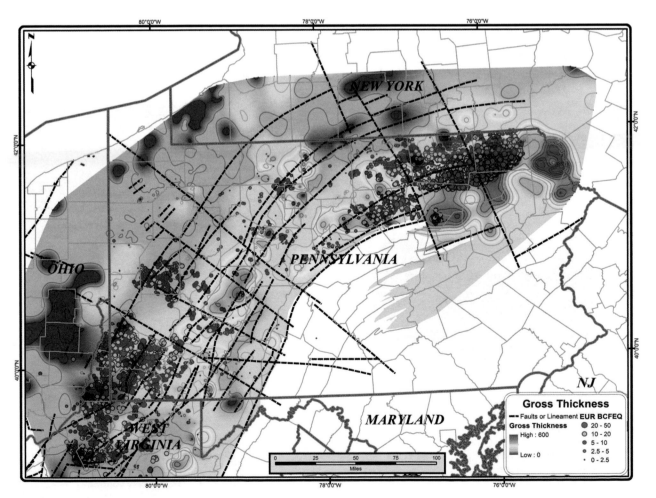

Figure 13. A map showing the gross thickness trends for the Marcellus shale and major basement faults (modified from Zagorski et al., 2012). DC = District of Columbia; DE = Delaware; NJ = New Jersey.

thickness of the Marcellus shale across the Appalachian basin together with major mapped basement fault trends. This map shows a general eastward thickening of the Marcellus shale within, or near, the Rome trough. The gross thickness of the Marcellus as mapped is defined by the top of the first occurrence of organic shale near the base of the Mahantango formation to the top of the Onondaga limestone. Gross thickness of the Marcellus increases generally eastward from the zero isopach in eastern Ohio and western West Virginia to a maximum thickness of more than 107 m (350 ft) in northeastern Pennsylvania. The gross thickness map has not been corrected for potential repeated sections or areas that encounter significant bed dips. The trend of thickening in the Marcellus generally parallels the Appalachian structural front. The gross depositional patterns of the Marcellus shale are highly influenced by basement fault patterns. They show general strike-parallel thickening within the Rome trough feature and related strike-parallel basement faults. Additionally, abrupt depositional terminations appear to exist at, or near, the cross-striking basement faults.

The generalized cross-section shown in Figure 14 illustrates the significant stratigraphic changes that occur

across the Marcellus shale play. On a regional basis, the entire section thickens considerably to the northeast, suggesting significantly higher sedimentation rates associated with the early Catskill delta compared with the southwestern play region. Also shown on the regional cross-section is the position of key maximum flooding surfaces in the Union Springs and Oatka Creek members of the Marcellus shale, which records episodes of maximum organic deposition and preservation in the condensed sections. These maximum flooding surfaces can be traced across the entire play and represent key pay intervals. Thicker gross Marcellus shale also relates to higher gas-in-place along isomaturity trends.

POROSITY, PERMEABILITY, AND PORE TYPES

High organic content, organic-sourced porosity, permeability, and overpressure are key gas productivity factors for the Marcellus shale. Organic content can be accurately estimated by gamma ray and density log data calibrated with core measurements. The high organic facies of the Marcellus is the key reservoir unit in terms of hydrocarbon storage. Porosity within

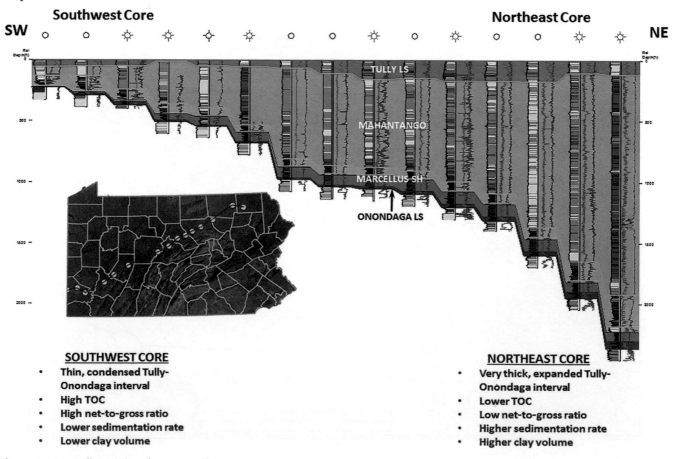

SOUTHWEST CORE
- **Thin, condensed Tully-Onondaga interval**
- **High TOC**
- **High net-to-gross ratio**
- **Lower sedimentation rate**
- **Lower clay volume**

NORTHEAST CORE
- **Very thick, expanded Tully-Onondaga interval**
- **Lower TOC**
- **Low net-to-gross ratio**
- **Higher sedimentation rate**
- **Higher clay volume**

Figure 14. Marcellus regional cross-section.

organic matter, either partially converted kerogen, bitumen, or pyrobitumen, is key for hydrocarbon storage in the Marcellus shale because the organic pores contain both absorbed and free gas with little to no water saturation. The organic content varies between approximately 2 and 18 (wt.%) average in southwestern Pennsylvania to approximately 4 to 10 (wt.%) average in north central Pennsylvania. Organic content and the development of intraorganic porosity are key factors that affect Marcellus shale gas in place and productivity. The observed intraorganic porosity displays a high degree of connectivity (Figure 15) and is responsible for a significant portion of the Marcellus shale's productivity and gas-in-place. Intraorganic pores range from less than 10 to more than 200 nm. Other pore types include intergranular, intercrystalline, and microcracks.

Core data and calibrated log data confirm that good porosity and permeability are present in the organic-rich lithofacies of the Marcellus shale across a large area. Core and log data acquired across the Marcellus shale play exhibit porosities ranging from 2 to 18% and permeability ranging from 130 to over 2000 nanodarcies (nd). Most workers consider minimum values of commercial permeability in gas shales to be in excess of 100 nd. Shale gas reservoirs with average permeability values of more than 500 nd are considered very high for unconventional shale plays. As such, observed ranges of permeability in the Marcellus shale play appear exceptional and unique compared with other North American gas shale plays.

The regional distribution of organic material and porosity and permeability can be mapped using gamma ray feet calculations as a proxy. As shown in Figure 16, gamma ray feet distribution patterns are concentrated in the northeastern and southwestern areas of the Marcellus shale play. Again, regional basement fracture trends clearly influence the distribution of organic matter throughout the play fairway. This regional mapping approach combined with the distribution of Marcellus shale estimated ultimate recovery (EUR) data highlights the location of the core producing regions of the Marcellus shale play.

White: Pyrite
Light gray: Minerals of density 2-3 g/cc
Dark gray: Kerogen
Black: Pore space

Blue: Connected porosity
Red: Non-connected porosity
Green: Kerogen (+ nano-pores)

Microns

Majority of porosity and permeability is associated with kerogen. Three visible pore types; large mega pores, smaller pores, and a third textural indication any level of smaller pores below resolution and included in Kerogen in the right image.

Figure 15. Three-dimensional FIB/SEM imagery of Marcellus pay interval in wet gas/liquid–rich area of southwestern Pennsylvania. Note well-developed and large pore size and high degree of connected porosity with nanopore network (modified from Yang et al., 2013).

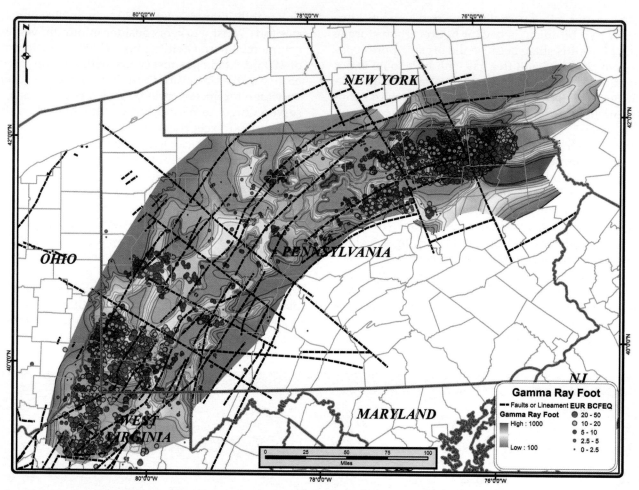

Figure 16. A map showing the total gamma ray feet (a proxy for total organic volume of total organic pore volume) for the Marcellus shale play and major basement faults (modified from Zagorski et al., 2013). DC = District of Columbia; DE = Delaware; NJ = New Jersey.

NATURAL FRACTURING

Natural fractures represent an important element of the Marcellus shale play on both a local and a field level. There is a major regional natural fracture network present in the Marcellus shale as documented by various core and outcrop studies. These regional fracture or joint sets are designated J1 (east-northeast trending) and J2 (north-northwest trending) by Engelder et al. (2009). The Devonian organic black shales exhibit predominately at the J1 set of joints. Natural fractures influence Marcellus production, but their role appears more subtle, suggesting that while they potentially significantly contribute to well performance, their role is less critical in defining commercial production. Interestingly, in highly fractured regions, it appears the higher degree of natural fracturing significantly negatively impacts well performance. Low Marcellus interval velocity anisotropy from three-dimensional seismic data and the predominately

J2 orientation of the joint sets correspond to higher Marcellus productivity (Inks et al., 2015). Based on available well performance data and extensive log and core data, it is evident that the Marcellus shale is regionally more strongly controlled by key reservoir characteristics such as thickness, porosity, permeability, gas-in-place, pressure gradient, and the ability to be fractured. There are several areas in southwestern Pennsylvania where higher observed initial test rates can be demonstrated to be related to the presence of natural fracture systems. However, it appears that once natural fracturing systems develop to a point where effective stimulation is compromised or the reservoir seal is compromised over time, their role changes from one of enhancement to one of detriment.

Nearly all horizontal wells drilled in the Marcellus shale play are oriented along a northwest by southeast azimuth. The current shear max (SHmax) direction for the Appalachian basin is observed to be northeast-southwest based on numerous studies by the EGSP, the world stress map, microseismic studies, and observed direction of drilling-induced fractures or bore-hole breakout observed in cores and formation microimaging (FMI) logs for the Marcellus shale and other EGSP wells. These are shown in Figure 17. As such, the northwest by southeast azimuth is the primary orientation for most horizontal Marcellus wells.

On a broad scale, most current activity in southwestern Pennsylvania and northern West Virginia is situated in relatively uncomplicated structural trends. Open natural fractures are rarely observed in whole cores of the Marcellus or in FMI logs. Most observed natural fractures appear to be healed and calcite filled. FMI logs run primarily in southwest Pennsylvania in the Devonian shale interval tend to favor a strong northwest by southeast orientation for healed fractures. Analysis of FMI patterns on several wells across the Marcellus play show the following types of fracture patterns: drilling-induced fractures, which trend northeast to southwest, paralleling the inferred SHmax direction (or conversely, bore-hole breakout oriented

northwest to southeast in the higher–pore pressure Marcellus); healed fractures defined by high resistivity patterns trend primarily in a northwest to southeast direction paralleling the J2 set proposed by Engelder et al. (2009); and many of the fracture patterns observed earlier in the EGSP cores. Possible faults and fractures with varying orientations show good representation of the proposed J1 and J2 joint and fracture sets. Other orientations also are well represented and are believed to represent features associated with slickensides (low-angle) and high-angle faults and fractures.

The effect of increased folding and faulting to the east can be depicted on the two cores shown in Figure 18. The core in the westernmost area (Washington County, Pennsylvania) demonstrates the presence of natural fracturing, but fracture density and width are low. This differs from the significantly higher fracture density and fracture width exhibited by the core of the well located near the Fayette anticline in eastern Greene County, Pennsylvania. This comparison illustrates the significant increase in natural fracturing observed in the many

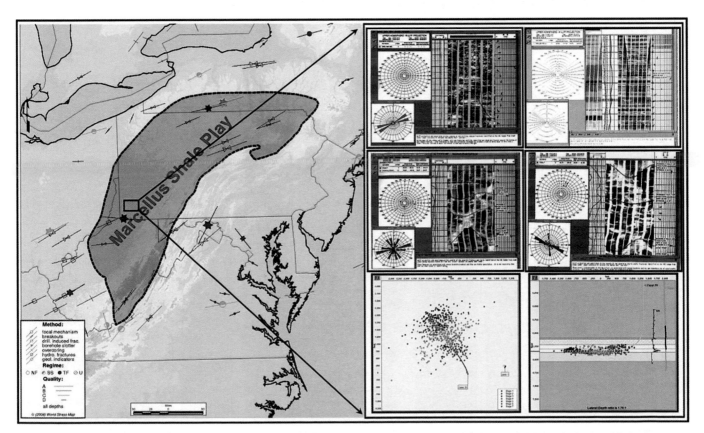

Figure 17. A stress map (modified from Heidbach et al., 2007) showing the observed SHmax trends, observed FMI features, and sample microseismic observations from the Marcellus shale play in southwestern Pennsylvania. Attached FMI images include (1) drilling-induced fractures (green), (2) healed natural fractures (yellow), (3) partially healed fractures (purple), and (4) possible faults (blue). Microseismic examples show the primary fracture growth direction in a northeast to southwest direction and good observed containment between the Tully limestone and Onondaga limestone intervals bounding the Marcellus shale (modified from Zagorski et al., 2012). FMI = formation microimaging; Drill. induced frac. = drilling-induced fracture; geol. indicators = geologic indicators; NF = normal faulted regime; SS = strike-slip faulted regime; TF = thrust faulted regime; U = unfaulted regime.

cores taken in the Marcellus shale interval. This appears to have a regional detrimental effect on Marcellus well productivity in the southwestern portions of the play.

CORE AREAS

Since the Marcellus play's vertical and horizontal commercialization in 2004 and 2007, two major core areas have developed along a 1295 km^2 (500 mi^2) southwest to northeast trending fairway (Figure 5). The prospective play area encompasses approximately 114,000 km^2 (44,030 mi^2) and includes large portions of Pennsylvania and northern West Virginia, as well as limited portions of eastern-most Ohio. Establishment of core producing areas is critical to effective development of unconventional shale plays. While the geographic extent of modern shale gas plays is enormous, as is

their in-place reserve potential, they each possess wide variations in production capabilities, and the core areas are the portions that are most economically viable. Only a limited portion of each play has the optimal reserve potential and reservoir characteristics needed for economic development. This is highly dependent, both geographically and temporally, on gas and oil prices, rock quality, completion efficiencies, and the level of technologic advancement and understanding of each play. These core areas are typically estimated at 15 to 25% of any one play's geographic extent.

In the Marcellus play, productive potential of core versus noncore areas can vary by 100% or more on an EUR per 1000 ft (305 m) basis. Two major core areas have developed across the play trend: southwestern Pennsylvania and northern West Virginia and northeastern Pennsylvania. Interestingly, the initial discovery areas in southwestern and northeastern Pennsylvania

Figure 18. Comparison of two Marcellus cores in southwestern Pennsylvania showing increased natural fracturing from west to east. Core locations shown on Figure 9 and are in detail area on Figure 17 (modified from Zagorski et al., 2013).

that were most successful evolved to be the core areas within the Marcellus play. These core areas of the Marcellus play each display unique combinations of controlling geologic factors. Thickness, depth, net-to-gross ratios, organic content, intraorganic porosity, overpressure, thermal maturity, structural position, and degree of natural fracturing represent key factors. In addition to the core areas themselves, between these two established core areas, there are large underexplored areas that have excellent future potential for Marcellus development. Gas takeaway capacity has influenced the rate of exploration and development in this play to date. Several pipeline expansion projects will become operational after 2017 that will influence future exploration and development patterns in the Marcellus play.

SOUTHWESTERN CORE AREA

The southwest core area of the Marcellus play encompasses large areas of southwestern Pennsylvania and northern West Virginia. Shown on Figure 19 are the horizontal well control and thermal maturity R_o trends. The southwestern play area was established by Range Resources Corporation's 2004 Renz Unit 1 vertical completion and the successful Range Gulla 9H horizontal test in 2007. Horizontal results in this area range from less than 1 MMCFe/day for early tests to over 43 MMCFe/day. Estimated ultimate recoveries calculated from reported production data in Pennsylvania and West Virginia range from 2 to over 20 BCF of gas equivalent per horizontal well. On a EUR per 1000 ft basis, projected recoveries range from 1.0 to over 4.5 BCF/1000 ft. Gas-in-place calculations for the southwestern portion of the play range from 40 to more than 150 BCF/mi^2. Natural gas liquids (NGL) production is significant throughout much of this core area, with 281,000 to 1 million barrels or greater of recoverable NGL per lateral in key areas.

In this region, drilling depths in the Marcellus range from 1371 to 2439 m (4500 to 8000 ft), and the Marcellus has a gross thickness ranging from 15 to 30 m (50 to 100 ft). Some of the highest observed total organic content percentages, porosity, and permeability in the Marcellus play are observed in the southwestern core area. Here, the Marcellus is represented by a relatively thinner, but more condensed, sedimentary section with very high total organic content, a high net-to-gross pay ratio, and overall higher porosity and permeability. Key pay intervals are represented as maximum flooding surfaces within the Marcellus interval. Log and core data for the southwestern core portion of the play shows higher volumes of carbonate content and reduced clay volumes. This reflects lower sedimentation rates and a relatively distal position from

sediment sources. Marcellus depositional patterns appear to be strongly influenced by basement faulting. Sedimentation rates appear low compared to other parts of the play, favoring the concentration of organic matter in the Marcellus shale. Typical log suites run in southwestern Pennsylvania display elevated gamma ray counts in the Marcellus shale compared with the northeastern part of the play. In the southwestern core area, key characteristics include high porosity and permeability, as well as high resistivity compared to the same intervals in the northeastern portion of the play. The key pore type in the Marcellus in the southeastern play is intraorganic porosity. Other pore types include intercrystalline/intergranular between pyrite crystals (which are significant in the southwest part of the play) and between platey clay crystals/grains. Silica (quartz), organic material, carbonates, and pyrite predominate in the southwestern play area.

Within the southwestern core areas of Marcellus play, thermal maturity observed is in the 1.0 to 2.8% R_o range. In the western-most portions of the southwestern play, thermal maturity is lower, and significant NGL production has been established. Pressure gradients in the southwest core range between 0.45 and 0.70 psi/ft. These overpressure trends closely coincide with the position of the Rome trough and thermal maturity levels of 1.0% R_o or higher. The best observed results are located in less tectonically disturbed areas west of the major fold belt structures of the Allegheny front (Chestnut ridge). Core, log, seismic, microseismic, and other data suggest that natural fracturing, while present throughout the Marcellus system, changes from a potential positive enhancer of reservoir quality in the west to a probable detriment to reservoir quality to the east. The thickness of the underlying Salina formation is considerably thinner in the southwestern core areas compared to the northeastern core area, suggesting that a higher regional level of natural fracturing present in the southwestern portions of the play translates into lower reservoir quality with less efficient completion potential. This is coincident with observed fold wavelength and intensity.

NORTHEASTERN CORE AREA

The northeastern core area of the Marcellus play encompasses large areas of northeastern Pennsylvania. Shown on Figure 20 are the horizontal well control and thermal maturity R_o trends. The northeastern play area was established by Cabot Oil & Gas Corporation's Ely 1 Unit vertical completion in December 2006 and subsequent horizontal tests completed in 2008. Horizontal results in this area range from less than 1 MMCFe/day from early tests to over 47.6 MMCFe/day.

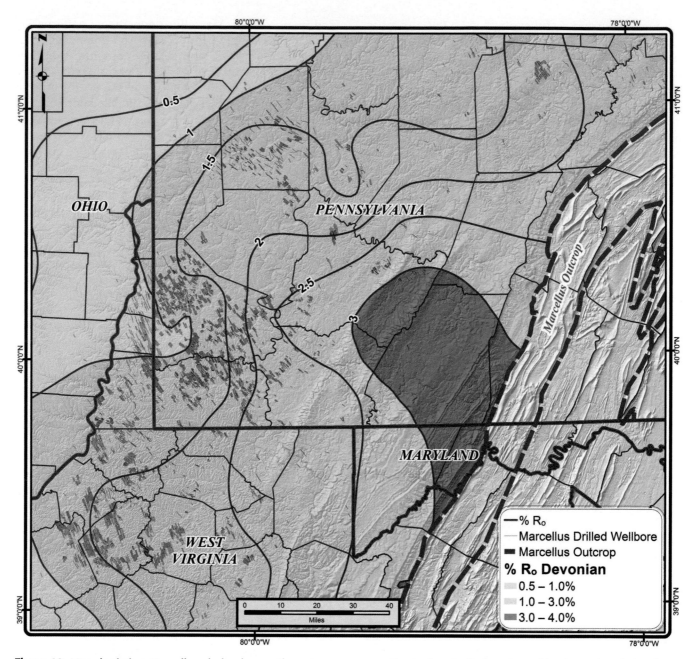

Figure 19. Map depicting Marcellus shale play southwestern core area, thermal maturity trends, and horizontal well development as of early 2016.

EUR calculations based on reported production data in Pennsylvania range from 2 to over 30 BCF per lateral. On a EUR per 1000 ft basis, projected recoveries range from 1.0 to over 5.0 BCF/1000 ft. Gas-in-place calculations for the northeastern portion of the play range from less than 75 to over 200 BCF/mi^2. Production from the northeast core area of the Marcellus is dry gas only with no liquid production.

In the northeastern core area, Marcellus typical TVD drilling depths range from 1067 to 2744 m (3500 to 9000 ft). The Marcellus attains a gross pay interval of 60 to 105 m (200 to 350 ft). Here, regional sedimentation rates appear to have been higher, favoring the additional clastic material concurrent with the deposition and preservation of organic matter. Well log and core data (Figure 14) show an expanded sedimentary section associated with greater levels of sediment influx. This is accompanied by an increase in clay deposition and overall reductions in carbonate content, suggesting a closer proximity to the source area compared with the southwestern Marcellus core area. The Marcellus here is represented by a relatively thick sedimentary section with fair-to-high total organic content and reduced net-to-gross pay ratios. Porosity and permeability values are somewhat lower

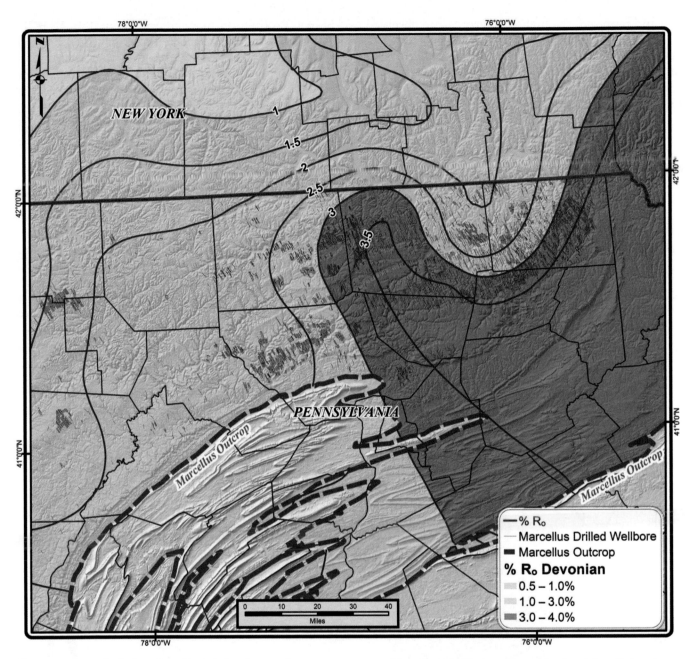

Figure 20. Map depicting Marcellus shale play northeasters core area, thermal maturity trends, and horizontal well development as of early 2016.

than the southern core region. Key pay intervals are represented as maximum flooding surfaces within the Marcellus interval. The key pore type in the Marcellus in the northeastern portion of the play is intraorganic porosity. Other pore types include intercrystalline/intergranular between pyrite crystals and platey clay crystals/grains. Silica (quartz), organic material, carbonates, and pyrite predominate in the northeast play area.

Within the northeastern portion of the Marcellus play, thermal maturity for established production is in the range of 2.0 to greater than 3.0% R_o. This suggests greater depth of burial history than the southwestern

core area. Marcellus production in the northeastern play area is in the dry gas window with a BTU content of 1000 to 1050 due to the elevated thermal maturity levels. Eastern commercial limits to the Marcellus play in the northeastern area are well defined and are related to areas where the Marcellus has reached a thermal maturity level of greater than 3.3 to 3.5% R_o combined with increased structural complexity. In addition, the eastern limit appears to coincide with the eastern limits of Salina deposition. Pressure gradients in the northeast core range from 0.50 to more than 0.82 psi/ft. These are significantly higher than in the southwestern core and represent the highest overpressure observed in the Marcellus play to date. In the northeastern core area, the Marcellus is generally more structurally complicated, with higher fold amplitudes and wavelength. Unlike the southwestern core area, significant Marcellus production is being developed relatively close to the Allegheny front. This may be attributed to broader fold wavelengths and a lesser degree of deformation at the Marcellus level caused by a tectonically thickened section of salt beds in the underlying Salina formation. However, the same dual role of natural fracturing and faulting is observed. In areas with extensive faulting and fracturing, the Marcellus is marginally productive, probably due to a breach of the Marcellus pressure cell and expulsion of gas and pressure from the Marcellus.

MARCELLUS SHALE RESOURCE POTENTIAL

There are enormous volumes of gas present within the Marcellus shale play. In 2013, the Marcellus shale became the largest producing gas field in the United States. Production reached approximately 16 BCFe /day in 2015 and is expected to reach over 20 BCFe /day by 2020. The Marcellus represents a continuous-type gas accumulation and when fully developed will be comprised of a large continuous field or series of fields. Engelder and Lash (2007) provided early recognition of the world-class potential of this resource at 50 tcf recoverable, which was quickly revised as the play grew. More recent estimates of the recoverable reserve potential range from 87 tcf and 3.5 billion bbl (USGS) to higher estimates of 489 tcf (Engelder, 2009). Other recent estimates fall within this general range.

Modern core and log analyses now show the Marcellus shale to have abundant to exceptional gas-in-place. A regional gas-in-place (GIP) map for the Marcellus play incorporating log, core, and pressure data is shown in Figure 21. This map assumes 1000 Btu, so in the liquids-rich regions, we are underestimating the total hydrocarbon-in-place. Gas-in-place estimates for the entire Marcellus play range from 40 to over 200 BCF/mi². Most development of the Marcellus shale is within areas of GIP greater than

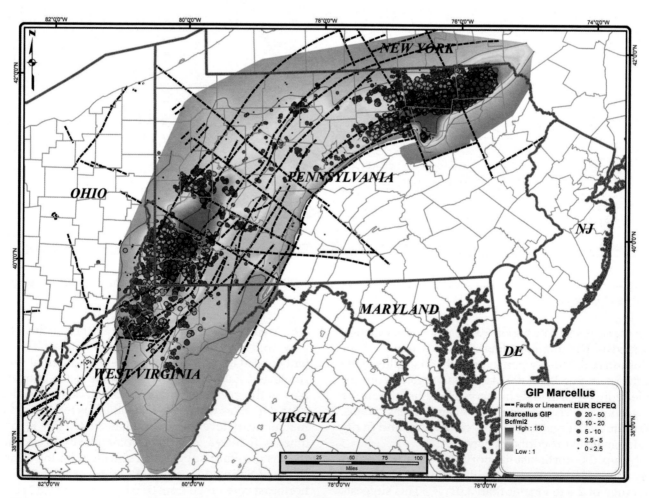

Figure 21. A map showing the gas-in-place trends for the Marcellus shale play and major basement faults. DC = District of Columbia; DE = Delaware; NJ = New Jersey.

50 BCF/mi². It is the authors' opinion that GIP values are being underestimated in the northeastern portion of the play, where some of the highest EUR wells are being drilled, yet GIP values are 100 to 200 BCF/mi². In the southwestern portion of the play, GIP values are also believed to be underestimated based on the higher hydrocarbon density and the 1100 to 1400 Btu value of the gas combined with the production of natural gas liquids. Initial nuclear magnetic resonance (NMR) log studies by Range Resources Corporation (RRC) and Schlumberger suggest similar findings when comparing standard log gas-in-place analysis with GIP calculations using NMR data. Other issues when calculating gas-in-place are accurate estimates (or lack) of pressure gradients, the negative effects of depletion and well interference, the significant contribution of adsorbed gas due to the high organic content of the Marcellus, and the effects of ethane absorption isotherms in liquids-rich areas.

When considering a giant field, it isn't just one horizon; it's all horizons comprising the play/field. The Marcellus play has significant stacked resource potential across most of its extent. There is excellent potential in the younger upper Devonian shale (Burket, Geneseo, Middlesex, and Rhinestreet) that lies above the Marcellus and from the deeper Ordovician-age Utica/Point Pleasant shale. Both of these associated plays have been successfully tested horizontally and have been steadily developed since 2010. The shallower upper Devonian shale units above the Marcellus and Tully intervals have now reached a level of testing, development, and characterization that supports the inclusion of these related/penetrated intervals to the resource assessment of the Marcellus play (Wrightstone, 2015). We believe that in the future when an adequate level of testing and characterization has been completed the deeper resource potential of the Ordovician-age Utica/Point Pleasant interval will be added to the resources/reserve estimates of the Appalachian basin Marcellus play.

Gas-in-place maps of the Marcellus, Burket /Geneseo/Rhinestreet, and combined Marcellus /Burket/Geneseo/Rhinestreet intervals are shown on Figures 21, 22, and 23. Using these maps and the

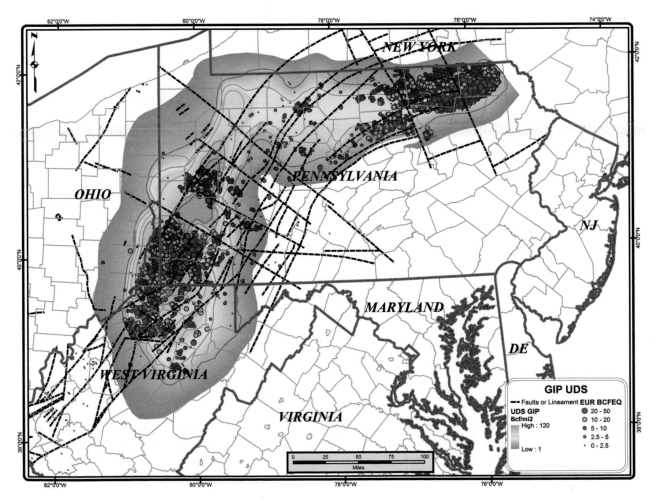

Figure 22. A map showing the gas-in-place trends for the middle Devonian Rhinestreet through Burkett shale interval and major basement faults. DC = District of Columbia; DE = Delaware; NJ = New Jersey.

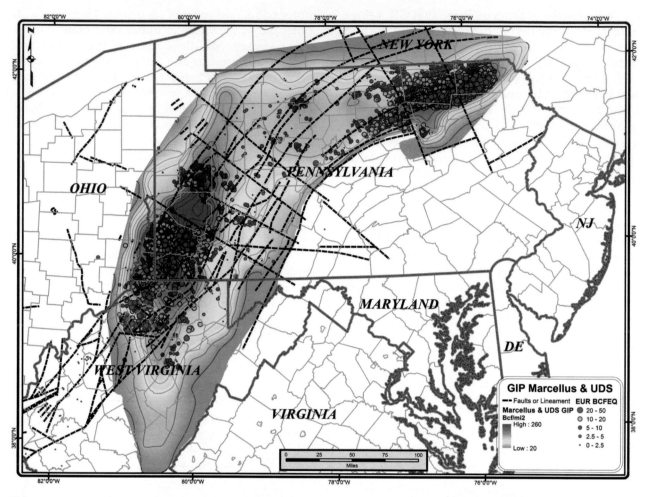

Figure 23. A map showing the gas-in-place trends for the combined Marcellus shale/Rhinestreet/Burket play and major basement faults. DC = District of Columbia; DE = Delaware; NJ = New Jersey.

regional play extents for the Marcellus and shallower upper Devonian shales suggests total in-place-gas resources of 2686 tcf for the Marcellus, 1012 tcf for the shallower Burket/Geneseo/Rhinestreet (upper Devonian shales), and 3698 tcf for the combined Marcellus/upper Devonian shale system. This calculated total GIP does not yet include the deeper Utica/Point Pleasant interval that, based on the very limited testing to date, may be highly productive across portions of the mapped Marcellus shale play. When compared to the gas-in-place estimates for the majority of top gas fields in the world, the Marcellus and the combined Marcellus/upper Devonian shales easily demonstrate in-place resources greater than the North Pars field. Another interesting comparison is that the total gas-in-place estimated for the combined Marcellus/upper Devonian shale (3698 tcf) is almost as great as the calculated gas-in-place for all of the conventional gas fields (3847 tcf).

The map in Figure 24 and Table 1 depicts the top 15 gas fields in the world together with their estimated in-place reserves and estimated recoverable reserves (Sandrea, 2006a; Sandrea, 2006b). Estimated reserve potential ranges from 40 to 1400 tcf. On a recoverable reserve basis, the Marcellus play comes in at number 2 behind the South Pars/North Dome field in Iran and Qatar. When compared on the basis of in-place reserves, the Marcellus clearly is significantly larger than all of the conventional giant fields. When the range of the recent reserve estimates for the Marcellus is compared against these top worldwide fields, the scope of the Marcellus play is clearly apparent.

ECONOMIC IMPACT OF THE MARCELLUS SHALE

Results from Marcellus wells continue to improve despite a declining rig count since 2012 and drops in commodity prices in 2014. When the Marcellus was first commercialized, conventional wisdom was that the EURs for the Marcellus wells might be 2.5 to 3.5

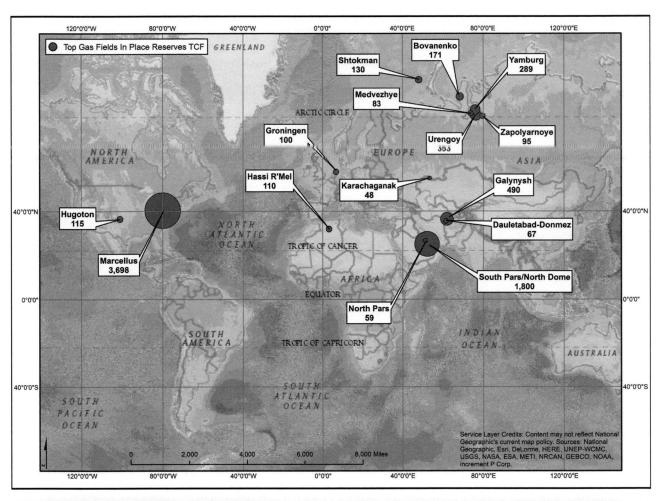

Figure 24. Map depicting the largest gas fields in the world and comparisons of in-place gas reserves and projected recoverable reserves (Marcellus reserve estimates from this study; Engelder [2009] and Wrightstone [2015]; worldwide reserve estimates from Sandrea [2006]).

BCF of gas equivalent per well, using the Barnett shale play as an analog. Drilling efficiency improvements, improved lateral targeting, optimizing completions, and longer laterals combined to drive the Marcellus shale well average EUR to 8.9 BCF of gas equivalent per well in 2014. This current study documents technical accessible in-place gas reserves in the Marcellus ranging from 2322 to 3698 tcf. This demonstrates the Marcellus gas system to be largest documented in-place gas reserves in the world. Marcellus liquids production now is supplying the northeastern United States, and Marcellus NGLs will soon be exported internationally. The Marcellus is transforming how natural gas moves across the United States. Instead of bringing Rocky Mountain gas east, the Marcellus gas now displaces gas from the Rockies Express pipeline.

The Marcellus play has been transformative to industry, economy, and environment. In 1979, the gas reserve life index in the United States was roughly estimated at about 10 years. Today, it is estimated to be at least 100 years, and some projections estimate over 200 years of reserve life. In less than a decade, the United States went from a country that was short of gas to one of the largest-producing nations in the world. Due to the abundance of natural gas, U.S. prices are now extraordinarily competitive. The price of natural gas in the United States as of early 2016 was approximately $2.40/MCF (million cubic feet). By comparison, in Europe, the cost of gas is $6.00 to $7.00/MCF, and in places around the world—including Japan and China—the price for gas is about $7.00 to $8.00/MCF. This abundance and low price has led to the rebirth of American manufacturing. The petrochemical industry overseas was using naphtha derived from crude oil as its main feedstock to manufacture products such as ethylene and plastics. Now, many are considering converting to ethane processed from natural gas as feedstock instead of naphtha. This is allowing some

Table 1. Summary of gas-in-place and recoverable reserves for top 15 gas fields worldwide.

Ranking	Field Name	Country	Size (km³)	In-Place Reserves (tcf)	Recoverable Reserves (tcf)
1	South Pars/North Dome	Iran and Qatar	35,000	1800	1235
2	Marcellus	United States	148,000	3698	489
3	Urengoy	Russia	6300	353	222
4	Yamburg	Russia	3900	289	138
5	Hassi R' Mel	Algeria	3500	110	123
6	Shtokman	Russia	3100	130	110
7	Galynysh	Turkmenistan	2800	490	98
8	Zapolyarnoye	Russia	2700	95	95
9	Hugoton[a]	United States	2300	115	81
10	Gronigen	Netherlands	2100	100	73
11	Bovanenko	Russia	2000	171	70
12	Medvezhye	Russia	1900	83	68
13	North Pars	Iran	1400	59	48
14	Dauletabad-Donmez[a]	Turkmenistan	1300	67	47
15	Karachaganak	Kazakhstan	1300	48	46
	Total GIP: All Fields			**7608**	
	Total GIP: Marcellus/UDS System			**3698**	
	Total GIP: Conventional Systems Only			**3910**	

[a]Published gas-in-place data not available. Gas-in-place estimated based on published recoverable reserves is assumed to be 70% of total GIP.

petrochemical industries to move back to the United States. Thanks to lower energy prices, the United States has provided an estimated $113 billion annual utility savings for domestic consumers.

The United States is now supplying about 84% of its energy needs. In contrast, in the mid-1970s, the consensus was that the United States was running out of oil and natural gas. But with the development of domestic resources such the Permian basin as well as Bakken and Eagleford plays, oil imports have dropped to levels of roughly 40%. This reduced dependency on foreign oil is due almost solely to the ingenious work of America's oil and gas industry. The success has been so significant that some projections suggest that by 2025, North America may be energy secure. The abundance of low-cost natural gas is changing how we generate electricity. These developments have had positive impacts not only on the cost of electricity but also on the quality of our environment. In 2003, natural gas supplied about 17% of power generation and in 2015, it reached about 30%. Coal historically has provided a large energy source to generate electricity in the United States, but now its share has decreased from 51 to 37%, with natural gas now providing a much bigger share of the fuel used for power generation.

Natural gas has many positive environmental benefits. It produces no sulfur dioxide, no nitrous oxide, and no mercury. It doesn't contain the particulates that burning coal releases and has about half the CO_2 content and therefore is a significantly better fuel environmentally and for public health. Based on a recent U. S. Environmental Protection Agency (EPA) reports, there has been a 14% decrease in toxic air emissions from the last reporting period in the mid-Atlantic region. Importantly, CO_2 reduction in the United States has been about two times what the entire world reduction has been over the past 20 years.

Finally, the Marcellus story is still unfolding. Our current estimates of gas-in-place and recoverable reserves are still evolving. Future technological breakthroughs not yet considered could further impact the ultimate recovery from this play. In addition, the potential for additional in-place and recoverable gas reserves from the Utica/Point Pleasant interval appears very promising across much of the Marcellus play area. Perhaps that will be the next giant unconventional discovery story of the current decade.

ACKNOWLEDGMENTS

The authors thank the senior management of Range Resources Corporation for their support and permission to publish. Special thanks go to Ray Walker, Alan

Farquharson, and John Applegath of Range Resources for their long-term vision and consistent encouragement in the process of unlocking and understanding the Marcellus shale play. Special thanks also to the excellent long-term research and mapping support provided by Range Resources Geoscience staff with special mention of Brad Hina, Chuck Moyer, Douglas Bowman, James Morris, Jared Van Meter, Nathan Dowey, Doug Odham, Mark Limbruner, Chris Pounds, Toni Eilerts, Steve Poe, Carl Dokter, Doug Odham, Taylor McClain, Matt Weber, Magell Candelaria, Josh Kuhn, and Chaoqing Yang. We also wish to acknowledge Mike Forrest and Jim Funk for their excellent long-term support and critical peer review. Sincere thanks and acknowledgment for the critical engineering and operational contributions and support from Range's engineering groups, with special mention of Mike Middlebrook, Dennis Degner, Don Robinson, Brad Grandstaff, Ken Brown, Joe Frantz, Zhong He, Greg Frazier, and Andrew Tullis. We also gratefully acknowledge the efforts of Core Lab, Geomark, Halliburton, Ingrain, Schlumberger, and Terra Tek for their excellent technical contributions to the understanding of this giant play.

REFERENCES CITED

Blakey, R., 2005, Global paleogeography, accessed October 10, 2015, http://jan.ucc.nau.edu/~rcb7/globaltext2.html.

Boyce, M., and T. Carr, 2010, Stratigraphy and petrophysics of the middle Devonian black shale interval in West Virginia and southwest Pennsylvania: AAPG ACE Conference Poster Proceedings, accessed January 9, 2017, http://www.searchanddiscovery.com/pdfz/documents/2010/10265boyce/ndx_boyce.pdf.html.

Cabot Oil and Gas, 2009, Cabot Oil & Gas Corporation discussion handout: Enercom 2009 Oil & Gas Conference of August 10, 2009, accessed January 9, 2016, http:www.cabotog.com/pdfs/Londonoil&gasconference09_presentation.pdf.

Canich, M. R., and D. P. Gold, 1977, A study of the Tyrone-Mt. Union lineament by remote sensing techniques and field methods: State College, Pennsylvania, Office of Remote Sensing and Earth Resources (ORDER) Technical Report 120-137, Pennsylvania State University, p. 59.

Colton, G. W., 1970, The Valley and Ridge and Appalachian Plateau: Stratigraphy and sedimentation; The Appalachian basin. Its depositional sequences and their geologic relationships, *in* G. W. Fisher, F. J. Pettijohn, and J. C. Reed Jr., eds., Studies of Appalachian geology: Central and southern: New York, New York, Interscience Publishers, p. 5–47.

Demaison, G. J., and G. T. Moore, 1980, Anoxic environments and oil source bed genesis: AAPG Bulletin, v. 64, p. 1179–1209.

de Witt, W., Jr., J. B. Roen, and L. G. Wallace, 1993, Stratigraphy of Devonian black shales and associated rocks in the Appalachian basin, *in* J. B. Roen and R. C. Kepferle, eds., Petroleum geology of the Devonian and Mississippian black shale of eastern North America: USGS Bulletin 1909, p. M1–M16.

Engelder, T., 2009, Marcellus 2008: Report card on breakout year for gas production in the Appalachian basin: Fort Worth Basin Oil and Gas Magazine, August, p. 18–22.

Engelder, T., G. G. Lash, and R. S. Uzcategui, 2009, Joint sets that enhance production from middle and upper Devonian gas shales of the Appalachian basin: AAPG Bulletin, v. 93, no. 7, p. 857–889.

Ettensohn, F. R., 1985a, The Catskill Delta complex and the Acadian Orogeny: A model, *in* D. W. Woodrow and W. D. Sevon, eds., The Catskill Delta: Geological Society of America Special Paper 201, p. 39–49.

Ettensohn, F. R., 1985b, Controls on development of Catskill Delta complex basis facies, *in* D. W. Woodrow and W. D. Sevon, eds., The Catskill Delta: Geological Society of America Special Paper 201, p. 65–77.

Ettensohn, F. R., 1992, Controls on the origin of the Devonian–Mississippian oil and gas shales, east-central United States: Fuel, v. 71, p. 1487–1492.

Ettensohn, F. R., 2004, Modeling the nature and development of major Paleozoic clastic wedges in the Appalachian basin, USA: Journal of Geodynamics, v. 37, p. 657–681.

Faill, R. T., 1985, The Acadian orogeny and the Catskill Delta, *in* D. W. Woodrow and W. D. Sevon, eds., The Catskill Delta: Geological Society of America Special Paper 201, p. 15–37.

Flaherty, K. J., 1992, Fractured middle Devonian Huntersville Chert and lower Devonian Oriskany sandstone, *in* John B. Roen and Brian J. Walker, eds., The Appalachian Oil and Natural Gas Research Contortium: The atlas of major Appalachian gas plays, p. 103–108.

Frey, M. G., 1973, Influence of Salina salt on structure in New York-Pennsylvania part of the Appalachian plateau: AAPG Bulletin, v. 57, no. 6, p. 1027–1037.

Gwinn, V. E., 1964, Thin-skinned tectonics in the Plateau and northwestern Valley and Ridge provinces of the central Appalachians: Geological Society of America Bulletin, v. 75, no. 9, p. 863–900.

Hamilton-Smith, T., 1993, Stratigraphic effects of the Acadian orogeny in the autochthonous Appalachian basin, *in* D. C. Roy and J. W. Skehan (eds.), The Acadian orogeny: Recent studies in New England, maritime Canada, and the authochthonous foreland: Geological Society of America, Special Paper, v. 275, p. 153–164.

Harper, J. A., 1992, Lower Devonian Oriskany sandstone structural play, *in* Gas Research Institute: The atlas of major Appalachian gas plays, p. 109–117.

Harper, J. A., 2008, The Marcellus shale: An old "new" gas reservoir in Pennsylvania: Pennsylvania Geology, v. 38, no. 1, p. 2–13.

Harper, J. A., and C. D. Laughrey, 1987, Geology of the oil and gas fields of southwestern Pennsylvania: Commonwealth of Pennsylvania Mineral Resource Report no. 87, p. 91–97.

Heidbach, O., K. Fuchs, B. Muller, J. Reinecker, B. Sperner, M. Tingay, et al., eds., 2007, The world stress map: Release

2005: Paris, Commission for the Geological Map of the World.

Hunter, C. D., 1935, Natural gas in Eastern Kentucky, *in* Henry A. Ley, ed., Geology of Natural Gas: AAPG Special Publication 7, p. 915–947.

Inks, T. L., T. Engelder, E. Jenner, B. Golob, J. S. Hocum, and D. G. O'Brien, 2015, Marcellus fracture characterization using P-wave azimuthal velocity attributes: Comparison with production and outcrop data: Interpretation, v. 3, no. 3, p. SU1–SU15.

Jarvie, D. M., R. J. Hill, and R. M. Pollastro, 2005, Assessment of the gas potential and yields from shales: The Barnett shale model, *in* Brian J. Cardott, ed., Unconventional Energy Resources in the Southern Midcontinent, 2004 symposium: Oklahoma Geological Survey Circular 110, p. 37–50.

Kohl, D., R. Slingerland, M. Arthur, R. Bracht, and T. Engelder, 2014, Sequence stratigraphy and depositional environments of the Shamokin (Union Springs) member, Marcellus formation, and associated strata in the middle Appalachian basin: AAPG Bulletin, v. 98, no. 3, p. 483–513.

Kulander, C. S., and R. T. Ryder, 2005, Regional seismic lines across the Rome trough and Allegheny plateau of northern West Virginia, western Maryland, and southwestern Pennsylvania, USGS Geologic Investigations Series Map I-2791, accessed January 9, 2017, https://pubs.er.usgs .gov/publication/pp1708E.5.1.

Lash, G. G., 2008, Stratigraphy and fracture history of the middle & upper Devonian succession, western New York: Significance to basin evolution and hydrocarbon exploration: Pittsburgh Association of Petroleum Geologists unpublished field trip guide, p. 85.

Lash, G. G., and Terry Engelder, 2009, The middle Devonian Marcellus shale: A record of eustacy and basin dynamics (abs.): AAPG Annual Convention and Exhibition, accessed September 21, 2016, http://www.searchanddiscovery .com/abstracts/html/2009/annual/abstracts/lash.htm.

Lash, G. G., 2009, Sequence stratigraphic framework of the middle Devonian Marcellus shale (abs.): AAPG 2009 Eastern Section Meeting, accessed September 21, 2016, http://www.searchanddiscovery.com/abstracts /html/2009/eastern/abstracts/lash.htm.

Lash, G. G., and T. Engelder, 2008, Marcellus shale subsurface stratigraphy and thickness trends: Eastern New York to northeastern West Virginia (abs.): AAPG Eastern Section Meeting and http://www.papgrocks.org/lash_p.pdf.

Lash, G. G., and T. Engelder, 2011, Thickness trends and sequence stratigraphy of the middle Devonian Marcellus formation, Appalachian basin: Implications for Acadian foreland basin evolution: AAPG Bulletin, v. 95, no. 1, p. 61–103.

Lash, G. G., and E. P. Lash, 2014, Early history of the natural gas industry, Fredonia, New York: Search and Discovery Article #70000.

Lavin, P. M., D. L. Chaffin, and W. F. Davis, 1982, Major lineaments and the Lake Erie–Maryland crustal block: Tectonics, v. 1, p. 431–440.

Lee, K. D., 1980, Subsurface structure of the eastern Kentucky gas field: Unpublished M.S. thesis, West Virginia University, 52 p.

Macquaker, J., D. McIlroy, S. J. Davies, and M. A. Keller, 2009, Not anoxia! How do you preserve organic matter then? (abs.): AAPG Annual Convention and Exhibition.

Milici, R. C., 2005, Assessment of undiscovered natural gas resources in Devonian black shales, Appalachian basin, eastern U.S.A.: USGS Open-file report, accessed September 15, 2009, http://pubs.usgs.gov/of/2005/1268/2005 -1268.ppt#313.

Milici, R. C., and C. S. Swezey, 2006, Assessment of Appalachian Basin oil and gas resources: Devonian shale–Middle and Upper Paleozoic total petroleum system: USGS Open-file Report, accessed January 9, 2017, https://pubs .usgs.gov/of/2006/1237/of2006-1237.pdf, 70 p.

Murphy, A. E., 2000, Physical and biochemical mechanisms of black shale deposition, and their implications for ecological and evolutionary change in the Devonian Appalachian basin: Unpublished Ph.D. dissertation, Northwestern University, 363 p.

Negus-deWyss, J., 1979, The eastern Kentucky gas field: A geological study of the relationship of oil shale gas occurrence to structure, stratigraphy, lithology, and inorganic geochemical parameters: Unpublished Ph.D. dissertation, West Virginia University, 199 p.

Pollastro, R. M, D. M. Jarvie, R. J. Hill, and C. W. Adams, 2007, Geologic framework of the Mississippian Barnett shale, Barnett-Paleozoic total petroleum system, Bend arch-Fort Worth basin, Texas: AAPG Bulletin, v. 91 no. 4, p. 405–436.

Powell, M. E., and W. Brackett, 2009, Best Barnett shale wells based on peak month daily average: Powell Barnett Shale Newsletter, July, p. 9.

Powell, M. E., and W. Brackett, 2015, Best Barnett shale wells based on peak month daily average: Powell Barnett Shale Newsletter, August 21, p. 9.

Range Resources Corporation, 2010, Range Resources company presentation, August: accessed August 2010, Unpublished internal document, Range Resources Corporation.

Reed, J. R., and D. Dunbar, 2008, Using ArcGIS to estimate thermogenic gas generation volumes by upper and middle Devonian shales in the Appalachian basin (abs.): AAPG Eastern Section Meeting, 2008.

Repetski, J. E., R. T. Ryder, J. A. Harper, and M. H. Trippi, 2002, Thermal maturity patterns (CAI and %R_o) in the Ordovician and Devonian rocks of the Appalachian basin in Pennsylvania: U.S. Geological Survey Open-File Report 2002-302, 57 p.

Repetski, J. E., R. T. Ryder, K. L. Avary, and M. H. Trippi, 2005, Thermal maturity patterns (CAI and %R_o) in the Ordovician and Devonian rocks of the Appalachian basin in West Virginia: U.S. Geological Survey Open-File Report 2005-1078, 72 p.

Repetski, J. E., R. T. Ryder, D. J. Weary, A. G. Harris, and M. H. Trippi, 2008, Thermal maturity patterns (CAI and %R_o) in the Ordovician and Devonian rocks of the Appalachian basin: A major revision of USGS Map I-917 using new subsurface collections: U.S. Geological Survey Scientific Investigations Map 3006.

Robinson, J. E., 1985, Development of gas-bearing reservoirs in the Trenton limestone formation of New York: New York State Energy and Development Authority (NYSERDA) Report: New York, The Authority, p. 85-18.

Rodgers, M. R., and T. H. Anderson, 1984, Tyrone-Mt. Union cross-strike lineament of Pennsylvania: A major Paleozoic basement fracture and uplift boundary: AAPG Bulletin, v. 68, p. 92–105.

Rowan, E. L., 2006, Burial and thermal history of the central Appalachian basin, based on three 2-D models of Ohio, Pennsylvania, and West Virginia: USGS Open File Report 2006-1019, accessed January 10, 2017, https:// pubs.er.usgs.gov/publication/ofr20061019.

Rowan, E. L., R. T. Ryder, J. L. Repetski, M. H. Trippi, and L. F. Ruppert, 2004, Initial results of a 2D burial/thermal history model: Central Appalachian basin, Ohio and West Virginia: USGS Open File Report 2004-1445, 37 p.

RSEG (Ross Smith Energy Group, Ltd.), 2007, The Marcellus shale: Get your lease on: RSEG Alert December 12, 7 p.

Ryder, R. T., M. H. Trippi, C. S. Swezey, R. C. Milici, J. E. Repetski, L. F. Ruppert, et al., 2011, A regional perspective of the Devonian shale and Ordovician Utica shale total petroleum systems of the Appalachian basin: AAPG Search and Discovery Article #90131, accessed September 21, 2016, http://www.searchanddiscovery.com/pdfz /abstracts/pdf/2011/eastern/abstracts/ndx_ryder.pdf .html.

Sageman, B. B., A. E. Murphy, J. P. Werne, C. A. Ver Straeten, D. J. Hollander, and T. W. Lyons, 2003, A tale of shales: The relative role of production, decomposition, and dilution in the accumulation of organic-rich strata; Middle–upper Devonian, Appalachian basin: Chemical Geology, v. 195, p. 229–273.

Sandrea, R., 2006a, Global natural gas reserves: A heuristic viewpoint (part 1 of 2): Middle East Economic Survey, v. 49, no. 11, accessed January 10, 2017, http://archives .mees.com/issues/298/articles/12167.

Sandrea, R., 2006b, Global natural gas reserves: A heuristic viewpoint (part 2 of 2): Middle East Economic Survey, v. 49, no. 11, accessed May 1, 2007, http://www.mees.com /postedarticles/oped/v49n12-5OD01.htm.

Sanford, B. V., 1993, St. Lawrence platform-economic geology, in D. F. Stott and J. D. Aitken, eds., Sedimentary cover of the craton in Canada: Boulder, Colorado, Geological Society of America, p. 787–798.

Scanlin, M. A., and T. Engelder, 2003, The basement versus the no-basement hypothesis for folding within the Appalachian plateau: Detachment sheet: American Journal of Science, v. 303, p. 519–563.

Schmoker, J. W., 1981a, Determination of organic-matter content of Appalachian Devonian shales from gamma-ray logs: AAPG Bulletin, v. 65, no. 7, p. 1285–1298.

Schmoker, J. W., 1981b, Organic-matter content of Appalachian Devonian shales determined by use of wire-line logs: Summary of work done 1976–80: U.S. Geological

Survey, accessed January 9, 2017, https://pubs.er.usgs .gov/publication/ofr81181.

Shumaker, R. C., 1993, Structural parameters that affect Devonian shale gas production in West Virginia and eastern Kentucky, in J. B. Roen and R. C. Kepferle, eds., Petroleum geology of the Devonian and Mississippian black shale of eastern North America: USGS Bulletin 1909, p. K1–K38.

Shumaker, R. C., 1996, Structural history of the Appalachian basin, in J. B. Roen and B. J. Walker, eds., The atlas of major Appalachian gas plays: Morgantown, West Virginia, West Virginia Geological Survey, p. 8–10.

Van Tyne, A. M., 1993, Detailed study of Devonian black shales encountered in nine wells in western New York state, in J. B. Roen and R. C. Kepferle, eds., Petroleum geology of the Devonian and Mississippian black shale of eastern North America: USGS Bulletin 1909, p. M1–M16.

Ventura, J. L., 2013, Range's path to discovery and commercialization of the Marcellus shale:

The largest producing gas field in the United States: Search and Discovery Article 110165, 2013 Michael T. Halbouty Presentation and Award, AAPG National Conference, Pittsburgh, Pennsylvania.

Ventura, J. L., et al., 2013, The Discovery of the Marcellus shale Play, An Operator's Experience: URTeC Conference Proceedings, accessed January 9, 2017, http://library .seg.org/doi/abs/10.1190/urtec2013-077.

Wendt, A. K., M. A. Arthur, R. Slingerland, D. Kohl, R. Bracht, and T. Engelder, 2015, Geochemistry and depositional history of the Union Springs member, Marcellus formation in central Pennsylvania: Interpretation, v. 3, no. 3, p. SV17–SV33.

Werne, J. P., B. B. Sageman, T. W. Lyons, and D. J. Hollander, 2002, An integrated assessment of a "type euxinic" deposit: Evidence for multiple controls on black shale deposits in the middle Devonian Oatka Creek formation: American Journal of Science, v. 302, p. 110–143.

Wheeler, R. L., 1980, Cross-strike structural discontinuities: Possible exploration tool for natural gas in Appalachian overthrust belt: AAPG Bulletin, v. 64, no. 12, p. 2166–2178.

Williams, H., and R. D. Hatcher, 1982, Suspect terranes and accretionary history of the Appalachian orogen: Geology, v. 10, p. 530–536.

Woodrow, D. L., and W. D. Sevon, eds., 1985, The Catskill delta: Geological Society of America, Special Paper, 246 p.

Wrightstone, G. R., 2015, Burket/Geneseo shale: Appalachia's little brother to the Marcellus and Utica: PAPG Eastern Section Meeting.

Yang C., D. Bowman, J. Morris, and W. Zagorski, 2013, Marcellus shale asset optimization through increased geological understanding: Search and Discovery Article 41144, accessed September 20, 2016, http://www.searchanddiscovery.com /pdfz/documents/2013/41144yang/ndx_yang.pdf.html.

Zagorski, W. A., 2010, The Appalachian Marcellus shale play: Discovery thinking, timing and technology: Search and Discovery Article 110138, accessed September 20, 2016, http://www.searchanddiscovery.com/pdfz /documents/2010/110138zagorski/ndx_zagorski.pdf. html.

Zagorski, W. A., G. R. Wrightstone, and D. C. Bowman, 2012, The Appalachian basin Marcellus gas play: Its history of development, geologic controls on production, and future potential as a world-class reservoir, *in* J. A. Breyer, ed., Shale reservoirs: Giant resources for the 21st century: AAPG Memoir 97, p. 172–200.

Zagorski, W. A., D. C. Bowman, M. Emery, and G. R. Wrightstone, 2011, An overview of some key factors controlling well productivity in core areas of the Appalachian basin Marcellus shale play: 2011 AAPG National Conference, Houston, Texas.

Zagorski, W. A., D. Bowman, J. Morris, and C. Yang, 2013, Marcellus shale: Geologic considerations for an evolving North American liquids-rich play: Search and Discovery Article 110166 , accessed January 9, 2017, http://www.searchanddiscovery.com/pdfz/abstracts /pdf/2015/90229playmaker/abstracts/ndx_zagorski .pdf.html.

6

Sonnenberg, Stephen A., Cosima Theloy, and Hui Jin, 2017, The giant continuous oil accumulation in the Bakken petroleum system, U.S. Williston Basin, *in* R. K. Merrill and C. A. Sternbach, eds., Giant fields of the decade 2000–2010: AAPG Memoir 113, p. 91–120.

The Giant Continuous Oil Accumulation in the Bakken Petroleum System, U.S. Williston Basin

Stephen A. Sonnenberg

Department of Geology, Colorado School of Mines, Golden, Colorado, U.S.A. (e-mail: ssonnenb@mines.edu)

Cosima Theloy

Independent Geologist, 1690 S. Deframe Ct., Lakewood, Colorado, U.S.A. 80228 (e-mail: ctheloy@gmail.com)

Hui Jin

BP America, Inc., 501 Westlake Park Blvd., Houston, Texas, U.S.A. 77079 (e-mail: hui.jin4@bp.com)

ABSTRACT

The Williston Basin Bakken petroleum system is a giant continuous accumulation. The petroleum system is characterized by low-porosity and -permeability reservoirs, organic-rich source rocks, and regional hydrocarbon charge. Total Bakken and Three Forks production to December 2014 was 1.289 billion barrels (bbl) of oil and 1.3 trillion cubic feet of gas (TCFG) from 12,051 wells. U. S. Geological Survey (USGS) (Gaswirth et al., 2013) mean technologically recoverable resource estimates for the Bakken petroleum system are 7.375 billion barrels of oil, 6.7 tcf of gas, and 527 million barrels of natural gas liquids.

The Bakken Formation regionally in the Williston Basin consists of four members: upper and lower organic-rich black shale, a middle member (silty dolostone or limestone to sandstone lithology), and a basal member recently named the Pronghorn. The Bakken Formation ranges in thickness from a wedge edge to over 140 ft (43 m) with the thickest area in the Bakken located in northwest North Dakota, east of the Nesson anticline.

The Three Forks is a silty dolostone throughout much of its stratigraphic interval. The Three Forks ranges in thickness from less than 25 ft (8 m) to over 250 ft (76 m) in the mapped area. Thickness patterns are controlled by paleostructural features such as the Poplar Dome, Nesson, Antelope, Cedar Creek, and Bottineau anticlines. Thinning and/or truncation occurs over the crest of the highs, and thickening of strata occurs on the flanks of the highs. The Three Forks can be subdivided into three units (up to six by some authors; e.g., Webster, 1984; Gutierrez, 2014; Gantyno, 2011). Most of the development activity in the Three Forks targets the upper Three Forks.

The upper Three Forks is dominated by silt-sized quartz and dolomite and some very-fine-grained sandstones and has low permeabilities and porosities. The upper Three Forks ranges in thickness from a wedge edge to over 40 ft (12 m) in areas east of the Nesson anticline. The unit thins toward the margins of the depositional basin because of erosional truncation.

DOI:10.1306/13572002M113508

The upper and lower shale members are potential source rocks and are lithologically similar throughout much of the basin. The shales are regarded as dominantly type II kerogens. The shales average 11 wt.% total organic carbon.

Measured core porosity and permeability are very low in the Bakken, Sanish, and Three Forks reservoirs (<10% porosity and <0.1 md permeability) in the Williston Basin, so productivity is assumed to be due to natural and artificial fracturing. The reservoirs generally require advanced technology to get them to produce (fracture stimulation and horizontal stimulation). For this reason, they should be considered to be technology reservoirs. Natural fractures in some areas (e.g., Billings Nose area and Antelope field) are sufficient for vertical well production.

Reservoir pressure in the Bakken is regarded as overpressured with pressure gradients exceeding 0.5 psi/ft. A new pressure map for the Bakken petroleum system was generated. The map is based on 92 BHP (bottom-hole pressure) and DFIT (diagnostic fracture injection test) data points, including six additional hydrostatic points at the eastern margin as well as six data points for the Sanish–Parshall area. High overpressures are found in large parts of the central basin and the Parshall area in the east, where gradients exceed 0.7 psi/ft. Elm Coulee has a pressure gradient around 0.55 psi/ft. Parshall is reported to have a gradient of 0.74 psi/ft. The area west of the Nesson anticline has pressure gradients of 0.6 to 0.7 psi/ft. Pressure gradients in Montana are generally in the 0.5+ psi/ft range.

INTRODUCTION

The Mississippian–Devonian Bakken petroleum system of the Williston Basin is characterized by low-porosity and -permeability reservoirs, organic-rich source rocks, and regional hydrocarbon charge. The unconventional play is the current focus of exploration and development activity by many operators.

The structure of the Williston Basin at the top of the Bakken is illustrated by Figure 1. The basin is semicircular in shape, and prominent structural features are the Nesson, Billings, Little Knife, Poplar, and Cedar Creek anticlines. Many of the structural features have a documented ancestral origin and influenced Paleozoic sedimentary patterns (Gerhard et al., 1990). Recurrent movement on Precambrian faults or shear zones is seen elsewhere in the Rocky Mountain region (Weimer, 1980). The Nesson anticline is the location of the first oil discoveries in the 1950s. The first oil production on the Nesson anticline was from the Silurian Interlake Formation in 1951, and subsequent oil production was established from the Mississippian Madison Group (the main producer in the basin). The Williston Basin produces mainly oil from several Paleozoic reservoirs (Figure 2). The probable source rock to reservoir rock petroleum systems is illustrated by Figure 2. Seven different petroleum systems have been identified in the Williston Basin (Lillis, 2013).

The Bakken petroleum system consists of the Bakken Formation, lower Lodgepole, and upper and middle Three Forks (Figures 2 and 3). A petroleum system consists of source beds and all the genetically related hydrocarbon accumulations. The Bakken Formation over most of the Williston Basin consists of four members: (1) upper shale, (2) middle silty dolostone or dolomitic siltstone

and sandstone, (3) lower shale, and (4) Pronghorn (LeFever, 2008; LeFever et al., 2011). The source beds for the petroleum system are the upper and lower organic-rich Bakken shales. Source bed potential also exists in the False Bakken interval of the lower Lodgepole (Stroud, 2010). The reservoir rocks for the petroleum system are all the members of the Bakken, the lower Lodgepole, and upper and middle Three Forks.

Previous workers have described significant Bakken source rock potential and estimates of oil generated

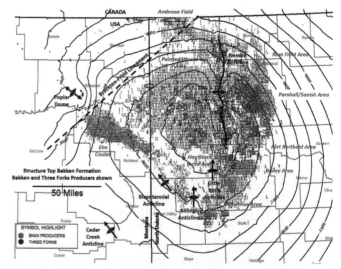

Figure 1. Structure map on top of Bakken. Contour interval is 500 ft (152 m). Prominent structural features in the Williston Basin include the Poplar, Cedar Creek, Billings, Bicentennial, Little Knife, and Nesson anticlines. The Nesson, Billings, and Little Knife anticlines trend north–south which is most likely related to the Precambrian geology. All the major structural features show evidence of recurrent structural movement during the Phanerozoic.

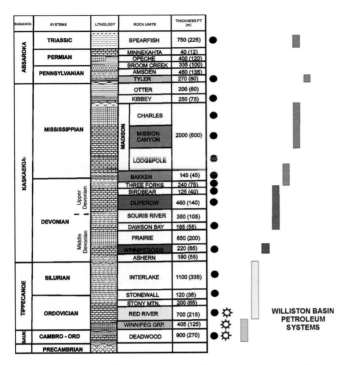

Figure 2. Stratigraphic column for Paleozoic producing units in the Williston Basin. Producing units shown by oil and gas symbols. The Bakken petroleum system consists of source beds in the Bakken and reservoirs in the lower Lodgepole, Bakken, and upper Three Forks. The upper Three Forks is the main producer in the Antelope field. Sedimentary sequences following Sloss (1963) are indicated. Thickness of stratigraphic units indicated in the column to the right (ft/m). Oil and gas symbols indicate producing formations. Modified from LeFever (1992). Petroleum systems are modified from Lillis (2013).

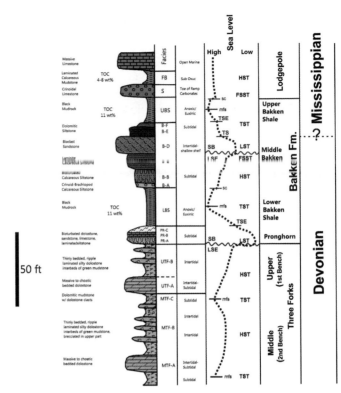

Figure 3. Diagram illustrating members of the Bakken petroleum system. Source beds are the Lower and Upper Bakken shales and the false Bakken member of the Lodgepole. Reservoirs are the middle and upper Three Forks, middle member of the Bakken, and the Scallion member of the Lodgepole

from the petroleum system range from 10 to 400 billion barrels (Dow, 1974; Williams, 1974; Meissner, 1978; Schmoker and Hester, 1983; Webster, 1984; Price et al., 1984; Meissner and Banks, 2000; Pitman et al., 2001; Flannery and Kraus, 2006; LeFever and Helms, 2006). The USGS (Gaswirth et al., 2013) mean technologically recoverable resource estimates for the Bakken petroleum system is 7.375 billion barrels oil, 6.7 tcf gas, and 527 million barrels of natural gas liquids (Gaswirth et al., 2013). The technologically recoverable resource estimates for the Bakken Formation are 3.644 billion barrels of oil, 3.1 trillion cubic feet of associated/dissolved natural gas, and 246 million barrels of natural gas liquids. The technologically recoverable resource estimate for the Three Forks is 3.731 billion barrels of oil, 3.5 trillion cubic feet of gas, and 281 million barrels of natural gas liquids.

The Bakken petroleum system is thought to have created a continuous type of accumulation in the deeper parts of the Williston Basin (Nordeng, 2009). A continuous accumulation is a hydrocarbon accumulation that has some or all of the following characteristics: pervasive hydrocarbon charge throughout a large area, no well-defined oil– or gas–water contact, diffuse boundaries, commonly abnormally pressured, large in-place resource volume but low recovery factor, little water production, geologically controlled "sweet spots," reservoirs commonly in close proximity to mature source rocks, reservoirs with very low matrix permeabilities, and water that occurs updip from hydrocarbons. The Bakken petroleum system meets all these characteristics.

Many of the reservoirs in the Bakken petroleum system have low permeability. Productive areas or sweet spots are localized areas of improved reservoir permeability through natural fracturing, the development of matrix permeability, or a combination of both. The Bakken petroleum system is a continuous system with no real boundaries between fields (Figure 1). Total Bakken and Three Forks production to December 2014 was 1.289 billion bbl of oil and 1.3 TCFG from 12,051 wells (Figure 4). Thus the petroleum system easily meets the definition of a giant accumulation (500 million barrels of oil). Total Bakken production to December 2014 was 1.022 billion bbl of oil and 1.0 TCFG (Figure 5). Total Three Forks production to December 2014 was 263,448 MBO and 294 billion cubic feet gas (Figure 6). The most notable sweet spot areas are the Elm Coulee, Sanish, and Parshall fields. Field names are abundant through the continuous

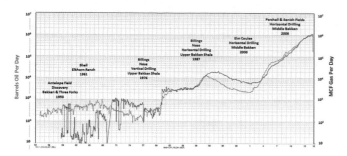

Figure 4. Total U.S.A. Williston Basin Bakken and Three Forks production. Current cumulative total is: 1,289,803,891 bbl of oil and 1,311,105,241 MCFG.

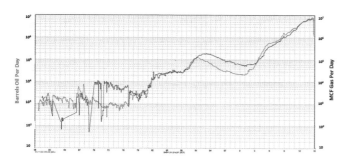

Figure 5. Total U.S.A. Williston Basin Bakken only production. Current cumulative total is: 1,022,855,380 bbl of oil and 1,011,814,857 MCFG.

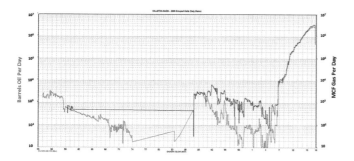

Figure 6. Total U.S.A. Williston Basin Three Forks only production. Current cumulative total is: 263,448,155 bbl of oil and 294,728,845 MCFG.

accumulation, but no barriers exist between the fields. At the end of 2014, the U.S. Williston Basin accounted for approximately 25% of domestic oil production.

This chapter summarizes the regional geology of the Bakken and Three Forks formations in the Williston Basin.

BAKKEN EXPLORATION: HISTORY OF BASIN

The Bakken Formation of the Williston Basin has seen three cycles of exploration and development since the 1950s (Figure 4) (LeFever, 2006, 2007; Sonnenberg, 2010a). The first cycle is the Antelope field discovery and development (Bakken and Three Forks vertical drilling). The next cycle is the upper Bakken shale Billings Nose edge play (vertical and horizontal drilling for the upper Bakken shale). The last cycle is the middle Bakken–Three Forks horizontal play.

The earliest discovery occurred in the Antelope field of North Dakota in 1953, and development continued into the 1960s. Sixty-three wells targeted the Bakken and upper Three Forks (referred to as the Sanish member) on a tightly folded structure. The Bakken and upper Three Forks are low-permeability, fracture-enhanced reservoirs in Antelope with fracturing related to the tight fold (Murray, 1968). The wells were drilled vertically and after a sand-oil fracture stimulation treatment were capable of producing an average of 209 BOPD. Antelope field has produced 11 million barrels of oil and 20 BCF of gas from the Three Forks Bakken interval. Average cumulative production per Three Forks well is 550 million bbl of oil and 1.4 BCF. Following the Antelope discovery, exploration proceeded slowly. All three members of the Bakken and the upper Three Forks were perforated in Antelope, and production established these formations as petroleum reservoirs in the basin.

The next significant discovery in the Bakken was by Shell in the Elkhorn Ranch field in 1961 (Billings Nose area) (Figures 1 and 4). The upper Bakken shale was completed in the well as a secondary objective after the deeper primary objective, the Red River zone (Ordovician), was not successful. The Elkhorn Ranch well was very significant in that it showed significant reserves could be found in the upper Bakken shale. Because of product prices and the remoteness of the area, the next Bakken well was not drilled until 1976. This area then became known as the Bakken fairway area. Wells drilled in the fairway targeted the upper Bakken shale and other Paleozoic horizons (both shallower and deeper). The area occurs along the southwest margin of the Bakken depositional basin in the general area of the Billings Nose (Figure 1). Reservoir characteristics for this area were described by Cramer (1986). Where the Bakken thins, fracture density increases (Sperr, 1991). Sand-oil fracture stimulation treatment was used on these wells.

Horizontal drilling in the upper Bakken shale commenced in 1987 in the Billings anticline (fairway) area (LeFever, 1992, 2006). The first horizontal well, drilled by Meridian, was the #33-11 MOI well (Sec. 11, T143N, R102W, Elkhorn Ranch field), which had a horizontal displacement of 2603 ft (793 m) in the Bakken. The well was completed for 258 BOPD and 299 MCFGD, and production was remarkably stable for the first 2 years. The success of this well set off the horizontal drilling phase of the upper Bakken shale. The play continued into the 1990s with over 20 operators. Product prices declined significantly in the 1990s, and this—along with the somewhat unpredictable production in the upper Bakken shale—brought this phase to a close. The fairway play met with mixed results. Good-producing wells were often offset with poor-producing wells. In addition, some pressure depletion and cross-well communication was reported (LeFever, 2006).

Because of mixed results in the fairway trend and low product prices, the Bakken again returned to the status of being a secondary objective type of reservoir rather than a primary objective of exploration. This status changed with the discovery of significant reserves in the middle Bakken in the Elm Coulee field. The discovery and development of the middle Bakken has resulted in the most significant exploration cycle to date.

The Elm Coulee field was discovered in 2000 with horizontal completions in the middle Bakken. The field is located in the western part of the Williston Basin in northeast Montana (Figure 1). Prior to the horizontal drilling in 2000, the area had scattered vertical well production (marginal to uneconomic) from the Bakken (the Bakken was a secondary objective for wells targeting deeper horizons). Horizontal drilling began in the field in 2000 and to date, over 1500 wells have been drilled. The estimated ultimate recovery for the field is over 200 million bbl of oil. Cumulative production from the Elm Coulee area from the Bakken to December 2014 was 152 million bbl of oil and 136 BCF. Horizontal drilling and fracture stimulation of the horizontal leg are key technologies that enable a low-permeability reservoir to produce. The original drilling and spacing unit at Elm Coulee was a 640-acre unit. Wells were drilled using bi- or trilaterals in a section and then were fracture stimulated with one hydraulic fracture stimulation stage (which became known as the pump and pray type of fracture stimulation). Stratigraphic trapping plays a key role at Elm Coulee (Sonnenberg and Pramudito, 2009; Alexandre, 2011). Horizontal wells in the Elm Coulee field target mainly the B facies of the middle Bakken (Figure 3). The unit is dominated by dolostone (Alexandre, 2011). The mineral composition in the main pay interval is 50 to 60% dolomite, 30 to 35% quartz, 10% feldspar, and 5% clay.

The Elm Coulee discovery and development prompted operators to also target the middle Bakken in North Dakota. Prior to Elm Coulee, most operators targeted only the upper shale in the Bakken. The expansion of the play into North Dakota is currently underway and has resulted in many new discoveries, including the Parshall and Sanish fields. The new discoveries in North Dakota suggest the existence of an extremely large unconventional resource play. Product prices will probably influence this cycle too.

The Parshall Field located on the east side of the Nesson anticline was discovered in 2006 with horizontal completion in the middle Bakken. EOG drilled and completed the 1-36 Parshall (Sec. 36, T150N, R90W) for 463 BOPD and 128 MCFGD. Through December 2014, the field had produced approximately 94 million bbl of oil and 46 BCF from 346 wells completed in the Bakken. This field illustrates that significant production from the middle Bakken and Three Forks exists in North Dakota. The field connects to the Sanish field to the west and the Ross field to the north. By the time Parshall was discovered, multistage fracture stimulation had been tried and tested in the Barnett shale play of the Fort Worth basin. Therefore, during the development of the Parshall field, multistage hydraulic stimulation in the Williston Basin was developed. Fracture stages were originally around 10 but have evolved up to 40 fracture stages.

The Sanish field was also discovered in 2006. Whiting drilled the discovery well: 44-1 Bartleson (Sec. 1, T152N, R93W). Through December 2014, the field had produced approximately 101 million bbl of oil and 74 BCF from 592 wells completed in the Bakken and Three Forks. The geology of the Parshall and Sanish areas has been described by Kowalski (2010), Kowalski and Sonnenberg (2011), Simenson (2010), and Simenson et al. (2011).

Horizontal wells in the Parshall–Sanish areas target specific facies (C, D, E) of the middle Bakken (Figure 3). Production is related to fracture development and matrix development in the middle Bakken. The original oil in place in the Parshall greater area is estimated by various operators to be 8 to 11 million barrels per section for the Bakken and 4 to 6 million barrels per section for the Three Forks. Wells are drilled on either 1280-acre spacing units or 640 spacing units. Estimated ultimate recoveries for the Bakken are 600,000 to 900,000 barrels of oil per section; estimated ultimate recoveries for the Three Forks are 350,000 to 500,000 barrels of oil per section. The recovery factor for the tight reservoirs is estimated to be approximately 3 to 10% (LeFever and Helms, 2006). Because of high production rates, wells can pay out in 4 to 6 months. Some operators prefer the 1280 spacing units over the 640 spacing units because of cost savings associated with the drilling of one well instead of two. Operators are fracture stimulating wells with 20-plus stages.

Various methods have been proposed to explore the Bakken (Sperr, 1991; Rogers and Mattox, 1985). The methods include exploring along the depositional or erosional edge (more susceptible to fracturing and fracture spacing decreases as bed thickness decreases); exploring structural flexures and lineaments; looking for Prairie dissolution areas, as they may be areas of more intense fracturing (Parker, 1967); looking for geothermal anomalies (intense hydrocarbon generation may cause more intense fracturing); looking for primary reservoirs (e.g., middle Bakken); and looking for fractured areas identified by well logs. The fracture signature on well logs has been described by Hansen and Long (1991) and Sonnenberg et al. (2011c).

The latest cycle of exploration and development in the Williston Basin is the most significant to date. Production for the U.S. part of the Williston Basin has gone from 2500 BOPD to close to a million BOPD.

REGIONAL GEOLOGY

The Williston Basin is a large intracratonic sedimentary basin that occupies parts of North Dakota, Montana, South Dakota, Saskatchewan, and Manitoba. The basin probably originated as a craton-margin basin and evolved to an intracratonic basin during the Cordilleran orogen (Gerhard et al., 1982, 1987, 1990) (Figure 7). Sedimentation occurred throughout much of the Phanerozoic, and the thickness of the stratigraphic section is approximately 16,000 ft (Figure 8). Many unconformities are described in the stratigraphic section, but rocks of all Phanerozoic time periods are represented by some deposits (Figures 2 and 8). Paleozoic strata consist mainly of cyclic carbonate deposits; the Mesozoic and Cenozoic strata consist mainly of siliciclastics.

During the late Devonian and early Mississippian, the basin was an area of active subsidence in a broad shelf area that existed along the western margin of

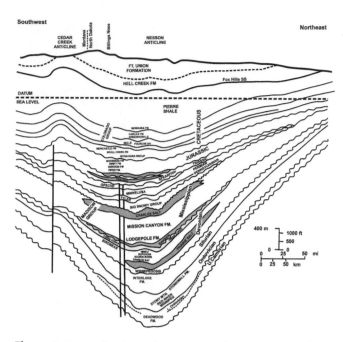

Figure 8. Generalized southwest to northeast cross section across Williston Basin. Modified from Peterson and MacCary (1987). The Cedar Creek anticline is a probably source of sediments for parts of the Bakken, Pronghorn, and Three Forks intervals.

North America. The proto-Williston Basin was an extension of the Devonian Elk Point basin of Canada and was situated in tropical regions near the equator.

Source areas for clastics found in the Bakken and Three Forks include the Cedar Creek High, Central Montana High, Black Hills Highland, Transcontinental Arch, and Canadian Shield.

The depositional and/or erosional limits of the Three Forks Formation and subsequent deposits of the Bakken members are shown in Figure 9 (Theloy, 2014). The

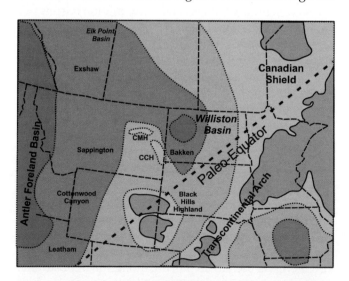

Figure 7. North America paleogeography and black shale deposits for Late Devonian, 360 Ma (modified from Blakey, 2005). Structural features: Canadian Shield, Transcontinental Arch, Black Hills Highland, Cedar Creek High (CCH), Central Montana High (CMH). Position of equator marked by dashed line (Paleo-Equator).

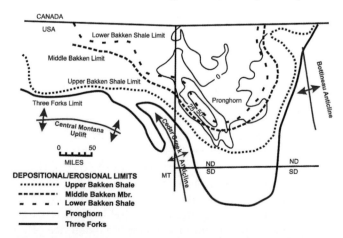

Figure 9. Depositional and erosional limits of the Bakken formation members and the Three Forks formation (modified from Theloy, 2014; after Meissner, 1978; Pronghorn limits from LeFever et al., 2011).

Three Forks has the largest areal extent. After a period of erosion and nondeposition, Pronghorn sediments filled in topographic lows. The Pronghorn has, unlike overlying Bakken strata, a depocenter at the southern margin of the basin with maximum thickness of 54 ft (16 m). The thickest Pronghorn accumulation extends in a linear trough shape, which coincides with both the edge of the Prairie salt and the Heart River fault on the southwestern side (LeFever et al., 2011; Bottjer et al., 2011). The fault may have facilitated movement of fluids into the Prairie salt, which in turn could have triggered dissolution and larger-scale salt collapse features.

After the major drop in sea level at the Three Forks–Bakken boundary, all four members of the Bakken exhibit a successively larger areal extent and onlapping relationships with the Three Forks at the basin margin, reflecting rising sea level conditions.

Three Precambrian provinces underlie the Williston Basin: the Superior craton, Trans-Hudson orogenic belt, and Wyoming craton (LeFever, 1992). These provinces trend north–south, and structures associated with them have strongly influenced later sedimentation and structural features. Notable structural features with a north grain in the Williston Basin include the Nesson, Billings, Little Knife, and Tree Top anticlines. Northwest-trending prominent structural feature include the Cedar Creek, Antelope, and Poplar anticlines. Periodically, these structural features are reactivated (LeFever, 1992; Gerhard et al., 1990).

The Devonian Prairie evaporite occurs about 800 to 1100 ft (244 to 335 m) beneath the Bakken Formation (Figure 8). Regional and local dissolution is known to have occurred in the Prairie (Parker, 1967; Rogers and Mattox, 1985; Gerhard et al., 1990; Martiniuk, 1991; LeFever and LeFever, 2005). Dissolution occurs both as a roughly linear front and also in isolated semicircular areas. Dissolution of the Devonian Prairie evaporite occurred at multiple times during the Paleozoic and Mesozoic (Rogers and Mattox, 1985; Parker, 1967). Isopach thicks in formations above Prairie thins help document the timing of dissolution. Models suggested for salt dissolution include (1) depositional facies control (dissolving fluids move through permeable beds adjacent to the salt horizon), (2) compaction and dewatering of surrounding sediments (supplies the fluid necessary for salt dissolution), (3) surface water recharge at the outcrop (resulting basinward flow dissolves salts), and (4) direct or indirect result from minor tectonic movement related to Precambrian basement features (e.g., faults create pathways for fluids) (Martiniuk, 1991; LeFever and LeFever, 2005). Dissolution of the Prairie occurred during Bakken time and affected Bakken sediments (Martiniuk, 1991; Rogers and Mattox, 1985; Sperr, 1991). Sonnenberg and Pramudito (2009) attributed

anomalous thickening in the middle Bakken member at the Elm Coulee field to be due to Prairie salt dissolution coincident with middle Bakken member deposition.

BAKKEN FORMATION: GEOLOGY AND PRODUCTION

The Bakken Formation regionally in the Williston Basin consists of four members: upper and lower organic-rich black shale, a middle member (silty dolostone or limestone to sandstone lithology), and a basal member recently named the Pronghorn (LeFever et al., 1991, 2011; LeFever, 2006) (Figures 3, 8, 9, 10, and 11). The Bakken Formation ranges in thickness from a wedge edge to over 140 ft (43 m) (Figure 12) with the thickest area in the Bakken located in northwest North Dakota, east of the Nesson anticline. The members of the Bakken thin and converge toward the margins of the Williston Basin and have an onlapping relationship with the underlying Three Forks (Figures 8 and 9). The contact between the Bakken and Three Forks is probably unconformable throughout much of the Williston Basin. The Bakken is sharply overlain by the Lodgepole. This sharp contact suggests a period of erosion or nondeposition prior to Lodgepole deposition. The lower, middle, and upper members of the

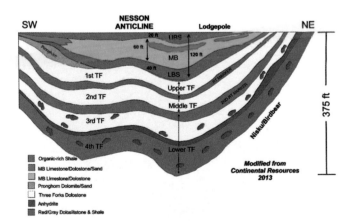

Figure 10. Generalized stratigraphic cross section southwest to northeast across the Williston Basin illustrating Bakken and Three Forks stratigraphy. The Bakken consists of the Pronghorn, Lower Bakken shale (LBS), middle member (MB), and upper Bakken shale (UBS). Industry generally divides the Three Forks into four units or benches (1st TF, 2nd TF, 3rd TF, 4th TF). In this chapter, the Three Forks is divided into three informal units (upper, middle, and lower units). Marker beds or anhydrites separate the units. The targets for horizontal drilling are currently the middle member of the Bakken and the first two units in the Three Forks.

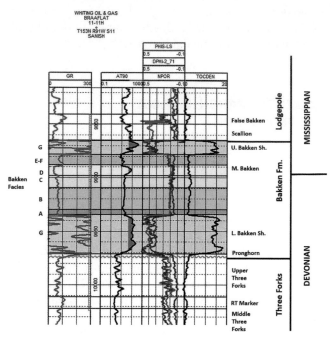

Figure 11. Well log display of the Bakken and upper Three Forks from the Whiting Braaflat 11-11H (Sec. 11, T153N, R91W). Upper and lower Bakken shales have very high GR readings (>200 API). Middle Bakken and Three Forks have low porosities (<10%). Middle Bakken can be subdivided into facies A–F. This well was completed in a horizontal leg for 2669 BOPD. GR = gamma ray; AT20 and AT90 = resistivity curves; PHIS = sonic porosity; DPHZ = density porosity; NPOR = neutron porosity; TOCDEN = calculated TOC from density log.

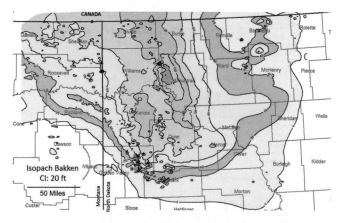

Figure 12. Isopach map of Bakken Formation. The Bakken ranges in thickness from a wedge-edge to over 140 ft (43 m). The thickest area is just east of the Nesson anticline in Mountrail County.

Bakken may represent two regressive–transgressive cycles of sedimentation (Meissner et al., 1984). Following Three Forks deposition, major uplift and erosion occurred along the margins of the Williston Basin

(Webster, 1984). This erosion resulted in deposition of the Pronghorn member of the Bakken. With a subsequent relative sea-level rise and low-energy transgression, the lower Bakken shales were deposited. Another regressive event resulted in the middle Bakken being deposited, which was then followed by the next transgressive event, which deposited the upper Bakken shale.

The middle member of the Bakken was deposited in a shallow-water setting following a sea-level drop, resulting in a regressive event (Meissner et al., 1984; Smith and Bustin, 1996, 2000). In the central part of the basin, the middle member consists of argillaceous, greenish-gray, highly fossiliferous, pyritic siltstones that indicate an environment that was moderately well oxygenated but occasionally suboxic. The upper parts of the middle member have cross-stratified sandy intervals that suggest strong current action (LeFever et al., 1991). The mineralogy of the middle Bakken is variable across the basin and consists of 30 to 60% siliciclastic material (quartz and feldspar), 30 to 80% carbonate (calcite and dolomite), and minor matrix material (illite, smectite, chlorite, and kaolinite) (LeFever, 2007). The sources of the detrital fraction in the middle Bakken are thought to be from the north and northwest (Webster, 1984). The middle member ranges in thickness from a wedge edge to over 70 ft (21 m) (Figure 13A and 13B). The thickest middle member occurs east of the Nesson anticline. Figure 13B shows thinning of the middle member east of the Sanish and Parshall fields. A thick also occurs in the general Elm Coulee area. Isolated thicks also occur along the east flank of the Williston, which may be due to Prairie salt dissolution (Cobb, 2013).

The middle Bakken can be subdivided into multiple facies (LeFever et al., 1991; Canter et al., 2009; Sonnenberg et al., 2011c) (Figures 3, 11, 13–19). All the facies are thought to be related to deposition in a shelf setting and appear to represent a shallowing upward sequence followed by a water-deepening event. The facies from bottom to top are facies A, a fossiliferous calcareous siltstone; facies B, bioturbated calcareous clay-rich siltstone to very fine-grained sandstone; facies C is a thinly bedded to laminated calcareous very-fine-grained sandstone; facies D is the highest energy facies and consists of alternating beds of fine-grained sandstone to carbonate grainstones (oolites and bioclastic debris); facies E represents the start of the water deepening and consists of thinly bedded, occasionally microbial laminated, to parallel laminated siltstone; and facies F consists of fossiliferous dolomitic to calcitic siltstone (Figures 14–16). The facies are widespread across the Williston Basin with some exceptions. Laminites in facies C were

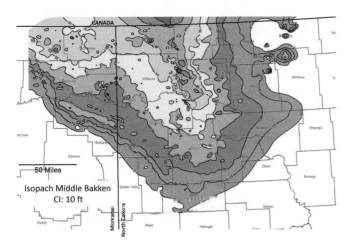

Figure 13A. Isopach map of middle Bakken. Contour interval equals 10 ft (3 m). The middle Bakken ranges in thickness from a wedge-edge to over 70 ft (21 m).

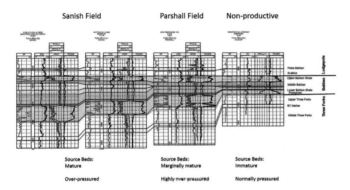

Figure 13B. Four well cross-section Sanish to Parshall fields (W–E). Upper and lower Bakken shales (facies G) have very high GR readings (>200 API). Middle Bakken and Three Forks have low porosities (<10%). Middle Bakken can be subdivided into facies A–F. GR = gamma ray; AT90 = deep resistivity curves; PHIS = sonic porosity; DPHI = density porosity; NPOR = neutron porosity; TOCDEN = calculated TOC from density log. Resistivity greater than 50 ohm-m shaded pink. Note decrease in resistivity to the east (decrease in thermal maturity). Note pinching out of facies C and D to the east. Horizontal wells were drilled from these pilot wells. Deadwood Canyon well completed for 362 BOPD and 364 MCFGD; Braaflat well completed for 2669 BOPD and 1968 MCFGD; N&D well completed for 1285 BOPD and 404 MCFGD.

recently interpreted to be the result of tidal energies (Gent, 2011). Facies D is only locally developed; the amount of dolomite changes from area to area; production is associated with matrix development in facies B, C, D, and E and microfracturing. Facies B and C produce at Elm Coulee (facies D is not present or very thin), whereas facies C, D, and E produce in the Sanish–Parshall areas. Typical facies found in the

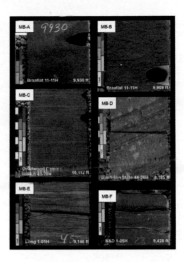

Figure 14. Core photographs of middle Bakken facies: MB-A) skeletal lime wackestone with crinoids, MB-B) characteristic helminthopsis burrows in argillaceous siltstone, MB-C) thinly interbedded silty sandstones and mudstones, MB-D) cross-stratified limy sandstone, MB-E) laminated to wavy, lightly bioturbated dolomitic siltstones and mudstones, and MF-F) massive skeletal dolomitic mudstone with brachiopod fragments. Well locations: Braaflat 11-11H, Sec. 11, T153N, R91W, Mountrail County; Deadwood Canyon Ranch 43-28H, Sec. 28, T154N, R92W, Mountrail County; Gunnison State 44-36H, Sec. 36, T161N, R91W, Burke County; Long 1-01H, Sec. 1, T152N, R90W, Mountrail County; N&D 1-05H, Sec. 5, T152N, R90W, Mountrail County. Core photos are from the North Dakota Industrial Commission (NDIC) and from Kowalski (2010), Simenson (2010), and Theloy (2014).

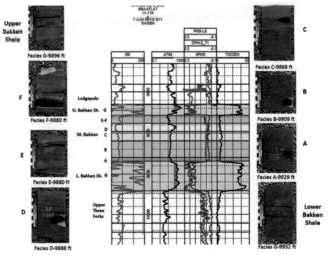

Figure 15. Well log display of the Bakken and upper Three Forks from the Whiting Oil and Gas Braaflat 11-11H (Sec. 11, T153N, R91W). Upper and lower Bakken shales have very high GR readings (>200 API). Middle Bakken and Three Forks have low porosities (<10%). Middle Bakken can be subdivided into facies A–F. GR = gamma ray; AT90 = resistivity curves; PHIS = sonic porosity; DPHI = density porosity; NPOR = neutron porosity; TOCDEN = calculated TOC from density log. Resistivity greater than 50 ohm-m shaded pink.

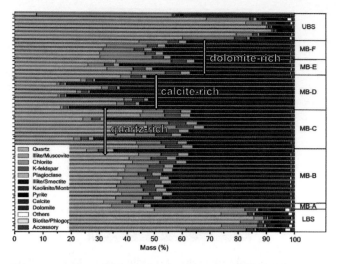

Figure 16. Mineralogical composition of middle Bakken facies and the Bakken shales based on quantitative evaluation of minerals by scanning electron microscope (QEM-SCAN) data from the well Braaflat 11-11H, Sec. 11, T153N, R91W, Mountrail County; LBS = Lower Bakken shale; MB-A through MB-F = middle Bakken facies; UBS = upper Bakken shale. From Theloy (2014).

Sanish–Parshall area is shown by Figures 14–16. Mineralogy changes in the middle Bakken across the Williston Basin (Vickery, 2010). Typical mineralogy found in the Sanish–Parshall field areas is shown by Figure 16.

For ease in mapping purposes, the middle Bakken is subdivided into three intervals (facies A–C, facies D, and facies E–F). The thickness of facies A–C is shown in Figure 17. The unit ranges in thickness from a wedge edge (0 ft) to over 50 ft (15 m). The thickest development is east of the Nesson anticline. A thick in the unit develops in the Elm Coulee field area. This thick may be due to two-stage Prairie salt dissolution (Sonnenberg and Pramudito, 2009). Facies B

is the main producer at Elm Coulee. Facies D represents the highest energy and shallowest water unit within the middle Bakken (Figures 3, 11, and 18). The unit is typically cross-stratified and consists of alternating beds of bioclast-rich grainstones and fine- to very-fine-grained sandstone. The unit ranges in thickness from 0 to over 20 ft (6 m). The thickest areas are east of the Nesson anticline in what may have been a sag area. A well-developed thick is also present in the northwest part of the mapped area. The reservoir quality of the D unit is variable and depends on the amount of carbonate cement present. Parts of the D represent sag deposits, and isolated shoal deposits are also present. Locally, facies C appears to be eroded by an unconformity at the base of facies D. This unconformity is thought to represent a low-stand surface of erosion. Facies E–F ranges in thickness from a wedge edge to over 20 ft (6 m) (Figure 19). This interval consists of very-fine-grained sandstone

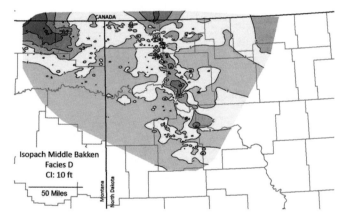

Figure 18. Isopach middle Bakken facies D. The unit ranges in thickness from less than 0 to over 20 ft (0 to over 6 m).

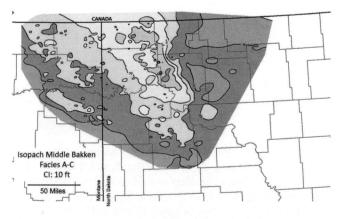

Figure 17. Isopach middle Bakken facies A–C. The unit ranges in thickness from less than 10 to over 50 ft (3 to over 15 m).

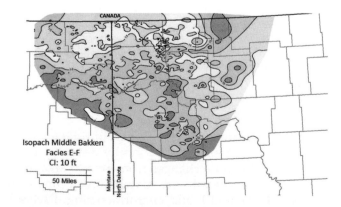

Figure 19. Isopach middle Bakken facies E–F. The unit ranges in thickness from less than 0 to over 20 ft (0 to over 6 m).

to siltstone and is planar to undulose laminated. Some burrowing is present, and fossil-rich beds occur in the F facies. Microbial laminations have been observed in the upper parts of facies C and lower parts of facies E.

A variety of geologic factors and technological factors influence middle Bakken productivity (Theloy, 2014). Technological factors include lateral length, number of hydraulic fracturing stages, proppant volume and type, proppant loading, fluid type used in hydraulic fracturing and volume, fluid–proppant ratio, injection rate, treatment pressure, choke sizes, well spacing, and plug and perf versus sliding sleeves completions. Theloy (2014) addresses each of these topics and notes that more aggressive completions (more fracture stimulation stages) result in high productivity. Geologic factors include reservoir quality (matrix porosity and permeability), reservoir thickness, oil and water saturations, hydrocarbon generation potential, source rock maturity, overpressure, structure and regional stress regime, natural fractures, mechanical stratigraphy, amount of migration, and types of traps. Theloy (2014) also addresses each of these topics. Geologic factors such as source rock maturity, overpressure, reservoir quality, and thickness generally outweigh technological factors.

Utilizing the (oil/oil + water) ratio from longer-term production data is a quick method, developed by Theloy (2014), to identify sweet spot areas characterized by high productivity in the Bakken play. The first 90 days of production (oil/oil + water) is a useful indication of productivity and sweet spots. Figure 20 illustrates areas that produce more oil than water

based on this production. The areas of highest oil-to-water production are Elm Coulee, the Billings Nose area, Parshall–Sanish, the Nesson anticline, and the Antelope anticline area.

Theloy (2014) mapped out estimated ultimate recovery (EUR) for the middle Bakken (Figures 21 and 22). Figure 22 illustrates by area EURs for wells drilled from 2010 to 2011. The best EURs are in the Sanish–Parshall area with 632,000 bbl of oil per well (MBO) per well. The Fort Berthold area is the second best with

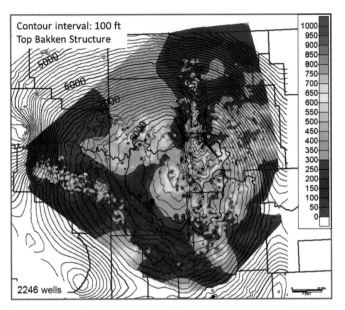

Figure 21. Bakken estimated ultimate recovery map (EUR). Note areas of low production along flanks of the Nesson anticline (suggest migration out of these areas). From Theloy (2014).

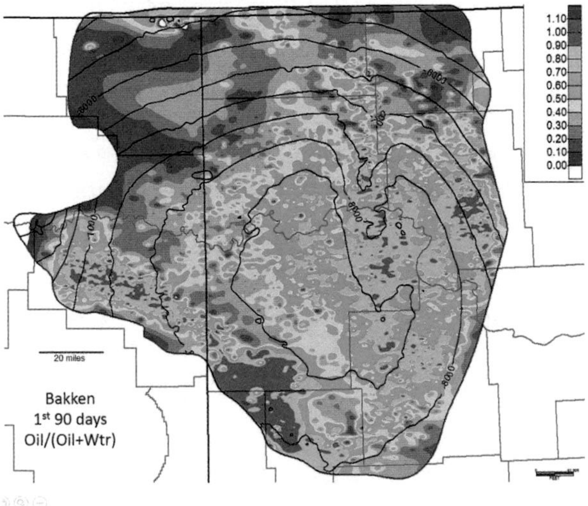

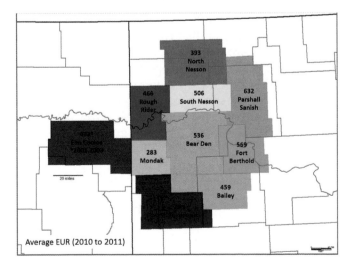

Figure 20. Bakken first 90 days of production: oil/(oil + water). Sweet spot areas with low water production are the warmer colors.

Figure 22. Average EUR 2010 to 2011 by area (thousand bbl). With exception of Elm Coulee, the average EUR was calculated from wells drilled between 2010 and 2011. From Theloy (2014).

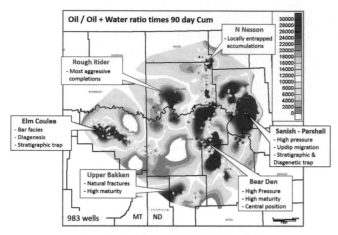

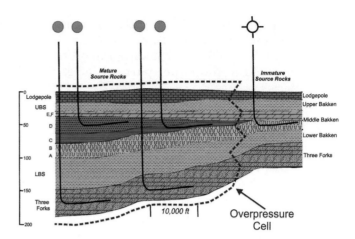

Figure 23. Bakken producing sweet spot areas. The accumulation is a continuous accumulation but individual sweet spot areas result from different causes. From Theloy (2014).

Figure 24. Stratigraphic cross section across Sanish and Parshall fields. Horizontal wells target middle Bakken facies C, D, and E. Stratigraphic thinning in the middle Bakken contributes to the trapping mechanism for the field. Note how facies C and D pinch-out to the east. Modified from Whiting (2010).

569 MBO per well. This is followed by the Bear Den (536 MBO per well) and South Nesson (506 MBO per well). Next is the Bailey area at 459 MBO per well. The updip eastern margin of the Bakken production is in an area of overpressuring (discussed later in this article). The crest of the Nesson anticline is a moderately producing area, which relates to structural controls on productivity (393 MBO per well). Consequently, the flanks of the anticline are a poorly producing area due to partial migration and depletion of hydrocarbons (updip). The poorest-producing areas are St. Demetrius (at 209 MBO per well) and Mondak (slightly better at 283 MBO per well) in the southern part of the basin. The poor production in these areas is probably related to the thinness of the middle Bakken and poor reservoir quality. Elm Coulee has an EUR per well of 433 MBO, which was calculated for the 2001–2003 time period that coincided with the onset of field development. Note that at this time, multistage fracture stimulation was not being performed in the field.

Figure 23 summarizes the various Bakken producing areas and reasons production differs from area to area. In general, structure, stratigraphy, and pore pressure are key ingredients to good production. Figure 24 is an illustration showing factors at Sanish and Parshall thought to be important to production. These factors include source bed maturity, overpressure, and stratigraphic pinchouts of units in an updip direction (Coskey and Leonard, 2009).

PRONGHORN

The Pronghorn is the basal member of the Bakken Formation and unconformably overlies the Three Forks (Figure 3) (LeFever et al., 2011). Johnson (2013)

subdivided the Pronghorn into four lithofacies, which are—from bottom to top—PH-1) heavily bioturbated fine-grained sandstone, PH-2) burrowed dolomitic silty mudstone with storm deposits, PH-3) skeletal lime wacke- to packstone, and PH-4) shale with siltstone and sandstone laminations. The Pronghorn shows an overall deepening- and fining-upward character (Bottjer et al., 2011).

The subtidal deposits of the Pronghorn overlie unconformably the Three Forks Formation, and usually, a lag of rip-up clasts and abundant pyrite is developed in the basal portion. The contact between the Pronghorn and the lower Bakken shale is interpreted as a transgressive surface of erosion (Bottjer et al., 2011; LeFever et al., 2011; Johnson, 2013), marking the Pronghorn as lowstand deposits. Johnson (2013) recognized a transgressive surface within the upper part of the Pronghorn, and it may be possible that more than one surface exists or that the vertical position of the surface varies depending on the location in the basin.

The Pronghorn ranges in thickness from a zero edge to over 50 ft (15 m) (Figure 25). Much of the Pronghorn interval may be derived from the Cedar Creek anticline area where the Three Forks and Pronghorn are absent due to erosional truncation (Figures 7–9).

THREE FORKS FORMATION

The name Three Forks shales was used by Peale (1893) for beds resting between the Jefferson Formation and Madison Limestone for outcrops near Three

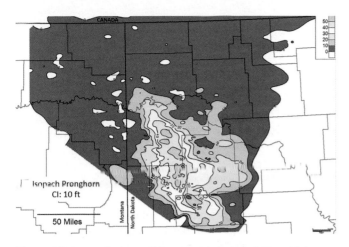

Figure 25. Isopach map of Pronghorn interval. The thickness ranges from a wedge-edge to over 50 ft (15 m). This largely dolomitic interval may largely be derived from erosion of Paleozoic units on the Cedar Creek anticline.

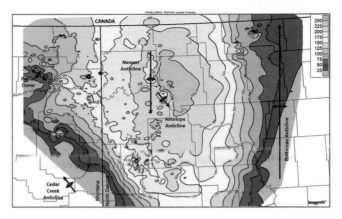

Figure 26. Isopach of total Three Forks interval. The Three Forks ranges in thickness from a wedge-edge to over 225 ft (69 m). Structural features control the thickness patterns seen on this map. Active structures during deposition include the Cedar Creek, Poplar, Nesson, and Bottineau anticlines. The thickest Three Forks area is east of the Nesson anticline.

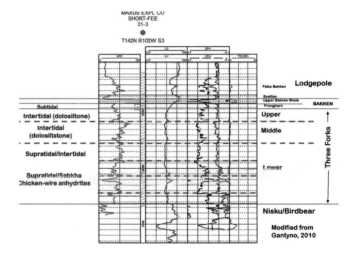

Figure 27. Well log display of the Bakken and Three Forks from the Maxus Short-Fee 31-3 (Sec. 3, T142N, R102W). GRD = gamma ray; ILD and ILM = resistivity curves; NPHI = porosity; DPHI = density porosity; TOCDEN = calculated TOC from density log. Modified from Gantyno (2011).

Forks, Montana (Sandberg, 1965). The name was later changed to Three Forks Formation by Haynes (1916). Sandberg (1965) published a detailed measured section of the Three Forks at its type section near Logan, Montana.

Sandberg and Hammond (1958) described the original Three Forks type section in the Mobil Producing Company No. 1 Solomon Bird Bear well, Sec. 22, T149N, R91W, Dunn County, North Dakota, using a clastic classification scheme. Poor preservation of the original type section core led to the selection of a new standard reference section for the Three Forks in the EOG Resources #2-11H Liberty well, Sec. 11, T151N, R91W, Mountrail County, North Dakota.

The Three Forks ranges in thickness from less than 25 to over 250 ft (8 to over 76 m) in the mapped area (Figure 26). Thickness patterns are controlled by paleostructural features such as the Poplar Dome, Nesson, Antelope, Cedar Creek, and Bottineau anticlines. Thinning and/or truncation occurs over the crest of the highs, and thickening of strata occurs on the flanks of the highs.

Many subdivisions have been proposed for the Three Forks (Berwick, 2008; Bottjer et al., 2011; LeFever et al., 2011; Gantyno, 2011; Gutierrez, 2014; Webster, 1984; Dumonceaux, 1984). For example, Gantyno (2011) subdivided the Three Forks into six units (Figure 27). For the sake of simplicity, the interval will be subdivided into three units in this chapter (upper, middle, and lower). These subdivisions are illustrated by Figure 27. The extents of each unit decreases upwards, with the lower Three Forks showing the largest areal distribution and the upper Three Forks showing the smallest areal distribution.

This in part is due to the unconformity at the top of the Three Forks.

X-ray diffraction (XRD) mineralogy for the Three Forks is illustrated in Figure 28. The Three Forks is an argillaceous, silty to very-fine-grained, dolostone throughout. The formation becomes anhydritic toward the base. The hematite content increases in the middle and lower Three Forks, whereas the pyrite content increases in the upper Three Forks. Small amounts of halite also show up in an XRD analysis of the formation showing the high salinity of the formation. Often,

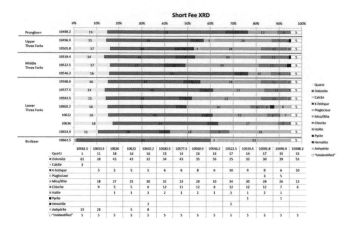

	10661.5	10653.9	10636	10622	10602.2	10583.5	10577.5	10560.9	10546.2	10522.5	10519.4	10501.8	10496.9	10488.2
Quartz	1	11	18	16	16	15	14	16	16	17	14	17	15	15
Dolomite	61	28	43	43	32	34	43	35	56	25	33	30	39	53
Calcite	3													
K-feldspar		5	5	5	5	6	6	8	6	10	9	9	6	10
Plagioclase											3	5		
Mica/illite		18	27	25	30	31	22	28	10	34	30	28	26	13
Chlorite		9	5	5	6	12	11	12	8	12	12	12	7	6
Halite				1	3	2	1	2	1	1	1	2	1	
Pyrite											1			
Hematite					2						2			
Anhydrite	33	28		5	8									
"Unidentified"	5	5	5	5	5	5	5	5	5	5	5	5	5	5

Figure 28. X-ray diffraction data (XRD) for the Three Forks Formation from the Maxus Short-Fee 31-3 (Sec. 3, T142N, R102W) well. Uppermost data are from the Pronghorn interval and lowermost data are from the Birdbear. Note the presence of dolomite, illite, and chlorite throughout the Three Forks. Note also the presence of evaporites (anhydrite and halite) in the Three Forks interval.

halite crystals will precipitate on slabbed core surfaces (post slabbing). Halite beds are not reported to occur in the Three Forks, which may be a result of local dissolution. Salt hoppers are present in outcrops in central Montana.

The lower and middle Three Forks is known for its red color. The presence of hematite gives the Three Forks its red color. The hematite occurs as a thin coating around grains. The source of the hematite, as in most red bed sequences, is probably diagenetic. The source of hematite is generally intrastratal dissolution of detrital silicates such as hornblende, augite, olivine, chlorite, biotite, and magnetite (Tucker, 2001). The Three Forks has a large percentage of chlorite in its composition. The source of the chlorite is unknown but may be from volcanic arcs to the west. The red color comes from the oxidizing diagenetic environment. Only a small amount of iron, 0.1%, is sufficient to impart a red color. If reducing conditions prevail, the iron will be in a ferrous state and impart a green color. Secondary alteration of the red color takes place when reducing solutions penetrate into red sediments. This commonly occurs along porous beds, fractures, and so on. The upper Three Forks has a distinct green color in mudrock intervals, which may be an alteration of a previous red color.

Most of the previous workers in the Three Forks have interpreted the depositional environment to be subtidal to supratidal (Figure 29) (Dumonceaux, 1984; Berwick, 2008; Gantyno, 2011; Bottjer et al., 2011; LeFever et al., 2011; Gutierrez, 2014). Overall, the

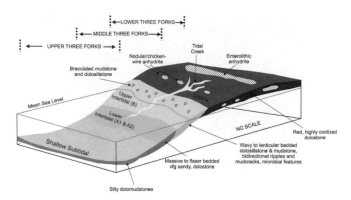

Figure 29. Three Forks schematic depositional model. Approximate settings for lower, middle, and upper Three Forks shown. Anhydrites mainly found in lower Three Forks. Modified from Berwick (2008), Gantyno (2011), and Franklin and Sonnenberg (2012).

Three Forks represents a water-deepening cycle with more coastal and inland sabkha deposits in the lower Three Forks, and intertidal deposits in the middle and upper Three Forks.

Lower Three Forks

The deposits of the lower Three Forks reflect mainly a low-energy, supratidal sabkha setting in dry, evaporative climate conditions. The very fine grain sizes of sediments and the abundance of anhydrite set the lower Three Forks deposits apart from the overlying units. Anhydrite occurs as massive, argillaceous mosaic anhydrite or as distinctive beds, stringers, and nodules within a mudstone matrix. The precipitation of anhydrite is interpreted to have occurred coevally with sedimentation or at very early stage of diagenesis. The dolomitic claystones within the lower Three Forks are either reddish-brown or green in color, and both variations can occur in close juxtaposition to each other. The dolomudstones contain minor amounts of silt and are typically noncalcareous, hard, fissile, and well cemented. Usually, the mudstones are structureless to faintly laminated. Other sedimentary structures include compaction-loading features, dewatering structures, distortion around anhydrite nodules and granule-sized clasts, as well as mud cracks, syneresis cracks, and brecciation. The breccias contain clay and dolomudstone fragments floating in a matrix-supported fabric. Common cementing agents are anhydrite, dolomite, and pyrite in disseminated form (Gantyno, 2011; Franklin and Sonnenberg, 2012).

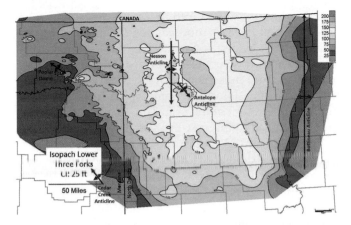

Figure 30. Isopach lower Three Forks. Thickness ranges from less than 25 to over 150 ft (8 to over 46 m) in mapped area. Thickest area is east of Nesson Anticline. Thinning occurs on Poplar, Nesson, Cedar Creek, and Boutineau anticlines.

The lower Three Forks ranges in thickness from less than 25 to over 150 ft (8 to over 46 m) in the mapped area (Figure 30). The thickest area is east of the Nesson anticline. Thinning of the lower Three Forks occurs toward the flanks of the basin.

Middle Three Forks

The middle Three Forks ranges in thickness from 20 to 60 ft (6 to 18 m) across the mapped area (Figure 31). Thinning occurs towards the flanks of the Williston Basin.

The middle Three Forks consists of beds of anhydritic, calcareous, argillaceous dolostone, silty

dolostone, and sandy argillaceous dolostone. Generally, the unit is very fine grained, and grain size decreases upward. The unit is similar to the upper Three Forks, with an overall shallowing upward sequence followed by a water deepening event (dolomudstone).

The middle Three Forks is dominated by chaotic and brecciated facies. Two types of brecciated fabrics occur in the middle Three Forks, including matrix-supported and clast supported breccia. The abundance of mud-supported breccia may be due to storm events (Bazzell, 2014). Original sedimentary structures such as parallel and ripple laminations are rarely preserved due to the high degree of brecciation and soft-sediment deformation (including dewatering structures).

A laminated facies often occurs near the base of the middle Three Forks. This facies consists of thin- to thick-bedded (millimeter to centimeter scale) alternating layers of mudstones and dolomitic siltstones.

The top of the middle Three Forks is a massive (possibly burrowed), structureless, subtidal mudstone. This unit is referred to as the RT marker bed and is 2 to 20 ft (0.6 to 6 m) thick. The unit is dominated by clay-sized material with silt-sized quartz and dolomite. The average composition of this upper unit is 38% dolomite, 30% clay, 27% quartz, and 2% pyrite.

Upper Three Forks

The upper Three Forks is dominated by silt-sized and some very-fine-grained sandstones and dolomite and has low permeabilities and porosities. The upper Three Forks ranges in thickness from a wedge edge to over 40 ft (12 m) in areas east of the Nesson anticline (Figure 32). The unit thins toward the margins of the depositional basin because of erosional truncation. On logs, the unit is difficult to separate from the overlying Pronghorn.

The upper Three Forks is evolving into a significant resource play in the Williston Basin. To date, over 2880 wells (including the older wells at Antelope) have been completed in the upper Three Forks (Figure 30). The upper Three Forks consists largely of pinkish-tan silty dolostones that are interbedded with green chloritic, dolomitic mudstone (Figure 33). A variety of facies have been reported in the upper Three Forks, ranging in depositional environment from subtidal to supratidal (Dumonceaux, 1984; Berwick, 2008; Gantyno, 2011; Bottjer et al., 2011). Typical sedimentary structures include parallel to subparallel laminations, uni- and bidirectional ripple cross-laminations, mudcracks,

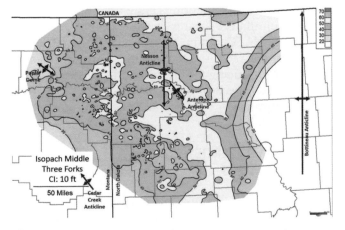

Figure 31. Isopach map of middle Three Forks. Thickness ranges from less than 20 to over 60 ft (6 to over 18 m) in mapped area.

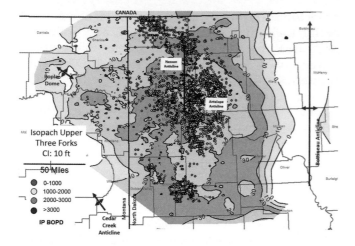

Figure 32. Isopach map upper Three Forks. Thickness ranges from a wedge-edge to over 30 ft (9 m). Thinning occurs towards Poplar dome and the Cedar Creek anticline. The vast majority of Three Forks wells are drilled in this interval. The colored dots indicate Three Forks initial production (see legend).

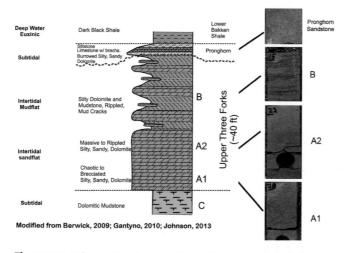

Figure 33. Schematic of upper Three Forks showing facies, core photographs, and interpreted depositional environment. Tidal environments dominate the upper Three Forks. Modified from Berwick (2008) and Gantyno (2011).

syneresis cracks, and soft sediment deformation. Deposition is a shallowing upward succession ranging from subtidal to upper intertidal. The Pronghorn member of the Bakken sits unconformably on the Three Forks.

The facies in the upper Three Forks is shown by Figure 33. The basal upper Three Forks (A1 and A2) is a sandy to silty dolostone unit that overlies the green mudstone facies of the middle Three Forks. The unit ranges in thickness from 10 to 25 ft (3 to 8 m). The mineralogic composition of the basal upper Three Forks is 57% dolomite, 29% quartz, 10% clay, and 2% pyrite. The

unit can be subdivided into two subfacies, A1 and A2. The lower A1 facies is mottled, possibly burrowed, and characterized by soft sediment deformation that resembles dewatering structures. Upward-directed dewatering features are present. The overlying A2 is laminated to massive, silty dolostone. Some ripple and wavy laminations are present in the unit. The A1 and A2 are interpreted as shallowing upward succession. The B facies shown in Figure 33 consists of interlaminated to interbedded green dolomitic mudstone and pinkish-tan silty dolostones. The green mudstones constitute 30 to 70% of the unit. Sedimentary structures are uni- and bidirectional ripple cross-laminations, double clay drapes, mudcracks, syneresis cracks, scour surfaces, soft sediment deformation, and rare intraclast conglomerates. The intraclast conglomerates may form in small tidal channels, by storm events, or by evaporite dissolution.

THREE FORKS PRODUCTION

The original discovery at the Antelope field in 1953 established the upper Three Forks as a viable reservoir in the Williston Basin. The upper Three Forks remained fairly dormant until recently drilled horizontal wells began again to indicate its large potential.

The North Dakota Industrial Commission (NDIC) has recently estimated that the Three Forks will have recoverable reserves of 1.9 billion bbl of oil across much of the Williston Basin (Nordeng and Helms, 2010). The Three Forks play coincides with the Bakken play, which adds significantly to the reserves across the basin. The USGS mean technologically recoverable resource estimate for the Three Forks is 3371 billion bbl of oil, 3.5 tcf of gas, and 281 million bbl of natural gas liquids (Gaswirth et al., 2013).

Three Forks production is shown by Figure 6. The current cumulative total is 263,448,155 bbl of oil and 294,728,845 MCFG. Figure 34 illustrates the first 90 days' production (oil/oil + water) for the Three Forks and low water producing areas. The southern Nesson anticline and areas east of the Nesson anticline show the highest oil-to-water ratio.

RESERVOIR PROPERTIES: BAKKEN AND THREE FORKS

Measured core porosity and permeability are very low in the Bakken, Sanish, and Three Forks reservoirs (<10% porosity and <0.1 md permeability) in the Williston Basin, so productivity is assumed to be due to natural and artificial fracturing. The reservoirs generally require advanced technology to get them to

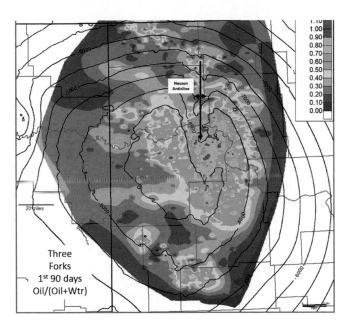

Figure 34. Three Forks production map for the first 90 days: oil/(oil + water). The warm colors (green to red) indicate wells which produce more oil than water. The cool colors (blue) indicate wells that produce more water than oil. The best production is associated with the Nesson anticline and areas to the east of the Nesson. After Theloy (2014).

produce (fracture stimulation and horizontal stimulation). For this reason, they should be considered to be technology reservoirs. Natural fractures in some areas (e.g., the Billings Nose area and Antelope field) are sufficient for vertical well production.

A core analysis from the Whiting Braaflat 11-11H (Sec. 11, T153N, R91W) provides the following information. The Scallion member of the Lodgepole has an average porosity of 2.3% and average permeability of 0.12 md (most permeability plugs had visible fractures). Average grain density is 2.7 gm/cc. The middle Bakken has average porosity of 6.7% and average permeability of 0.33 md (including plugs with visible fractures). Excluding core plugs with fractures, the average permeability number drops to 0.028 md. Average grain density in the middle Bakken is 2.7 gm/cc. The Three Forks has an average porosity of 7.6% and average permeability of 1.1 md (including core plugs with visible fractures). The average permeability excluding the plugs with fractures is 0.23 md. Average grain density in the Three Forks is 2.8 gm/cc. Most of the visible fractures in the core are horizontal. The Braaflat 11-11H (Figure 11) was completed as a horizontal well in the middle Bakken for 2669 BOPD and 1968 MCFGD. The well has a cumulative production of 359 million bbl of oil and 232 MMCFG.

Measured core porosity and permeability are also very low in the Bakken shale, Pronghorn, and Three

Forks reservoirs at the Antelope field. The core analysis from the Duncan Rose #1 (Sec. 33, T15N, R94W) provides the following information. The lower Bakken shale has porosities of 3.8% and permeabilities of 0.01 md. The Pronghorn (formerly known as the Sanish) has porosities ranging from 6 to 9% and permeabilities ranging from 0.08 to 0.33 md. The upper Three Forks has porosities ranging from 8.3 to 10.6% and permeabilities ranging from 0.01 to 0.18 md. One foot of Three Forks 10,609–10,610 reported a permeability of 6.88 md, but this is interpreted to be due to a horizontal fracture.

LOWER AND UPPER BAKKEN SHALES

The upper and lower shale members are potential source rocks and are lithologically similar throughout much of the basin (Dow, 1974; Webster, 1984). The shales predominantly contain type II kerogens but may also contain some type I and type III (Sonnenberg, 2010b, Sonnenberg et al., 2011a, 2011b, 2001c, Jin, 2013) (Figure 35). The shales are potential source beds for the Bakken, Three Forks, and Lodgepole formations (Meissner et al., 1984; Sonnenberg, 2011; Longman et al., 2014). The shales are dark gray to black, hard, siliceous, slightly calcareous, dolomitic, pyritic, and massive to fissile, and they generally either break along horizontal fractures or with conchoidal fractures (Figures 36 and 37). Detrital silt grains are disseminated throughout the shale interval as scattered grains. Some discontinuous laminae of silt grains

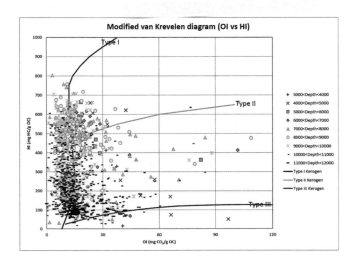

Figure 35. Modified van Krevelen diagram for the Bakken Formation of Williston Basin. Published data from Webster (1984) and Price et al. (1984). Majority of samples indicate a Type I and II oil-prone kerogen (algal origin). Legend shows source rock data by depth interval; EC Vaira from Elm Coulee (only 2 data points available). HI is hydrogen index (S2/TOC). OI is oxygen index (S3/TOC). From Jin (2013).

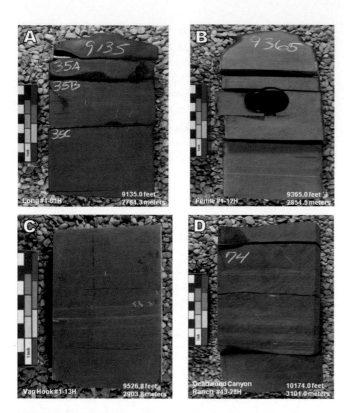

Figure 36. Core photos of facies G—organic rich pyritic brown/black mudstone. Photos A and B are from the upper Bakken shale, and photos C and D are from the lower Bakken shale. Small vertical fractures cemented by calcite and pyrite are visible in photo C.

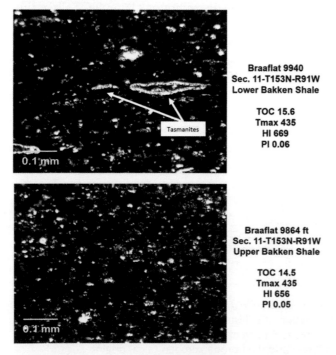

Figure 37. Thin section photomicrographs of upper and lower Bakken shales. Note abundance of Tasmanites in lower Bakken shale.

are present. The silt-sized material is probably eolian in origin. The shales contain radiolaria, conodonts, ostracodes, small cephalopods, small brachiopods, and *Tasmanites* (algae) fossils (Webster, 1984). The shales lack bioturbation but do contain flattened fecal pellets and lack evidence of bottom current transport except in the transitional foot to 3 ft (1 m) at the base and tops of the shales (Longman et al., 2014). The shales are dissimilar in that the upper shale lacks limestone and greenish-gray shale beds found locally in the lower shale (Pitman et al., 2001). The lower shale has a greater abundance of *Tasmanites*. Secondary pyrite occurs disseminated throughout the shale interval and as individual laminations and lenses. The shales consist of dark organic material, clay, silt-sized quartz, and some calcite and dolomite (both detrital and authigenic). The shale is kerogen rich in the deeper parts of the basin, and the organic material is distributed throughout. The Bakken kerogen is an amorphous kerogen inferred to be sapropelic, and the composition consists of 70 to 95% amorphous material, 0 to 20% herbaceous material, up to 30% coaly material (recycled opaque material), and 5% woody material (Webster, 1984). Because of the high hydrocarbon-generating capacity of the material determined from pyrolysis (>500 mg HC/g OC at shallow depths), Webster (1984) believes the amorphous material has an algal origin. Webster (1984) describes the total organic carbon content of the Bakken shales as averaging 11.3 wt.% in thermally mature areas of the basin. The shales average 15 to 20 wt.% total organic carbon (TOC) where thermally immature (Longman et al., 2014).

Schmoker and Hester (1983) derived an equation to calculate TOC content using bulk density logs. They derived the following equation for calculating TOC from bulk density: $TOC = (154{,}497/\rho) - 57.261$, where TOC is total organic carbon and ρ is the bulk density of the shale. Figure 11 illustrates the calculated TOC for the Braaflat 11-11H (Sec. 11, T153N, R91W) from the Sanish field. The calculated TOC is comparable to the actual measured TOC of 10 to 18 wt.%.

The upper and lower shale are interpreted to have been deposited in an offshore marine anoxic or oxygen-restricted environment during periods of sea-level rise (Price et al., 1984; Webster, 1984; LeFever et al., 1991; Pitman et al., 2001). The anoxic conditions may have resulted from a stratified hydrologic regime (Webster, 1984; Smith and Bustin, 1996, 2000). The stratified water column is envisioned as having an upper water layer that is well oxygenated and nutrient rich. High organic production occurred in this layer (probably planktonic algae). Following the death of the organisms, they sank through stagnant bottom waters and were deposited. Anoxic conditions are created by restricted circulation and in part by destruction of organic matter by consuming organisms that remove oxygen and release hydrogen sulfide (Meissner et al., 1984; Webster, 1984). Anoxic conditions are indicated by the lack of benthic fauna and burrowing, as well as high TOC content. The Bakken may be part of continent-wide anoxic event that took place from late Famennian through Kinderhookian time (Meissner et al., 1984). The Bakken is correlative with the Woodford-Percha-Leatham-Sappington-Exshaw-Cottonwood Canyon source rock facies of the western Cordilleran and southern craton-margin geosynclines and the Antrim-Sunbury-New Albany-Chattanooga and equivalent source rock facies of the Appalachian geosyncline (Meissner et al., 1984).

The Bakken is not thermally mature throughout the Williston Basin. The shales are thermally immature in the eastern part of the basin and characterized on well logs by low resistivity (i.e., water-wet) (Figure 38). In the western Williston, the shales are characterized by high resistivity and thought to be oil-wet (Meissner, 1978). Hydrocarbons are nonconductive, which results in extremely high resistivities. Further evidence of the presence of hydrocarbon saturation comes from core analyses and also plots of pyrolysis data (i.e., production index versus depth plots or pyrolysis S1 versus depth plots) with depth (Price et al., 1984; Webster, 1984). These data clearly indicate that the Bakken shales are oil saturated where they have high resistivity. Wettability tests in the Bakken illustrate that the upper and lower shales are oil-wet while the Lodgepole, middle Bakken, and Three Forks intervals are water-wet (Cramer, 1986, 1991). Price (1999) and Price and LeFever (1992) noted the extremely high oil-to-water ratios associated with Bakken production,

suggesting that most of the water has been displaced by hydrocarbon generation. The oil–water ratios are 200 to 800 bbl of oil to one bbl of water, with the mean being 300 bbl of oil to one bbl of water. The small amount of co-produced water may be dissolved in Bakken oil and exsolved during production, or it can be produced from the matrix of the reservoir rocks. Figure 38 illustrates the areas of high resistivities in the Bakken shales. The 100 ohm-m line is used as a cutoff value where generation has occurred.

Organic maturity has recently been modeled using the Time-Temperature Index (TTI) method by Nordeng and LeFever (2008) and Jin (2013). Their models suggest that organic maturity started approximately 100 Ma. Carlisle et al. (1992) suggest that hydrocarbon generation started in the early Cretaceous. Webster (1984) utilized TTI plots to conclude that oil generation began approximately 75 Ma (late Cretaceous).

Most of the oil generated in the Bakken black shales may have been expelled into the middle member of the Bakken or the upper Three Forks. Price and LeFever (1994) also presented evidence that most of the oil generated in the Bakken stayed in the Bakken and did not migrate into the overlying Madison Group. Earlier investigators thought the Bakken shales sourced reservoirs in the Bakken and entire Madison Group (Dow, 1974; Williams, 1974; Meissner, 1978).

The lower Bakken shale ranges in thickness from 0 to over 50 ft (0 to over 15 m) (Figure 39). The thickest area is a north–south trending area just east of the Nesson anticline. Slightly updip from the axis of the thick lies the greater Sanish-Parshall-Fort Berthold producing area. The lower Bakken shale is the main source bed for this sweet spot production area.

A plot of hydrogen index (mg HC/g OC) versus T_{max} °C for the lower Bakken shale illustrates Bakken source rock data that falls into immature, oil window, and

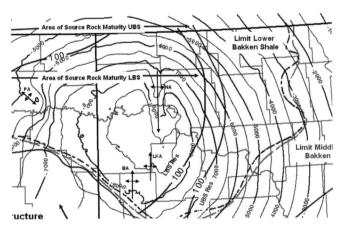

Figure 38. TStructure map on top of Bakken and limits of lower Bakken shale, middle Bakken, and upper Bakken shale across Williston Basin. Areas of source rock maturity for upper Bakken shale and lower Bakken shale are indicated by 100 ohm-m contour lines.

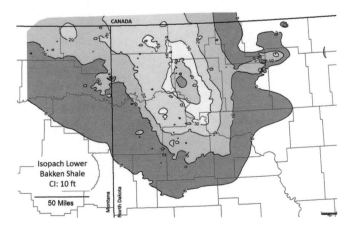

Figure 39. Isopach map of lower Bakken shale. Thickness ranges from a zero edge to over 50 ft (15 m).

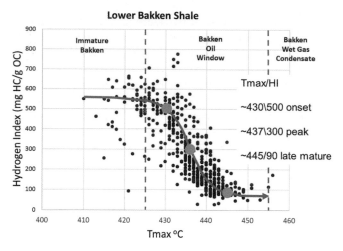

Figure 40. Hydrogen index versus T_{max} °C for the lower Bakken shale. Onset of intense hydrocarbon generation coincides with T_{max} values of 430° Celsius (806° Farenheit) and HI values of 500. Data are from the USGS (2016) and CSM Bakken (2015) data sets.

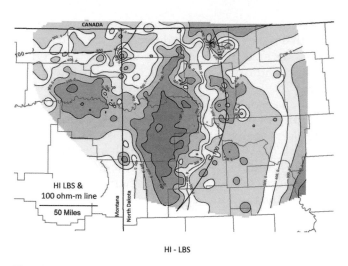

HI - LBS

Figure 42. Hydrogen index (HI) contour map for the lower Bakken shale (LBS). Onset of generation is thought to occur at a HI number of 500. Data are from the USGS (2016) and CSM Bakken (2015) data sets.

wet-gas condensate categories (Figure 40). The oil window ranges in value from 425 to 455 T_{max}. Onset of intense oil generation coincides with values of 500 HI and 430 for T_{max}. Peak generation is approximately 300 HI and 437 T_{max}. Late mature values are 90 HI and 445 T_{max}. These values can be mapped to illustrate mature and immature areas for the lower Bakken shale (Figures 41 and 42).

Figure 41 illustrates mapped T_{max} for the lower Bakken shale. These values are compared to the 100 ohm-m line taken from Hester and Schmoker (1985). The 100 ohm-m line coincides with T_{max} values of 425 to 430. The hot colors on Figure 40 are high geothermal gradient areas previously noted by Sonnenberg (2011a) and Jin (2013).

Figure 41 illustrates mapped HI values for the lower Bakken shale. These values are compared to

the 100 ohm-m line taken from Hester and Schmoker (1985). The 100 ohm-m line approximately coincides with HI values of 500.

The upper Bakken shale is also an important source rock in the Bakken petroleum system (Figure 43). The upper Bakken shale ranges in thickness from 0 to approximately 25 ft (0 to ~8 m) in the mapped area. No obvious structural controls on thickness variations are suggested other than a Prairie salt dissolution-related thick shown in the southern part of the mapped area in Stark County. This anomalous area is also the area of prolific Lodgepole mounds.

A plot of hydrogen index (mg HC/g OC) versus T_{max} °C for the upper Bakken shale illustrates Bakken source rock data which falls into immature, oil window, and wet-gas condensate categories (Figure 44). The oil window ranges in value from 425 to 455 T_{max}. Onset of intense oil generation coincides with values of 500 HI and

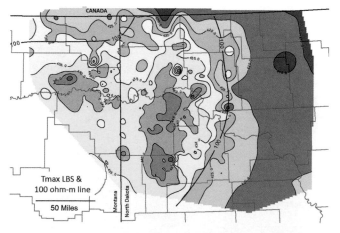

Figure 41. T_{max} values for lower Bakken shale (LBS). Also shown is the 100 ohm-m resistivity line for the lower Bakken shale (from Hester and Schmoker, 1985). The thermal mature areas of the lower Bakken shale are shown by the warmer colors. Immature areas are the blue colors. Data are from the USGS (2016) and CSM Bakken (2015) data sets.

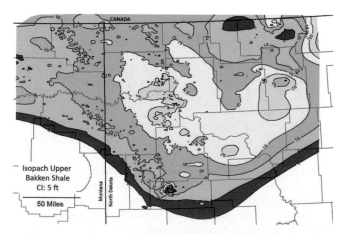

Figure 43. Isopach upper Bakken shale. The unit ranges in thickness from a wedge-edge to over 25 ft (7 m).

Upper Bakken Shale

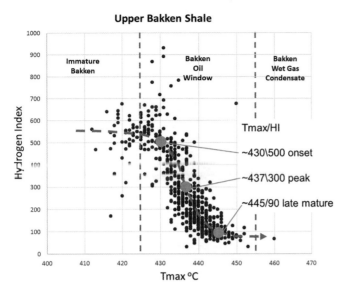

Figure 44. Hydrogen index versus T_{max} °C for the upper Bakken shale. Onset of intense hydrocarbon generation coincides with T_{max} values of 430° Celsius (806° Fahrenheit) and HI values of 500. Data are from the USGS Geochemistry Database (2016) and CSM Bakken Consortia data base (2015).

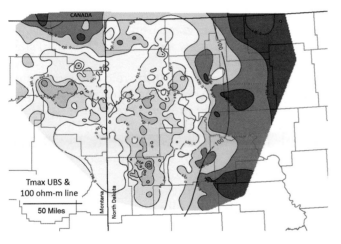

Tmax – UBS & 100 ohm-m line

Figure 45. T_{max} values for upper Bakken shale (UBS). Also shown is the 100 ohm-m resistivity line for the Upper Bakken Shale (from Hester and Schmoker, 1985). The thermal mature areas of the upper Bakken shale are shown by the warmer colors. Immature areas are the blue colors. Data are from the USGS Geochemistry Database (2016) and CSM Bakken Consortia data base (2015).

430 for T_{max}. Peak generation is approximately 300 HI and 437 T_{max}. Late mature values are 90 HI and 445 T_{max}. These values can be mapped to illustrate mature and immature areas for the upper Bakken shale (Figures 45 and 46).

Figure 45 illustrates mapped T_{max} values for the upper Bakken shale. Also shown is the 100 ohm-m resistivity line for the upper Bakken shale (from Hester and Schmoker, 1985). The thermal mature areas of the

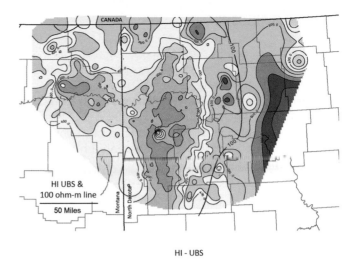

HI - UBS

Figure 46. Hydrogen index (HI) contour map for the upper Bakken shale (UBS). Onset of generation is thought to occur at a HI number of 500. Data are from the USGS Geochemistry Database (2016) and CSM Bakken Consortia data base (2015).

lower Bakken shale are shown by the warmer colors. Immature areas are the blue colors. The 100 ohm-m line coincides approximately with the 425 T_{max} contours.

Figure 46 shows a contoured HI map for the upper Bakken shale. These values are compared to the 100 ohm-m line taken from Hester and Schmoker (1985). The 100 ohm-m line approximately coincides with HI values of 500 to 600. The warm colors (yellow to red) are thermally mature areas, and the cool colors (light blue to purple) are thermally immature areas.

Although there is general agreement between different means to map thermally mature areas (resistivity versus HI versus T_{max}), the best correlations exist with T_{max} and resistivity.

BAKKEN AND THREE FORKS OILS

The oil produced from the Bakken and Three Forks reservoirs is different from oil produced from Madison reservoirs (Jarvie, 2001; Jiang et al., 2001; Lillis, 2013). Bakken-reservoired oils and Madison-reservoired oils are different based on a number of factors, including biomarker geochemistry. The Bakken-reservoired oils have high diasterane/sterane values, indicating argillaceous source rocks; the Madison-reservoired oils have low pristane/phytane and diasterane/sterane values and high norhopane/hopane values, indicating sourcing from carbonate rocks.

Bakken oils are moderate to high gravity (26 to 46° API), have low sulfur contents (less than 0.35 wt.%), and low pour points (average –25° Fahrenheit [–32° Celsius]). Madison oils have higher sulfur contents (0.2 to over 3.6 wt.%) and higher pour points (average 38° Fahrenheit [3° Celsius]).

RESERVOIR PRESSURE

Reservoir pressure in the Bakken is regarded as over-pressured with pressure gradients exceeding 0.5 psi/ft (Figure 47) (Sonnenberg, 2010b). A new pressure map for the Bakken petroleum system was generated by Theloy (2014). The map is based on 92 BHP (bottom-hole pressure) and DFIT (diagnostic fracture injection test) data points, including six additional hydrostatic points at the eastern margin as well as six data points for the Sanish–Parshall area. High overpressures are found in large parts of the central basin and the Parshall area in the east, where gradients exceed 0.7 psi/ft. Elm Coulee has a pressure gradient around 0.55 psi/ft. Parshall is reported to have a gradient of 0.74 psi/ft. The area west of the Nesson anticline has pressure gradients of 0.6 to 0.7 psi/ft. Pressure gradients in Montana are generally in the 0.5+ psi/ft range.

A plot of pressure versus depth for Bakken and Three Forks data is shown in Figure 48 (from Theloy, 2014). Onset of oil generation is extrapolated to approximately 8400 ft (2560 m). In general, the Three Forks is slightly higher pressured than the Bakken. Parshall data points suggest that the Parshall field is

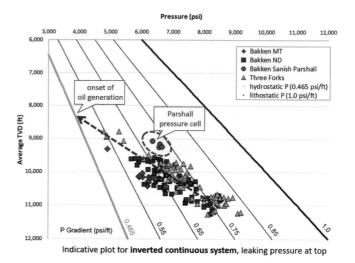

Figure 48. Pressure depth plot for Bakken and Three Forks using BHP and DFIT data points. The plot suggests onset of oil generation occurring at a depth of 8400 ft (2560 m). Data from the Parshall field plots off the main data trend suggesting a separate pressure compartment. The Three Forks appears to be slightly higher pressured than the Bakken pressures. From Theloy (2014).

a well-sealed pressure compartment. Data from Montana (mainly Elm Coulee and areas to the north) suggest more of a leaky seal.

Meissner (1978) described the role of overpressuring in the Bakken at Antelope and the creation of open tension fractures. The pressure gradient at Antelope is 0.73 psi/ft in the Bakken and upper Three Forks intervals (Folsom et al., 1959; Murray, 1968; Finch, 1969; Sonnenberg, 2010b). Normal pressures are found above and below the Bakken.

The abnormal pressures in the Bakken and Three Forks suggest that the oil generated in the Bakken petroleum system has largely stayed in the Bakken petroleum system. Lower pressures indicate dissipation of pressure in areas where migration has taken place.

A summary diagram illustrating areas of thermal maturity and overpressuring in the Bakken petroleum system is shown in Figure 49 (from Theloy, 2014).

FRACTURES

Fractures enhance the reservoir quality of the tight Bakken reservoir (Murray, 1968; Meissner, 1978; Pitman et al., 2001; Sonnenberg et al., 2011c; Theloy, 2014). Three types of fractures are reported to occur in the Bakken: (1) structural-related tectonic fractures, (2) stress-related regional fractures, and (3) diagenetic fractures associated with overpressuring due to hydrocarbon generation (Druyff, 1991; Carlisle et al., 1992;

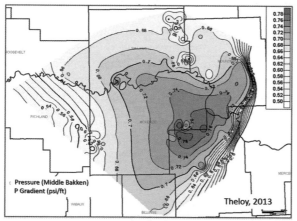

Figure 47. Pressure data for the middle Bakken reservoir. The map is based on 92 BHP (bottom-hole pressure) and DFIT (diagnostic fracture injection test) data points, including six additional hydrostatic points at eastern margin as well as six data points for the Sanish–Parshall area. Parshall is reported to have a gradient of 0.74 psi/ft. High overpressures are found in large parts of the central basin and the Parshall area in the east, where gradients exceed 0.7 psi/ft. Elm Coulee has a pressure gradient around 0.55 psi/ft. The area west of the Nesson anticline has pressure gradients of 0.6 to 0.7 psi/ft. Pressure gradients in Montana are generally in the 0.5+ psi/ft range. From Theloy (2014).

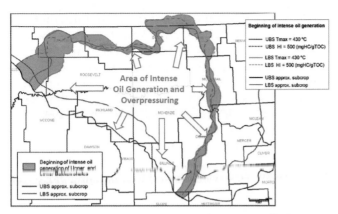

Beginning of intense oil generation based on Tmax and HI constraints of both Upper and Lower Bakken shales

Figure 49. Area of intense oil generation and overpressuring based on T_{max} and HI data. Subcrops of the upper and lower Bakken shales also shown. From Theloy (2014).

Price, 1999; Pitman et al., 2001; Hill, 2010). LeFever (1992) states that the best production comes from hydrocarbon-generated, related pervasive microfracturing within the Bakken, Three Forks, and Lodgepole combined with larger-scale fracturing (i.e., structural-related or stress-related regional fractures).

Fracturing of source rocks has been frequently discussed as a mechanism that enhances primary migration and increases the permeability of the source rock (Momper, 1980; Lempp et al., 1994). Fracturing observed in source rocks is commonly horizontal; however, oblique and perpendicular to bedding plane fractures also occur.

Structural-Related Tectonic Fractures

Structure-related fractures are associated with specific features like folds or faults (Stearns and Friedman, 1972). These types of fractures may pervade entire regions where similar structural features also are common. Changes in the structural trend, however, alter the trend of orientation of structure-related fractures. These fractures often occur in conjugate patterns. A complete conjugate pattern contains a left-lateral shear, a right-lateral shear, and an extension fracture.

Fractures associated with faults are assignable to the same stress state that caused the fault. The orientation of the fractures can be predicted from the orientation of the fault because they are miniatures of the fault. The width of the fracture zone is difficult to determine. The directional strike of the fracture trends is the same as the fault, so fluid movement direction and possible communication between wells can be predicted.

Fractures related to folding fall into two categories, hinge perpendicular and hinge parallel (Stearns and Friedman, 1972). The high rates of production at Antelope field suggest that the hinge-parallel type of fractures may be dominant in controlling production in this field.

Hinge-parallel and perpendicular fractures may also play roles associated with other anticlines and noses in the Williston Basin (i.e., Nesson, Cedar Creek, Poplar, Billings, and Little Knife anticlines).

Regional Fractures

Regional orthogonal fractures are common in little-deformed strata in many sedimentary basins (Lorenz et al., 1991). These fracture sets consist of a set of smooth, subparallel fractures, along with a more irregular set of cross-fractures. The fractures of the first set are considered to be systematic and parallel each other at very closely spaced intervals; fractures of the second set are nonsystematic and terminate against members of the first set. These fractures are important contributors to reservoir performance. The fractures are normal to bedding, occur throughout a basin, and are independent of local structure. The systematic fractures make good targets for deviated wells. The systematic fractures form during far-field compression and propagate in the plane of the maximum and intermediate compressive stresses. The fractures may form at depth in extension and parallel to the direction of regional horizontal tectonic compression.

Studies conducted on the regional stress field in the Williston Basin suggest a northeast–southwest orientation of the maximum horizontal stress (Zoback and Zoback, 1980; Narr and Burrus, 1984; Breig, 1988; Cramer, 1991; Whiting Petroleum, 2010; O'Brien et al., 2011; Sonnenberg et al., 2011c). Vertical fractures paralleling the maximum horizontal stress are thought to be the direction of open fractures (Figure 50). Natural fractures in the Mission Canyon in the Little Knife field trend in a general east–west direction, which is perpendicular to the trace of the Little Knife anticline. These fractures were related to the regional stress field. Oriented cores in the Elkhorn Ranch and Roosevelt field areas of the Billings anticline suggest that the maximum horizontal stress direction is N45E (Cramer, 1991). Multiwell interference testing in the Billings Nose area indicated restricted hydraulic communication exists between wells off the N45E trend. Natural fractures in the Mission Canyon at Big Stick field have a preferred orientation of N50°E. These fractures play a key role in Mission Canyon reservoir performance.

Regional Fractures

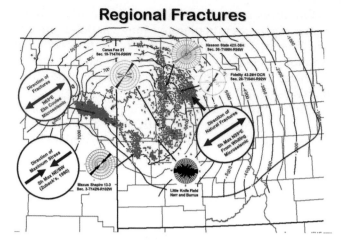

Figure 50. Regional fracture orientation based on literature, oriented core and microseismic data. Modified from Sonnenberg (2011b).

Microseismic data also supports the northeast–southwest orientation of regional fractures (Whiting Petroleum, 2010; O'Brien et al., 2011). In Parshall field microseismic surveys confirm a maximum horizontal stress direction of N55°E and for Elm Coulee N63°E.

Diagenetic Fractures

Microfracturing due to overpressuring of enclosed pore fluids is reviewed by Meissner (1978), Momper (1978), and Tissot and Welte (1984). The model proposed is that a large increase in pore pressure may be sufficient to overcome the capillary pressure or even exceed the mechanical strength of the rock and induce microcracking. These types of microfractures are restricted to deeply buried, compacted, low-permeability rocks. With thermal maturity, organic matter generates liquid or gaseous low-molecular-weight compounds. The mechanical strength of a rock is exceeded, and fracturing occurs if the internal fluid pressure in a rock or in local pressure centers inside the pores is greater than a factor of 1.42 to 2.4 over the hydrostatic pressure in the immediate surroundings (Tissot and Welte, 1984). Pressures that exceed normal hydrostatic and even lithostatic pressure are possible whenever massive generation of gas and oil from kerogen takes place.

The Bakken shales were probably indurated when hydrocarbon generation began (Dembicki and Pirkle, 1985). Fracturing, therefore, may be an important factor in the expulsion of oil generated in the Bakken shales.

Vertical and subhorizontal expulsion fractures have been reported in the Bakken shales in clay- and organic-rich intervals (Carlisle, 1991; Carlisle et al., 1992; Pitman et al., 2001; Vernik, 1994; Hill, 2010; Sonnenberg et al., 2011c; Theloy, 2014; Al Duhailan, 2014). Both micro- and macroexpulsion fractures have been observed (Carlisle et al., 1992). Carlisle et al. (1992), Pitman et al. (2001), and Price and Stolper (1999) discuss hydrocarbon generation resulting in superlithostatic pressures that could create the horizontal fractures. Price (1999) also discusses the model using early CO_2 generation and light hydrocarbons also creating high overpressures. The microexpulsion fractures have a "cracked-tip" morphology and have widths of 10 to 20 microns and lengths of approximately or ½ inch (1.3 cm) or longer. Connected vertical and horizontal macroexpulsion fractures also exist (Carlisle et al., 1992). These types of fractures are difficult to distinguish from small tectonic fractures, small-scale regional fractures, and bedding-plane partings.

ESTIMATES OF OIL GENERATED FROM BAKKEN SHALES

Numerous authors have estimated the amount of oil generated from the Bakken shales (Dow, 1974; Schmoker and Hester, 1983; Webster, 1984; Price, 1999; Meissner and Banks, 2000; Flannery and Kraus, 2006; Bohrer et al., 2008). Debate exists about how much oil has been generated and what formations have been sourced. Estimates of generated oil range from 10 to 500 billion bbl of oil. Different methodologies were used by various authors, resulting in the wide spread of estimates. The first estimate by Dow (1974) using an average of 4 wt.% TOC suggested 10 billion bbl of oil were generated. Webster (1984) calculated generation capacities to be 92 billion bbl of oil for North Dakota only based on the extent of thermal kerogen breakdown as observed on pyrolysis data. Schmoker and Hester utilized log-derived TOC and maturity (resistivity) data in their calculations and determined that 132 billion bbl of oil were generated. Price (1999) used an extensive data set to estimate generation of between 271 and 503 billion bbl of oil. More recent estimates (from 2000 to 2008) utilize computer mapping and modeling programs. Meissner and Banks (2000) estimated 32 billion bbl of generated oil. Flannery and Kraus (2006) used sophisticated computer modeling with extensive data input supplied by the North Dakota Geological Survey to estimate 300 billion bbl of generated oil. Most of the estimates are in excess of 100 billion bbl of oil generated in the Bakken petroleum system.

Oil generated in the Bakken shales is thought to have migrated into adjacent formations (Lodgepole and Three Forks) and into the middle Bakken member (Price and LeFever, 1994). And some of the generated oil stays within the Bakken shales. Thus much of the oil generated by the Bakken shales stays in the Bakken petroleum system reservoirs. The oils produced in the overlying upper Madison reservoirs are distinctly different from Bakken oils, and this suggests that they are self-sourced from the Madison (Jiang et al., 2001; Jarvie, 2001; Lillis, 2013). These reservoirs were previously thought to have been sourced from the Bakken shales (Dow, 1974; Meissner, 1978). The recovery factors for Bakken and Three Forks wells are often reported to be 3 to 10% of the oil in place (LeFever and Helms, 2006). The estimates of the amount of oil generated in the Williston Basin by the Bakken shales indicate a very large resource. How much of this resource can be recovered will be based on future technology and oil prices.

SUMMARY

The Bakken and Three Forks are an important tight oil resource play. The production in the Williston Basin is increasing dramatically because of the excellent results in recent drilling. The amount of technically recoverable oil has recently been estimated by Gaswirth et al. (2013) to be 7.3 billion bbl (3.7 from the Three Forks and 3.6 from the Bakken). New technology and enhanced recoveries may add to the number in the future. Total Bakken and Three Forks production to December 2014 was 1.289 billion bbl of oil and 1.3 tcf of gas from 12,051 wells (Figure 3). Thus the play is in its early stages. Production from both the Three Forks and Bakken is excellent. Both fracture and matrix permeability are important in the play.

Fracturing in the Bakken petroleum system occurs from a variety of causes: pore pressure, regional stress field, local structures (including salt dissolution features), and recurrent movement on basement fault systems. The regional stress field appears to play a significant role in how operators are orienting their laterals and overall production.

Many of the reservoirs in the Bakken petroleum system have low permeability. Productive areas or sweet spots are localized areas of improved reservoir permeability through natural fracturing or development of matrix permeability, or combination of both. Reservoir facies with matrix permeability are key ingredients to sweet spot areas.

REFERENCES CITED

Al Duhailan, M., 2014, Petroleum-expulsion fracturing in organic-rich shales: Genesis and impact on unconventional pervasive petroleum systems: Ph.D. theses, Colorado School of Mines, Golden, Colorado, 206 p.

Alexandre, C. S., 2011, Reservoir characterization and petrology of the Bakken Formation, Elm Coulee Field, Richland County, MT: M.S. thesis, Colorado School of Mines, Golden, Colorado, 159 p.

Bazzell, A., 2014, Origin of brecciated intervals and petrophysical analyses, the Three Forks Formation, Williston Basin, North Dakota, USA: M.S. thesis, Colorado School of Mines, Golden, Colorado, 140 p.

Berwick, B., 2008, Depositional environment, mineralogy, and sequence stratigraphy of the Late Devonian Sanish Member (upper Three Forks Formation), Williston Basin, North Dakota: M.S. thesis, Colorado School of Mines, Golden, Colorado, 262 p.

Blakey, R., 2005, Paleogeography and geologic evolution of North America: Northern Arizona University, Ron Blakey webpage, accessed March 15, 2009, http:jan.ucc.nau.edu/~rcb7/nam.html.

Bohrer, M., S. Fried, L. Helms, B. Hicks, B. Juenker, D. McCusker, et al., 2008, Bakken Formation resource study project: North Dakota Department of Mineral Resources Report, 23 p.

Bottjer, R. J., R. Sterling, A. Grau, and P. Dea, 2011, Stratigraphic relationships and reservoir quality at the Three Forks-Bakken Unconformity, Williston Basin, North Dakota, in J. W. Robinson, J. A. LeFever, and S. B. Gaswirth, eds., The Bakken-Three Forks petroleum system in the Williston Basin: Rocky Mountain Association of Geologists, p. 173–228.

Breig, J. J., 1988, Mississippian Mission Canyon reservoirs of the Billings Nose, Billings County, North Dakota, in S. M. Goolsby and M.W. Longman, eds., Occurrence and petrophysical properties of carbonate reservoirs in the Rocky Mountain Region: Rocky Mountain Association of Geologists, p. 357–369.

Canter, L., O. Skinner, and M. Sonnenfeld, 2009, Facies and mechanical stratigraphy of the middle Bakken, Mountrail County, North Dakota (abs): Rocky Mountain Section SEPM Luncheon, January 27.

Carlisle, W., 1991, The Bakken Formation of the Williston Basin: Deposition, maturation, and fracturing (abs.), in B. Hansen, ed., Geology and horizontal drilling of the Bakken Formation: Montana Geological Society, p. 89.

Carlisle, W. J., L. Dryff, M. Fryt, J. Artindale, and H. Von Der Dick, 1992, The Bakken Formation: An integrated geologic approach to horizontal drilling, in J. E. Schmoker, E. Coalson, and C. Brown, eds., Geologic studies relevant to horizontal drilling: Examples from western North America: Rocky Mountain Association of Geologists, p. 215–226.

Cobb, D., 2013, Characterization of thickness anomalies in the Bakken and Three Forks formations, North Central North Dakota, U.S.A.: M.S. thesis, Colorado School of Mines, Golden, Colorado, 196 p.

Coskey, R. J., and J. E. Leonard, 2009, Bakken oil accumulations: What's the trap?: AAPG Search and Discovery Article #90090, AAPG Annual Convention and Exhibition, Denver, Colorado, June 7–10, 2010, accessed September 22, 2016, http://www.searchanddiscovery.com /abstracts/html/2009/annual/abstracts/coskey.htm.

Cramer, D. D., 1986, Reservoir characteristics and stimulation techniques in the Bakken Formation and adjacent beds, Billings Nose area, Williston Basin, in S. Goolsby and M. W. Longman, eds., Proceedings from SPE Rocky Mountain Region Technical Meeting, Society of Petroleum Engineers, Paper No. 15166, p. 331–344.

Cramer, D. D., 1991, Stimulation treatments in the Bakken Formation: Implications for horizontal completions, in W. B. Hansen, ed., Geology and horizontal drilling of the Bakken Formation: Montana Geological Society, p. 117–140.

CSM Bakken Consortia data base, 2015, Source rock analysis data on Bakken wells Williston Basin: Unpublished source rock data from miscellaneous wells Williston Basin, Colorado School of Mines Bakken Consortia.

Dembicki, H., and F. L. Pirkle, 1985, Regional source rock mapping using a source potential rating index: AAPG Bulletin, v. 69, p. 567–581.

Dow, W. G., 1974, Application of oil-correlation and source-rock data to exploration in Williston Basin: AAPG Bulletin, v. 58, no. 7, p. 1253–1262.

Druyff, L., 1991, Reservoir properties of the Bakken shale (abs.), in W. B. Hansen, ed., Geology and horizontal drilling of the Bakken Formation: Montana Geological Society, p. 91.

Dumencaoux, G. M., 1984, Stratigraphy and depositional environments of the Three Forks Formation (upper Devonian), Williston Basin, North Dakota: M.S. thesis, University of North Dakota, 114 p.

Finch, W. C., 1969, Abnormal pressure in the Antelope Field, North Dakota: Journal of Petroleum Technology, July, p. 821–826.

Flannery, J., and J. Kraus, 2006, Integrated analysis of the Bakken petroleum system, U.S. Williston Basin: AAPG Search and Discovery Article #10105. Accessed December 15, 2008, http://www.searchanddiscovery.net /documents/2006/06035flannery/index.htm.

Folsom, C. B., C. Carlson, and S. B. Anderson, 1959, Geology of the Antelope Field: North Dakota Geological Survey Report of Investigation No. 32, 38 p.

Franklin, A. L., and S. A. Sonnenberg, 2012, Regional stratigraphic analysis of the Three Forks Formation, Williston Basin, USA: AAPG Search and Discovery Article #90142 © 2012 AAPG Annual Convention and Exhibition, accessed September 28, 2016, http://www.searchanddiscovery.com /abstracts/html/2012/90142ace/abstracts/frankl.htm.

Gantyno, A. A., 2011, Sequence stratigraphy and microfacies analysis of the late Devonian Three Forks Formation, Williston Basin, North Dakota and Montana, U.S.A.: M.S. thesis, Colorado School of Mines, Golden, Colorado, 201 p.

Gaswirth, S. B., K. R. Marra, T. A. Cook, R. R. Charpentier, D. L. Gautier, D. K. Higley, et al., 2013, Assessment of undiscovered oil resources in the Bakken and Three Forks formations, Williston Basin Province, Montana, North Dakota, and South Dakota: U.S. Geological Survey Report, accessed September 22, 2016, http://pubs.usgs .gov/fs/2013/3013/, 4 p.

Gent, V. A., 2011, Fourier analysis of the laminated facies of the middle Bakken Member, Sanish-Parshall Field, Mountrail County, North Dakota: M.S. thesis, Colorado School of Mines, Golden, Colorado, 135 p.

Gerhard, L. C., S. B. Anderson, and D. W. Fischer, 1990, Petroleum geology of the Williston Basin, in M. W. Leighton, D. R. Kolata, D. T. Oltz, and J. J. Eidel, eds., Interior Cratonic Basins: AAPG Memoir 51, p. 507–559.

Gerhard, L. C., S. B. Anderson, and J. A. LeFever, 1987, Structural history of the Nesson anticline, North Dakota, in M. W. Longman, ed., Williston Basin: Anatomy of a Cratonic Oil Province: Rocky Mountain Association of Geologists, p. 337–354.

Gerhard, L. C., S. B. Anderson, J. A. LeFever, and C. G. Carlson, 1982, Geological development, origin, and energy mineral resources of Williston Basin, North Dakota: AAPG Bulletin, v. 66, p. 989–1020.

Gutierrez, C., 2014, Stratigraphy and petroleum potential of the upper Three Forks Formation, North Dakota, Williston Basin, USA: M.S. thesis, Colorado School of Mines, Golden, Colorado, 180 p.

Hansen, W. B., and G. Long, 1991, Criteria for horizontal and vertical prospects in the Bakken Formation, Williston Basin, in W. B. Hansen, ed., Geology and horizontal drilling of the Bakken Formation: Montana Geological Society, p. 151–163.

Haynes, W. P., 1916, The fauna of the upper Devonian of Montana: Part 2. The stratigraphy and the Brachiopoda: Pittsburgh Carnegie Museum Annals, v. 10, p. 13–54.

Hester, T. C., and J. W. Schmoker, 1985, Selected physical properties of the Bakken Formation, North Dakota and Montana part of the Williston Basin: USGS Oil and Gas Investigations Chart OC-126, map scale 1:2,500,000, accessed September 22, 2016, http://ngmdb.usgs.gov /Prodesc/proddesc_5153.htm.

Hill, R., 2010, Bitumen filled fractures in the Bakken Formation and implications for gas shale systems: AAPG Search and Discovery Article #90108, AAPG International Convention and Exhibition, Calgary, Alberta, Canada, accessed September 22, 2016, http://www .searchanddiscovery.com/pdfz/abstracts/pdf/2010 /intl/abstracts/ndx_hill02.pdf.html.

Jarvie, D. M., 2001, Williston Basin petroleum systems: Inferences from oil geochemistry and geology: Mountain Geologist, v. 38, no. 1, p. 19–41.

Jiang, C., M. Li, K. G. Osadetz, L. R. Snowdon, M. Obermajer, and M. G. Fowler, 2001, Bakken/Madison petroleum systems in the Canadian Williston Basin: Part 2. Molecular markers diagnostic of Bakken and Lodgepole source rocks: Organic Geochemistry, v. 32, p. 1037–1054.

Jin, H., 2013, Characterization for source rock potential of the Bakken shales in the Williston Basin, North Dakota and Montana: Ph.D. thesis, Colorado School of Mines, Golden, Colorado, 240 p.

Johnson, R. L., 2013, The Pronghorn member of the Bakken Formation, Williston Basin, USA: Lithology, Stratigraphy, and Reservoir Properties: M.S. thesis, Colorado School of Mines, Golden, Colorado, 166 p.

Kowalski, B., 2010, Quantitative mineralogic analysis of the middle Bakken member, Parshall Field, Mountrail County, North Dakota: M.S. thesis, Colorado School of Mines, Golden, Colorado, 126 p.

Kowalski, B. L., and S. A. Sonnenberg, 2011, Mineralogic analysis of the middle Bakken member, Parshall Field area, Mountrail County, North Dakota, in J. W. Robinson, J. A. LeFever, and S. B. Gaswirth, eds., The Bakken-Three Forks petroleum system in the Williston Basin: Rocky Mountain Association of Geologists, p. 102–126.

LeFever, J., 2006, Oil production from the Bakken Formation: A short history: North Dakota Geological Survey Newsletter, v. 32, no. 1, p. 1–6.

LeFever, J., 2007, Evolution of oil production in the Bakken Formation: RMS-AAPG Meeting and North Dakota Industrial Commission Geologic Investigation 49: NDIC website PowerPoint presentation, accessed December 15, 2008, https://www.dmr.nd.gov/ndgs/bakken/Papers/Petroleum%20Council%202004.ppt.

LeFever, J. A., 1992, Horizontal drilling in the Williston Basin, United States and Canada, in J. W. Schmoker, E. B. Coalson, and C. A. Brown, eds., Geological studies relevant to horizontal drilling: Examples from Western North America: Rocky Mountain Association of Geologists Guidebook, p. 177–198.

LeFever, J. A., 2008, Isopach of the Bakken Formation: North Dakota Geological Survey Geologic Investigations No. 59, Bakken Map Series: Sheet 1-5, scale: 1:1,000,000.

LeFever, J. A., and L. Helms, 2006, Bakken Formation reserve estimates: North Dakota Geological Survey website, accessed December 15, 2008, https://www.dmr.nd.gov/ndgs/bakken/newpostings/07272006_BakkenReserveEstimates.pdf, 6 p.

LeFever, J. A., and R. LeFever, 2005, Distribution of salts in the Williston Basin, North Dakota: North Dakota Geological Survey Report of Investigations no. 103, 41 p., two plates.

LeFever, J. A., R. LeFever, and S. Nordeng, 2011, Revised nomenclature for the Bakken Formation (Mississippian-Devonian), North Dakota, in J. W. Robinson, J. A. LeFever, and S. B. Gaswirth, eds., The Bakken-Three Forks petroleum system in the Williston Basin: Rocky Mountain Association of Geologists, p. 11–26.

LeFever, J. A., C. D. Martiniuk, E. F. R. Dancsok, and P. A. Mahnic, 1991, Petroleum potential of the middle member, Bakken Formation, Williston Basin, in J. E. Christopher and F. Haidl, eds., Proceedings of the Sixth International Williston Basin Symposium: Saskatchewan Geological Society, Special Publication 11, p. 76–94.

Lempp, C., O. Natau, U. Bayer, and D. Welte, 1994, The effect of temperature on rock mechanical properties and fracture mechanisms in source rocks: Experimental results: Society of Petroleum Engineers Paper No. 28039, p. 147–154.

Lillis, P. G., 2013, Review of oil families and their petroleum systems of the Williston Basin: Mountain Geologist, v. 50, no. 1, p. 5–31.

Longman, M., K. Kocman, and L. Wray, 2014, Petrography of the Bakken black "shales" in the eastern Williston Basin of North Dakota: AAPG Datapages/Search and Discovery Article #90193, Rocky Mountain Section AAPG Annual Meeting, Denver, Colorado, July 20–22, accessed September 22, 2016, http://www.searchanddiscovery.com/abstracts/html/2014/90193rms/abstracts/1956909.html.

Lorenz, J. C., L. W. Teufel, and N. R. Warpinski, 1991, Regional fractures I: A mechanism for the formation of regional fractures at depth in flat-lying reservoirs: AAPG Bulletin, v. 75, p. 1714–1737.

Martiniuk, C. D., 1991, Regional geology and petroleum potential of the Bakken Formation, southwestern Manitoba, in B. Hansen, ed., Geology and horizontal drilling of the Bakken Formation: Montana Geological Society, p. 43–67.

Meissner, F. F., 1978, Petroleum geology of the Bakken Formation, Williston Basin, North Dakota and Montana, in D. Estelle and R. Miller, eds., The economic geology of the Williston Basin, 1978 Williston Basin Symposium, September 24–27, Montana Geological Society, p. 207–230.

Meissner, F. F., and R. B. Banks, 2000, Computer simulation of hydrocarbon generation, migration, and accumulation under hydrodynamic conditions: Examples from the Williston and San Juan Basins, USA: AAPG Search and Discovery Article #40179, accessed December 15, 2008, http://www.searchanddiscovery.net/documents/2005/banks/index.htm?q=%2Btext%3Ameissner.

Meissner, F. F., J. Woodward, and J. L. Clayton, 1984, Stratigraphic relationships and distribution of source rocks in the Greater Rocky Mountain Region, in J. Woodward, F. F. Meissner, and J. L. Clayton, eds., Hydrocarbon source rocks of the Greater Rocky Mountain Region: Rocky Mountain Association of Geologists Guidebook, p. 1–34.

Momper, J. A., 1978, Oil migration limitations suggested by geological and geochemical considerations: AAPG Course Notes 8, Physical and chemical constraints on petroleum migration, B1–B60.

Momper, J. A., 1980, Oil expulsion: A consequence of oil generation: American Association of Petroleum Geologists slide/tape series, produced by Science-Thru-Media Co., New York, New York.

Murray, G. H., 1968, Quantitative fracture study: Sanish Pool, McKenzie County, North Dakota: AAPG Bulletin, v. 52, no. 1, p. 57–65.

Narr, W., and R. C. Burruss, 1984, Origin of fractures in Little Knife Field, North Dakota: AAPG Bulletin, v. 68, no. 9, p. 1087–1100.

Nordeng, S. H., 2009, The Bakken petroleum system: An example of a continuous petroleum accumulation: North Dakota Department of Mineral Resources Newsletter, v. 36, no. 1, p. 19–22.

Nordeng, S. H., and J. LeFever, 2008, The Bakken: A question of maturity: 16th Annual Williston Basin Petroleum Conference, April 28–30, North Dakota Geological Survey, PowerPoint presentation, accessed December 15, 2008, https://www.dmr.nd.gov/ndgs/wbpc/wbpc2008.asp.

Nordeng, S.H., and L. D. Helms, 2010, Bakken Source System, Three Forks Formation Assessment: Department of Mineral Resources, North Dakota Industrial Commission, accessed September 27, 2016, https://www.dmr.nd.gov/ndgs/bakken/bakkenthree.asp.

O'Brien, D. G., R. T. Larson, R. C. Parham, B. L. Thingelstad, W. W. Aud, R. A. Burns, et al., 2011, Using real-time downhole microseismic to evaluate fracture geometry for horizontal packer-sleeve completions in the Bakken Formation, Elm Coulee Field, Montana: Society of Petroleum Engineering Paper 139774, 22 p.

Parker, J. M., 1967, Salt solution and subsidence structures Wyoming, North Dakota, and Montana: AAPG Bulletin, v. 51, no. 10, p. 1929–1947.

Peale, A. C., 1893, Paleozoic section in the vicinity of Three Forks, Montana: U.S. Geological Survey Bulletin 110, 56 p.

Peterson, J. A., and L. M. MacCary, 1987, Regional stratigraphy and general petroleum geology of the U.S. portion of the Williston Basin and adjacent areas, in M. W. Longman, ed., Williston Basin: Anatomy of a cratonic oil province: Denver, Colorado, Rocky Mountain Association of Geologists, p. 9–43.

Pitman, J. K., L. C. Price, and J. A. LeFever, 2001, Diagenesis and fracture development in the Bakken Formation, Williston Basin: Implications for reservoir quality in the middle member: U.S. Geological Survey Professional Paper 1653, 19 p.

Price, L. C., 1999 (unpublished), Origins and characteristics of the basin-centered continuous reservoir unconventional oil-resource base of the Bakken Source System, Williston Basin: Unpublished, accessed September 22, 2018, http://www.undeerc.org/Price/.

Price, L. C., T. Ging, T. Daws, A. Love, M. Pawlewicz, and D. Anders, 1984, Organic metamorphism in the Mississippian-Devonian Bakken shale North Dakota portion of the Williston Basin, in J. Woodward, F. F. Meissner, and J. C. Clayton, eds., Hydrocarbon source rocks of the greater Rocky Mountain Region: Denver, Colorado, Rocky Mountain Association of Geologists, p. 83–134.

Price, L. C., and J. A. LeFever, 1992, Does horizontal drilling imply a huge oil-resource base in fractured shales? in J. W. Schmoker, E. B. Coalson, and C. A. Brown, eds., Geologic studies relevant to horizontal drilling: Examples from Western North America: Rocky Mountain Association of Geologists, p. 199–214.

Price, L. C., and J. A. LeFever, 1994, Dysfunctionalism in the Williston Basin: the mid-Madison/Bakken petroleum system: Bulletin of Canadian Petroleum Geology, v. 42, no. 2, p. 187–218.

Price, L. C., and K. Stolper, 1999, Evidence and causes of super-lithostatic fracturing, in L. C. Price, ed., Origins and

characteristics of the basin-center continuous-reservoir unconventional oil-resource base of the Bakken Source System, Williston Basin: Unpublished, accessed May 6, 2010, http://www.undeerc.org/Price/.

Rogers, M. H., and W. A. Mattox, 1985, Solution of Devonian Prairie Formation salt: Seismic recognition and exploration implications, in R. R. Gries and R. C. Dyer, eds., Seismic exploration of the Rocky Mountain Region: Rocky Mountain Association of Geologist Guidebook, p. 137–142.

Rogers, M., and W. Mattox, 1985, Solution of the Devonian Prairie Formation salt: Seismic recognition and exploration implications, in R. R. Gries, ed., Seismic exploration of the Rocky Mountain Region: Rocky Mountain Association of Geologists, Boulder, Colorado, U.S.A., p. 137–141.

Sandberg, C. A., 1965, Nomenclature and correlation of lithologic subdivisions of the Jefferson and Three Forks formations of southern Montana and northern Wyoming: U.S. Geological Society Bulletin 1194-B, 18 p.

Sandberg, C. A., and C. R. Hammond, 1958, Devonian system in Williston Basin and central Montana: AAPG Bulletin, v. 42, p. 2293–2334.

Schmoker, J. W., and T. C. Hester, 1983, Organic carbon in Bakken Formation, United States portion of Williston Basin: AAPG Bulletin, v. 67, no. 12, p. 2165–2174.

Simenson, A., 2010, Depositional facies and petrophysical analysis of the Bakken Formation, Parshall Field, Mountrail County, North Dakota: M.S. thesis, Colorado School of Mines, Golden, Colorado, 198 p.

Simenson, A. L., S. A. Sonnenberg, and R. M. Cluff, 2011, Depositional facies and petrophysical analysis of the Bakken Formation, Parshall Field and Surrounding Area, Mountrail County, North Dakota, in J. W. Robinson, J. A. LeFever, and S. B. Gaswirth, eds., The Bakken-Three Forks petroleum system in the Williston Basin: Rocky Mountain Association of Geologists, p. 48–101.

Smith, M. G., and M. Bustin, 1996, Lithofacies and paleoenvironments of the upper Devonian and lower Mississippian Bakken Formation, Williston Basin: Bulletin of Canadian Petroleum Geology, v. 44, no. 3, p. 495–507.

Smith, M. G., and M. Bustin, 2000, Late Devonian and early Mississippian Bakken and Exshaw Black shale source rocks, Western Canada Sedimentary basin: A sequence stratigraphic interpretation: AAPG Bulletin, v. 84, no. 7, p. 940–960.

Sonnenberg, S. A., 2010a, Focusing on the Bakken: The Bakken petroleum system of the Williston Basin: Harts Magazine, July, p. 4–20.

Sonnenberg, S. A., 2010b, Abnormal pressure analysis in the Bakken Formation, Williston Basin: A key to future discoveries (abs.): 2010 Annual AAPG Meeting Abstracts, p. 242, accessed September 22, 2018, http://www.searchanddiscovery.com/pdfz/abstracts/pdf/2010/annual/abstracts/ndx_sonnenberg.pdf.html.

Sonnenberg, S. A., 2011, TOC and pyrolysis data for the Bakken shales, Williston Basin, North Dakota and Montana, in J. W. Robinson, J. A. LeFever, and S. B. Gaswirth, eds.,

The Bakken-Three Forks petroleum system in the Williston Basin: Rocky Mountain Association of Geologists, p. 308–331.

Sonnenberg, S. A., V. James, C. Theloy, and J. F. Sarg, 2011a, Middle Bakken facies, Williston Basin, USA: A key to prolific production: AAPG Annual Convention and Exhibition, Houston, Texas, Poster Session Presentation, Search and Discovery Article #50449, April 10–13, accessed September 22, 2016, http://www.searchanddiscovery.com/abstracts/html/2011/annual/abstracts/Sonnenberg3.html.

Sonnenberg, S. A., H. Jin, and J. F. Sarg, 2011b, Bakken mudrocks of the Williston Basin, world class source rocks: AAPG Annual Convention and Exhibition, Houston, Texas, Poster Session Presentation, Search and Discovery Article #80171, April 10–13, accessed September 22, 2016, http://www.searchanddiscovery.com/abstracts/html/2011/annual/abstracts/Sonnenberg2.html.

Sonnenberg, S.A., J. A. LeFever, and R. J. Hill, 2011c, Fracturing in the Bakken petroleum system, Williston Basin, in J. W. Robinson, J. A. LeFever, and S. B. Gaswirth, eds., The Bakken-Three Forks petroleum system in the Williston Basin: Rocky Mountain Association of Geologists, p. 393–417.

Sonnenberg, S. A., and A. Pramudito, 2009, Petroleum geology of the giant Elm Coulee Field, Williston Basin: AAPG Bulletin, v. 93, no. 9, p. 1127–1153.

Sperr, J. T., 1991, Exploration models for Bakken Reservoirs: Williston Basin, North Dakota and Montana, in B. Hansen, ed., Geology and horizontal drilling of the Bakken Formation: Montana Geological Society, p. 143–149.

Stearns, D. W., and M. Friedman, 1972, Reservoirs in fractured rock: AAPG Bulletin, p. 82–106.

Stroud, J., 2010, The role of the lower Lodgepole Formation in the Bakken petroleum system, Billings Nose, North Dakota: M.S. thesis, Colorado School of Mines, Golden, Colorado, 104 p.

Theloy, C., 2014, Integration of geological and technological factors influencing production in the Bakken play, Williston Basin: Ph.D. thesis, Colorado School of Mines, Golden, Colorado, 223 p.

Tissot, B. P., and D. H. Welte, 1984, Petroleum formation and occurrence (2nd ed.): Berlin, Heidelberg, New York, and Tokyo, Springer-Verlag, 699 p.

Tucker, M. E., 2001, Sedimentary petrology: Malden, Massachusetts, Blackwell Publishing, 262 p.

U. S. Geological Survey Geochemistry Database, 2016, Geochemistry Database: Energy Resources Program Geochemistry Laboratory Database (EGDB), U.S. Geological Survey, accessed September 28, 2016, http://energy.usgs.gov/GeochemistryGeophysics/GeochemistryLaboratories/GeochemistryLaboratoriesGeochemistryDatabase.aspx.

Vernik, L., 1994, Hydrocarbon generation induces microcracking of source rocks: Geophysics, v. 59, no. 4, p. 555–563.

Vickery, J. O., 2010, Lithofacies, mineralogy, and ichnology of the Bakken Formation (Mississippian and Devonian), Williston Basin, Montana and North Dakota, USA: M.S. thesis, Colorado School of Mines, Golden, Colorado, 254 p.

Webster, R. L., 1984, Petroleum source rocks and stratigraphy of the Bakken Formation in North Dakota, in J. Woodward, F. F. Meissner, and J. C. Clayton, eds., Hydrocarbon source rocks of the Greater Rocky Mountain Region: Denver, Colorado, Rocky Mountain Association of Geologists, p. 57–81.

Weimer, R. J., 1980, Recurrent movement of basement faults: A tectonic style for Colorado and adjacent areas, in H. C. Kent and K. W. Porter, eds., Colorado Geology: Rocky Mountain Association of Geologists Guidebook, p. 23–35.

Whiting Petroleum, 2010, Current corporate information, December 2010: accessed December 23, 2010, http://www.whiting.com/investor-relations/presentationsand-media-events/.

Williams, J. A., 1974, Characterization of oil types in Williston Basin: AAPG Bulletin, v. 58, p. 1243–1252.

Zoback, M. L., and M. Zoback, 1980, State of stress in the conterminous United States: Journal of Geophysical Research, v. 85, no. B11, p. 6113–6156.

Stoneburner Richard K., 2017, The Eagle Ford Shale Field in the Gulf Coast Basin of South Texas, U.S.A.: A "Perfect" Unconventional Giant Oil Field, *in* R. K. Merrill and C. A. Sternbach, eds., Giant Fields of the Decade 2000–2010: AAPG Memoir 113, p. 121–140.

7

The Eagle Ford Shale Field in the Gulf Coast Basin of South Texas, U.S.A.: A "Perfect" Unconventional Giant Oil Field

Richard K. Stoneburner

Pine Brook Partners, 1301 McKinney Street, Suite 3550, Houston, Texas, U.S.A. 77010 (e-mail: dstoneburner@pinebrookpartners.com)

ABSTRACT

The Eagle Ford shale Formation (Upper Cretaceous) in the Gulf Coast basin of south Texas was first commercially produced in 2008 and has since achieved production and reserve growth that is virtually unprecedented in the history of onshore North American oil and gas development. Through December 2014, the field had cumulative production of approximately 1.1 billion bbl of oil and condensate and 4.8 trillion cubic ft of natural gas (TCFG). Average daily production during 2014 was approximately 1.3 million bbl of oil and condensate per day and 4.9 billion cubic ft per day of natural gas (BCFGD). The horizontal rig count in October 2014 was approximately 200, resulting in approximately 300 wells drilled per month (RigData). While the entire resource potential of the Eagle Ford is still quite subjective, it has been estimated to be as high 25 to 30 billion bbl of oil equivalent (BBOE).

The Eagle Ford shale covers a vast area that spans approximately 7 million ac (2,832,799 ha) of continuous prospective reservoir and therefore should be considered as one oil and gas accumulation, or field. As a result of the aerial extent of the field occurring at depths ranging from approximately 5000 ft (1524 m) to the north to approximately 13,000 ft (3962 m) to the south, the product mix covers the entire spectrum from low gravity–low gas oil-ratio oil to dry gas, and everything in between.

The Eagle Ford Formation lies above the Buda limestone and beneath the Austin chalk over the entire field area. The formation varies in thickness from approximately 250 ft (76 m) to as much as 600 ft (183 m) and is composed of a variety of facies. The primary reservoir facies, herein referred to as the Hawkville facies, is the primary reservoir and is located near the base of the formation. The Hawkville facies, named for the field area located in LaSalle and McMullen Counties where the net reservoir thickness is found to be in excess of 300 ft (91 m), is a calcareous mudstone that was deposited in an anoxic environment as part of the Cretaceous seaway that traversed north to south through west-central United States and Canada. Long known as a source for oil and gas production from other Cretaceous reservoirs such as the Buda, Austin chalk, Olmos, and others, the Eagle Ford has moderate to high total organic

DOI:10.1306/13572003M1133682

content (TOC) ranging from 3 to 5% and thermal maturities based on vitronite reflectance ranging from approximately 0.7 to 1.3.

Operationally, the field has proven to be one that has been relatively benign from a drilling perspective. The Tertiary is at the surface and is a sand-dominated section extending to as deep as approximately 8000 ft (2438 m) near the down dip limits of the field and results in excellent rates of penetration. The Cretaceous Midway, Taylor, and Austin formations also provide consistent drilling conditions. Wells in the field that are in the measured depth range of 15,000 to 18,000 ft (4572 to 5486 m) are commonly drilled from spud to total depth in 8 to 12 days or less. Completion operations are similarly advantaged. The reservoir is extremely brittle and is very receptive to the high-rate hydraulic fracturing processes that are necessary to establish commercial production, with a very low percentage of screened out fracture stimulation stages. Production operations vary widely based on product type, gas-to-oil ratio, and the volatility of the liquid. However, to date, there have not been material changes in the gas-to-oil ratio of the producing wells that would suggest degradation of ultimate recoveries based on bubble point or dew point effects.

The regulatory and community effects have also been relatively benign in terms of impediments to the development of the field. The state of Texas and the oil and gas industry have a long history of working in a collaborative manner. Very early in the field's history, the Eagle Task Force, led by railroad commissioner David Porter, was organized with members from the state bureaucracy, industry, and community with the intent of promoting economic activity, establishing best practices across the play, and reacting to issues that affected the constituencies within the group. One of the most significant issues is water usage, which is a common issue in all unconventional development that utilizes isolated multistage hydraulic fracturing. One of the benefits to the field is the presence of the Carrizo aquifer, which underlies a vast majority of the field. The Carrizo is a fresh-water aquifer that has proven to be an excellent source of water without experiencing material depletion, primarily because of its extremely large amount of available water and because it is actively replenished except in times of severe drought.

HISTORY OF UNCONVENTIONAL SHALE EXPLORATION AND DEVELOPMENT

A discussion of unconventional shale exploration can start in only one place, and that is the Barnett shale in the Fort Worth Basin. Likewise, there is only one person that should be involved in that initial discussion, and that is George Mitchell.

George's company, Mitchell Energy, had been exploiting the Fort Worth Basin, in an area specifically known as the Boonsville Bend Conglomerate field, for over three decades when he made the decision to test the Barnett shale to determine if it could produce hydrocarbons commercially. The decision to do so was a combination of both economic necessity and scientific curiosity. The necessity aspect was a function of a depleting natural gas asset across Wise and Denton Counties in conjunction with a contractual obligation to deliver gas under a long-term contract. The scientific aspect was a function of George Mitchell being a geologic visionary who became convinced, and maybe a bit obsessed, that the Barnett could become a commercial gas reservoir.

The initial test of the Barnett was in 1981 when Mitchell completed the C.W. Slay 1 in Wise County. The well, fracture stimulated with nitrogen foam, was noncommercial but did validate the most basic premise, which was that natural gas could be produced from the Barnett.

It has been estimated that over the next two decades Mitchell Energy spent approximately $250 million drilling and completing Barnett shale wells and was woefully short of getting a return on that investment. The biggest breakthrough for Mitchell came in 1997, when a Mitchell Energy petroleum engineer, Nick Steinsberger, suggested that a slickwater frac might be the most effective means of stimulating the reservoir (Gold, 2014). Slickwater fracs had been widely used in other conventional low-permeability reservoirs such as the Cotton valley sands in east Texas but had not been tried yet in the Barnett. The result was both a dramatic increase in productivity and a significant decrease in total well cost. Prior to this time, Mitchell had a monopoly on the Barnett. However, it became apparent to the industry that a new play had been proven and by 2001, there were more wells drilled by other operators than by Mitchell.

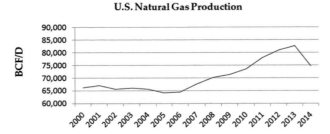

Figure 1. U.S. natural gas production vs. time (2000–2014) (EIA, 2015).

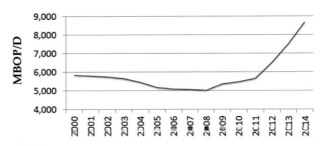

Figure 2. U.S. crude oil production vs. time (2000–2014) (EIA, 2015).

In 2002, Devon Energy became convinced that the Barnett shale was for real and acquired Mitchell Energy for $3.5 billion. Shortly after the acquisition, Devon concluded that horizontal drilling should dramatically improve the commerciality of the play due to the low permeability of the reservoir and the cultural challenges of drilling in the play's largely urban area. Conceptually, they were entirely correct. However, the challenge became stimulating the horizontal lateral and having confidence in both where the stimulation went and how much of the wellbore was actually stimulated to the point of achieving flow.

After several years of trying a wide variety of completion techniques, the concept of cementing casing in the lateral and employing the isolated multistage hydraulic fracturing method of completion, often referred to as plug and perf, was proven. Not only did the results in the Barnett improve dramatically but it became the catalyst for successful exploration and development of other shale gas reservoirs.

Figure 1 is a graph showing total U.S.A. natural gas production from 2002 through 2014 and the New York Mercantile Exchange (NYMEX) price for natural gas. The growth from 2006 until 2009, which saw an unprecedented collapse of natural gas prices, was coincident with the advent of isolated multistage hydraulic fracturing in horizontally drilled shale reservoirs. Even though growth has diminished dramatically over the past 5 years, the resource is in place and can provide the country adequate supplies of natural gas for many decades to come.

While natural gas exploration peaked from 2006 through 2009, the industry began taking the lessons learned from shale gas exploration and began exploring for more liquids-rich shale reservoirs. Beginning with the Bakken and Eagle Ford and followed by the Niobrara, Permian, and others, the growth of U.S.A. oil production from oil and condensate shale reservoirs has proven to be equally as prolific as that from shale gas reservoirs. Figure 2 displays the growth in oil and condensate production from 2004 to 2014, whereby total daily production increased by ~100%.

The impact of the shale reservoirs, both oil and natural gas, can be seen not only by the previous graphs but also by the ranking of the most prolific producing fields in the U.S.A. Figure 3 is the ranking of the top 10 natural gas fields of 2014 by annual production, and Figure 4

2013 Rank	Field Name	Location	2013 Proved Reserves	2013 Estimated Production	Discovery Year
1	MARCELLUS SHALE AREA	PA & WV	-	2,836,043	2008
2	NEWARK EAST (BARNETT SHALE)	TX	-	1,951,750	1981
3	B-43 AREA (FAYETTEVILLE SHALE)	AR	-	1,025,153	2005
4	SAN JUAN BASIN GAS AREA	CO & NM	-	1,024,962	1927
5	HAYNESVILLE SHALE UNIT	LA	-	1,425,661	2008
6	PINEDALE	WY	-	568,153	1955
7	CARTHAGE	TX	-	653,093	1936
8	JONAH	WY	-	239,233	1977
9	WATTENBERG	CO	-	304,540	1970
10	PRUDHOE BAY	AK	-	147,554	1967
	Group 1 -10 Volume Subtotal		144,614,724	10,176,142	

Figure 3. Top 10 U.S. natural gas fields by 2013 total production (EIA, 2015).

2013 Rank	Field Name	Location	2013 Proved Reserves	2013 Estimated Production	Discovery Year
1	EAGLEVILLE (EAGLE FORD SHALE)	TX	-	238,050	2009
2	SPRABERRY TREND AREA	TX	-	99,787	1949
3	PRUDHOE BAY	AK	-	79,080	1967
4	WATTENBERG	CO	-	47,259	1970
5	BRISCOE RANCH (EAGLE FORD SHALE)	TX	-	62,046	1962
6	KUPARUK RIVER	AK	-	29,487	1969
7	MISSISSIPPI CANYON BLK 778 (THUNDER HORSE)	Fed Gulf	-	15,833	1999
8	WASSON	TX	-	19,996	1937
9	BELRIDGE SOUTH	CA	-	23,703	1911
10	GREEN CANYON BLK 699 (ATLANTIS)	Fed Gulf	-	27,346	1998
	Group 1-10 Volume Subtotal		9,659,688	642,587	

Figure 4. Top 10 U.S. oil fields by 2013 total production (EIA, 2015).

is the ranking of the top 10 oil fields. Five of the top 10 natural gas fields are shale reservoirs, and five of the top 10 oil/condensate reservoirs are shale reservoirs.

HISTORY OF THE EAGLE FORD DISCOVERY AND DEVELOPMENT

It was simply a matter of time before the Eagle Ford shale, a well-known source rock throughout south Texas, became an exploration target. In fact, multiple companies were testing the concept during 2008. The differentiating factors between the companies that were involved in the play appeared to be a combination of completion techniques and geological variability.

Some of the first attempts to establish commercial production from the Eagle Ford were by Newfield and The Exploration Company (TXCO). Newfield completed a 2700 ft (823 m) horizontal lateral well in March 2008 in Maverick County with a small one-stage fracture stimulation that resulted in an initial production rate of 81 thousand cubic feet of gas per day (MCFGD) and 2 barrels of oil per day (BOPD). TXCO completed a 4800 ft (1463 m) open-hole horizontal lateral in May 2008 in Zavala County for 61 BOPD. In July 2008, Cornerstone E & P completed a 1600 ft (488 m) horizontal lateral in Maverick County with a four-stage fracture stimulation that resulted in a rate of 40 BOPD. Anadarko completed two wells in August and October 2008 in Dimmit County: the first was a 2900 ft (884 m) lateral that tested at a rate of 337 MCFGD and 37 BOPD, and the second was a 3100 ft (945 m) lateral that tested at a rate of 192 MCFGD and 43 BOPD. As intimated above, all of these wells suffered from at least one of two limiting factors: inferior reservoir quality and/or thickness and inadequate fracture stimulation.

The exploration of the Eagle Ford by Petrohawk began in January 2008 when Petrohawk's geological staff joined forces with Gregg Robertson, a very successful geologist with a tremendous amount of experience working the Cretaceous trend of south Texas. Together they began a concerted evaluation of the subsurface across the entire Texas Gulf Coast region with the intent of identifying the type of reservoir characteristics in the Eagle Ford that were known to be requisite for a commercially productive shale reservoir.

Within several months of initiating this effort, an area had been identified that was clearly anomalous. Not only was there the appearance of outstanding petrophysical properties in the Eagle Ford, but the thickness of the reservoir was more than anywhere else along the entire trend of the Eagle Ford. Even though the well control was sparse, you can see in Figure 5 a well log with over 250 ft (76 m) of what appeared to be continuous reservoir-quality rock in the Eagle Ford at a depth of approximately 11,000 ft (3353 m).

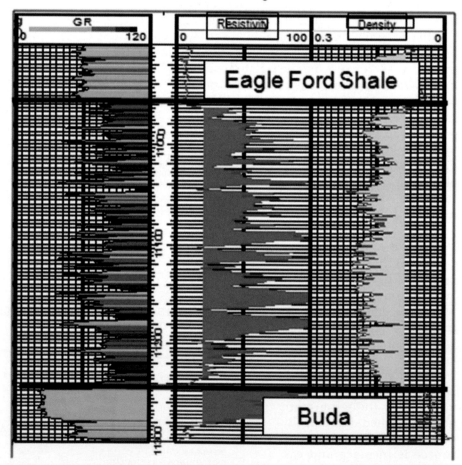

Figure 5. Open-hole log Swift #1 Pielop; LaSalle County, Texas, U.S.A. (Stoneburner, 2014).

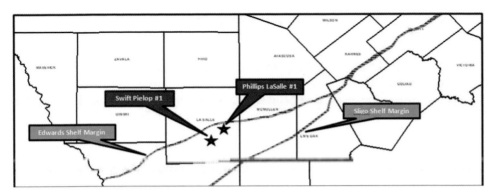

Figure 6. Regional map of south Texas with location of Cretaceous shelf margins and key well control (Stoneburner, 2014).

As shown in Figure 6, the area around this well, located in LaSalle and McMullen Counties, was actually between the Edwards and Sligo shelf margins where a natural mini-basin had formed to allow for lower Eagle Ford reservoir thicknesses two to three times greater than what had been observed anywhere else along the trend.

While these findings were extremely supportive of the play concept, the question of shale geochemistry was still uncertain. Prior to the discovery of the Eagle Ford, all of the commercial shale gas reservoirs had been from rocks that were Paloezoic in age (with the exception of the Jurassic-aged Haynesville, which was just beginning to emerge as a shale reservoir), and knowledge of the thermal maturity of a Cretaceous shale reservoir seemed to be a component of the play that was needed to reduce the risk.

To mitigate this point, the exploration team located drill cuttings at the Bureau of Economic Geology from a well located in the mini-basin, the Phillips 1 LaSalle. Samples of the cuttings were sent to a lab to be analyzed for certain geochemical properties, most notably vitinite reflectance (Ro) and total organic carbon (TOC). The results of the analysis strongly supported the Eagle Ford being a thermogenic reservoir with R_o being in the range of 1.1 (gas condensate window) and TOC in the 3 to 5% range, which was consistent with readings from other commercial shale reservoirs.

These data in conjunction with the petrophysical support provided a level of confidence for the company to initiate a leasing effort. The challenge to that, however, was that the lack of subsurface control made the establishment of a buy outline quite problematic. The answer to that dilemma was found with the utilization of a fairly robust two-dimensional seismic grid. As shown in Figure 7, seismic data quickly verified that the seismic signature of the Eagle Ford was such that it

became a straightforward exercise to confidently build an isochron map that allowed the construction of a buy outline that approximated the area where the lower Eagle reservoir was greater than approximately 150 ft (46 m).

The leasing effort began in April 2008. Due to sparse existing production in the area and the presence of many large ranches, over 160,000 ac (64,750 ha) were leased within a 3-month time frame. The STS 241 1H was spudded on July 8 in LaSalle County and reached total depth on August 23. A 10-stage hydraulic fracture stimulation over an approximately 3200 ft (975 m) horizontal lateral was pumped in early October. The well tested at a rate of 7.6 MMCFGD and 240 BCPD and became the first commercial Eagle Ford completion. The Dora Martin 1H, also located in LaSalle County, was completed in January 2009 approximately 10 mi (16 km) to the southwest at a rate of 8.3 MMCFGD from a 12-stage hydraulic fracture stimulation over an approximately 4200 ft (1280 m) horizontal lateral and the Donnell Minerals 1H, located in McMullen County, was completed approximately 10 mi (16 km) to the northeast at a rate of 398 BOPD and 3.4 MMCFGD from a 10-stage hydraulic fracture stimulation over an approximately 3600 ft (1097 m) horizontal lateral. In April 2010, EOG announced its successful exploration in the Eagle Ford with the completion of its Milton 1H in April 2009,

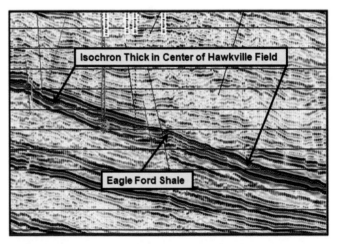

Figure 7. 2-D seismic line through the Hawkville field area (Stoneburner, 2014).

located in Karnes County, at a rate of 608 BOPD from an approximately 1800 ft (549 m) horizontal lateral. With the completion of the Milton 1H, located over 100 mi (161 km) northeast from the STS 241 1H, the Eagle Ford was validated as a potentially incredibly large oil and gas resource.

Further validation of the size of the resource is reflected in Figures 8 through 10, which represent the growth of oil and condensate production, natural gas production, and number of drilling permits issued from 2008 through 2014.

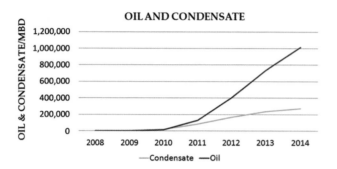

Figure 8. Eagle Ford oil and condensate production vs. time (2008–2014) (Texas Railroad Commission, 2017).

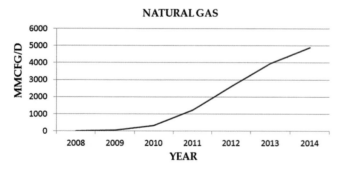

Figure 9. Eagle Ford oil natural gas production vs. time (2008–2014) (Texas Railroad Commission, 2017).

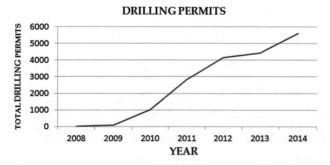

Figure 10. Eagle Ford drilling permits vs. time (2008–2014) (Texas Railroad Commission, 2017).

UPPER CRETACEOUS STRATIGRAPHY

The Cretaceous period along the Gulf Coast was dominated by a series of carbonate platforms that were amalgamated into a single platform called the Comanche shelf. The shelf is characterized by a series of stacked, prograding carbonate platforms separated by transgressive, organic-rich facies. The Sligo limestone was the initial carbonate development on the Comanche shelf. It formed as a shallow, rimmed carbonate platform that was very a broad, restricted interior platform with a narrow, high-energy well-circulated outer platform that had a well-defined margin and gently dipping foreslope (Workman, 2013). The Sligo carbonate development was followed by a rapid marine transgression, resulting in the deposition of the organic-rich Pearsall shale. Figure 11 shows relationships between the Glen Rose, Edwards, Georgetown, and Buda limestones. They represented another period of carbonate shelf deposition during late Albian to early Cenomonian that amalgamated into what is locally referred to as the Stuart City reef complex at the margin of the Comanche shelf. This period of platform and reef carbonate deposition was once again followed by a rapid transgression, resulting in the deposition of the Eagle Ford shale

With the exception of minor outcrops in the San Antonio area, Eagle Ford outcrops are limited in south Texas. As a result, much of the descriptions, stratigraphic divisions, and correlations have been done using wire-line and core data. Figure 12 provides a summary and comparison of the Eagle Ford and equivalent units in south and east Texas. Cusack et al. (2010) subdivided the Eagle Ford in south Texas into the upper and lower Eagle Ford.

The lower Eagle Ford was deposited during a second-order transgressive systems tract and attains a maximum thickness of over 91 m (300 ft) in the Hawkville field area in LaSalle and McMullen Counties. This interval thins to the southeast toward the Sligo shelf margin and northeastward toward the San Marcos arch, as shown in Figure 13. It consists predominately of dark-gray mudrocks with TOC values between 1.0 and 8.3% and high gamma ray values typically between 90 and 135 API units (Hentz and Ruppel, 2010, sourced from Workman, 2013). Light-gray calcareous mudrocks, marls, and limestones with low gamma ray values also occur locally.

The upper Eagle Ford was deposited during a marine transgression and is generally restricted to areas southwest of the San Marcos arch. It reaches a maximum thickness of 146 m (480 ft) in the Maverick Basin. It also thins to the southeast toward the Sligo and Edwards shelf margins and to the northeast toward the San Marcos arch. It consists primarily of light-gray calcareous

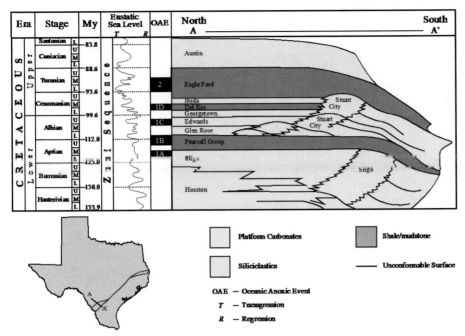

Figure 11. Diagrammatic representation of the evolution and architecture of Cretaceous carbonate platforms in the Northern Gulf Coast (reprinted with permission from Workman, 2013, whose permission is required for further use).

mudrocks with low organic content and low gamma ray values between 35 and 60 API units (Hentz and Ruppel, 2010, sourced from Workman, 2013). Thin beds of organic, dark-gray noncalcareous mudrocks with gamma ray values as high as 120 API units are locally present.

Figure 14 represents the mineralogical content of the Eagle Ford taken from a core provided by Core Laboratories. The entire section is dominated by calcite with lesser amounts of quartz, dolomite, various clay minerals, and kerogen. The primary difference between the upper and lower Eagle Ford is the percentage of kerogen, which has a direct relationship with effective porosity and permeability as a result of the conversion of kerogen to hydrocarbon product.

STRUCTURAL ELEMENTS AFFECTING THE EAGLE FORD

The Eagle Ford has been structurally influenced by a variety of features across the entirety of the state. Figure 15 is a map of the state of Texas with (1) the outcrop highlighted, (2) the subsurface representation of the Cretaceous Comanche shelf, and (3) a number of structural elements that significantly affect on the deposition and reservoir development of the Eagle Ford.

Mesozoic tectonism led to the development of the predominant structural and geologic features in the study area and surrounding regions. These features greatly influenced the deposition and spatial distribution of the carbonate facies in the Eagle Ford. A good example of that influence is the regional variations in thickness of the Eagle Ford, with thins toward and over the arches and thickening into the bordering embayments.

The San Marcos arch is a southern subsurface expression of the Llano uplift and is characterized as a low-amplitude, south to southeast plunging anticline, as shown in Figure 15. During the upper Cretaceous, the arch formed a topographic high in central Texas that experienced less subsidence than the flanking east Texas and Gulf Coast/Maverick Basin areas did (Laubach and Jackson, 1990, sourced from Workman, 2010). This decrease in subsidence established shallow-marine platform environments over the arch with numerous internal unconformities.

S. Central Texas Maverick Basin *Subsurface*	N. Central Texas - Waco *Outcrop*	N. Central Texas - Dallas *Outcrop*	East Texas Basin *Subsurface*		
Cusack *et al.*, (2010)	Brown & Pierce (1962)	Brown & Pierce (1962)	Hentz & Ruppel (2010)	Coniacian	UPPER CRETACEOUS
Austin Chalk	Austin Chalk	Austin Chalk	Austin Chalk		
Upper Eagle Ford	South Bosque Formation	Arcadia Park Formation	Eagle Ford Group	Turonian	
		Britton Formation	Pepper Shale / Woodbine Group		
Lower Eagle Ford	Lake Waco Formation	Tarrant Fm.			
	Pepper Shale	Woodbine Group / Lewisville Member	Maness Shale	Cenomanian	
Buda Limestone					
Del Rio Shale					
Georgetown Limestone					

Platform Carbonates   Shale/mudstone

Siliciclastics   — Unconformity

Figure 12. Summary and comparison of nomenclature for the Eagle Ford and equivalent units in South Texas and east Texas (reprinted with permission from Workman, 2013, whose permission is required for further use).

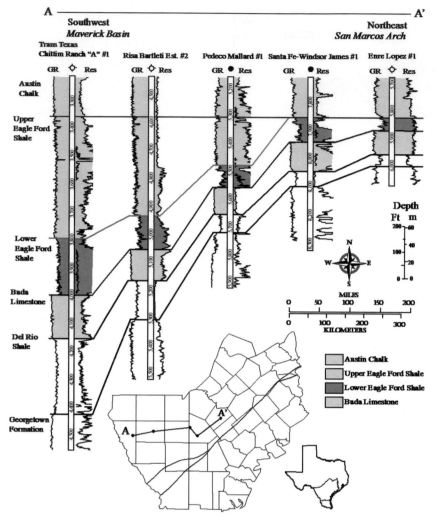

Figure 13. Strike oriented cross section (A—A') illustrating thickness and stratigraphic trends of the Eagle Ford and related sections from the Maverick Basin to the San Marcos Arch area (reprinted with permission from Workman, 2013, whose permission is required for further use).

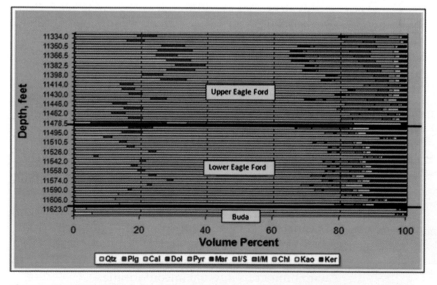

Figure 14. Mineralogical diagram from Eagle Ford core (Stoneburner, 2014).

The Maverick Basin is an intrashelf depocenter that developed on the southeast flank of the Edwards platform, which is also shown in Figure 15. The increased sedimentation within the Basin resulted from prolonged subsidence and the development of accommodation for the sediments. Sediment loading and thermal subsidence was the result and is associated with underlying basement structures that formed during the failed Rio Grande rifting event (Hull, 2011, sourced from Workman, 2013). Movement of the underlying Louann salt began soon after it was deposited and is believed to have continued through the Paleogene, which compounded the effects of thermal subsidence in the Maverick Basin.

Between the Maverick Basin and the San Marcos arch is what is commonly referred to as the Gulf Coast Basin area of the Eagle Ford. Numerous structural features are present in this area, most notably the Atascosa and Karnes troughs, which are regionally significant graben features. They were initiated during the late Albain and continued into the Eocene and likely resulted from salt withdrawal and sediment loading. These graben systems experienced contemporaneous growth with Cretaceous sedimentation and accumulated thickened Eagle ford sections (Corbett, 2010, sourced from Workman, 2013).

SUBSURFACE MAPPING

Figure 16 is a regional structure map of the top of the Eagle Ford. The region is dominated by monclinal dip to the southeast. There is not any large-scale faulting that manifests itself at this regional scale. However, as is shown in Figure 15, the Karnes and Atascosa troughs are two areas with faulting that is readily mappable from subsurface data. Additionally, there is a moderate amount of localized faulting, with both up to the coast faults and down to the coast faults present. The other notable feature in Figure 16 is the expression of the Chittum anticline in the western area of the map in the vicinity of the Red

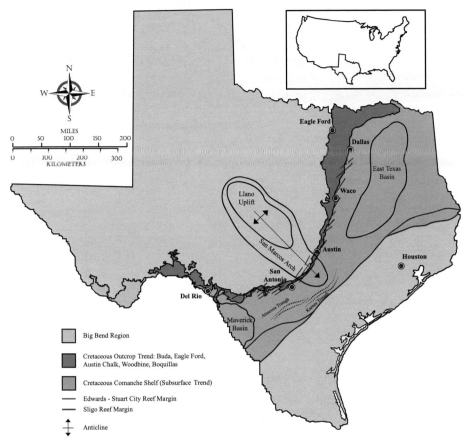

Figure 15. Map of Texas that shows prominent structural and geologic features (reprinted with permission from Workman, 2013, whose permission is required for further use).

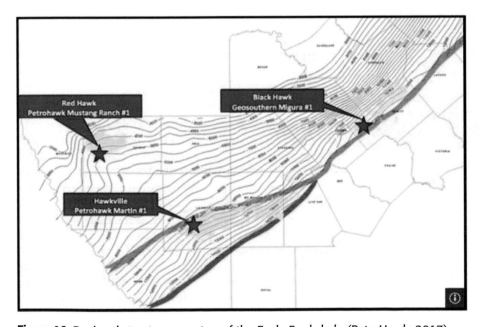

Figure 16. Regional structure map top of the Eagle Ford shale (PetroHawk, 2017).

Hawk prospect. The anticline represents the boundary between the Maverick Basin to the west and the Gulf Coast Basin to the east.

Figure 17 is a regional net isopach map of the lower Eagle Ford reservoir, commonly referred to as the Hawkville facies. The Hawkville area is the location of the discovery well, and it contains the thickest development of the Hawkville facies in the entire trend areas with in excess of 300 ft of net reservoir. The anomalously thick section is a result of it being located in a minibasin between the Edwards shelf margin, denoted by blue-stippled trend, and the Sligo shelf margin, denoted by purple-stippled trend. Updip of the Edwards shelf margin, the reservoir gradually thins and eventually has insufficient thickness for commercial reserves. The Red Hawk area, as discussed above, is on the flank of the Maverick Basin and represents another area of thickening of the Hawkville facies.

PALEOGEOGRAPHY AND DEPOSITIONAL ENVIRONMENT OF THE UPPER CRETACEOUS

Early Mesozoic tectonism initiated the fragmentation of Pangea and the opening of the proto-Gulf of Mexico. At this time, the northern Gulf Coast was situated within the Caribbean province of the Tehyan seaway and paralleled the pantropic equatorial belt, as shown in Figure 18 (Scott, 1993, in Workman, 2013). The North American plate drifted northward as seafloor spreading continued to open the Gulf of Mexico. During the Cretaceous period, the Gulf Coast region was located near the junction of the southern end of the western Interior seaway and the westernmost part of the Tethys Ocean, also shown in Figure 18.

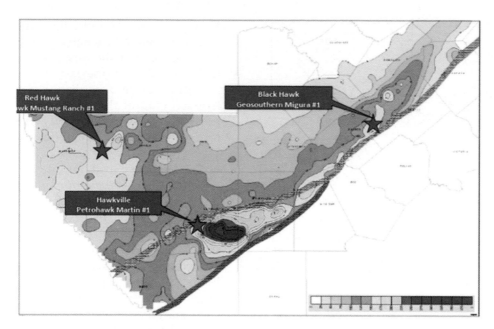

Figure 17. Regional net isopach map of lower Eagle Ford reservoir or Hawkville facies (PetroHawk, 2017).

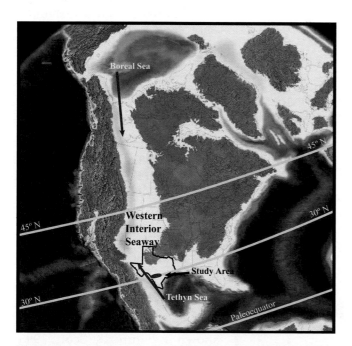

Figure 18. Late Cretaceous (85 Ma) paleogeographic map of North America (reprinted with permission from Workman, 2013, whose permission is required for further use).

The Cretaceous was also characterized by marine transgressive and regressive cycles (Figure 19) with the most significant transgressive events corresponding to worldwide phases of bottom-water anoxia, otherwise known as oceanic anoxic events, or OAE. OAE were first recognized in association with deposition of the Pearsall shale during the

Aptian–Albian and the deposition of the Eagle Ford shale during the Cenomanian–Turonian (Schlanger and Jenkyns, 1976, sourced from Workman, 2013). Global OAE correspond to worldwide deposits of thick organic-rich black shales. The OAE associated with the Eagle Ford is characterized by large-scale pulses of magmatic activity during the late Cretaceous (Turgeon and Creaser, 2008).

Figure 20 is a subsurface cross-section from the northern flank of the Maverick Basin, through the Stuart City/Edwards shelf margin and terminating near the Sligo shelf margin. During the period of maximum transgression, such as existed during lower Eagle Ford deposition, deep-water organic deposits filled the Basin, resulting in sediments exhibiting the primary reservoir facies of the Eagle Ford, which was a result of this facies containing the highest total organic content. The upper Eagle Ford is still dominated by marine shale deposits, but the TOC has moderated, and the resultant porosity and permeability as a result of the conversion of kerogen has moderated as well. The return to carbonate-dominated platform deposits occurred with the deposition of the Austin chalk.

PETROPHYSICS OF THE EAGLE FORD RESERVOIR FACIES

Understanding the nano-level composition of a shale reservoir, and what that implies in terms of reservoir characteristics, is one of the most important aspects in the exploration and appraisal of shale reservoirs. Virtually every discovery of a commercial shale reservoir began with the evaluation of a whole core taken from the initial exploratory well drilled. The analysis of a shale reservoir goes way beyond the approach to evaluating conventional reservoirs, whose primary focus was porosity, permeability, and water saturations with lesser need to understand the mineralogical, geochemical, and geomechanical attributes of the rock. While the details of the core analysis are beyond the scope of this chapter, it is clear that tests, measurements, readings, and images extracted from the whole core were critical to ascertaining whether the rock was capable

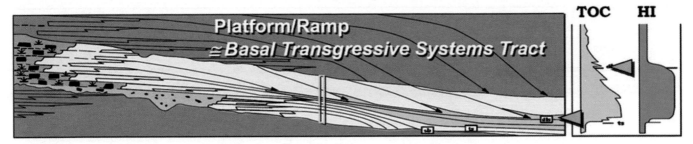

Figure 19. Diagrammatic cross section of Comanche style platform and transgressive depositional model (Passey et al., 2012, reprinted with permission from Q. Passey, whose permission is required for further use).

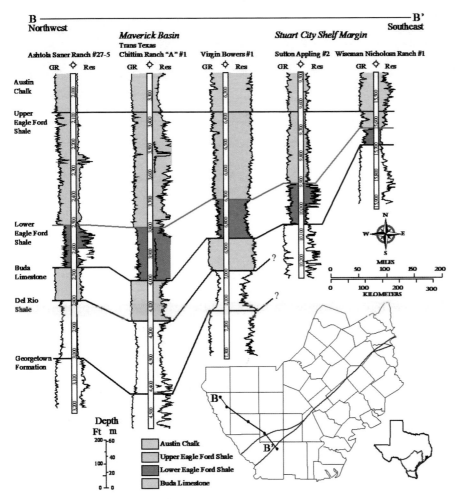

Figure 20. Dip oriented cross section (B–B') showing thickness and stratigraphic trends of the Eagle Ford and related sections from the Maverick Basin to the Sligo shelf margin (reprinted with permission from Workman, 2013, whose permission is required for further use).

becomes prohibitive when compared with the added benefit. However, this phase of geologic reconnaissance is driven by the calibration of the existing core database to the existing subsurface database. The utilization of cross-plot analyses of certain metrics such as porosity, hydrocarbon-filled porosity, TOC, Young's modulus, and Poisson's ratio as well as many other attributes allows the use of more widespread subsurface data to become calibrated to the core specific data, thereby providing a much more robust data set to be utilized in the geologic modeling process. Figure 21 is a representative set of log curves that can be utilized to calibrate the data from both core and open-hole logs. The solid curves represent the open-hole log data, and the multicolored dots represent core-derived data for the particular readings such as TOC, permeability, porosity, water saturation, and mineralogy. The combined uses of these data have been instrumental in gaining a more complete understanding of the nature of the rock.

DRILLING, COMPLETION, AND PRODUCTION PRACTICES FOR HORIZONTAL EAGLE FORD WELLS

of producing commercial volumes of hydrocarbons and, equally important, what type of hydrocarbons it would likely produce.

Once the exploration and early appraisal of a play is complete, the acquisition of whole core data diminishes, if not ceases entirely, as the cost of acquisition

As is the case with most every large-scale resource play that has been under development during the past decade, remarkable strides have been made in all phases of the engineering processes.

The Eagle Ford covers a wide range of depths at which the reservoir is encountered, from as shallow

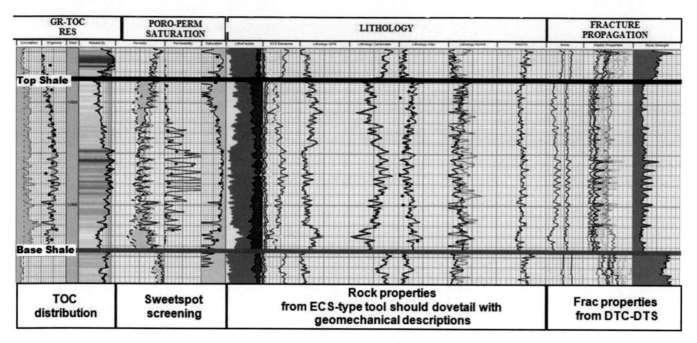

Figure 21. Petrophysical data derived from open-hole logs in conjunction with data derived from whole core analysis (Stoneburner, 2014).

as ~5000 ft (~1520 m) to as deep as ~13,000 ft (~3960 m). Additionally, both normal and abnormal reservoir pressure exist within the trend. However, even in light of such a wide range of depths and pressures, the Eagle Ford drilling operations have proven to be as accommodating a drilling environment as exists in the realm of shale plays. The following is a summary of most drilling operations as they have evolved over the past 7 years:

- Drill 12 3/4-in. (32.4 cm) surface hole to the base of the fresh water bearing Carrizo sand (ranging from ,3000 to ,5500 ft [,910 to ,1670 m]) and set 9 5/8-in. (24.5 cm) surface casing. This is often done with a spudder rig prior to mobilizing the actual rig that will drill the well to total depth.
- Mobilize drilling rig with top drive unit to drill 8 3/4-in. (22.2 cm) hole out from under the surface casing to total depth with oil-based mud and set 7-in. (17.8 cm) production casing.

There are a few areas where contingent strings need to be set should abnormal pressure, lost circulation, unstable hole conditions, or other drilling-related issues cause the need for intermediate casing to be run. The most notable of these areas is in the far eastern area of the play where the upper Eagle Ford has a tendency to create unstable hole conditions. However, in the vast majority of the play, a two-string program is all that is necessary.

Completion operations have also proven to be relatively risk free. The reservoir is extremely brittle and generally very receptive to the isolated multistage hydraulic fracturing process. Early in the development of the play, most operators would validate their fracture stimulation coverage by acquiring microseismic data such as those shown in Figures 22 and 23. In these images, it is apparent that the areal coverage of each stage was consistent in creating a significant amount of SRV, or stimulated reservoir volume. While early in the play companies tried a variety of fluid systems ranging from slickwater, hybrid systems utilizing slickwater and gel to all cross-linked gel, the vast majority of operators are currently pumping slickwater and Ottawa sand, even though in some of the deeper, higher-pressure wells, resin-coated sand or ceramic proppant is recommended.

Another variable in the completion recipe is the amount of sand that is pumped. The trend over the past few years has been to dramatically increase the proppant load from less than 1000 lb/lateral ft (305 lb/lateral m) to as much as 3000 lb/lateral ft (914 lb/lateral m). Figure 24 is a plot of pound per lateral foot on the x-axis and a lateral-normalized test rate of BOE per day per 1000 ft (305 m) on the y-axis. As can be seen on the plot, there is a definitive trend of increasing productivity with increasing proppant load. The variable that is not apparent is whether the increased cost of the proppant diminishes the rate of return or

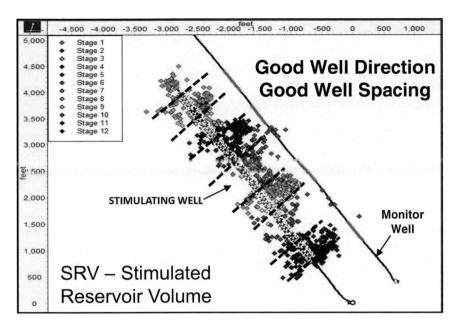

Figures 22. Microseismic data in aerial view and plan view (Stegent, 2011, reprinted with permission from N. Stegent, whose permission is required for further use).

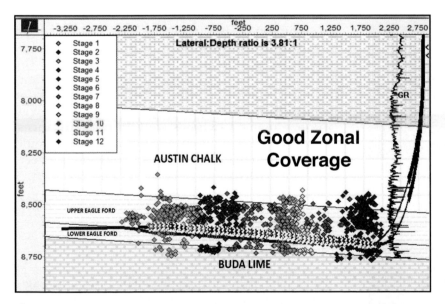

Figures 23. Microseismic data in aerial view and plan view (Stegent, 2011, reprinted with permission from N. Stegent, whose permission is required for further use).

if the increased productivity increases the rate of return. Considering that proppant, particularly regular-strength proppant such as Ottawa sand, is a relatively small component of the cost of a completion, it is most likely that the increased proppant load results in improved economics.

Another trend that is taking place in the industry, and particularly in the Eagle Ford, is the concept

of geometric completions as opposed to engineered completions. Figures 25 and 26 are generalized representations of both approaches. In a geometric completion, the lateral is indiscriminately divided into equal stages, generally in the 200 to 250 ft (61 to 76 m) range, with a set number of perforation clusters equally spaced apart, generally in the 50 to 75 ft (15 to 23 m) range. The rational for the geometric concept is that it is imperative to stimulate as much of the wellbore as possible and that this would be the most efficient method of doing that. In an engineered, or sometimes referred to as a geologic, completion, open-hole logs are run in the lateral to gain more knowledge as to the petrophysical and geomechanical properties of the reservoir. The log suite will typically be comprised of a quad combo, including a gamma ray, resistivity, density-neutron, and dipole sonic. These logs would then quantitatively define which areas of the lateral were the most prospective and contrarily would identify which areas were least prospective. The most influential data from the log suite is the dipole sonic, which is capable of identifying geomechanical heterogeneity in the lateral by focusing on sections of the wellbore that should be most receptive to hydraulic fracturing and eliminating those sections of the wellbore that appear to be much less receptive to hydraulic fracturing. By utilizing reservoir analysis in the lateral and designing the fracture stimulation accordingly, it is believed that the wellbore will become more economic as a result.

Production engineering also plays a key role in an economically successful shale play. Several of those practices are briefly discussed below:

- Choke management, sometimes referred to as restricted rate production: Many shale reservoirs, particularly those that are abnormally pressured, benefit from limiting the drawdown on the reservoir, which in turn minimizes the degradation of the permeability that was created by the hydraulic

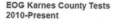

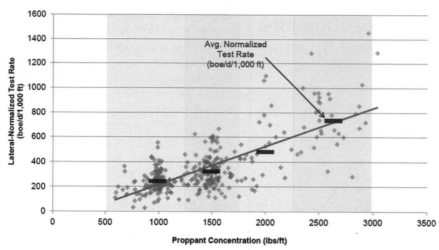

Figure 24. Test rate of EOG wells in Karnes County normalized to 1000 BOPD/d/1000 lateral ft vs. proppant concentration in #/lateral ft.

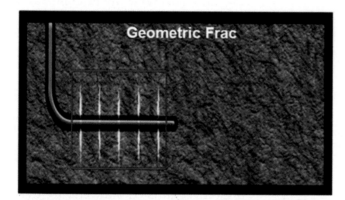

Figure 25. Diagrammatic representation of geometrically designed isolated multi-stage hydraulic fracturing and engineered designed isolated multi-stage hydraulic fracturing (Banks, 2014).

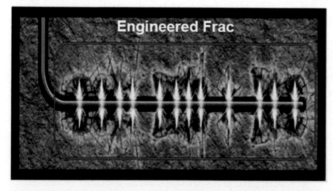

Figure 26. Diagrammatic representation of geometrically designed isolated multi-stage hydraulic fracturing and engineered designed isolated multi-stage hydraulic fracturing (Banks, 2014).

fracturing process. While it has not been universally accepted as a beneficial production practice in the Eagle Ford, it is one that is emplyed by a number of operators.

• Artificial lift: The unique aspect of artificial lift in the Eagle Ford is a function of the wide range of depths, pressures, and gas-to-oil ratios that exist across the play. As a result of the variability of reservoir conditions, a wide range of lift mechanisms are employed, with rod pump and gas lift being the most common.

Another aspect of the Eagle Ford that has caused uncertainty as what are best production practices is the question of how reaching the bubble point or dew point of the reservoir will affect ultimate recovery. While this subject is well beyond the scope of this chapter, a few examples of these effects display the variability that exists in the reservoir. Figure 27 is a plot of eight downspaced wells in Dimmit County with gas–oil ratio (GOR) on the y-axis and time on the x-axis. The plot shows a definitive increase in GOR with time. Figure 28 show two plots of GOR versus time for two wells in Karnes County, one being an oil well and one being a rich gas well. In both instances, there is no discernible change in GOR, which would suggest that the bubble point and dew point effects have not occurred.

RESERVE AND RESOURCE POTENTIAL OF THE EAGLE FORD

With over 10,000 wells on production from the Eagle Ford, the evaluation of reserves and resource for the play can be based on a reasonable amount of technical data and therefore should be considered to be reasonably certain assumptions.

One source of credible analysis for the resource associated with the Eagle Ford is ITG and Associates, a research firm located in Calgary, Canada. ITG is widely considered to be one of the foremost engineering firms specializing in unconventional reservoir analysis. The following are several conclusions the company published in its analysis of the data through 2014:

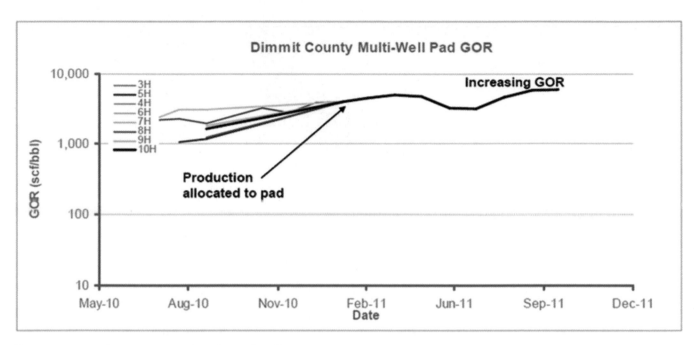

Figure 27. Gas–oil ratio vs. time of Eagle Ford wells in Dimmitt County, Texas.

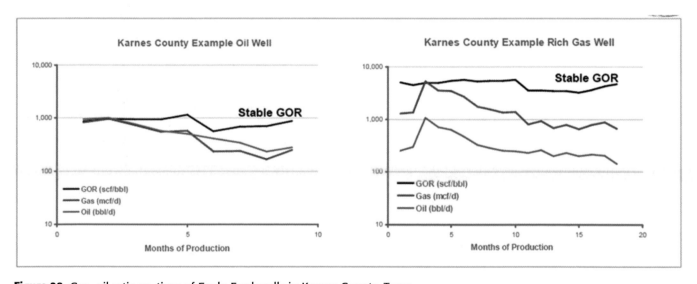

Figure 28. Gas–oil ratio vs. time of Eagle Ford wells in Karnes County, Texas.

- The Eagle Ford has been adding approximately 170,000 BOPD per month
- ITG analyzed decline curves from 10,119 Eagle Ford wells in order to calculate the economics of those wells
- Calculated break-even price across the entire play to average $65/barrel West Texas Intermediate (WTI)
- If the NYMEX gas price were to remain flat at $4.00, the break-even price would be reduced to $53/barrel WTI

- The remaining resource in the Eagle Ford is approximately 26 billion BOE

Gong (2013) divided the Eagle Ford into eight distinct regions, as shown in Figure 29. Within each region, the highest established well density (HEWD) within each region was determined, with those densities ranging from 2.0 wells/section (320 ac [129 ha] spacing) to 11.2 wells/section (57 acre [23 ha] spacing).

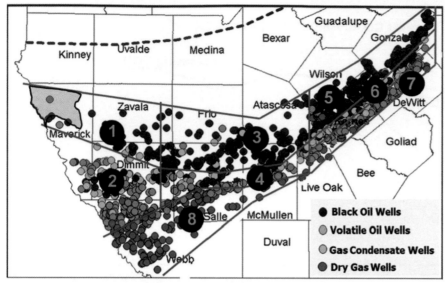

Figure 29. Fluid type changes from black oil to dry gas from north to south (Gong, 2013, reprinted with permission from X. Gong, whose permission is required for further use).

- Percentiles of thickness of upper and lower Eagle Ford
- Percentiles of initial reservoir pressure
- Percentiles of matrix permeability
- Percentiles of fracture permeability by region
- Percentiles of bubble point pressure for black oil
- Percentiles of dew point pressure for volatile oil and condensate
- Percentiles of recovery factor for oil, condensate, and gas

These parameters then led to the generation of type probabilistic decline curves by region that resulted in the TRR20 volumes summarized in Figure 31.

Figure 32 calculates the reserves and resources for the Eagle Ford based on the per-well resource in Figure 28 multiplied by the total number of wells to be drilled in each region represented in Figure 27. That calculation, assuming a P90 result, implies a total resource of 2.95 billion barrels of oil and 34.3 tcf. Assuming a P50 result the resource is 8.25 billion barrels of oil and 90.57 tcf, and assuming a P10 result the resource is 23.53 billion barrels of oil and 266.17 tcf.

While it is difficult to compare ITG's resource of 26 billion BOE to the range Gong (2013) calculated primarily because ITG takes the wells to commercial limits while Gong cuts it off at 20 years, it is

Figure 30 is a table assigning the total acres for each region, specifying which acres are allocated to proven/contingent resource and which are allocated to prospective resource, and a calculation of the well count for each area and resource type based on the HEWD.

An assignment of technically recoverable resource over 20 years (TRR20) for each region was made based on a Monte Carlo based analysis. The methodology in concluding the distribution of TRR20 by region included, but was not limited to, analysis of the following parameters of the reservoir by region:

Table 3.31— Summary of P_{50} Well Count for Reserves and Resources									
Production Region	PR1	PR2	PR3	PR4	PR5	PR6	PR7	PR8	Total
Area (Acres)	799,836	942,734	1,617,410	584,070	977,484	338,000	478,888	1,201,185	6,939,607
Reserves/Contingent Area (Acres)	173,590	550,944	1,017,488	414,105	675,539	318,336	370,863	565,281	4,086,146
Prospective Area (Acres)	626,246	391,790	599,922	169,965	301,945	19,664	108,025	635,904	2,853,461
Current Well spacing (Acres/Well)	206	57	160	96	57	61	106	320	
Drilling Efficiency Factor	0.7875	0.7875	0.7875	0.7875	0.7875	0.7875	0.7875	0.7875	
Existing Well Count	102	839	913	428	1020	561	310	229	4,402
Reserves Well Count	235	2,035	2,710	965	2,710	1,545	730	365	11,295
Contingent Well Count	327	4,738	1,385	2,004	5,603	2,004	1,715	797	18,572
Prospective Well Count	2,394	5,413	2,953	1,394	4,172	254	803	1,565	18,947
Total Well Count	3,058	13,025	7,961	4,813	13,505	4,364	3,558	2,956	53,216

Figure 30. Summary of P50 well count by region (Gong, 2013, reprinted with permission from X. Gong, whose permission is required for further use).

Table 3.29— Summary of TRR20 Oil and Gas for All Production Regions										
	Oil TRR20, STB					Gas TRR20, BCF				
Production Regions	P_{90}	P_{50}	P_{10}	Mean	SD	P_{90}	P_{50}	P_{10}	Mean	SD
PR1	23,059	72,345	199,612	100,688	96,760	0.04	0.19	0.71	0.32	0.38
PR2	26,699	124,438	382,868	173,595	169,270	0.48	2.43	8.16	3.62	3.89
PR3	71,994	199,662	488,506	254,858	226,309	0.14	0.55	1.73	0.81	0.94
PR4	27,941	93,645	282,178	133,376	129,414	0.48	1.97	6.54	2.97	3.27
PR5	84,686	204,650	457,435	247,402	172,769	0.16	0.54	1.57	0.75	0.70
PR6	136,613	318,489	925,599	453,708	412,886	0.51	1.66	6.35	2.79	3.35
PR7	28,227	151,288	653,800	269,239	318,648	0.54	2.70	11.35	4.75	5.89
PR8						0.04	2.42	6.30	3.25	3.11

Figure 31. Summary of Monte Carlo distribution of TRR20 by region (Gong, 2013, reprinted with permission from X. Gong, whose permission is required for further use).

Table 3.36— Reserves and Resources of the Eagle Ford Play						
	Oil, BBO			Gas, TCF		
	P_{90}	P_{50}	P_{10}	P_{90}	P_{50}	P_{10}
Cumulative	0.264	0.264	0.264	1.37	1.37	1.37
Existing Reserves	0.59	0.74	0.89	5.50	7.89	10.28
Undeveloped Reserves	1.71	2.75	4.25	13.64	23.32	37.01
Total Reserves	2.30	3.49	5.14	19.13	31.21	47.28
Contingent Resources	0.92	4.52	14.59	11.25	47.93	155.19
Prospective Resources	2.03	3.72	8.93	23.05	42.63	110.98
Total Resources	2.95	8.25	23.53	34.30	90.57	266.17

Figure 32. Summary of Monte Carlo distribution of total resources by region (Gong, 2013, reprinted with permission from X. Gong, whose permissions is required for further use.).

interesting to compare the two. Gong's P50 BOE, assuming the same 22.5:1 revenue-based gas conversion that ITG assumes, is 12.27 billion BOE, and the P90 is 35.3 billion BOE, putting the ITG resource of 26 roughly between those two and probably much closer to the P50 if the Gong resource were not assuming a 20-year life.

REGULATORY AND COMMUNITY ISSUES ASSOCIATED WITH EAGLE FORD DEVELOPMENT

The oil and gas regulatory environment in Texas has long been recognized as being rational and well intentioned to both the industry and to other stakeholders, specifically the mineral owners and the communities in which the operations are taking place. It is this long history of oil and gas exploration and production that has helped establish the Eagle Ford play as one that provides an operating environment that is conducive to all parties involved.

One development that helped establish trust and collaborative relationship between the operators, the regulators, and the community was the establishment of the Eagle Ford Task Force by Texas railroad commissioner David Porter in 2010. This group, the members of which Porter picked himself, is comprised of 24 individuals from all facets of the play with five from the upstream sector, two from the midstream sector, four from the service sector, seven from state and local government, two from environmental NGOs, and four from institutions. By having such a diverse collection of stakeholders, the task force felt empowered to study the effects of the play from virtually all facets and encourage a range of findings that were not biased toward any one sector. The task force met 10 times from July 2010 to November 2011 to study the following issues related to developing the Eagle Ford shale:

- Infrastructure: roads, pipelines, and housing
- Water quality and quantity
- Railroad Commission regulations
- Economic benefits
- Flaring and air emissions
- Health, education, and social services
- Landowner, mineral owner, and royalty owner issues

One of the most controversial elements of all unconventional resource development that depends

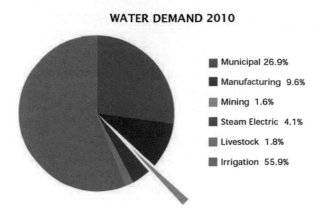

WATER DEMAND 2010

- Municipal 26.9%
- Manufacturing 9.6%
- Mining 1.6%
- Steam Electric 4.1%
- Livestock 1.8%
- Irrigation 55.9%

Figure 33. Pie chart depicting water demand in the State of Texas for 2010 as per the Texas Water Development Board, as presented in the 2012 State Water Plan (modified from Texas Railroad Commission, 2017).

on isolate multistage hydraulic fracturing is water usage. Because of the relatively arid nature of south Texas, the primary source of water for hydraulic fracturing needs to be from the subsurface. Fortunately, a world-class fresh-water aquifer called the Carrizo sandstone exists under a large portion of the play. Figure 33 is a pie chart showing the region's water usage from the Carrizo. As can be seen, mining (which includes not only oil and gas operations but coal mining operations as well) comprised only 1.6% of the total usage in 2010. While that volume has increased as the level of activity has increased, it is still a very small percentage of the water drawn from this critically important water resource.

One of the foremost experts of water usage in south Texas is Dr. Darrell Brownlow, who testified before the task force and offered the following findings regarding the use of subsurface water, particularly the Carrizo Formation which is a Wilcox aged sandstone.

Projected south-central Texas water usage for the year 2060 would be 1.27 million acre-ft (.953 million hectare-meter) of water:

- Municipality use at 637,236 acre-ft (477,927 hectare-meter), or 50.1%
- Agricultural irrigation use at 301,679 acre-ft (226,259 hectare-meter), or 23.7%
- Steam-electric power generation use at 109,776 acre-ft (82,332 hectare-meter), or 8.6%
- Industrial needs use at 67,016 acre-ft (50,262 hectare-meter), or 5.9%

- Livestock use at 25,954 acre-ft (19,466 hectare-meter), or 2.0%
- Oil and gas and other mining use at 18,644 acre-ft (13,983 hectare-meter), or 1.5%

Brownlow quantified his estimates of industry's annual water usage related to Eagle Ford operations:

- Average water usage for drilling and hydraulically fracturing a well in the Eagle Ford shale is 15 acre-ft (11.25 hectare-meter), or 116,000 bbl of water with approximately 0.5 acre-ft (.38 hectare-meter) required for drilling (162,500 gal [615,129 L] of water) and 14.5 acre-ft (10.9 hectare-meter) are required for hydraulic fracturing (over 4.7 million gal [17,791,435 L] of water).
- He estimated that between 20,000 and 25,000 new wells would be drilled over the next 10 to 20 years, resulting in 300,000 to 375,000 acre-ft (225,000 to 281,250 hectare-meter) of cumulative future water use.
- His estimate does not take into account or address the use of recycled water. He added that via the industry's recycling efforts, many operators could decrease that by one-third to an average of 10 acre-ft (7.5 hectare-meter), or 77,000 bbl, of water per well.

Brownlow spoke to specific usage from the subsurface aquifer, most specifically the Carrizo:

- Annual groundwater pumpage from the portion of the Carrizo aquifer located in the area of Eagle Ford development is 285,000 acre-ft (213,750 hectare-meter)
- Total groundwater pumpage from all aquifers located in the area of Eagle Ford development is 426,000 acre-ft (319,500 hectare-meter) per year
- He emphasized that if hydraulic fracturing-related water use in the Eagle Ford shale equals 15,000 acre-ft (11,250 hectare-meter), then the industry's current annual Carrizo usage is approximately 5%

Another aspect related to water usage is the maintenance of water quality. The Texas Railroad Commission is in the process of amending its rules for injection and disposal wells, well integrity, wellhead control, waste management, and water recycling. All of these issues are of paramount importance to the state, local communities, and industry.

Economic benefits are another significant result of the development of the Eagle Ford shale. During a task force meeting on April 18, 2012, the director of local government assistance and economic development for the Texas comptroller of public accounts, Robert Wood, reported that employment in the oil and gas industry, including the refining of oil, manufacturing of chemicals, and related manufacturing sectors, increased by 11% from 2010 to 2011, compared to a growth rate of 2% for all industries. He added that wage and salary income in the oil and gas industry increased by 18% from 2010 to 2011, versus just 2% for all industries. He further reported that the average 2011 income for workers in the oil and gas industry was $117,000, compared to the all-industry average of $49,000.

CONCLUSIONS

It is clear that the discovery of the Eagle Ford shale oil and gas resource has been an incredibly important event in the state of Texas and the United States. In addition, it has had repercussions throughout the world. The growth of production to over 2.1 million BOED in just in the course of just over 6 years is an unprecedented level of growth. What made that growth possible is a combination of factors that collectively resulted in the success of the play:

- Superior petrophysical and geomechanical properties of the reservoir rock
- Abnormal pressure reservoir conditions
- A range of hydrocarbon product that covered every generating window from dry gas to low-GOR black oil
- Very large area of commercial production
- A high percentage of unleased acreage in an area of sophisticated, oil- and gas-literate mineral owners, providing ready access for operators to acquire meaningful acreage positions
- A large source of accessible fresh water without causing stress to the community or environment
- A regulatory environment that encouraged and allowed for development that was properly engineered, environmentally prudent, and aligned with local and state authorities as well as stakeholders

All of these factors support the contention that the Eagle Ford play could be considered the "perfect" unconventional giant oil field.

REFERENCES CITED

Banks, B., 2014, Gaining efficiencies in monetizing Eagle Ford pay: 2014 DUG Eagle Ford Conference, Proceedings, accessed February 15, 2017, http://www.adstrategiesconference.com/dugef-conf14.

Corbett, K., 2010, Eagleford Shale exploration models: Depositional controls on reservoir properties: AAPG Search and Discovery Article #10242, accessed October 3, 2016, http://www.searchanddiscovery.com/pdfz/documents/2010/10242corbett/ndx_corbett.pdf.html.

Cusack, C., J. Beeson, D. Stoneburner, and G. Robertson, 2010, The discovery, reservoir attributes, and significance of the Hawkville Field and Eagle Ford Shale trend, Texas: Gulf Coast Association of Geological Societies Transactions, v. 60, p. 165–179.

EIA, 2015, Top 100 U.S. Oil and Gas Fields: U.S. Department of Energy. U.S. Energy Information Administration, accessed February 15, 2017, http://www.eia.gov/naturalgas/crudeoilreserves/top100/pdf/top100.pdf.

Gold, R., 2014, The boom, how fracking ignited the American energy revolution and changed the world: New York, Simon & Schuster Paperbacks, 84 p.

Gong, X., 2013, Assessment of Eagle Ford Shale Oil and Gas Resources: Ph.D. Dissertation, Texas A&M University, 159 p.

Hentz, T. F., and S. C. Ruppel, 2010, Regional lithostratigraphy of the Eagle Ford Shale: Maverick Basin to East Texas Basin: Gulf Coast Association of Geological Societies Transactions, v. 60, p. 325–337.

Hull, D. C., 2011, Stratigraphic architecture, depositional systems, and reservoir characteristics of the Pearsall shale-gas system, Lower Cretaceous, South Texas: M.S. Thesis, University of Texas at Austin, 192 p.

Laubach, S. E., and M. L. W. Jackson, 1990, Origin of arches in the northwestern Gulf of Mexico basin: Geology, v. 18, p. 595–598.

Passey, Q. R., K. M. Bohacs, W. L. Esch, R. Klimentidis, and S. Sinha, 2012, My source rock is now my reservoir: Geologic and petrophysical characterization of shale-gas reservoirs: AAPG Distinguished Lecture, 2012, accessed February 15, 2017, http://www4.unileoben.ac.at/fileadmin/shares/unileoben/erdoelgeologie/docs/AAPG_2012_European_Distinguished_Lecture_Quinn_Passey.pdf.

PetroHawk, 2017, Eagle Ford Shale: PetroHawk Energy Corporation, accessed February 15, 2017, http://eaglefordshale.com/companies/petrohawk-energy/.

Schlanger, S. O., and H. C. Jenkyns, 1976, Cretaceous oceanic anoxic events: Causes and consequences: Geologie en Mijnbouw, v. 55, p. 179–184.

Scott, R. W., 1993, Cretaceous carbonate platform, U.S. Gulf coast, in J. A. Simo, R. W. Scott, and J. P. Masse, eds., Cretaceous carbonate platforms: AAPG Memoir 56, p. 97–109.

Stegent, Neil, P. E., 2011, Let's Put Engineering Back into Fracture Stimulation!: Norman, Oklahoma: Oklahoma Geological Society Presentation, accessed February 15, 2017, http://ogs.ou.edu/docs/meetings/OGS-workshop-shales_moving_forward_2011-stegent.pdf.

Stoneburner, R.K., 2014, The Discovery, Reservoir Attributes, and Significance of the Hawkville Field and Eagle Ford Shale Trend: Implications for Future Development, accessed February 15, 2017, http://www.searchanddiscovery.com/documents/2014/20251stoneburner/ndx_stoneburner.pdf.

Texas Railroad Commission, 2017, Eagle Ford Shale Information: Railroad Commission of Texas, accessed February 15, 2017, http://www.rrc.state.tx.us/oil-gas/major-oil-gas-formations/eagle-ford-shale/

Turgeon, S. C., and R. A. Creaser, 2008, Cretaceous oceanic anoxic event 2 triggered by a massive magmatic episode: Nature, v. 454, p. 323–327.

Workman, S. J., 2013, Integrating depositional facies and sequence stratigraphy in characterizing unconventional reservoirs: Eagle Ford Shale, south Texas: M.S. thesis, accessed February 15, 2017, http://scholarworks.wmich.edu/cgi/viewcontent.cgi?article=1154&context=masters_theses.

8

Castillo, Veronica, Laszlo Benkovics, Carlos Cobos, Daniel Demuro, and Alejandro Franco, 2017, Perla field: The largest discovery ever in Latin America, *in* R. K. Merrill and C. A. Sternbach, eds., Giant fields of the decade 2000–2010: AAPG Memoir 113, p. 141–152.

Perla Field: The Largest Discovery Ever in Latin America

Veronica Castillo, Laszlo Benkovics, and Carlos Cobos

Repsol USA, 2455 Technology Forest Blvd., The Woodlands, Texas 77381, U.S.A.
(e-mails: mvcastillodeo@repsol.com, lbenkovicsb@repsol.com, carlos.cobos@repsol.com)

Daniel Demuro

Repsol Colombia, Calle 77 # 7 – 44 piso 13, Apto. Aéreo 110221, Bogotá D.C., Colombia
(e-mail: ddemur@repsol.com)

Alejandro Franco

Repsol, c/ Mendez Alvaro 44, 2, Madrid 28045, Spain
(e-mail: afrancog@repsol.com)

ABSTRACT

Perla gas field is a world-class giant and one of the most significant in Latin America in the last decade. The field was discovered in August 2009. It is the largest gas field in Latin America with approximately 17 trillion cubic feet (tcf) of gas in place, or 3.1 BBOE. The field, located in the shallow waters of the Gulf of Venezuela, was discovered, and is operated by Cardon IV S.A., a 50/50 joint operating company formed by Repsol and Eni.

The Perla discovery is important because it is a Play opener for the southern Caribbean domain, triggering a new exploration cycle in the region and proving a previously unknown Tertiary thermogenic petroleum system. The discovery well encountered a thick carbonate section (240 m [787 ft] thick) with excellent primary reservoir properties. The trap is a combination structural and stratigraphic, defined by a northwest–southeast trending asymmetric faulted structure and pinch-out of the carbonate reservoir rock to the north. The proven hydrocarbon column exceeds 350 m (1148 ft) and is in complete hydraulic continuity, and the structural-stratigraphic closure exceeds 100 km² (39 mi²).

INTRODUCTION

The Gulf of Venezuela is located in the northwest part of Venezuela and has an area of 20,000 km² (7722 mi²), where water depths range from 15 to 60 m (49 to 197 ft). To the north of the basin is the Caribbean Sea; to the south, the Maracaibo Basin (the most important hydrocarbon province of Venezuela); to the southeast, the Falcon Basin; to the east, the Paraguana Peninsula; and to the west, the Guajira Peninsula (Figure 1).

DOI:10.1306/13572004M1133683

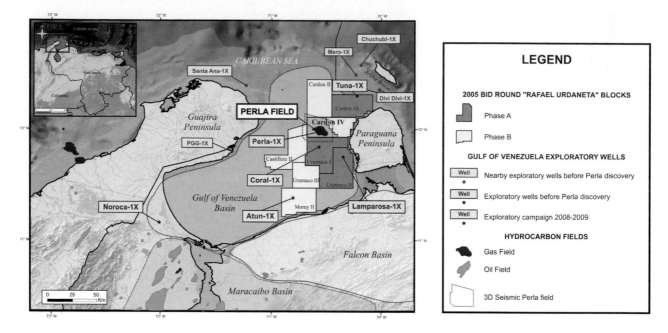

Figure 1. Location of the Gulf of Venezuela Basin. The map shows: 1) the Maracaibo and Falcon basins, 2) the two exploratory wells (Noroca-1X and Lamparosa-1X) drilled in the Gulf of Venezuela before the Perla discovery, 3) the wells drilled during the 2008–2009 exploratory campaign, and 4) other wells in the Guajira Peninsula and Aruba Basin. The blocks offered in the Phase A of the "Rafael Urdaneta" bid round are highlighted in red, whereas the blocks offered in Phase B are highlighted in yellow. Cardon IV block is outlined in red, and its darker western portion is the current shape, after relinquishing the eastern part of the block at the end of the exploratory phase.

The Gulf of Venezuela Basin is one of the few unexplored basins in Venezuela, yet it is surrounded by areas that have been well studied during the past 80 years, including the well-known Maracaibo and Falcon hydrocarbon basins. This frontier basin had only two wells drilled before the 2005 Rafael Urdaneta bid round, Noroca-1X well and Lamparosa-1X well (Figure 1).

The region records geological evidence of the tectonic interaction between the Caribbean and South American plates since the Cretaceous. This geodynamic history played an important role in the development of petroleum systems through time. To define this evolution, five major tectonic phases have been described by several authors (Pindell and Barret, 1990; Lugo and Mann, 1995; Audemard, 1993; Castillo, 2001; Lugo, 2001). These tectonic phases are (1) Cretaceous passive margin development, (2) late Paleocene–early Eocene depocenter formation and erosion in the area where tectonic compensation occurs, (3) late Eocene tectonic flexure and block faulting, (4) Oligocene–late Miocene transtensional block faulting, and (5) Pliocene to present Andean uplift.

The interaction of these tectonic events defined the current configuration of the basement, with the existence of a relatively stable area to the west, defined as the Dabajuro platform, and a major subsidence area to the east known as the Urumaco trough (Figure 2). These two major tectonic elements define two distinctive geologic provinces in the Gulf of Venezuela. The western province has an autochthonous basement of continental affinity, covered by passive margin successions ranging in age from Cretaceous to early Eocene and showing similar stratigraphy and petroleum system to those of the Maracaibo Basin. The eastern province has an allochthonous basement of island arc affinity, covered by Paleogene and Neogene rocks deposited under extensional and transtensional stresses and showing similar stratigraphy and petroleum system to those of the Falcon Basin (Figure 2).

The proximity to the petroleum-prolific Maracaibo and Falcon basins, together with the launching in 2005 of the Rafael Urdaneta bid round, started a new exploration phase in this unique tectonic setting of the Gulf of Venezuela. Exploration companies focused on better understanding the region, specifically on the coalescence of three very different petroleum systems: the prolific and well-known Cretaceous–Cretaceous and Cretaceous–Tertiary Maracaibo-type

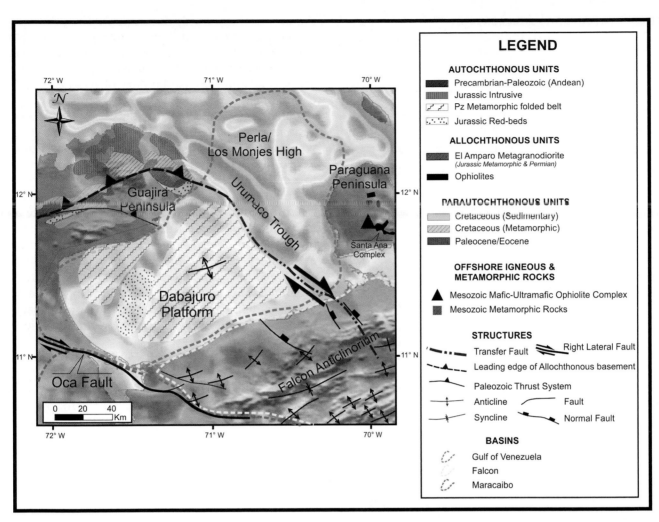

Figure 2. Map showing the main tectonic elements in the Gulf of Venezuela area. The background is the first vertical derivative of the Bouguer anomaly map depicting very clearly the basement trend in this region. The main transfer fault zone in the central area is oriented northwest–southeast and defines the tectonic boundary between the autochthonous geologic province in the west, and the allochthonous geologic province to the east. This transfer fault system connects to the northwest with the Cuiza fault zone, which represents the leading edge of the allochthonous basement on the Guajira Peninsula. The eastern limit of the Dabajuro platform with the major transfer fault zone continues to the west toward the Guajira Peninsula and finally plunges to the southeast. The northwest–southeast-trending Urumaco trough (gravity low) and the Paraguana Peninsula (gravity high) show very prominent gravimetric anomalies. The Falcon anticlinorium, which is defined by west–east parallel-subparallel anticlinal structures extends toward the east from the Dabajuro platform, developing a curved morphology near the coastline. The map also depicts a basement low north of the Oca fault, perhaps related to a pull-apart basin developed during the lateral offset of the fault.

petroleum systems, and the less prolific Tertiary-Tertiary Falcon-type petroleum system.

The Perla discovery well encountered a thick carbonate section (240 m [787 ft] thick) with excellent primary reservoir properties (Table 1) and proved a previously underestimated Tertiary thermogenic petroleum system. Four additional exploration/appraisal wells were drilled after the discovery well in 2010 and 2011, confirming the areal extent and properties of the carbonate reservoir. This discovery defined

a new play concept in the southern Caribbean domain, triggering a new exploration stage in the region. Previous exploration efforts were focused on the well-known Cretaceous petroleum system.

EXPLORATION HISTORY

Although the hydrocarbon exploration activities in the Gulf of Venezuela began in the 1950s with the

Table 1. Perla field reservoir average properties.

Initial pressure (psi)	4608
Dew point (psi)	4135
P_e (psi)	4608
Depth (ft)	8899–10000
Reservoir temperature (°F)	208
Porosity (%)	16–31
Permeability (md)	0.06–517 (average 14)
Water saturation (%)	17–37
Type of fluid	Gas and Condensate
API	46–48°
Initial GOR (scf/stb)	44930 Perla-1X
CO_2 (%)	1–3.5
H_2S (ppm)	0

acquisition of gravimetric, magnetic, and seismic data, it was not until 40 years later that drilling activities began (Figure 1). The first well was Noroca-1X, which was drilled onshore in 1994 in the southwestern part of the basin and which tested 1000 BOPD of 33° API from the early Cretaceous succession. The second well was the Lamparosa-1X well, drilled offshore in 1995 12 km (7 mi) west of Paraguana Peninsula, which had only minor gas shows in the early Miocene–Oligocene successions. The results from these two wells confirmed the existence of an active petroleum system in two very distinctive geological provinces of the Gulf of Venezuela. These results were key for the recent exploration success in recent years.

In 2004, the Venezuelan government through the Ministerio para el Poder Popular de la Energia y el Petroleo (MPPEP) launched the Rafael Urdaneta gas bid round in two phases (Figure 1). In 2005, during phase B, the Eni-Repsol joint venture was awarded the Cardon IV block license for a period of 30 years effective February 2, 2006. The operator of this license is Cardon IV SA (equally comprised by Eni and Repsol), a Venezuelan company formed as required by the government under the terms defined in the license agreement.

The exploration period was of 4 years, with a possible extension of 1 year, divided into three phases. During the first exploratory phase, Cardon acquired and processed 693 km² (268 mi²) (700 km² full fold) of 3-D seismic data (Figure 1). Interpretation of the new data confirmed the presence of two overlapping exploratory opportunities, previously identified with two-dimensional seismic data (the two-dimensional seismic data were delivered by the Venezuelan government in the data package for the bid round). The primary objective was an early Miocene–Oligocene target (main exploratory objective and reservoir in Perla field) and a secondary objective of possible middle Miocene age. The second and third exploratory phases had one well commitment each.

During the interpretation, an unconstrained elastic inversion of the three-dimensional seismic volume was done using a velocity model that incorporated Repsol's rock physics database. This work contributed to a better understanding of the relationship between reservoir properties and seismic signatures. Using the seismic inversion, Cardon IV interpreters were able to relate seismic signatures to different geologic scenarios and rock physical conditions to help reduce exploratory risk. The study and analysis of these data confirmed previous interpretations based on old 2-D seismic data. The identified exploration opportunities were defined as structural-stratigraphic prospects in the Oligocene–early Miocene and middle Miocene successions.

The first exploratory well, Perla-1X, was spudded in June 2009 and reached total depth (TD) in September 2009. This well, drilled in 60 m (197 ft) of water depth, encountered a 233-m (763-ft) hydrocarbon column. The second exploratory well, Perla 2 (January 2010) found 299 m (982 ft) of net pay in a carbonate sequence with excellent reservoir characteristics. During 2010 and 2011, three appraisal wells were drilled. During this drilling campaign, 573 m (1880 ft) of core was obtained and studied; the conclusion was that the field's hydrocarbon section is over 350 m (1150 ft) thick, with both horizontal and vertical hydraulic reservoir continuity. Production from the Perla gas field began in July 2015. The development concept includes four platforms that connect to 26 wells, and the gas is transported to coast facilities through a 30-in. (76-cm)-diameter pipeline of approximately 72 km (116 mi) long.

TECTONOSTRATIGRAPHY

The Gulf of Venezuela Basin is characterized by a northwest–southeast trending steeply dipping transform fault system, which defines the Urumaco Trough (Figures 2 and 3). This fault system separates two very distinctive geological provinces characterized by different basement rocks and geologic history. The western province has an autochthonous basement consisting of Meso-Neoproterozoic to Paleozoic continental rocks, most probably made up of a diverse mosaic of blocks, including fragments of the Putumayo orogen (Baquero et al., 2015), Late Paleozoic

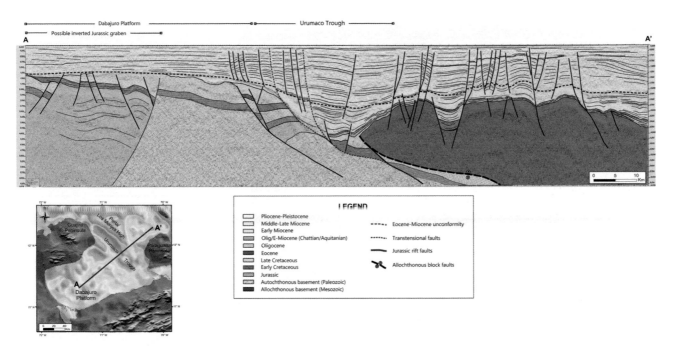

Figure 3. Southwest–northeast oriented regional seismic profile along the Gulf of Venezuela. In the western area, the Dabajuro platform shows the interpreted Cretaceous passive margin overlying autochthonous basement. The basement is interpreted as consisting of a metamorphic Paleozoic folded belt and continental Jurassic redbeds. The platform is bounded to the east by the transfer fault system that accommodates sedimentation along the northwest–southeast trending Urumaco trough. In the eastern area, allochthonous Mesozoic basement is overlain by Paleogene rocks. Geologic interpretations suggest that the older rocks are Eocene in age, and possibly Paleocene. On basement highs, older successions are interpreted as upper Oligocene (Chattian). In this seismic profile, the blue succession correlates with both zones of the Perla reservoir rocks dated as upper Oligocene–lower Miocene (Chattian–Aquitanian).

granite and gneiss, similar to the rocks outcropping on Toas island, in the northernmost part of the Maracaibo Lake (Blaser and Dusembury, 1960; Pimentel, 1973), and the Guajira Peninsula (Renz, 1960; Rollins, 1965). The eastern province has a late Mesozoic island-arc allochthonous basement.

In this basin, four major megasequences have been defined based on the sequence stratigraphic analysis, well and outcrop data correlation with age-controlled formal successions, and seismic interpretation. Many authors have integrated these data to define the megasequences and to correlate them with the major tectonic phases that shaped the Gulf of Venezuela Basin from Cretaceous to Present (Van Andel, 1958; Wheeler, 1963a, b; Coronel, 1967, 1970; Feo Codecido, 1968; Mac Donald, 1968; Zambrano et al., 1970; Hunter and Bartok, 1974; Cabrera, 1975; Diaz de Gamero, 1977; Gonzalez de Juana et al., 1980; Pitelli and Molina, 1989; Boesi and Goddard, 1991; Curet, 1992; Diaz de Gamero et al., 1993; Macellari, 1995; Parnaud et al., 1995; Di Croce et al., 2000) (Figure 4). These tectonic settings are (1) Cretaceous passive margin, (2) Paleogene collisional margin, (3) Oligocene–Early Miocene

transtension, and (4) Middle Miocene–Present transtension and Andean uplift.

The chronostratigraphic chart in Figure 4 shows the four major megasequences within the two distinctive geologic provinces that controlled the evolution of the Gulf of Venezuela Basin. After the tectonic coupling in the early Paleogene during the eastward escape of the Caribbean plate, these two provinces shared a common sedimentary history until Present (Flinch and Castillo, 2015).

In the western geologic province of the basin, the sedimentary cycle started with the deposition of a passive margin succession that is very well preserved in most of western Venezuela (similar sequences are in the Maracaibo Basin and Guajira Peninsula; Figure 4). It is assumed that the entire gulf area and the Maracaibo Basin were below sea level with continuous marine sedimentation. This cycle began with a transgressive phase during the early Cretaceous, becoming more influenced by marine processes with the deposition of Cogollo Group carbonates and sandstones, followed by the deposition of euxinic facies of the La Luna Formation and ending with the open marine Colon Formation shales. Based on seismic

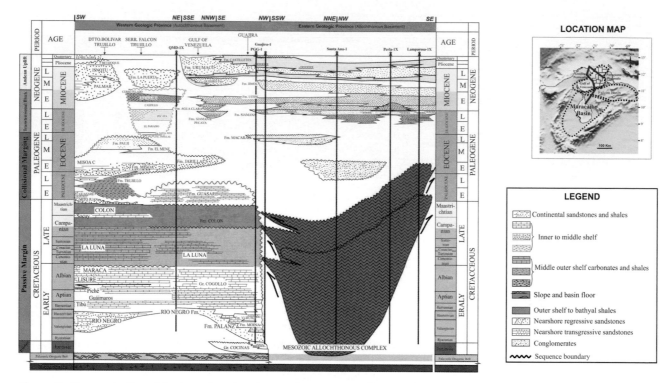

Figure 4. Chronostratigraphic chart showing the northeast Maracaibo, northwest Falcon, and Gulf of Venezuela basins. The chart integrates seismic data, recent exploratory well results in the Perla field, and information from nearby areas. It also includes the work of several authors cited in the manuscript. All integrated data record the lateral and vertical stratigraphic evolution of the sedimentary basins, as described in detail in the western and eastern areas of the Gulf of Venezuela.

data, well correlation, and outcrops, we also interpret the presence of Jurassic strata filling grabens in some areas of the western province. These grabens were probably formed during the rift stage that separated the North and South American plates forming the Proto-Caribbean (Mann, 1999) (Figures 2 and 3). During late Cretaceous–early Paleogene time, the Caribbean allochthonous terrane reached the Guajira area, while the Dabajuro platform was exposed in response to tectonic loading. These events caused erosion of the complete Cretaceous megasequence in the southwestern Gulf of Venezuela, leaving an erosional remnant in the central part.

In the eastern geologic province of the basin, the sedimentary history started with the deposition of Eocene sediments preserved along the Urumaco Trough, capping the allochthonous basement. By this time, the allochthonous Caribbean terrain reached the eastern Maracaibo Basin and had already overridden the eastern Gulf of Venezuela (Figures 2 and 3). There is no sedimentary record of Eocene rocks being deposited on the Guajira Peninsula nor the Paraguaná Peninsula. Eocene igneous bodies are believed to have been emplaced at this time. In the Maracaibo Basin, a thick sedimentary succession was deposited

in the foreland basin in response to oblique collision between the Caribbean and South American plates (Lugo, 1991).

During the Oligocene–early Miocene, the eastern Gulf of Venezuela was part of a wide shallow-water platform deepening toward the west. This moment in time is especially relevant for the new Tertiary play because the easternmost area of the basin was under shallow water, resulting in the deposition of carbonate reservoir rocks, while deposition and preservation of source rocks occurred in the deeperwater environments of the western part (Urumaco trough).

The Perla field is located in the eastern province of the basin, where shallow waters covered the area and extended toward the southeast. This setting favored the development of the carbonate reservoir succession deposited on top of a basement high defined by a northwest–southeast faulted anticline structure (Figures 2 and 5). This basement structure controlled the depositional geometry and facies distribution of the carbonate reservoir. A stratigraphic pinchout of the carbonate succession developed toward the northern part of the basement high during late Oligocene–early Miocene time (Figures 5 and 6).

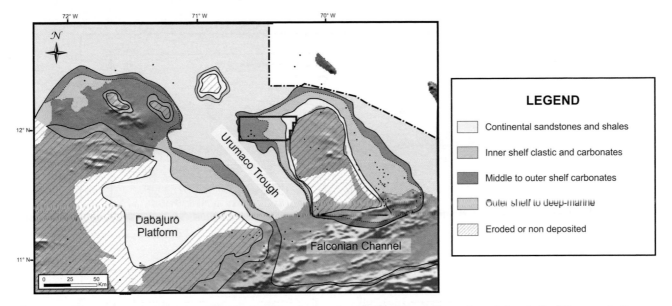

Figure 5. Oligocene-early Miocene (Chattian–Aquitanian) paleogeographic configuration of the Gulf of Venezuela Basin and surrounding areas. The paleogeographic setting is dominated by the Dabajuro platform in the western area, and the Urumaco trough in the eastern part of the basin. Perla field is located on the eastern part of the Urumaco trough. The reservoir succession developed in a middle-external carbonate ramp, on a narrow platform surrounding the Paraguana basement high. The paleogeographic transition from Paleogene to Neogene shows a strong control of the main tectonic elements shown in Figures 2 and 3, as well as on the depositional systems developed at that time.

The northwest–southeast trending faults were active during the carbonate deposition, and they were also reactivated later from Neogene through Present.

RESERVOIR AND SOURCE ROCKS

The Perla reservoir consists of a Chattian to Aquitanian carbonate succession, deposited on a distally steepened ramp, bulging in the middle-outer ramp, with a transgressive, deepening-upward stacking pattern, which is overlain by deposition of glauconite and pyrite related to the drowning of the platform. Red algae and large benthic foraminifera are dominant in the carbonate factory and are mainly represented by floatstones and rudstones of rhodoliths, fragments of branching red algae, larger benthic foraminifers, echinoderms, bivalves, barnacles, bryozoans and, locally, finger corals (Borromeo et al., 2011; Pinto et al., 2011; Benkovics et al., 2012; Pomar et al., 2015) (Figures 6 and 7). This carbonate succession lies unconformably on the allochthonous basement, and in some places, is underlain by basal siliciclastic rocks. The latter consists of small synsedimentary wedges of siliciclastic sandstone, siltstone, and mudstone deposited in grabens developed in the basement. The clastic succession lacks diagnostic fossils; however, based on their stratigraphic position and the

basin history, they might be Oligocene in age (Pinto et al., 2011) (Figures 6 and 7).

The geometry and stacking pattern of the reservoir succession in Perla field show a strong structural control during its depositional history. Evidence of this structural control includes a sharp erosional surface with siliciclastic sands present in the lower part of the carbonate section (Pinto et al., 2011) and retrograding and prograding depositional cycles of different orders of magnitude, apparently controlled by synsedimentary faults (Benkovics et al., 2012) (Figure 6). Pomar et al. (2015) made a detailed depositional lithofacies interpretation based on core analysis of textures, skeletal components, and vertical transitions into other lithofacies. In general, the basal terrigenous dominated facies is separated by a sharp boundary from the carbonate facies that are transitional through the column (Figure 7).

This reservoir is a continuous carbonate succession without interlayered mud. The main pore types are primary, inter- and intraparticle porosity with secondary biomoldic and microporosity. Pores have a complex distribution caused by depositional and diagenetic controls (Borromeo et al., 2011; Pinto et al., 2011; Benkovics et al., 2012; Pomar et al., 2015). The most important diagenetic event in terms of reservoir property enhancement (best reservoir areas) is late leaching. This leaching is most likely controlled

A

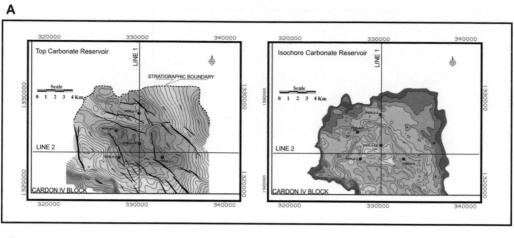

B

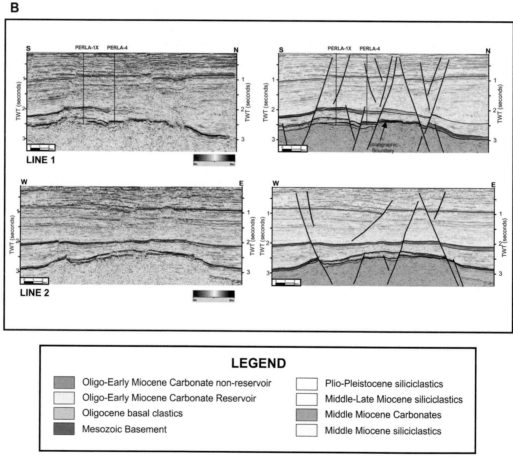

LEGEND

Oligo-Early Miocene Carbonate non-reservoir	Plio-Pleistocene siliciclastics
Oligo-Early Miocene Carbonate Reservoir	Middle-Late Miocene siliciclastics
Oligocene basal clastics	Middle Miocene Carbonates
Mesozoic Basement	Middle Miocene siliciclastics

Figure 6. Maps and seismic sections illustrating the components of the Perla field. A) (Left) Structural map at the top of the carbonate reservoir. The top of the reservoir shows a northwest–southeast-oriented, three-way closure faulted anticline, with a stratigraphic pinch-out toward the north. This map was constructed after Perla-1X was drilled, and before the continuation of the exploration/appraisal campaign. (Right) Isochore map interpreted after Perla-1X was drilled. The reservoir thickness decreases toward the north, west, and eastern flanks of the structure. The thicker succession is located in the central part of the anticline and extends toward the south. B) Seismic profiles indicated on the maps. Line 1 is a north–south seismic profile across the Perla field and through wells Perla-1X and Perla-4. This profile shows the stratigraphic pinchout towards the north, as well as the structural control during the deposition of the different sedimentary successions in this part of the basin. Some parts of the reservoir are deposited directly above the basement, but others, on top of a basal clastic wedge, deposited in few areas directly on top of the basement. Line 2 shows the east–west stratigraphic component of the trap for Perla field. A northwest–southeast-striking Paleogene graben is interpreted on the eastern part of the seismic profile. This graben probably developed during the transtensional event that generated the Urumaco trough. This same graben is also interpreted on the seismic transect in Figure 3.

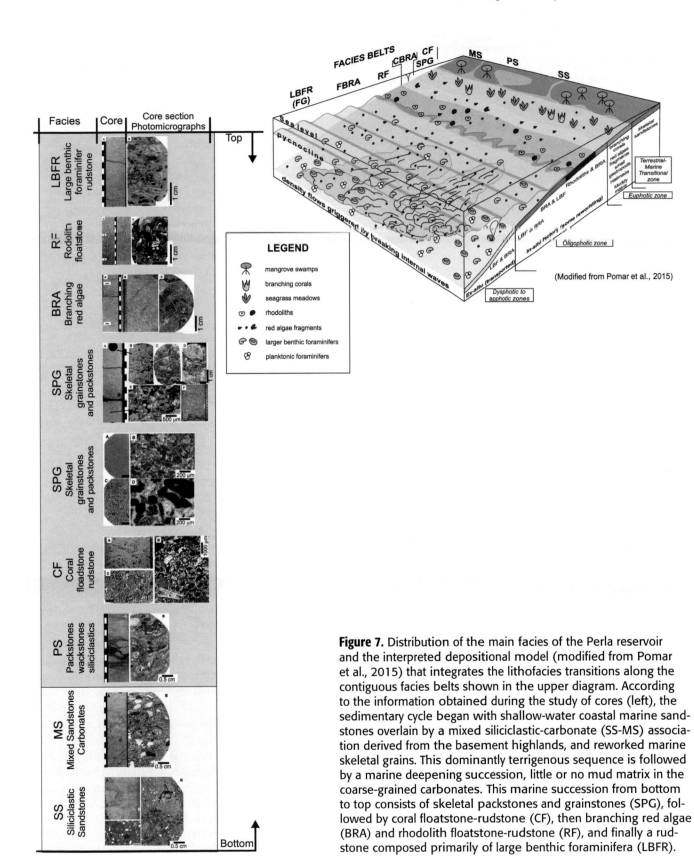

(Modified from Pomar et al., 2015)

Figure 7. Distribution of the main facies of the Perla reservoir and the interpreted depositional model (modified from Pomar et al., 2015) that integrates the lithofacies transitions along the contiguous facies belts shown in the upper diagram. According to the information obtained during the study of cores (left), the sedimentary cycle began with shallow-water coastal marine sandstones overlain by a mixed siliciclastic-carbonate (SS-MS) association derived from the basement highlands, and reworked marine skeletal grains. This dominantly terrigenous sequence is followed by a marine deepening succession, little or no mud matrix in the coarse-grained carbonates. This marine succession from bottom to top consists of skeletal packstones and grainstones (SPG), followed by coral floatstone-rudstone (CF), then branching red algae (BRA) and rhodolith floatstone-rudstone (RF), and finally a rudstone composed primarily of large benthic foraminifera (LBFR).

by deep-seated faults that funneled ascending fluids into the carbonate, from the basement through the reservoir beginning in the middle Miocene. Table 1 summarizes the Perla field reservoir properties.

Results of geochemical analysis show that the Perla gas is mainly thermogenic; however, some minor input of biogenic gas has likely contributed to the accumulated hydrocarbons. Estimated TOC (%) values in the Perla field average 1 to 2%. Results suggest a source rock maturity range between $R_o \sim 0.8$ % and $R_o \sim 1.9$ %. This diverse maturity information coming from biomarkers suggest that different source rocks or maybe one but very thick source rock sequence generated the Perla fluids. The source rock organofacies show a mixed marine-type kerogen (type II/III) and a terrestrial kerogen (type III/II) of early Tertiary age. Additional geochemical data indicate that the gas was generated in the Urumaco trough from latest late Miocene to Present.

PRODUCTION DATA

Perla field was discovered in August 2009. The first well, Perla 1X well, drilled in 60 m (197 ft) water depth, encountered a 233-m (763-ft) hydrocarbon column. During production testing, it produced 20.7 MMCFD of high-quality gas with a capacity of 600,000 cubic meters per day (cu m/d) (~3700 BOED) and 500 bbl/day of condensate. The second exploratory well, Perla 2, drilled almost 60 m (197 ft) downdip of Perla-1X, found 299 m (982 ft) of net pay in the same carbonate sequence with excellent reservoir characteristics. During production testing, the Perla 2 well flowed 50 MMCFD plus 1500 bbl/day of condensate. After these two exploratory wells, three appraisal wells were drilled to define the extension and characteristics of the carbonate reservoir. The Perla 3 well was drilled in 70 m (230 ft) of water and encountered 205 m (674 ft) of net pay carbonate sequence, with excellent reservoir characteristics. This well is located in a faulted block east of Perla-1X. During production testing, it was determined that the two wells were in the same hydraulic regime. The Perla-3 well flowed 68 MMCFD of gas and 1350 bbl/day of condensate during the production test. The Perla 4 appraisal well was drilled in the most distal carbonate facies of the reservoir and found a column of 95 m (313 ft). This well flowed 17 MMCFD of gas and 560 bbl/day of condensate during a production test. Perla-5X, the first horizontal well (lateral length less than 305 m [1000 ft]), has the highest production rate. Today, this well produces 118 MMCFD.

Presently, the field is producing from five wells, one vertical and four horizontal. Of these five wells, Perla-1X and Perla 5 are from the exploration and appraisal campaigns, respectively. Perla-1X, the only vertical well in the field, produces 59.6 mmcsf/d. The three horizontal wells produce a minimum of 118.36 and a maximum of 182.12 MMSCF gas/day. In February 2016, the field production average was 510 MMSCF gas/day and 13,857.4 b/d of condensate.

The three-phase development includes four offshore platforms connected to 26 wells, with gas exported to the coast through a 30-in. (76-cm)-diameter pipeline of approximately 72 km (116 mi) long. Presently, the production of one platform is centralized and transported to the coast trough this pipeline.

CONCLUSIONS

Perla field is the largest gas field ever discovered in Venezuela and is considered to be a world-class giant gas field (~17 tcf). The proven hydrocarbon column exceeds 350 m (1148 ft), in complete hydraulic continuity, and the trap accumulates original hydrocarbons in place in excess of 3.1 billion BOE.

This discovery opened a new exploration play and proved the existence of a Tertiary thermogenic petroleum system offshore in the south Caribbean area. In addition, this play incorporates a carbonate reservoir succession that has not been described before in the Gulf of Venezuela Basin.

The discovered reservoir unit consists of upper Oligocene–lower Miocene (Chattian to Aquitanian) limestone deposited in a distally steepened ramp. It shows a continuous carbonate succession without interlayered mud. The depositional facies of this carbonate unit can be described, from base to top, as a carbonate succession deposited in a relatively shallower middle ramp, with grainstone facies with larger foraminifera and branching red algae debris, overlain by outer ramp facies dominated by rhodolith floatstones/rudstones and planktonic foram-bearing grainstones, ending in a drowning unconformity.

The excellent reservoir properties were enhanced by diagenetic events controlled mainly by facies distribution and structural configuration of the basement. Much of the porosity is facies-related, which has a strong correlation with diagenesis. Leaching is considered the most important diagenetic effect in Perla field, and leached areas correlate with the best reservoir areas.

The trap shows a strong structural overprint, but a clear stratigraphic component is locally recognizable, and its proven closure is larger than 100 km².

ACKNOWLEDGMENTS

The authors gratefully acknowledge the contributions of the Exploration Departments of Repsol and Eni during the exploration phase of the project. We have to express our appreciation to Claudio Bartolini and Mikel Erquiaga for their comments on earlier versions of the manuscript. We thank Robert Merrill for his help in editing the manuscript.

REFERENCES CITED

Audemard, F. A., 2001, Quaternary tectonics and present stress tensor of the inverted northern Falcon basin, northwestern Venezuela: Journal of Structural Geology, v. 23, p. 431–453.

Baquero, M., S. Grande, F. Urbani, U. Cordani, C. Hall, and R. Armstrong, 2015, New evidence for Putumayo crust in the basement of the Falcon basin and Guajira peninsula, northwestern Venezuela, in C. Bartolini and P. Mann, eds., Petroleum geology and potential of the Colombian Caribbean margin, Tulsa: AAPG Memoir 108, p. 31–40.

Benkovics, L., V. Castillo, A. Asensio, M. Esteban, C. Cobos, V. Barletta, et al., 2012, Descubrimiento del Campo Perla: Un nuevo campo gigante en el Mar Caribe: 11th Simposio Bolivariano, Exploracion Petrolera en las Cuencas Subandinas, p. Extended abstract.

Blaser, R., and A. N. Dusembury, 1960, The geology of Toas, San Carlos and Zapara islands, Maracaibo, Venezuela: Sociedad Venezolana de Geologos, p. 8.

Boesi, T., and G. Goddard, 1991, A new geologic model related to the distribution of hydrocarbon source rocks in Falcon basin, northwestern Venezuela, in K. T. Biddle, ed., Active margin basins: AAPG Memoir 52, p. 303–319.

Borromeo, O., S. Miraglia, D. Sartorio, E. M. Bolla, O. Andrea, S. Reali, et al., 2011, The Perla World-class Giant Gas Field, Gulf of Venezuela: Depositional and diagenetic controls on reservoir quality in early Miocene Carbonates: AAPG Search and Discovery Article 90135, accessed October 3, 2016, http://www.searchanddiscovery.com /abstracts/html/2011/ice/abstracts/abstracts066.html.

Cabrera, E., 1975, Evolucion estructural de Falcon Cantral: Geologic engineer thesis, Universidad Central de Venezuela, Caracas, 125 p.

Castillo, M. V., 2001, Structural analysis of Cenozoic fault systems using 3D seismic data in the southern Maracaibo basin, Venezuela: Ph.D. thesis, University of Texas at Austin, 188 p.

Coronel, G., 1967, A geological outline of the Gulf of Venezuela: VII World Petroleum Congress, p. 799–812.

Coronel, G., 1970, El Golfo de Venezuela y sus problemas geológicos: Boletin Sociedad Venezolana de Geologos (SVG), p. 1–13.

Curet, E. A., 1992, Stratigraphy and evolution of the tertiary Aruba basin: Journal of Petroleum Geology, v. 15, p. 283–304.

Di Croce, J., B. De Toni, A. Navarro, R. Ysaccis, E. Alvarez, S. Gosh, et al., 2000, Key petroleum system elements of the Venezuelan basins in an improved chronostratigraphic framework (abs.): AAPG Annual Meeting, accessed October 3, 2016, http://www .searchanddiscovery.com/abstracts/html/2000/annual /abstracts/0168.htm.

Diaz De Gamero, M. I., 1977, Estratigrafia y micropaleontologia del Oligoceno y Mioceno Inferior del centro de la cuenca de Falcon, Venezuela: GEOS, Universidad Central de Venezuela, v. 22, p. 3–60.

Diaz De Gamero, M. L., G. Giffuni, and M. Castro, 1993, Biostratigraphic sequence analysis of two lower Miocene to Pliocene sections, eastern Falcon, northwestern Venezuela: AAPG International Meeting and Exhibition, p. 313–314.

Feo Codecido, G., 1968, Geologia y recursos naturales de la Peninsula de Paraguana: Coloquio sobre investigraciones del Mar Caribe, p. 7.

Fioretta, A., A. Schiroli, and V. Barletta, 2011, The Perla worldclass giant gas field, Gulf of Venezuela: An overview on successful case history in a virtually unexplored basin: AAPG International Conference and Exhibition, accessed October 3, 2016, http://www.searchanddiscovery.com /abstracts/html/2011/ice/abstracts/abstracts160.html.

Flinch, J., and V. Castillo, 2015, Records and constrains of the eastward advance of the Caribbean plate in northern South America, in C. Bartolini and P. Mann, eds., Petroleum geology and potential of the Colombian Caribbean margin: AAPG Memoir 108, p. 1–20.

Gonzalez de Juana, C., J. M. Iturralde, and X. Picard, 1980, Geología de Venezuela y de sus Cuencas Petrolíferas: Caracas, Ediciones Foninves, v. 1, 407 p. and v. 2, 624 p.

Hunter, H., and P. Bartok, 1974, Age and correlation of the tertiary sediments of the Paraguana peninsula, Venezuela: VII Caribbean Geologic Conference, p. 497–503.

Lugo, J., 1991, Cretaceous to Neogene tectonic control on sedimentation: Maracaibo basin, Venezuela: Ph.D. thesis, University of Texas at Austin, 219 p.

Lugo, J., and P. Mann, 1995, Jurassic-Eocene tectonic evolution of Maracaibo basin, Venezuela, in J. Tankard, S. Suarez, and H. J. Welsink, eds., Petroleum basins of South America: AAPG Memoir 62, p. 699–725.

Lugo, J., 2001, Tectonic model for northern Venezuela: Simposio Norte de Monagas, p. 42.

Macellari, C., 1995, Cenozoic sedimentation and tectonics of the southwestern Caribbean pull-apart basin in Venezuela and Colombia, in A. J. Tankard, R. Suarez, and H. J. Welsink, eds., Petroleum basins of South America: AAPG Memoir 62, p. 757–780.

Mann, P., 1999, Caribbean sedimentary basins, in K. J. Hsu, ed., Sedimentary basins of the world: Amsterdam, Elsevier Science B.V., p. 3–31.

Parnaud, F., Y. Gou, J.-C. Pascual, M. Capello, O. Truskowski, and H. Passalacqua, 1995, Stratigraphic synthesis of western Venezuela, *in* A. J. Tankard, R. Suarez, and H. J. Welsink, eds., Petroleum basins of South America: AAPG Memoir 62, p. 681–698.

Pimentel, N., 1973, Falla de Oca, Isla de Toas y San Carlos. Guia de excursion No. 3: II Congreso Latinoamericano de Geologia, p. 19.

Pindell, J. L., and F. Barrett, 1990, Geological evolution of the Caribbean region: A plate-tectonic perspective, *in* G. Dengo and J. E. Case, eds., The Caribbean region: The geology of North America: Geological Society of America, p. 405–431.

Pinto, J., S. Ortega, Z. Martin, I. Berrios, A. Perez, and M. Pirela, 2011, Controls on the newly-discovered gas accumulations in the Miocene "Perla" carbonate bank, Gulf of Venezuela: A preliminary assessment: I South American Oil and Gas Congress, p. 1–4.

Pitelli, R., and A. Molina, 1989, El Grupo Agua Negra de la Cuenca de Falcon, Boletin Sociedad Venezolana de Geologos (SVG), p. 5–12.

Pomar, L., M. Esteban, W. Martinez, D. Espino, V. Castillo, L. Benkovics, et al., 2015, Oligocene–Miocene carbonates of the Perla field, offshore Venezuela: Depositional model and facies architecture, *in* C. Bartolini and P. Mann, eds., Petroleum geology and potential of the Colombian Caribbean margin: Tulsa, Memoir AAPG 108, p. 647–674.

Renz, O., 1960, Excursión de los Andes suroccidentales, sección Santo Domingo a San Antonio (Estado Táchira): III Congreso Venezolano de Geología, Publicación Especial, p. 87–91.

Rollins, J. F., 1965, Stratigraphy and structure of the Goajira peninsula: Northwestern Venezuela, and northeastern Colombia: University of Nebraska Studies, Lincoln, University of Nebraska, p. 102.

Van Andel, T., 1958, Origin and classification of Cretaceous, Paleocene and Eocene sandstones of western Venezuela: AAPG Bulletin, v. 42, p. 734–763.

Wheeler, C. B., 1963a, Estratigrafia del Oligoceno y Mioceno Inferior de Falcon occidental y nororiental: III Congreso Geologico Venezolano, p. 407–465.

Wheeler, C. B., 1963b, Oligocene and lower Miocene stratigraphy of western and northeastern Falcon basin, Venezuela: AAPG Bulletin, v. 47, p. 35–68.

Zambrano, E., E. Vasquez, B. Duval, M. Latreille, and B. Coffinières, 1970, Synthèse Paleogéographique et Petroliére du Venezuela Occidentale: Publication Technique, v. 25, p. 1449–1499.

Heidmann, Jean-Claude, Jacques Durand, Philippe Mallard, Jean-François Ballard, and Jean-Marc Moron, 2017, Discovery of a Bolivian Foothills Giant Gas Field: Incahuasi, in R. K. Merrill and C. A. Sternbach, eds., Giant Fields of the Decade 2000–2010: AAPG Memoir 113, p. 153–164

9

Discovery of a Bolivian Foothills Giant Gas Field: Incahuasi

Jean-Claude Heidmann, Jacques Durand, and Philippe Mallard

Total Exploration & Production, 75018 Paris La Défense, France (e-mails: jean-claude.heidmann@total.com; jacques-pierre.durand@total.com; philippe.mallard@total.com)

Jean-Francois Ballard and Jean-Marc Moron

Total Exploration & Production, 64018 Pau cedex, France (e-mails: jean-françois.ballard@total.com; jean-marc.moron@total.com)

ABSTRACT

This chapter will address the innovative and bold exploration approach that has led the French company Total and its Argentinean partner Tecpetrol to achieve what is one of the largest gas discoveries of the south Bolivian sub-Andean basin of the 2000–2010 decade.

This discovery, named Incahuasi, is the result of multidisciplinary teamwork covering a period of 4 years from the initial geological concept definition to the drilling and testing of the discovery well Incahuasi-X1.

The overall approach can be summarized as a combination of controlled risk decision making based on a regional geological knowledge and the development of new techniques such as the definition of dedicated biostratigraphy charts. This approach enabled the multidisciplinary team to manage most of the uncertainties attached to this specific foothills context and define a workflow that led to success.

The successful testing of the Incahuasi-X1 exploration well in 2004 led to a multi-tcf discovery currently under development. Located more than 120 km (75 mi) north of the existing Devonian gas fields, it opened a new exploration domain. It also highlights the benefit of a multidisciplinary and innovative approach in challenging areas such as the fold belts from prospect generation to discovery in a time constraint domain.

INTRODUCTION

Before the Incahuasi discovery in 2004 (Figure 1), at the end of the 1990s, several multi-tcf gas/condensate discoveries were made in the southern part of the sub-Andean basin near the Bolivia/Argentina border such as San Alberto, Itau, San Antonio, and Margarita (Figure 2). Except for Margarita, Total was involved in all of these discoveries. Therefore, Total had a very good knowledge of the geological configuration of this part of the basin, the definition of the petroleum parameters, and a comprehensive database following previous studies and fieldwork in the area.

DOI:10.1306/13572005M1133684

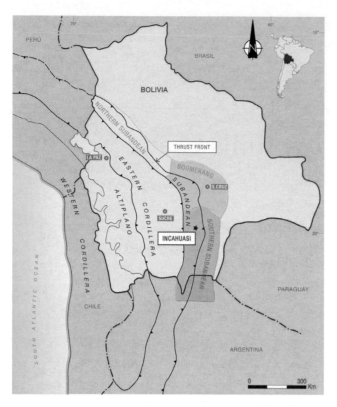

Figure 1. Incahuasi discovery location in the major geological provinces and basins of Bolivia.

Main characteristics of these discoveries can be described as follows:

- Regional north–south surface anticline trends indicating the existence of large subsurface structures. Significant conformity exists between surface and subsurface structures in this part of the basin.
- A Devonian-age and thick Huamampampa deltaic tight sands reservoir with poor matrix porosity (1 to 4%), but heavily fractured. This was a good indication of the existence of regional widespread Devonian deltaic systems. However, its paleogeography, away from the existing discoveries (Figure 2), was not clearly understood due to the difficulty to correlate the sandy reservoir extension between the different wells.
- A prolific petroleum system, with a thick and mature Devonian source rock known as the Los Monos Formation acting as source rock and a thick seal for the underlying reservoir that plays a major role in the structure generation, especially as a major decollement surface. Migration and sourcing from Los Monos source rock was not considered to be an issue given the existing discoveries.
- Based on the analysis of the petroleum system, the yet to find (YTF) in the Devonian series

was considered to be very important and as having a very large potential for additional discoveries.

In addition to these technical elements, potential access to new exploration acreage was considered to be favorable either through a bidding round to be announced shortly or business opportunities with companies divesting some of their interest.

Therefore, anticipating strong competition from the industry and because timing was seen as tight, a new venture evaluation team was set up in early 2001 to assess and define the most promising areas for exploration in this sub-Andean basin.

This new venture team was convinced after years of operations in Bolivia, and although several past exploration wells drilled in the northern part of the sub-Andean basin had been unsuccessful, the potential for large discoveries was still present in the sub-Andean fold belt, and not only in its southern part.

When launching the study, it became clear that a new conceptual approach was needed, especially for defining the Devonian depositional facies model, in order to better assess the distribution of the Huamampampa target reservoir. There was an obvious need for a new exploration tool that could be used over the entire basin.

FOUNDATION FOR A REASSESSMENT OF THE BASIN

Although regional routine work was still ongoing with the incorporation of new well data when available, it was decided upon the arrival of new members to the evaluation team (geologists and geophysicists) to revisit the existing in-house regional synthesis study. This decision was mostly based on the fact that we were dealing with a world-class prolific petroleum basin, exemplified by the discovery of multi-tcf gas fields such as Margarita, Itaú, San Alberto, San Antonio, and Madrerones. These discoveries provided geological information, but only in a limited part of the basin (Figure 2). The regional context was poorly known and very poorly understood.

Many unresolved technical aspects related to the Paleozoic petroleum components remained to be addressed at the basin scale:

- Poorly understood reservoir model:
  - Lack of understanding of the regional extension and distribution of reservoirs with unreliable well correlations
  - Poor understanding of matrix porosities and fracture distribution as well as generation models

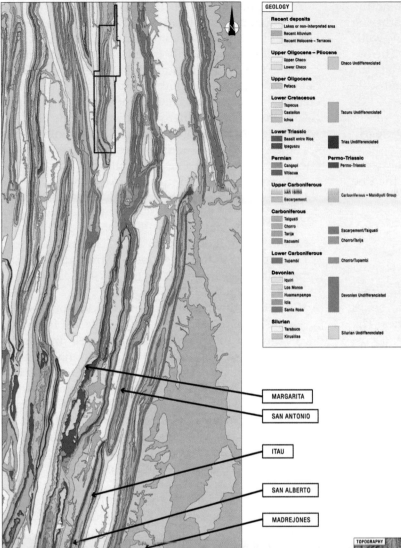

GEOLOGY

Recent deposits
Lakes or non-interpreted area
Recent Alluvium
Recent Holocene – Terraces

Upper Oligocene – Pliocene
Upper Chaco
Lower Chaco
Chaco Undifferenciated

Upper Oligocene
Petaca

Lower Cretaceous
Tapecua
Castellon
Ichoa
Tacuru Undifferenciated

Lower Triassic
Basalt entre Rios
Ipaguazu
Trias Undifferenciated

Permian
Cangapi
Vitiacua
Permo-Triassic
Permo-Triassic

Upper Carboniferous
San Telmo
Escarpement
Carboniferous – Mandiyuti Group

Carboniferous
Taiguati
Chorro
Tarija
Itacuami
Escarpement/Taiguati
Chorro/Tarija

Lower Carboniferous
Tupambi
Chorro/Tupambi

Devonian
Iquiri
Los Monos
Huamampampa
Icla
Santa Rosa
Devonian Undifferenciated

Silurian
Tarabuco
Kirusillas
Silurian Undifferenciated

MARGARITA

SAN ANTONIO

ITAU

SAN ALBERTO

MADREJONES

0   25 Km

Figure 2. Southern sub-Andean geological map. Relative locations of the major fields from 1998 to 2000 discoveries and of the Aquio-Ipati blocks (black rectangles).

- Prospect ranking: Because of all these uncertainties, as well as difficulty in ranking prospects, leads, and even structural trends, there was an inability to be efficiently proactive on acreage selection.

Due to uncertainties attached to these structurally very complex traps associated with very poor seismic images, the new team started to challenge the existing knowledge of this area with a new approach and new ideas.

This new approach was put in place based on two major principles:

- The need for a basin tool was addressed by gathering all existing techniques and expertise and then focusing on major correlation issues. It was felt that a local chronostratigraphic framework was clearly needed. This new chart would allow correlations within Devonian series using biostratigraphy and palynology. It could then be used during drilling operations to pilot the wells.

- Complex hydrocarbon maturation history in relation to the complex structural history
- Variable seal and fluid distribution: Highly variable fluid and hydrocarbon columns associated with the poorly predictive regional migration model
- Poorly defined structural models due to very poor imaging from existing seismic data led to difficulty in establishing a convincing structural model
- Wells postmortem analysis: The structural complexity of the basin associated with very bad imaging led to a poor understanding of the causes of failure for many dry wells; in the other hand, positive elements that led to discoveries could not be clearly established either

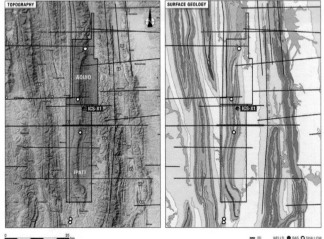

Figure 3. Discovery well location (ICS-X1) in the Aquio–Ipati exploration blocks. The white dots correspond to pre-existing shallow wells. The blue lines represent the 2-D seismic cover available at that time and the red line localizes the seismic line of Figure 7. Color chart as in Figure 2.

- An iterative approach was needed using trend-by-trend, and a morpho-structural analysis gathering data from remote sensing, surface geology, wells data and very poor seismic information. The objective was to be able to continuously update the structural model at both local and regional scale when new information was coming in.

The outcomes and deliverables of this study clearly provided a better view of the remaining exploration potential with identification and ranking of new associated prospects and exploration blocks to then be integrated into a global business approach.

DEFINITION OF THE STRATIGRAPHY AND BIOSTRATIGRAPHY TOOL

Among the major remaining uncertainties, the stratigraphic framework of the Devonian and Silurian series within this basin was one of our main priorities. The Devonian series, mainly constituted of silicoclastic deposits, has been encountered through wells and outcrops in different Bolivian basins such as Madre de Dios, Altiplano, Chaco-Beniana, sub-Andean, and Interandean.

The ongoing basin evaluation focused only on the southern sub-Andean area (Figure 1), and the main target was the Huamampampa Formation originally defined by Ulrich (1892) in La Candelaria-type locality. The Devonian stratigraphical units used are those defined in the Bolivian Stratigraphical Glossary (Suarez-Sorucco and Diaz Martinez, 1996) as illustrated in Figure 4. The Silurian and Devonian series interpretation was thoroughly discussed by Racheboeuf et al. (1993).

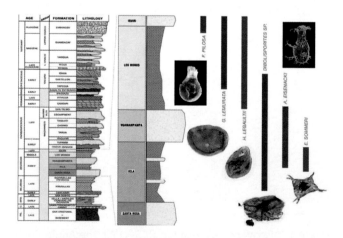

Figure 4. Stratigraphical series modified from Moretti et al. (1996). Detailed view of the Devonian series with the biozonations based on main chitinozoan, acritarch, and spores occurrences as recognized in the regional study.

At the time of the Itáu and Sabalo gas field discoveries, important correlational inconsistencies appeared between Devonian reservoirs in the wells and outcrops. Correlations were mainly based on lithostratigraphic criteria. There was little available biostratigraphical data, and what was present was mostly unreliable. This created incoherency and uncertainty in the stratigraphical attribution of the different reservoirs levels.

A large biostatigraphy study of the Devonian series was then launched to address these observed incoherencies in the stratigraphical attributions.

Different steps of the study were as follows:

1. To review the palynological samples analysis protocol to investigate the true occurrence of the three main palynomorphs (acritarchs, chitinozoans, and miospores) in four well tests (Parapetti X-2, Inau X-2, Itau X-2, Iniguazu X-4) (Paris et al., 2001; Paris and Le Hérissé, 2002) (Figure 4).
2. To extend the methodology to 10 additional wells.
3. To be prepared for the biostratigraphical follow-up of the first Incahuasi exploration well drilling, by sponsoring a Ph.D. thesis in order to formalize the biostratigraphical reference chart (Perez-Leyton, 2007).
4. To review, describe, and sample the Huamampampa outcrops-type section in the locality La Candelaria (Bolivia) during a field trip taken by J. Durand, W. Marquez, and M. Perez-Leyton in December 2002 (in Durand, 2005) (Figure 5). Analysis of the samples was carried out by Paris et al. (2003).

Following efficient protocols and procedures recommended by Paris et al. (2003) (in Durand, 2005), the palynological analysis revealed palynomorph assemblages with an abundance of chitinozoan species, terrestrial miospores, and phytoclasts, and relatively few acritarchs, a common characteristic of the Malvinokaffric realm in western Gondwana.

A special effort was made to study the chitinozoans, whose efficiency is well known in the ante-Carboniferous Paleozoic biostratigraphy. This group requires a specific approach and had not really been taken into account in previous work by other oil companies and consultants.

To carry out this biostratigraphical study under the umbrella of academic and world-famous palynologists was clearly one of the major keys in constructing the chart. The proposed age assignment is based on chitinozoan and acritarch evidence reported to classical Conodont standard zonation. The results were presented as a system of biozonations based on assemblages with chitinozoan, acritarch peak species, and spore zonation (Figures 4 and 5).

One of the most remarkable results of this biozonation of the Devonian Bolivian series was the

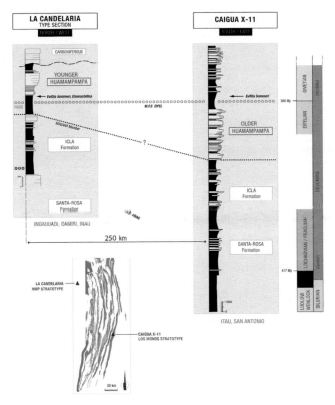

Figure 5. Correlation between the reviewed Huamampampa Formation stratotype in the outcrop (La Candelaria section) (Ulrich, 1892) and one of the ten wells investigated (Caigua X-11) based on acritarch (*Evitia Sommeri*) and chitinozoan (*Eisenachitina aranea*) peaks occurring in a condensed section MFS (maximum flooding surface). It shows the discrepancy in the sandy facies previously attributed to the Huamampampa reservoir in the well correlation. From this correlation, is now distinguished a younger (or Bolivian) Huamampampa and an older (or Argentinian) Huamampampa. Reprinted from Durand, 2005, with permission from Total Exploration Production, whose permission is required for further use.

demonstration of the existence of several different disconnected deltaic sandy systems, both attributed to the Huamampampa Formation. The most recent one (Givetian basal to upper Eifelian), called younger (or Bolivian) Huamampampa, occurs mainly in the northern part of the sub-Andean basin, while the oldest (probably Eifelian) is mainly developed in the southern part and is called older or Argentinian Huamampampa (Figure 6). The La Candelaria-type section was described by Durand, Marquez, and Peyrez-Leyton (in Durand, 2005). The palynological study was conducted by Paris et al. (2003) (Figure 5).

With regard to the sedimentological and stratigraphy sequential approach, it appeared that specific peak species were correlated to four main maximum flooding surfaces (MFS), used as markers for correlation purposes (Figure 6). These MFS were called the Prag MFS (*Angochitina comosa* peak species) between the Santa-Rosa and Icla Formations, the Eifel MFS (*Eisechitina aranea* peak species) distinguishing the older Huamampampa from the younger Huamampampa, the top Huamampampa MFS (*Alpenachitina eisenacki* peak species), and the Givet MFS characterized by *Ancyrochitina* species and the base AD lem spore zone, belonging to the spore zonation as defined by Streel et al. (1987), into the Los Monos Formation.

As a consequence of these new correlations of the Huamampampa reservoirs, an additional potential objective was clearly identified to be the deltaic reservoirs of the Santa Rosa Formation in the northern part of the basin (Figure 6). The outcome of this new study proved to be very important for defining the play on the Incahuasi structural trend and even more important for steering the well. That is why this method was named biosteering.

INITIAL REGIONAL GEOLOGIC CONCEPTS AND BID ROUND DEADLINE CONSTRAINTS

In March 2001, only a few months after the initiation of this new study, the Bolivian authorities announced a bidding round with a preliminary phase in which interested companies would nominate the blocks they would like to see proposed in the bid round. Time was therefore becoming crucial. The challenge was to be able to identify potential attractive open blocks to nominate before having any significant feedbacks from our ongoing study.

From our past experience, it was clear that the seismic data (only a few 2-D lines of poor quality were available at that time) would not allow trap identification and definition due to the structural complexity associated with high/subvertical dip (Figures 3 and 7). Therefore, the first preliminary geologic concepts had to be based on the structural analysis at a regional scale. We had to be able to identify the structural style and define the typology of each portion of north–south structural trends in order to rank them based on surface criteria. Our initial interpretation was to avoid fold propagation fault structures (possibly related to dry structures), and we needed to focus on buried blind thrust, as illustrated in the regional cross-section (Figure 8).

At the prospect level (or a potentially attractive part of a trend) we had, at that stage, very little technical information data. Then, more questions than answers. Therefore, the only possible approach was to focus on the approximate localization of potential closed rock volumes at the Huamampampa objective over part of a trend. Continuous updates of the vision of the regional potential—integrating available data—allowed

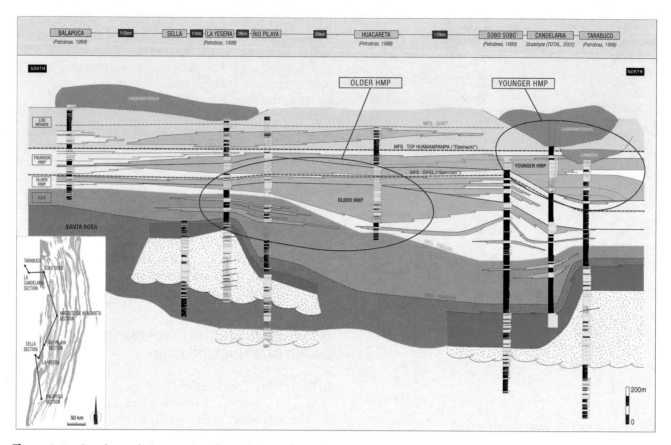

Figure 6. Regional correlation section through the sub-Andean basin leading to a new paleogeography based on sedimentological and sequential stratigraphy concept (modified from Durand, 2005). The used time-lines MFS (maximum flooding surfaces) were defined from the type section and based on maxima of deepening in the basin and on correlated acritarch, chitinozoan, and spore assemblages (Moron in Durand, 2005). Note the development of a regressive phase with settling of a lowstand delta in the northern part. This explains the difference between the older and younger Huamampampa reservoirs.

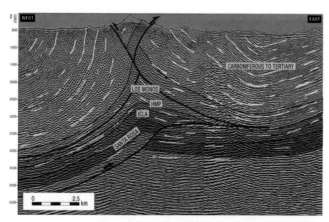

Figure 7. Example of interpreted seismic line over Incahuasi structure (line location on Figure 3), illustrating the poor seismic quality and the structural complexity of the trap.

us to compare all structural trends regardless of the acreage situation. Based on this structural criteria, in May 2001, two open zones were identified and selected, allowing Total to proactively nominate two blocks. Aquio block was one of them.

The Aquio block was an open part of a north–south structural trend (Figure 9). The initial structural model led to the possible existence of a closed volume nearby at the Huamampampa Devonian objective time map. This hypothesis was based on the integration and interpretation of multiple data sets:

- Outcrop analysis and surface mapping combined with the near surface seismic data
- Longitudinal trend analysis in terms of structural style
- Balanced reconstructions on specific regional cross sections
- A numerical field model (MNT) built using satellite data and aeromagnetic surveys, magneto telluric acquisition, and microgravity

Despite the lack of data, Total did apply for the Aquio block. The Aquio lead was estimated as a multi-tcf lead with a possible closure between 60 and 120 km² (23 to 46 mi²). The major risk was related to the description and geometry of a trap with an ill-defined closure

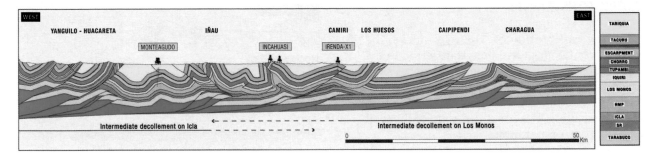

Figure 8. Balanced regional geological cross-section showing the structural style and the typology of the different trends.

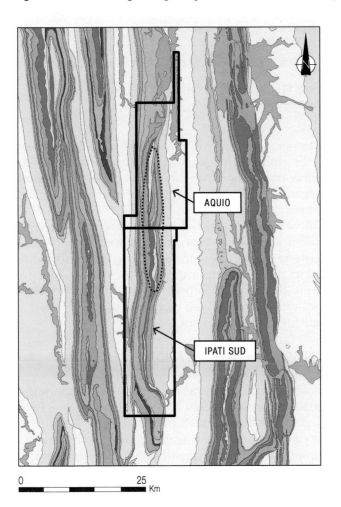

0   25 Km

Figure 9. Speculative structural contours at the top younger Huamampampa reservoir of the Incahuasi field prior to the drilling (color chart shown in Figure 2).

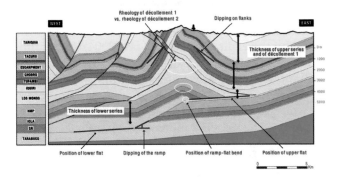

Figure 10. Initial geological model of the Incahuasi lead prior to drilling identifying the different uncertainties linked to it.

held by Tecpetrol 100%. The first phase of this audacious approach was successful in July 2001 when the Aquio block was awarded to Total (100%).

TO GET ACREAGE POSITION OVER THE WHOLE STRUCTURE, IPATI BLOCK

In September 2002, ongoing analysis of the structural trend of Aquio confirmed the extension of the Incahuasi prospect southward on the adjacent block of Ipati (100% Tecpetrol) with a potential structural closure located further south (Figure 9). Potential risk was better assessed with estimated lower reservoir and fracturation risks, and increased risk on the sealing capacity of the Los Monos. Incahuasi was, however, still a sizeable multi-tcf prospect. The probablized resource estimation of the prospect had risen. Total then approached Tecpetrol to swap interests in order to cover the full structural trend from north to south on the Aquio and Ipati blocks.

Total and Tecpetrol finally agreed on 80 and 20%, respectively, of Aquio and Ipati, covering the whole structural trend and potentially including a 60-km (37-mi) long prospect. The work commitment was one exploration well targeting the Huamampampa Devonian reservoir at a total depth of 5600 m (18,373 ft) (see the initial well location in Figure 3).

and unknown depth and location of the top of younger Huamampampa reservoir (Figure 9). The structural model consisted of a blind thrust under the Los Monos shales (Figure 10). This large identified structural trend was continued, however, on the Ipati block operated by Tecpetrol to the south. It was decided to first acquire the open Aquio acreage through the bidding round and then approach Tecpetrol to enter the Ipati block

OPERATIONAL CONSTRAINTS

Concerning the exploration of the two blocks, the main technical challenges were then transferred to the Total Bolivia subsidiary with, on the Geosciences side, the selection of the X, Y, and Z of the bottom hole Huamampampa target and on the operational side, the selection of the drilling location, the design of the well architecture, and its preparation.

In this context and with the very tight license deadlines as well as the time-consuming well planning and preparation phase (rig and services contract, civil works, long lead drilling material, etc.), managing time appeared to be a critical parameter (Ipati licensure, including the exploration well, had to be completed by the expiration date of late 2004). In addition to that preparation, drilling progress in these Paleozoic formations is very slow, and a normal well duration is considered to be in the range of a year. Therefore, the well preparation had to be handled with different preparation tasks being managed in parallel.

The close collaboration between the Drilling and Exploration departments during the well design phase and while drilling was fundamental. Having everyone understand the significant geological uncertainties and the constructive dialog between drillers and geologists were key factors during operations and eventually led to the success of the Incahuasi X-1 exploration well. We had to use a workflow that allowed enough flexibility to integrate new information as it became available.

Only shallow wells and some vintage two-dimensional seismic data of very poor quality were available for interpretation (see Figure 3). These data did not allow proper imaging of the top Huamampampa reservoir and its position in the core of the anticline, especially with regard to the possible offset between surface and subsurface structures. As previously described in many works on the sub-Andean area (Dunn et al., 1995; Moretti et al., 1996; Baby et al., 1995), the intermediate decollement surface of Devonian age (Los Monos Formation) decouples the upper deformation and surface anticline from the deep-seated structures at the Huamampampa reservoir. Such decoupling between surface and depth did not allow us to use surface data as a reliable and precise constraint for locating the possible top of the Huamampampa along an east–west as well as a north–south axis (Figure 11). Moreover, sharp topography relief, cliffs, and near-surface complexity with weathered zone and high velocity vertical beds outcropping on the flank of the structure strongly affected the seismic quality.

Because the end of the license was coming soon, it was thought there was not enough time to acquire a complete two-dimensional seismic survey prior

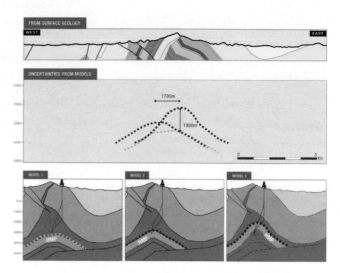

Figure 11. Uncertainties on the location of the Incahuasi structure apex.

to target selection, which would have allowed us to better evaluate the geometry along the Incahuasi anticline. It was therefore decided to define the preliminary exploratory well location only from surface data and structural models.

A new geological field campaign and a series of structural cross-sections along the trend were built to illustrate the north–south varying style of deformation and its potential implication for the depth of the reservoir. Based on this work, it was considered that the northern part of the Ipati block was the most favorable zone for locating the well.

EXPLORATION WELL LOCATION

Location of the well was decided by the beginning of 2003 in order to quickly initiate the 6 months of civil works (access road, well platform, etc.). Despite the very short planning, it was decided to optimize the sequence with the acquisition of a two-dimensional seismic line along the east–west direction through the well location. This line would be available only for possible steering during drilling of the well, not to specify the well target.

This seismic line was associated with a gravimetric and magneto-telluric (MT) acquisition along this single line (Figure 12). The MT method consists of passive measurements at Earth's surface of naturally occurring electro-magnetic field. This EM field, generated by the impact of solar wind on Earth's magnetosphere and the storm activity, diffuses into the Earth and generates a secondary field, which gives information on the subsurface resistivity distribution. In areas where a resistivity contrast exists between reservoir

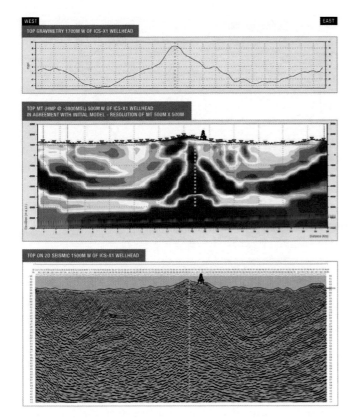

Figure 12. Structural crest at well location deduced from gravimetry, magneto-tellurics, and seismic data.

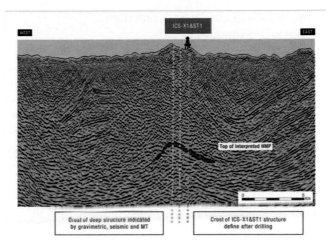

Figure 13. Well location proposal on the new two-dimensional time seismic line acquired in 2003 and prospect structural crest interpretation of the top younger Huamampampa reservoir (in red) prior to drilling.

and cover, for example, MT could be an additional tool for structural model building at a reasonable cost (Ravault et al., 2002). Nevertheless, the resolution of the method is quite poor (500 m × 500 m). However, the objective was to use subsurface information to add coherency to the structural model.

As stated above, the geometry of the anticline was controlled mainly by lithology and the presence of several detachment layers. These decoupling layers partly disconnect the deformations observed at the surface (tertiary to lower Carboniferous series) from what happens at depth at the Huamampampa reservoirs. Some sub-Andean wells suggest that deep anticline at the reservoir level may be shifted from the surface anticline axial plane.

On a given section through the location of the well, surface data provide only a very rough and qualitative estimate of the location of the top of the deep structure (Figure 13). Therefore, different geologic elements contribute to the general uncertainty over the apex of the structure (as summarized in Figure 11).

Taking into account the numerous structural possibilities on schematic models, a range of uncertainty for the top reservoir was defined to be given to the drillers as a target box. The order of magnitude of the uncertainty on the location of the structural apex of the structure was quite wide, with 1700 m (5577 ft) in an east–west direction and 1300 m (4265 ft) vertically. Well architecture and deviation were designed to be compatible with this target box. For well preparation and design, a base case scenario was selected, including space for potential sidetracks.

DRILLING AND STEERING

Once the Huamampampa target was selected, the most appropriate surface location was sought. Unfortunately, the most adequate location was offset from the selected bottom hole location, and the exploration well had to be designed as a deviated well from the flank of the surface anticline. Well ICS-X1, located on the eastern flank of the surface anticline (Figure 13), was spudded in October 2003 and planned to reach the main target 6 to 7 months later. Initial versions of processing the newly acquired seismic profile and MT data were delivered by the end of 2003 during drilling of the first phases.

Prior to drilling, due to the biostratigraphy synthesis, an accurate palynologic zonation from the base of the Carboniferous to the middle Devonian based on chitinozoans, acritarchs, and spores was available. The biosteering of the well was therefore the main tool used to compensate for the absence of reliable seismic imaging, especially in the core of the anticline. This part was expected to be complex, with many possible thrusts and internal deformation in the shale of the Los Monos Formation.

From Surface to Los Monos Formation in Line with Expectations

Drilling in the tertiary down to the top of the Devonian Los Monos Formation roughly conformed to the initial well prognosis. Depth estimates as well as dip and thickness of the successive formations indicated that field data could be used to build the general envelope of the anticline. The newly acquired seismic line also confirmed the general geometry of the eastern flank and showed a strong reflector similar to the expected geometry of the target, with a possible top some 1500 m (4921 ft) west of the wellhead. MT and gravimetry data defined a top respectively 500 and 1700 m (1640 and 5577 ft) west of the wellhead. MT data have low resolution and strongly depend on initial models, while gravimetry data do not give a unique solution and are influenced by the surface (Figure 12).

The biosteering tool was used extensively during the drilling phase. As was mentioned earlier, rock samples needed a specific preparation to allow the use of the defined chrono-stratigraphic chart. Because of the slow drilling rate penetration in Paleozoic sediments, this biosteering approach was based on almost real time sample analysis, with the cuttings sent from the remote rig area in Bolivia to the south of France for analysis at Total's research center.

This trip was taking up to 5 days, and the analysis and results were available only after an 8-hour analysis sequence. An innovative automated procedure that included electronic imagery detection and image capture was set up to speed up the process. The stratigraphic referential rapidly became operational with sufficient resolution. The structural model was then continuously updated and calibrated based on these data. During drilling that deviated to the west—from the surface location—into the Los Monos Devonian cover, biosteering clearly identified the top of Los Monos and then a progressive stratigraphic sequence that deepened as expected.

Surprise in the Los Monos Formation: Not as Expected

An intermediate dipmeter logging did indicate progressive steepening of series up to vertical while the biostratigraphy markers showed that the series were progressively getting younger downward. At the same time, analysis of cutting samples' vitrinite reflectance was showing a decrease in maturity with depth. Eventually, interpretation of the available data indicated that we were drilling a vertical to overturned flank, progressing up into the stratigraphic section. We reached the top of the Devonian Los Monos instead

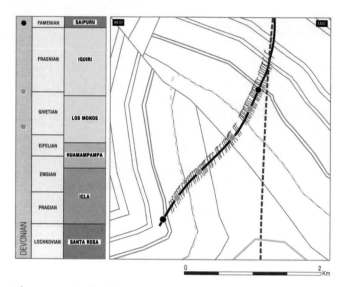

Figure 14. Updated geological cross-section during the drilling using biosteering tool results and dipmeter data. The red dash line was the proposed side-track to retarget the Huamampampa reservoir inside the overturned fold.

of the expected reservoir at 5187 m measured depth (mMD). An updated geological section (Figure 14) was performed, and it indicated a possible top structure approximately 300 m (984 ft) west of the wellhead, thus contradicting seismic, MT, and gravimetry initial prognosis. Without the real-time biosteering tool, it would have been impossible to clearly understand the trap configuration in such detail and so rapidly while the rig was still in location.

Structural Model Change, Sidetrack, Top Huamampampa Reservoir

A side track was decided based on this new structural model (see the trajectory in red in Figure 14). This new well (kickoff point at 2406 mMD finally reached the top reservoir 11 months after spud at 4905 mMD (−3352 m in true vertical depth sub sea [TVDSS]) and was drilled down to the final total depth of 5600 mMD. The Huamampampa was found to have very steep dips (between 50° and 80° toward the west), suggesting that the real top of the structure was located more to the east and probably just below the surface location.

A barefoot drill stem test (DST) was performed between 4905 and 5150 mMD. It produced 1093 km³/d (38,6 MMScfd) of gas, one of the best tests in south Bolivia. The most striking figure related to the Incahuasi anticline is the fact that the surface anticline was overturned after the main thrust emplacement with a vertical western flank and a 30° east-dipping forelimb.

Appraisal well ICS-2, drilled 5 km south of the discovery well, found a triplication of the reservoir and also

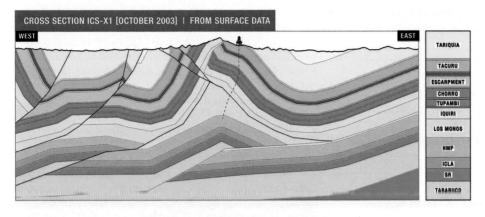

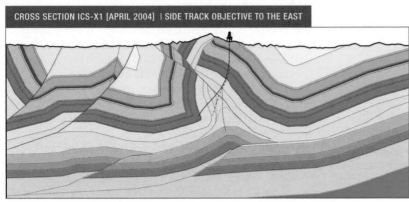

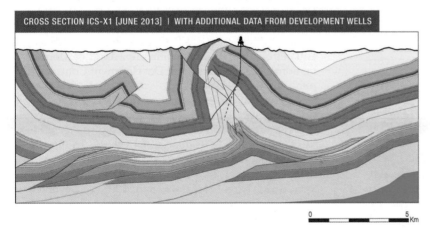

Figure 15. Evolution of the structural model before the drilling (2003), during the drilling (2004) and integrating the most recent data from development wells (2013).

an overturned series of the Huamampampa, suggesting that the initial thrusts had been recently passively rotated. Figure 15 illustrates the evolution—from the initial concept—of the structural model while drilling.

TAKEAWAYS

The first of the major lessons learned from the structural evaluation was that in the Bolivian foothills

where almost no imaging is available, constraints on the target's geometry remain very poor. Second, in this old-fashioned exploration approach, all relevant data have to be used together in order to reduce uncertainties. A multi-hypothesis and multidisciplinary approach is mandatory to anticipate and facilitate reactivity during drilling. Finally, using analogues from the field and models may help; however, the alternate models remain beyond our imagination.

CURRENT STATUS

A successful appraisal campaign did include three delineation wells located along a north–south axis of the structure over the Aquio and Ipati blocks. They all reached the Huamampampa reservoir at similar depth with some surprises, but all used the biostrat chart to steer the wells (Ballard et al., 2013, 2016; Lesnikov et al., 2015). Phase 1 development of the Incahuasi field was launched in September 2013 and included three production wells connected to a gas treatment plant which started its production in August 2016. Today, the field is operated by Total (50%) together with its partners Tecpetrol de Bolivia (20%) and with Gazprom (20%) and YPFB Chaco (10%) which joined the joint venture since the discovery well.

CONCLUSIONS

The discovery of Incahuasi field—a process carried out in a province with very complex geology—had a significant impact on both the rejuvenation of exploration activity and the attractiveness of this geological basin. It was the result of a quite original and proactive approach from prospect generation to discovery, which can be summarized as follows:

- A relatively short (3-year) cycle of exploration from the initial concept definition, acreage acquisition, and discovery
- A technically based and managed risk strategy of acreage acquisition
- The development of innovative techniques (e.g., the stratigraphic biosteering tool) used in real-time operations
- A discovery well which gave birth to a new major gas field and fostered exploration in the northern part of the southern sub-Andean zone.

As a result, one of the largest fields of south Bolivia was discovered. In addition to a new vision of the remaining potential of the basin, this work brought a new vision of the petroleum system, improved understanding of the stratigraphy, the paleogeography and then the Huamampampa reservoir geometries extension with a more accurate understanding of tectonic history. All of this has been made possible via permanent integration and transversal knowledge sharing across most of the main professional disciplines of the exploration domain. Flexibility, multidisciplinary team work, and adaptability to change were the key success factors of this adventure.

ACKNOWLEDGMENTS

In addition to all the experts involved in this adventure, we would like to thank Patrick Charron, Catherine Grasset, Olivier Jocktane, Miguel Peyrez-Leyton (consultant), Patrick Orsolini, Florentin Paris (University of Rennes), Patrick Rachebeuf (University of Brest), Patrick Ravaut, Philippe Rochat, Martin Specht, Philippe Werner, Jean-Paul Xavier, and all our colleagues from the Total Bolivian Task Force for their contributions to this successful team effort. We would also like to thank YPFB Corporation, Total and its partners Tecpetrol, Gazprom and YPFB Chaco for permission to publish this case study of the Incahuasi discovery. We are particularly grateful to Serge Nicoletis (Geosciences Manager Total E&P Bolivia) and to Michel Le Vot (Vice-President Geosciences Total E&P Americas LLC) for their helpful comments and reviews of the manuscript.

REFERENCES CITED

Baby, P., I. Moretti, B. Guillier, R. Limachi, E. Mendez, J. Oller, et al., 1995, Petroleum system of the northern and central Bolivian sub-Andean zone, *in* A. J. Tankard, R. Suarez S., and H. J. Welsink, eds., Petroleum basins of South America: AAPG Memoir 62, p. 445–458.

Ballard, J. F., J. C. Ringenbach, F. Clement, and J. M. Moron, 2013, 3D structural geological interpretation: Earth, mind and machine. AAPG Hedberg Research Conference, accessed October 4, 2016, http://www.searchanddiscovery.com/abstracts/html/2014/120140hedberg/abstracts/ballard.html.

Ballard, J. F, V. Spina, F. Clement P. E. Lardin, J. M. Fleury, P. Chaffel, et al., Structural characterization of the Incahuasi structure (Bolivia) and integrated approach to de-risk complex field appraisal, *in* Petroleum basins and hydorcarbon potential of the of Perú and Bolivia: AAPG Memoir (in review).

Dunn, J. F., K. G. Hartshorn, and P. W. Hartshorn, 1995, Structural styles and hydrocarbon potential of the sub-Andean thrust belt of southern Bolivia, *in* A. J. Tankard, R. Suarez, and H. J.Welsink, Petroleum basins of South America: AAPG Memoir 62, p. 523–543.

Durand, J., ed., 2005, La Thématique Dévonienne dans le Subandin sud de Bolivie. Internal report, New Exploration Ventures: Total Exploration Production (unpublished), 8 vol., 629 fig., 90 pl., 37 ann., 9 tab., 1702 p.

Lesnikov, V., M. Verliac, J. F. Ballard, and J. M. Fleury, 2015, Use of VSP for improving drilling decisions in the Bolivian foothills: Third EAGE Workshop on Borehole Geophysics Unlocking the Potential, Athens, 18–22 April, 2015, accessed January 16, 2017, http://www.eage.org/event/index.php?eventid=1247&evp=13996.

Moretti, I., P. Baby, E. Mendez, and D. Zubieta, 1996, Hydrocarbon generation in relation to thrusting in the sub Andean Zone from 18 to 22°S, Bolivia: Petroleum Geosciences, v. 2, p. 17–28.

Paris, F., and A. Le Hérissé, 2002, Chitinozoans, acritarchs and spores from wells Iniguazu X-4 and Itau X-2 (Bolivia): Internal Report TotalFinaElf (unpublished), 26 p.

Paris, F., A. Le Hérissé, and M. Streel, 2001, Palynomorphs from wells Inau X-2 and Parapetti X-2 (Bolivia): Internal Report TotalFinaElf (unpublished), 42 p.

Paris, F., D. Bernard, M. P. Dabard, A. Le Herissé, P. Steemans, and M. Streel, 2003, Organic-walled microfossils and petrology of the Huamampampa and Los Monos formations: Total Research and Development Contract, (unpublished), p. 1–79.

Perez-Leyton, M. A., 2007, Analyse des assemblages de palynomorphes du Silurien supérieur et du Dévonien de Bolivie: Proposition de mise en place d'une échelle biostratigraphique de référence: Ph.D. thesis, Université de Bretagne occidentale (unpublished), p. 1–407.

Rachebeouf, P. R., A. Le Hérissé, F. Paris, C. Babin, F. Guillocheau, M. Truyols-Massoni, et al., 1993, Le Dévonien de Bolivie: Biostratigraphie et chronostratigraphie : Comptes Rendus de l'Académie des Sciences de Paris, v. 317, no. 2, p. 795–802.

Ravault, P., S. Russell, P. Mallard, J. F. Ballard, D. Watts, and S. Hallinan, 2002, 3D magneto-tellurics for imaging a Devonian reservoir (Huamampampa) in the southern Sub-Andean basin of Bolivia: 72nd Annual International Meeting, Salt Lake City, Society of Exploration Geophysicists, Expanded Abstracts, 5 p.

Streel, M., K. Higgs, S. Loboziak, W. Riegel, and P. Steemans, 1987, Spore stratigraphy and correlation with faunas ans floras in the type marine Devonian of the Ardenne-Renish regions: Review of Palaeobotany and Palynology, 50, p. 211–229.

Suarez-Sorucco, R., and E. Diaz Martinez, 1996, Lexico estratigráfico de Bolivia. Revista Tecnica de Yacimientos petrolliferos fiscales bolivianos, v. 17, no. 1–2, p. 1–227.

Ulrich, A., 1892, Palaeozoische Versteinerungen aus Bolivien: Neues Jahrbuch für Mineralogie Geologie und Paläontologie Beilage, v. 8, p. 5–116.

10

Carlotto, Marco Antonio, Rodrigo Correia Baptista da Silva, Arlindo Akio Yamato, et al., 2017, Libra: A newborn giant in the Brazilian Presalt Province, *in* R. K. Merrill and C. A. Sternbach, eds., Giant fields of the decade 2000–2010: AAPG Memoir 113, p. 165–176.

Libra: A Newborn Giant in the Brazilian Presalt Province

Marco Antonio Carlotto, Rodrigo Correia Baptista da Silva, Arlindo Akio Yamato, Wagner Luz Trindade, Jobel Lourenço Pinheiro Moreira, Ricardo Augusto Rosa Fernandes, and Orlando José Soares Ribeiro

Petrobras (Petróleo Brasileiro S.A.), Rio de Janeiro, Brazil (e-mails: carlotto@petrobras.com.br, rodrigo .baptista@petrobras.com.br, yamato@petrobras.com.br, wtrindade@petrobras.com, jobel@petrobras.com.br, rrosa@petrobras.com, orlandor@petrobras.com.br)

Wenceslau Peres Gouveia Jr.

Shell Brasil Petróleo Ltda., Rio de Janeiro, Brazil (e-mail: wences.gouveia@shell.com)

Julien Philippe Carminati

Total E & P do Brasil Ltda., Rio de Janeiro, Brazil (e-mail: julien.carminati.TOTAL_E-P@petrobras.com.br)

Deng Qicai

CNOOC Petroleum Brasil Ltda., Rio de Janeiro, Brazil (e-mail: deng.qicai.CNOOC_PETROLEUM@ petrobras.com.br)

Zhao Junfeng

CNODC Brasil Petróleo e Gás Ltda., Rio de Janeiro, Brazil (e-mail: zhaojunfeng@cnpcint.com)

Augusto Carlos da Silva-Telles Jr.

PPSA (Pré-Sal Petróleo S.A.), Rio de Janeiro, Brazil (e-mail: augusto.telles@ppsa.gov.br)

ABSTRACT

As the operator of several exploratory blocks in ultradeep waters, Petrobras was responsible for many presalt oil discoveries in Santos Basin such as Tupi, Carioca, Guará, and Iara. In partnership with the National Petroleum, Natural Gas and Biofuels Agency (ANP), Petrobras drilled well 2-ANP-2A, which resulted in the Libra discovery. In 2013, Libra was offered in the first bidding round executed by the Brazilian government under the new Production Sharing Contract for presalt areas. The winning consortium is comprised of Petrobras (operator), Shell, Total, CNOOC (China National Offshore Oil Corporation), CNPC (China National Petroleum Corporation), and PPSA (Pré-Sal Petróleo S.A.).

The Libra discovery is sitting over a structural trap of about 550 km² (212 mi²) closure at the Aptian top reservoirs level presenting a maximum oil column that can reach up to 900 m (2953 ft).

The main reservoirs are lacustrine carbonates, deposited from the Neobarremian until the Aptian. Preliminary estimates indicate a volume of oil in place between 8 and 12 billion BOE.

The development proposed for Libra started with Phase 0, in 2014, and is focused on information gathering, including appraisal wells, extended well tests (EWT), early production systems (EPS), and a pilot project. Phase 1 encompasses the definitive production systems and is expected to start in 2022 and finish in 2030.

INTRODUCTION

The Libra discovery is located in the northeastern portion of Santos Basin, in southeastern Brazil, in the ultradeep waters of the Atlantic Ocean between 1900 and 2300 m (6234 and 7546 ft) of water depth (Figure 1). Initial estimates indicate the volume of oil in place to be between 8 and 12 billion BOE in carbonate reservoirs (coquinas, grainstones, and stromatolites) deposited from the Neobarremian until the Aptian.

Discovery well 2-ANP-2A was proposed to investigate a seismic feature interpreted as a microbial mound (Figure 2). This feature displays chaotic to progradational seismic facies favorably positioned on the northwestern flank of a structural trap with a closure larger than 500 km^2 (193 mi^2) at the base of salt level (top seal).

After the discovery, three-dimensional seismic data were acquired to image the whole field area and revealed a structural closure of 550 km^2 (212 mi^2). The main axis of the Libra structure extends along 50 km

(31 mi) in a northwest–southeast direction, exhibiting three well-defined highs elongated in north/northeast–south/southwest direction roughly splitting the structure in three sectors: northwest, central, and southeast (Figures 3 and 4). The first appraisal well, 3-RJS-731 well, drilled by the Petrobras/Shell/Total/CNOOC/CNPC/PPSA consortium is located in the northwest sector and confirmed the great potential of the area. The second appraisal well, 3-RJS-735A well, drilled in the central sector, is currently under evaluation.

The appraisal/development strategy of Libra consists of a systematic process of obtaining information to de-risk the concept selection for the development systems. Mitigation of existing uncertainties will be done progressively and gradually during Phase 0. During this phase, up to 11 appraisal wells and 5 EWT/EPS are planned to be deployed over the Libra field.

The planning of Phase 1 will start once the uncertainties are gradually mitigated and the risks associated to the full field development are reduced. The studies for such systems shall include evaluation of several hosts with different levels of production capacity, subsea technologies and system designs, optimized well designs, and strategies to enhance hydrocarbon production and recovery.

EXPLORATION HISTORY

The first hydrocarbon discovery in the presalt province of Santos Basin took place in 2005 by the well 1-RJS-617D (Parati), drilled by Petrobras in the BM-S-10 block (in partnership with BG and Partex). In 2006, Petrobras and partners in block BM-S-11 (BG and Petrogal) made the first commercial discovery of oil in the province with the 1-RJS-628 (Tupi) well in the area that later became known as the Lula giant field. In the following years, several discoveries such as Carioca (currently Lapa field), Guará (currently Sapinhoá field), and Iara (currently Berbigão, Sururu, and Atapu fields) (Figure 1) confirmed the potential of the presalt interval of Santos Basin. All of these discoveries were made in exploratory blocks under the Concession Contract regime.

In 2010, in collaboration with ANP (National Petroleum, Natural Gas and Biofuels Agency), Petrobras drilled two wells in the northern portion of Santos Basin with the intention of assessing the presalt potential

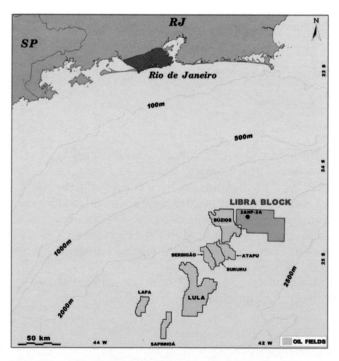

Figure 1. Santos Basin location map with bathymetric curves and main presalt oil fields. Libra block is represented by the green polygon.

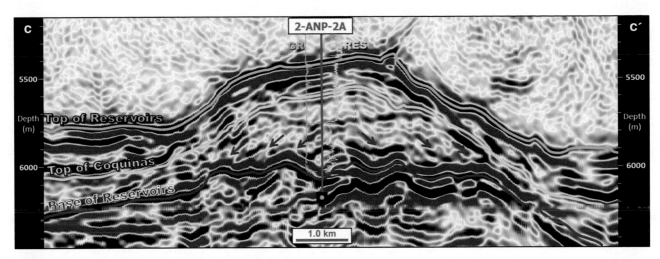

Figure 2. CC' seismic line, crossing 2-ANP-2A well (location in Figure 3). Observe the very clear mound geometry of the Itapema Formation (between yellow and blue horizons). Blue arrows correspond to progradational seismofacies of the coquinas, dipping southwest and northeast. The gamma ray log is green, the resistivity log is blue. (CGG Santos VI-A seismic data courtesy of CGG.)

in that area, at the time considered an exploration frontier. Well 2-ANP-1 resulted in the discovery of Franco, currently the Búzios giant oil field (100% Petrobras, under the Cession of Rights regime). Well 2-ANP-2A

resulted in the Libra discovery, which is the subject of this paper.

With well 2-ANP-2A (Libra), located in the northeasternmost portion of Santos Basin, Petrobras and

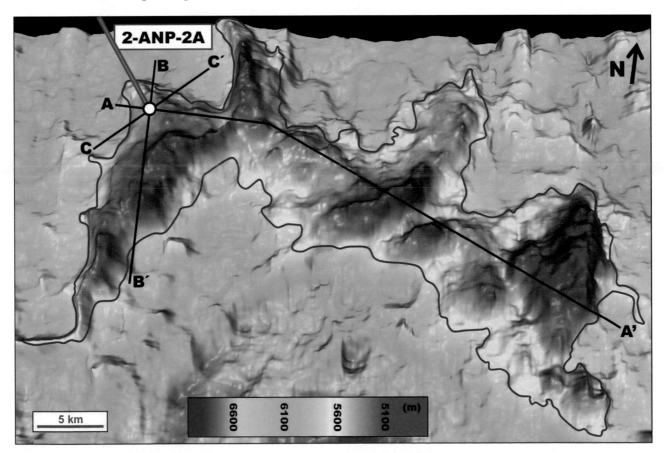

Figure 3. Base of salt (top reservoir) depth structural map, with the location of the 2-ANP-2A well and AA', BB', and CC' seismic lines. The blue polygon corresponds to the last closed curve of the structure, coincident with the oil–water contact at –5702 m (–18,707 ft).

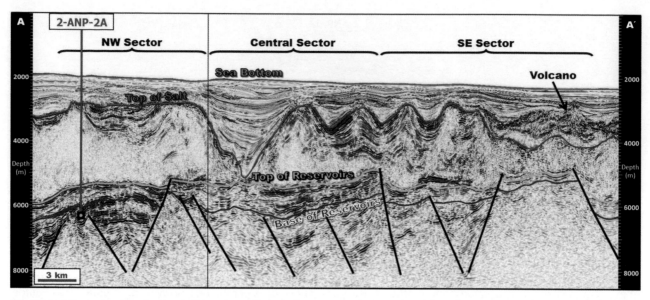

Figure 4. AA' semiregional seismic line, along the northwest–southeast axis of the Libra structure (location in Figure 3). Observe good presalt seismic quality in the northwest and central sectors and poor presalt seismic quality in the southeast sector due to the presence of postsalt volcanic rocks. Such volcanic rocks are represented by high amplitude and chaotic reflectors. (CGG_SantosVI-A seismic data courtesy of CGG.)

ANP intended to investigate a seismic feature interpreted as a microbial mound (Carlotto, 2009) (Figure 2), located in the northwest flank of a structure elongated in a northwest–southeast direction, showing a structural closure of more than 500 km^2 (193 mi^2) at the top reservoir level (Figure 3). The location chosen for the well was also influenced by the fact that at that moment, three-dimensional seismic data were available only over the northwest sector, covering only 20% of the structure. The discovery well revealed 329 m (1079 ft) of 27° API oil column in carbonate reservoirs displaying excellent porosity and permeability ranges. The feature initially interpreted as a microbial mound was in fact a bivalve coquina mound.

During 2011 and 2012, motivated by the 2-ANP-2A results, CGG acquired a speculative three-dimensional seismic data of about 2850 km^2 (1100 mi^2) (known as CGG Santos VI-A), covering the whole Libra structure. Pre-stack depth migration (PSDM) processing was made available to the market in early 2013. This speculative data showed fair to good image quality for the northwest and central sectors. However, in the southeast portion, the presalt seismic image is extremely deteriorated by the occurrence of igneous rocks in the postsalt interval (Figure 4). Nonetheless, the top reservoir is seismically mappable and indicates a 550 km^2 (212 mi^2) closure with a hydrocarbon column of up to 900 m (2953 ft) in the highest portions of the structure. Moreover, the oil–water contact found in the 2-ANP-2A well coincides with the spill-point of the structure (Figure 3), suggesting that Libra is filled to spill.

In October 2013, in the first bidding round of presalt areas under the shared production agreement, the ANP offered a 1550 km^2 (598 mi^2) area exploratory block that covered the totality of the Libra structure. The winning consortium included Petrobras (operator, 40%), Shell (20%), Total (20%), CNOOC (10%), and CNPC (10%). A very positive factor in the success of the Libra project is the high technical quality of the members of the consortium that won the bid. The diversity of companies— both in kind and in geography—has turned into a great opportunity to build a very robust partnership working together as part of an integrated project team, with very talented people sharing expertise, knowledge, and funding. This collaborative environment can be very fruitful for new ideas by leveraging Petrobras's strengths for the benefit of the Libra project.

Besides the international oil companies, Pré-Sal Petróleo S./A. (PPSA), the Brazilian government managing company, is an important player and has 50% voting participation in the consortium. Its board has a highly technical staff with extensive experience in the oil industry, which increases optimism for the success of the project.

The exploratory phase started in December 2013, and the first appraisal well, 3-RJS-731 well, was drilled in the northwest sector during the second half of 2014. The well evaluation, concluded in 2015, confirmed the same potential presented by the discovery well. The second appraisal well, 3-RJS-735A well, located in the central sector of Libra, is currently under evaluation. A comprehensive seismic reprocessing is currently occurring to improve seismic image quality of the presalt section, particularly in the southeast portion of Libra. This processing effort consists of advanced imaging techniques such as full waveform inversion and reverse time migration that can potentially mitigate the effect of complex heterogeneities in the postsalt on the reservoir image. Additionally, the Libra venture will tender a new full-azimuth seismic acquisition that will provide the necessary illumination to properly image the reservoir in its entirety.

REGIONAL SETTING

Stratigraphy of the Libra Area

The Santos Basin is located between latitudes of 23° and 28°S in the southeast portion of the Brazilian passive continental margin (Figure 7) and encompasses about 350,000 km² (135,136 mi²) with water depths in excess of 3000 m (9843 ft). The Cabo Frio high is the northern limit of the basin, and the Florianopolis high is its southern limit (Moreira et al., 2007).

The basin-fill history starts with the deposition of Camboriú Formation basalts in the upper Valanginian/Hauterivian (138 to 130 million years ago [m.y.a.]) as a response to the first signs of the Gondwana break-up (Figure 5). During the early rift stages, sandstones, siltstones, and shales of talc-stevensitic composition were deposited in a lacustrine environment and represent the Piçarras Formation of Barremian age.

From the Neobarremian until the Eoaptian, high-energy bivalve grainstones and rudstones (coquinas) of the Itapema Formation were deposited. These rocks are the best reservoir facies shown by well 2-ANP-2A. In a lower-energy setting, dark shales rich in organic matter occur interlayered with the coquinas basinward and are considered the main source rocks of Santos Basin hydrocarbons.

The Barra Velha Formation carbonates were deposited in the Aptian, during the postrift stage characterized by the transition from continental to a shallow marine setting (SAG interval). Grainstones and packstones composed of stromatolite fragments predominate at the base of the Barra Velha Formation. In the discovery well, these facies show reservoir characteristics as good as the coquinas from the Itapema Formation. To the top, in situ carbonates such as stromatolites and laminites are the prevalent facies. Stromatolites are also good reservoir facies.

By the end of the Aptian, after the establishment of an open marine setting, a thick salt sequence from the Ariri Formation was deposited. This sequence of mainly halite and anhydrite composition in addition to more exotic salts, such as tachydrite, carnallite, and sylvinite, covers the previous sediments and works as a seal for the Libra accumulation. On top of the salt, marine sediments of Camburi, Frade, and Itamambuca groups were deposited during the thermal subsidence stage, from Albian until recent, forming the drift sequence.

STRUCTURAL GEOLOGY OF THE LIBRA AREA

The origin of Santos Basin is linked to the Gondwana break-up and the opening of the South Atlantic, during the early Cretaceous. This extensional tectonics resulted in the separation between South America and Africa, controlling the tectono-stratigraphic evolution of the basins in the Brazilian eastern margin. The basin orientation is northeast–southwest and locally east–west, inherited from basement structures, which made possible an oblique opening with a sinistral component (Szatmari et al., 1984, 1985; Meisling et al., 2001; Lima et al., 2005; Milani et al., 2005; Magnavita et al., 2010). In the northeast part of the basin, the rifting kinematics generated a feature named Libra transfer zone

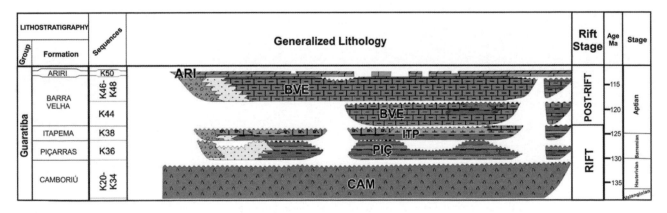

Figure 5. Stratigraphic chart of Santos Basin presalt interval. (Modified from Moreira et al., 2007.)

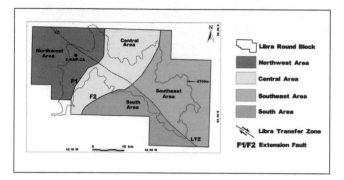

Figure 6. Schematic map showing the main structural features in the Libra area (modified from Dehler and Yamato, 2015).

(LTZ), an important structural element in the north-west–southeast direction (Figure 6) that was active during the tectono-sedimentary evolution of the Libra area (Dehler and Yamato, 2015).

The majority of the most distal portion of Santos Basin, a bit further from the continental rise, lies over a structural mega-feature named São Paulo Plateau (Figure 7). This feature extends in northeast–southwest direction from Santos to Espírito Santo basins and possibly represents a huge area of anomalously extended continental crust (Kumar et al., 1977; Carminatti et al., 2008, 2009; Gomes et al., 2008). Another major northeast–southwest structural feature occurs in the central area of São Paulo Plateau and is named Santos External High (Carminatti et al., 2008) (Figure 8) or Outer High of the Santos Basin (Gomes et al., 2002, 2008). In the direction of the external high, all presalt sequences thin out (Figure 9). It is interpreted that this structural high represents a portion of less extended continental crust inside São Paulo Plateau, approximately 340 km (211 mi) long and 130 km (81 mi) wide (Figure 8), which kept this area more elevated than its surroundings (Carminatti et al., 2008).

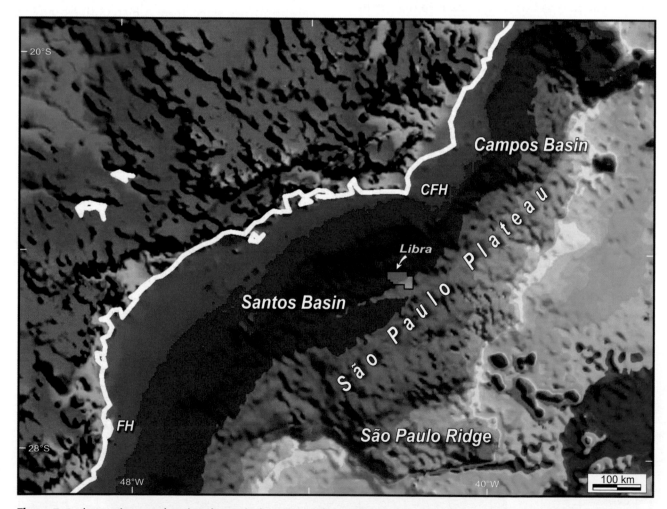

Figure 7. Bathymetric map showing the main features of the Santos and Campos basins, including São Paulo Plateau. The white line represents the shoreline. FH = Florianópolis High (limit between Santos and Pelotas basins), CFH = Cabo Frio High (limit between Santos and Campos basins). (Modified from Carminatti et al., 2008.)

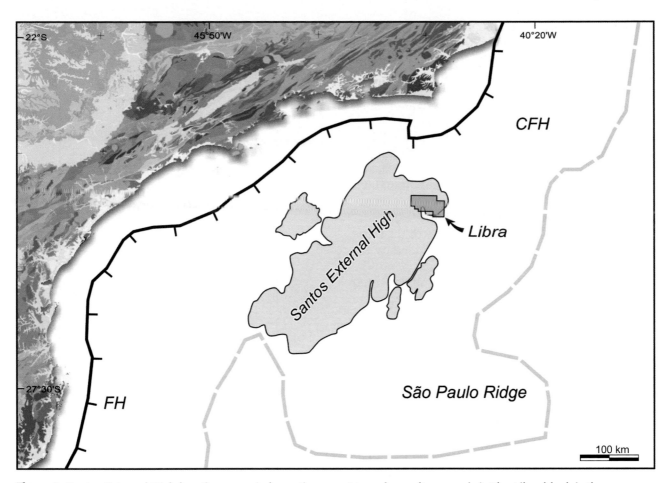

Figure 8. Santos External High location map (schematic map at top of presalt reservoirs). The Libra block is the green polygon. The black line High represents the Aptian Hinge Line. The gray dashed line represents the limit between continental and oceanic crusts. FH = Florianópolis High (limit between Santos and Pelotas basins); CFH = Cabo Frio High (limit between Santos and Campos basins). (Modified from Carminatti et al., 2008.)

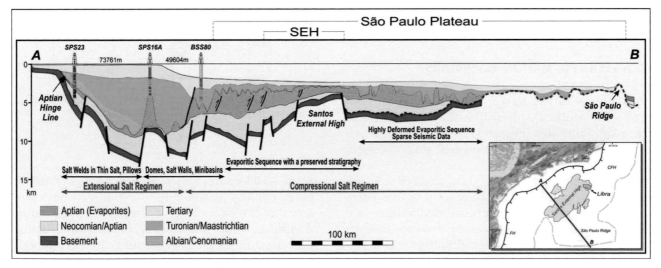

Figure 9. AB schematic geological section crossing Santos External High (SEH). Note the isopach thinning of presalt sequences over the Santos External High area. (Modified from Carminatti et al., 2008.)

The Libra structure is situated in the extreme northeast of Santos External High in the vicinity of Cabo Frio High. This region was kept structurally elevated since the early rift stage and away from any significant siliciclastic input, working as an ideal site for high-energy carbonate deposition in shallow waters, such as coquinas, grainstones, and stromatolites.

Detailed structural analysis of Libra block (Dehler and Yamato, 2015) individualized four areas with distinct characteristics: northwest, central, southeast, and south. Each of these areas is limited by important fault zones: F1, F2, and LTZ (Figure 6). These elements, together with the rifting style in the region, were fundamental for the definition of the geometry of the Libra structure. The northwest area is characterized by rift faults oriented north–south. On the other hand, the central area is characterized by major faults oriented north–south at its north and south limits, inflecting to northeast–southwest in its central portion. The southeast area is characterized by normal faults oriented in a north–south direction that are related to deep detachment faults. The south area displays faults with a northeast–southwest orientation.

RESERVOIR GEOLOGY AND FLUID PROPERTIES

Libra reservoirs are Aptian carbonates from the Guaratiba Group. In the 2-ANP-2A well, the coquinas and microbial carbonates from Itapema and Barra Velha formations are both in the oil zone (Figure 10). Fluid samples from 2-ANP-2A revealed an oil of 27° API with a 375 to 448 gas-to-oil ratio, CO_2 content ranging between 38 and 42% and less than 0.5 to 16 ppm of H_2S. The oil–water contact is well defined at –5702 m (–18,707 ft) true vertical depth sub sea (TVDSS) in the resistivity logs and pressure plots.

BARRA VELHA FORMATION RESERVOIRS

Typical facies in the Barra Velha Formation consist of stromatolites, spherulitic limestones, grainstones, and laminites (Figure 11A–C) deposited in a transitional setting during the postrift stage (Moreira et al., 2007).

Correlations using seismic data, 2-ANP-2A well logs, and petrographic descriptions show that Barra Velha Formation reservoirs can be subdivided into two major intervals. The upper interval, located immediately beneath the salt, shows a predominance of in situ facies where stromatolites, peloidal mudstones, and laminites are commonly recognized (Silva et al., 2014). This upper interval displays a net pay of 53 m (174 ft)

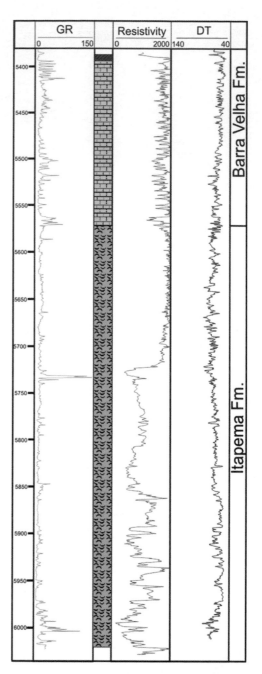

Figure 10. Representative log for Libra area (2-ANP-2A) showing Barra Velha and Itapema reservoirs.

at the well location and average porosities of 10%, with permeabilities reaching up to 353 mD. At the lower interval of the Barra Velha Formation, reworked facies dominate, with rudstones and grainstones being the prevailing facies (Silva et al., 2014). In this interval, the net pay is 80 m (262 ft) at the well location as a result of a 92% net-to-gross, the average porosity is 14%, and permeabilities reach up to 2540 mD.

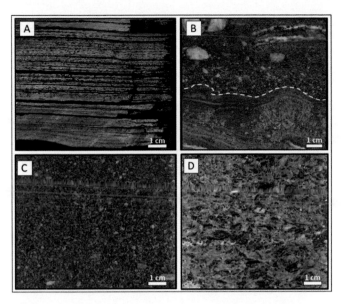

Figure 11. Detailed core photographs of representative facies in 2-ANP-2A. (A) Microbial laminite. (B) Top: Intraclastic rudstone; Bottom: Stromatolite. (C) Intraclastic grainstone. (D) Bivalve coquina.

In seismic sections, Barra Velha Formation reservoirs show plane parallel seismofacies with medium to high amplitude values in the 2-ANP-2A area (Figure 12).

ITAPEMA FORMATION RESERVOIRS

Itapema Formation is composed of bivalve rudstones (coquinas) (Figure 11D), bioclastic grainstones, packstones, wackestones, and shales deposited during the late stage of the rift phase in a lacustrine setting. This deposition occurred under variable paleoenvironmental conditions in regard to salinity and alkalinity (Moreira et al., 2007).

Correlation using seismic data, 2-ANP-2A well logs, and petrographic descriptions shows that Itapema Formation reservoirs can be subdivided into three major intervals. The Itapema Formation upper interval is entirely in the oil zone, exhibiting bivalve rudstones with intense dissolution and occasionally displaying karstification and brecciation surfaces, oncoids, and pisoids. The middle interval presents bivalve rudstones with

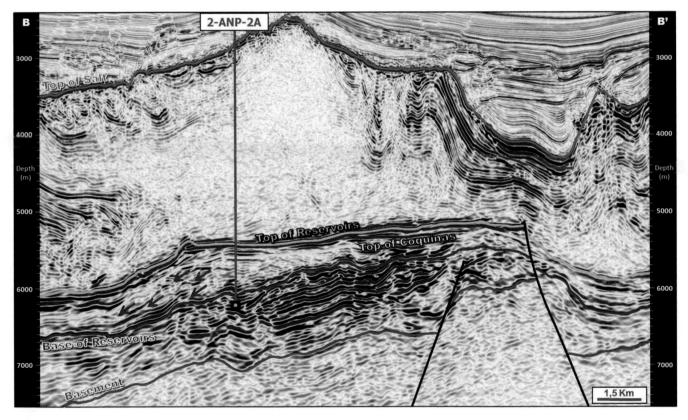

Figure 12. BB' seismic line, crossing 2-ANP-2A well (location in Figure 3). Note plane-parallel seismofacies of the Barra Velha Formation (between the green and yellow horizons) and progradational to chaotic seismofacies of the Itapema Formation (between the yellow and blue horizons). Blue arrows correspond to coquina wedges prograding in a north–northwest direction. (CGG Santos VI-A seismic data courtesy of CGG.)

moderate to high dissolution and moderate calcite cementation, which is also locally cemented by quartz. The lower interval is entirely in the water zone and displays bivalve rudstones with very low to moderate dissolution and intense quartz cementation (Silva et al., 2014).

At the 2-ANP-2A well location, the coquinas revealed a net pay of 144 m (472 ft) with an average porosity of 15% and permeabilities reaching up to 2990 mD.

The coquinas section typically shows chaotic to progradational seismofacies with weak amplitudes in the 2-ANP-2A area. In the southwest–northeast direction, the external geometry of the coquinas section shows a mound feature (Figure 2). Inline seismic sections from the CGG_SantosVI-A three-dimensional (north–south oriented) allow interpreting several coquina wedges that prograde toward north–northwest (Figure 12).

PRODUCTION PLAN

The extended well test (EWT), expected to start production in early 2017, will initiate the production of the Libra field, three years after the signing of the production sharing agreement. The pilot project is scheduled to start production in 2020. These two units will have a higher degree of flexibility in their design than the definitive systems, as they are constrained by fewer data than the definitive systems eventually will be; therefore, they are subjected to higher levels of uncertainty. The dynamic information acquired from these two systems is key for the definition of the future definitive production systems of Phase 1. The timeline of Libra development is shown in Figure 13.

As the project is still in its exploration phase, several reservoir scenarios have been defined. To establish development alternatives for the mapped scenarios, several conceptual studies are in progress, including (1) evaluation of different production capacity

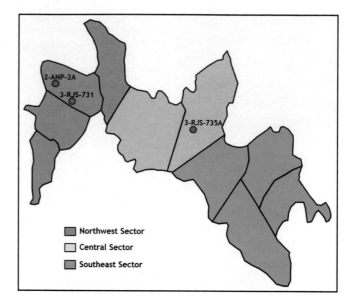

Figure 14. Preliminary development plan.

hosts, subsea technologies, and system design; (2) gas and oil export logistics; (3) accelerated production ramp-up; (4) local content requirements; (5) evaluation of different technologies to optimize production and recovery; and (6) optimization of well design and placement.

The current base case indicates that 4 floating production units (FPU) may be required for the development of the northwest sector. The number of FPUs for central and southeast sectors will depend on future exploratory well results. A schematic view of the preliminary field development is shown in Figure 14. This base case, defined with little information considering the huge area of Libra field, will be updated during the appraisal phase of the project.

The strategy of development while appraising is key to anticipating production. The reservoir risk management strategy and a combination of standardized and innovative technologies create a robust field development alternative to handle the reservoir and fluid uncertainties and associated risks.

HEALTH, SAFETY, AND ENVIRONMENT

Protection of people and the environment are core values for the Libra consortium. Understanding and mitigating health, safety, and environmental (HSE) risks creates a platform for safe and environmentally conscious operations.

Consortium members share HSE best practices. In line with the collaborative environment discussed earlier, the consortium developed Libra HSE principles

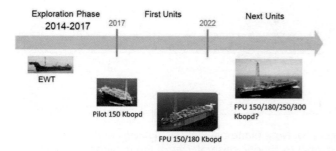

Figure 13. Timeline of Libra development. EWT = Extended Well Test; FPU = Floating Production Unit.

and established an HSE committee that meets quarterly to address relevant HSE topics and knowledge gained from global operations to strengthen the Libra HSE framework.

Collaboration with contractors and suppliers who have relevant ultra-deep water experience ensures a high level of competence to execute the complex development, including HSE expertise in specific areas, which complement the operator's processes to mitigate the project risks.

The Libra consortium developed a joint assurance process that enables peer reviews with participation of consortium member companies' experts. The joint assurance process focuses on key investment decisions. This process facilitates the sharing of best practice on process safety.

The Libra team is committed to driving continuous improvement in HSE practices, from exploration through design, construction, and production operations, promoting the culture of zero incidents to protect people, the environment, and facilities from the consequences of unsafe acts.

SUMMARY

The world-class presalt hydrocarbon accumulation in Libra was discovered in 2010 and since late 2013 has been the first block under a production sharing contract regime in Brazil. Libra block is operated by Petrobras with Shell, Total, CNOOC, CNPC, and PPSA as partners in the joint venture. Preliminary estimates indicate volumes of oil in place ranging between 8 and 12 billion BOE.

The trap is a four-way closure, approximately 550 km^2 (212 mi^2) in area, located in the northeast flank of a positive structural feature known as Santos External High, where the majority of the most significant Brazilian presalt discoveries lie.

The discovery well 2-ANP-2A displays a 27° API oil column of 329 m (1079 ft) in carbonate reservoirs comprising coquinas of the Itapema Formation and grainstones, stromatolites, and laminites of the Barra Velha Formation. The predominantly shallow water and probable high-energy paleoenvironment over the Santos External High decisively influenced the deposition of lacustrine carbonates with excellent porosities and permeabilities. The source rocks are interpreted to be organic-rich shales deposited in the distal lower-energy areas of the Itapema Formation. The top seal is the thick salt sequence deposited during the late Aptian.

The combination of a strategic development plan that provides a robust program of static and dynamic data acquisition with a phased project to balance the value of anticipated production against acceptable levels of risk exposure has been the strategy to exploit the Libra giant field in Santos Basin, off the coast of Brazil.

ACKNOWLEDGMENTS

The authors are thankful to Petrobras, Shell, Total, CNOOC, CNPC, and PPSA for the opportunity to publish this chapter. We would also like to thank Rogério Luiz Fontana for the initial drive and for motivating the authors to write this chapter. We are also thankful to Nolan Maia Dehler for the figures and insights on the structural analysis of the Libra area. The authors are thankful to Keith Lewis for his valuable contribution on the HSE topic. We also appreciate the discussion on the exploration history of Santos Basin presalt fields with Marcos Francisco Bueno de Moraes. The authors are also thankful to Arcioni Geraldo Pena, Haroldo Moraes Ramos, João Alberto Bach de Oliveira, José Sergival da Silva, and Rafael Cavalcante de Paiva for the assistance with figure drafting.

REFERENCES CITED

Carlotto, M. A., 2009, Evidências sísmicas de bioconstruções aptianas na seção pré-sal, porção norte da Bacia de Santos, VII Seminário de Interpretação Exploratória, Petrobras Internal Report, 6 p.

Carminatti, M., J. L. Dias, and B. Wolff, 2009, From turbidites to carbonates: Breaking paradigms in deep waters: Houston, TX, Offshore Technology Conference, OTC Proceedings, accessed January 17, 2017, http://dx.doi.org/10.4043/20124-MS.

Carminatti, M., B. Wolff, and L. A. P. Gamboa, 2008, New exploratory frontiers in Brazil: Madrid, Spain, 19th World Petroleum Congress, WPC Proceedings, accessed January 17, 2017, https://www.onepetro.org/conference-paper/WPC-19-2802.

Dehler, N. M., and A. A. Yamato, 2015, Contribuição à Estrutura e à Evolução Tectono-Sedimentar da Área de Libra: Petrobras Internal Report, 73 p.

Gomes, P. O., J. Parry, and W. Martins, 2002, The Outer high of the Santos Basin, southern São Paulo Plateau, Brazil: Tectonic setting, relation to volcanic events & some comments on hydrocarbon potential: AAPG Hedberg Conference "Hydrocarbon Habitat of Volcanic Rifted Passive Margins," Search and Discovery Article #90022, accessed October 21, 2016, http://www.searchanddiscovery.com/pdfz/abstracts/pdf/2002/hedberg_norway/extended/ndx_gomes.pdf.html.

Gomes, P. O., W. Kildonsk, J. Minken, T. Grow, and R. Barragan, 2008, The outer high of the Santos Basin, southern São Paulo Plateau, Brazil: Pre-salt exploration outbreak, paleogeographic setting and evolution of the syn-rift structures: Cape Town, South Africa, AAPG International Conference and Exhibition, accessed October 21, 2016, http://www.searchanddiscovery.com/abstracts/html/2008/intl_capetown/abstracts/471514.htm.

Kumar, N., L. A. P. Gamboa, B. C. Schreiber, and J. Mascle, 1977, Geologic history and origin of São Paulo plateau (southeastern Brazilian margin): Comparison with the Angolan margin and early evolution of the northern South Atlantic: Initial Reports of the Deep Sea Drilling Project, Washington, D.C., v. 39, p. 927–945.

Lima, C. C., M. R. Fetter, A. T. Silva, A. Moraes, C. M. O. Falcone, J. G. R. Silva, et al., 2005, Regimes Transcorrentes na Evolução da Margem Leste Brasileira: o Papel Ativo do Embasamento na Estruturação de Manati, Roncador e Jubarte, V Seminário de Interpretação Exploratória, Petrobras Internal Report, 8 p.

Magnavita, L. P., N. M. Dehler, L. C. Gomes, M. V. Sant'Ana, A. E. C. M. Souza, J. R. C. Menezes, et al., 2010, Arcabouço Tectônico e Cinemática do Pré-Sal do Sudeste Brasileiro, Petrobras Internal Report, 160 p.

Meisling, K. E., P. R. Cobbold, and V. S. Mount, 2001, Segmentation of an obliquely rifted margin, Campos and Santos basins, southeastern Brazil: AAPG Bulletin, v. 85, no. 11, p. 1903–1924.

Milani, E. J., J. A. B. Oliveira, J. L. Dias, P. Szatmari, and J. A. Cupertino, 2005, Basement control on structural styles and sediment pathways of southeast Brazil Atlantic margin basins (Brazil deep seas–deep-water sedimentation in the Southeast Brazilian Margin Project): Paris, France, AAPG International Conference and Exhibition, accessed October 21, 2016, http://www.searchanddiscovery.com/documents/abstracts/2005intl_paris/milani.htm.

Moreira, J. L. P., C. V. Madeira, J. A. Gil, and M. A. P. Machado, 2007, Bacia de Santos: Boletim de Geociências da Petrobras, v. 15, no. 2, p. 531–550.

Silva, C. M. A., V. S. S. Santos, R. P. Silva Filho, C. O. N. Leite, V. C. B. Oliveira, P. B Guimarães, et al., 2014, Análise Sedimentológica, Estratigráfica e Correlação Rocha-Perfil do Poço 2-ANP-02A-RJS, Área de Libra, Bacia de Santos: Petrobras Internal Report, 56 p.

Szatmari, P., J. C. Conceição, M. C. Lana, E. J. Milani, and A. P. Lobo, 1984, Mecanismo tectônico do rifteamento sul-atlântico: 33th Congresso Brasileiro de Geologia, v. 4, p. 1589–1601.

Szatmari, P., E. J. Milani, M. C. Lana, J. C. Conceição, and A. P. Lobo, 1985, How South Atlantic rifting affects Brazilian oil reserves distribution: Oil & Gas Journal, v. 83, no. 2, p. 107–113.

11

Vieira de Luca, Pedro Henrique, Hugo Matias, José Carballo, Jose Luis Algibez
Alonso, Jordi Tritlla, Mateu Esteban, et al., 2017, Breaking barriers and
paradigms in presalt exploration: The Pão de Açúcar discovery (offshore Brazil),
in R. K. Merrill and C. A. Sternbach, eds., Giant fields of the decade 2000–2010.
AAPG Memoir 113, p. 177–194.

Breaking Barriers and Paradigms in Presalt Exploration: The Pão de Açúcar Discovery (Offshore Brazil)

Pedro Henrique Vieira de Luca, Hugo Matias, José Carballo, Diana Sineva, Gustavo Antunes Pimentel

REPSOL SINOPEC, Praia de Botafogo, 300, 3rd Floor, Rio de Janeiro, Brazil (e-mails: ph.vieira@repsolsinopec .com, hmatias@repsol.com, jrcarballog@repsolsinopec.com, diana.sineva@repsolsinopec.com, gantunesp@ repsolsinopec.com)

Jordi Tritlla, Mateu Esteban, Rubén Loma

Repsol Exploración S.A., Madrid, Spain (e-mails: jordi.tritlla@repsol.com, mateu@szalai.com, ruben.loma@ repsol.com)

José Luis Algibez Alonso, Ricardo Perona Jiménez, Matthieu Pontet

Repsol USA, 2455 Technology Forest Boulevard, The Woodlands, Texas, U.S.A. (e-mails: jlalgibeza@repsol .com, rperonaj@repsol.com, mpontet@repsol.com)

Pedro Bonillo Martinez

Repsol Exploración, Novinskiy Boulevard 31, Moscow, Russia (e-mail: pbonillom@repsol.com)

Victor Vega

V&G Exploration, Inc., 2 Camden Ct., Sugar Land, Texas, U.S.A. (e-mail: victor@vngexploration.com)

ABSTRACT

Pão de Açúcar is certainly one of the most impressive and challenging hydrocarbon accumulations found in the prolific Campos Basin, offshore Brazil. This discovery opened a new frontier for exploration in Brazil´s ultradeep waters, in depths ranging from 2500 to 2900 m (8202 to 9514 ft). Pão de Açúcar is the third discovery made by a consortium integrated by Repsol Sinopec Brasil (operator), Statoil do Brasil, and Petrobras in the Concession BM-C-33, with estimated resources of 700 million bbl of light oil and 3 tcf of gas. This discovery is the result of the integrated work of a multidisciplinary international team using some of the most advanced technologies available today in the oil exploration industry in seismic imaging, drilling, formation evaluation, and fluid-rock sampling analysis. This discovery consists of a significant hydrocarbon column hosted within a unique reservoir made up of a variety of basic volcanic rocks overlain by pervasively silicified microbial carbonate platform/ramps, grading toward profundal lake facies. This chapter summarizes the main results of the exploration and ongoing appraisal work regarding this unique hydrocarbon accumulation, highlighting both the complexity of the discovered reservoirs and the operational and technical challenges faced, and still to overcome, before beginning production.

INTRODUCTION

The Pão de Açúcar (PdA) gas and condensate discovery is located within the BM-C-33 (C-M-539 block) concession in Campos Basin, offshore Brazil (Figure 1). The discovery is located offshore, approximately at 200 km (124 mi) from the coastline and in 2500 to 3000 m (8202 to 9843 ft) of water depth. The block was awarded during the seventh bid round to a consortium composed by Repsol Sinopec Brasil, as operator, and Statoil do Brasil. In 2009, Petrobras joined the consortium, acquiring a 30% interest in the project; Repsol Sinopec Brazil and Statoil each retained a 35% interest. PdA was discovered in 2012 by PdA1 exploration well (total depth [TD]: –7035 m [–23,081 ft] measured depth [MD], water depth [WD]: 2788.8 m [9450 ft]) (Figure 2).

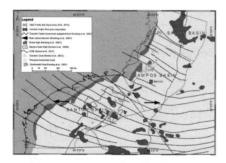

Figure 1. Regional map of the southeastern Brazilian continental margin showing the main structural elements and location of the BM-C-33 Concession (Pão de Açucar discovery).

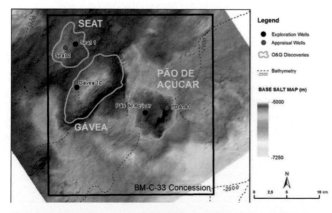

Figure 2. BM-C-33 map with drilled well and main discoveries inside the concession. Green polygons show the three oil and gas (O&G) discoveries in the BM-C-33 block.

The PdA structure holds a world-class retrograde gas–condensate accumulation with estimated resources of 700 million bbl of light oil and 3 tcf of gas. The PdA play is comprised of a structural-stratigraphic trap formed by lower Cretaceous silicified carbonates on top of a paleovolcanic edifice. Carbonate deposition occurred in an alkaline lacustrine environment. The structure was then sealed off by profundal lacustrine facies and the thick Aptian evaporitic section. Hydrocarbons are sourced from the underlying rift shales of the Lagoa Feia group.

REGIONAL GEOLOGICAL FRAMEWORK

The South Atlantic passive margins formed during Mesozoic times as a result of lithospheric extension followed by break-up of the Paleozoic Gondwana supercontinent. The initial structural style of the South Atlantic opening is dominated by rifting. A key element in this tectonic stage is the presence of asymmetric half grabens (Szatmari, 2000; Gibbs et al., 2003; Dias, 2005). This seems to be the dominant structural geometry on both the South American and African margins. This rifting event was diachronous, beginning in the south during the Jurassic and propagating northward to the equatorial segment during the early Cretaceous (Kumar et al., 2012) as the South American continent rotated clockwise relative to Africa with a pole located in northeast Brazil (Szatmari, 2000). Transfer zones divided the main Campos and Santos basins into structural domains; each developing several half grabens or grabens (Meisling et al., 2001). The margin inherited an east–northeast–west–southwest orientation, so rifting was oblique to this margin (Meisling et al., 2001). Significant tholeiitic continental magmatism affected the presalt section between 145 and 129 Ma across the Parana-Etedenka province of South America and West Africa (Hawkesworth, 1992; Meisling et al., 2001) with late Jurassic–Cretaceous basalt flows flooring the rift basins and covering intracratonic prerift successions. In central offshore Brazil (Santos, Campos, and Espírito Santo basins) (Figure 1) and in the African counterpart (Kwanza and lower Congo basins), this first stage of opening was followed by a postrift, thermal sag phase, initiated in the early Aptian and characterized by broad regional subsidence associated with cooling of the lithosphere (Thompson et al., 2015). This period, initially dominated by nonmarine (primarily lacustrine) facies during the Barremian, evolved to a shallow-water engulfment, culminating with an extensive evaporitic sequence in the Aptian. Current salt thickness is highly variable because of the extreme amount of salt halokinesis the area has experienced from the Cretaceous to the present (Mohriak et al., 2008). The dominant postsalt sediment filling in Campos and Santos basins consists of a thick sequence of upper Cretaceous carbonates and Cenozoic clastics, which include the main reservoirs of postsalt fields.

Campos Basin originated after the first phase of Mesozoic rifting that split apart South America and Africa. The associated transform and normal faults (Figure 1) acted as main focusing conduits for subaerial to sublacustrine volcanic piling in a general off-axis volcanic setting. The resulting horst-grabens and half grabens controlled the main depositional settings where shallow microbial carbonates, fine grained siliciclastics, and chemical sediments deposited in alkaline lacustrine environments during presalt times (Figure 3). The sag phase (transitional megasequence) (Guardado et al., 1989) was dominated by carbonate sedimentation in shallow-water environments (Carvalho et al., 2000; Gibbs et al., 2003; Dias, 2005), which probably evolved from brackish lacustrine environments to a wide alkaline/saline lake, with punctual marine transgressions. The sag sequence is dominated by lacustrine microbial carbonate facies.

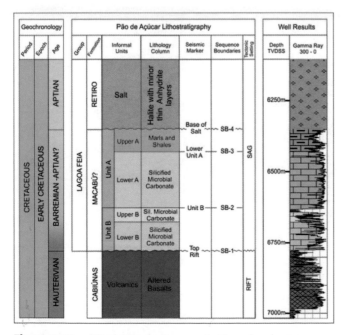

Figure 3. Simplified Pão de Açúcar stratigraphy chart.

EXPLORATION HISTORY AND PETROLEUM SYSTEM

Exploration History

The offshore basins of Campos, Santos, and Espírito Santo are the most prolific basins in Brazil, with presalt reservoirs recently playing a crucial role, therefore renewing interest in the postsalt turbidites that was present in the late 1990s. Giant discoveries like Libra, Sapinhoá, Lapa, Sagitário, and PdA are possibly the tip of the iceberg of as-yet undiscovered volumes of hydrocarbons in these world-class reservoirs. The first exploration well targeting the presalt reservoirs in Santos Basin deep waters was Parati (2005). Subsequently, the Tupi well resulted in the Lula field discovery (>8500 million bbl; from Upstream Data Tool™, Wood Mackenzie). Following this discovery, the drilling effort boosted to an accumulated total of more than 70 wildcats in 2015. Presently, more than 25 discoveries have been reported in the presalt play, with Lula ranking number one, followed by Libra and Franco. The overall presalt discoveries account for more than 30 billions of barrels (bbl) recoverable resource with current production set at 926,000 bbl/d (ANP, 2015).

The exploration in Concession BM-C-33 was initiated in 2006, based on the interpretation of the available three-dimensional seismic data. Several presalt targets were identified, and a drilling campaign of three exploration wells (Figure 2) resulted in two oil discoveries, Seat (2009–2010) and Gávea (2010–2011), and a gas and condensate discovery, PdA (2011–2012). These wells had significant technological challenges to overcome in order to drill beyond water depths of 2500 m (8282 ft) and TD of –7036 m (–23,084 ft) total vertical depth subsea (TVDSS). In 2013, the positive results led the consortium to decide to move to the appraisal phase and undertake an ambitious data acquisition campaign that included a three-dimensional HD-HR MAZ (high-density–high-resolution multiazimuth) seismic acquisition and several appraisal wells (including reservoir testing).

Petroleum System

The presalt petroleum system is reasonably well understood in the Santos Basin and has been addressed by several authors (Pontet and Sciamanna, 2012; Pontet and Merino, 2013; Pimentel et al., 2014; Pontet et al., 2014; Matias, 2015; Matias et al., 2015). In the Campos Basin, this prolific petroleum play lacks the same level of attention, and the main aspects of the PdA petroleum system are discussed below.

- Source rocks: Deposition of the main source rock sequences in the Brazilian presalt province occurred during the Barremian–lower Aptian rift stage. In Campos Basin, these rocks correspond to the Lagoa Feia group and are mainly composed of laminated shales with thicknesses ranging from 100 to 300 m (328 to 984 ft) (Guardado et al., 2000). The organic-rich Jiquiá shale is thought to be the main source of hydrocarbons in Campos (Winter et al., 2007; Tritlla et al., 2014), feeding both the recent presalt discoveries and traditional postsalt productive reservoirs. Campos Basin source rock typically has total organic carbon (TOC) varying from 2 to 6%, reaching up to 9% in some areas (Mello et al., 1994). The hydrogen index (HI) indicates a type I kerogen, with values of up to 900 mg HC/mg TOC (Mello et al., 1994). Although the Barremian–lower Aptian source rock had been extensively proved to be the main source rock of Campos Basin, its occurrence in the BM-C-33 block

area was one of the major uncertainties before the first drilling in the area.

- Reservoirs: PdA's productive interval contains a gas condensate column of around 476 m (1562 ft) comprising the following lithostatigraphic units: Hauterivian-Barremian basalts of Cabiúnas Formation and silicified microbial carbonates, probably of the Aptian Macabu Formation (Winter et al., 2007). The volcanic reservoir is separated by a tight shaly section approximately 50 m (164 ft) thick from the silicified carbonate section. The silicified carbonates reservoir section is divided into three main intervals with good reservoir properties, from bottom to top, lower Unit B, upper Unit B, and lower Unit A (Figures 3 and 4). The silicified carbonate units have undergone several pervasive diagenetic events that obliterated most of the original rock mineral composition, pore system characteristics, and sedimentary fabrics and structures, generating a peculiar reservoir

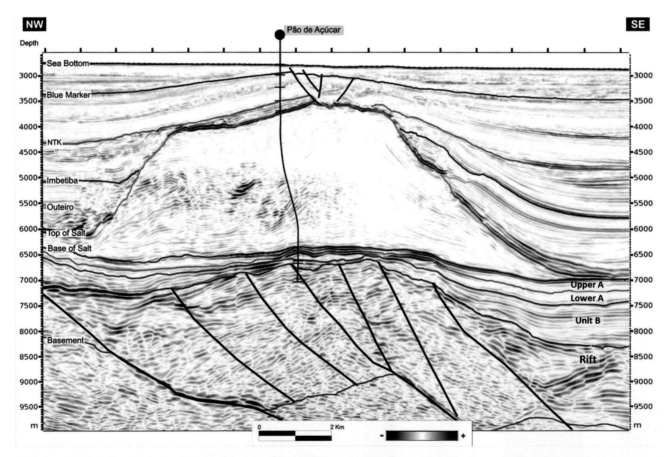

Figure 4. Regional seismic line illustrating the main seismic units and interpreted horizons drilled by the Pão de Açucar discovery well.

previously not recognized in the Brazilian presalt systems.

- Seals: The regional seal for the presalt carbonate reservoirs is the thick evaporitic sequence. Upper A unit forms a semiregional continuous sequence that, according to pressure measurements, can hold the thick fluid column height found in PdA. Specifically, at the top of the reservoir, a thin layer identified on the log by high resistivity and fast sonic velocity and on the seismic image by its high reflectivity and draping character may act as a major seal for the entire structure. No major faults are believed to affect seal integrity.

- Fluid types and hydrocarbon charge: According to Rangel et al. (2003), the Barremian–Aptian source rock entered the generation window during the Albian to Coniacian–Santonian and reached generation peaks in Turonian–Santonian and Miocene. Pressure–volume–temperature (PVT) data in PdA show a hydrocarbon whose characteristics range from 42 to 46° API and a gas/oil ratio (GOR) of approximately 5800 standard cubic feet per barrel (scf/bbl). Current basin modeling for the PdA area predicts hydrocarbon with 45° API and shows a good correlation with the PVT samples. On the other hand, the GOR predicted in the model (3200 scf/bbl) was highly underestimated, suggesting that additional dry gas charges from deeper kitchens might have occurred later in the basin's history. This hypothesis was corroborated by the use of slope factors derived from hydrocarbon composition (Thompson, 2004).

SEISMIC IMAGING CHALLENGES, INTERPRETATION, AND STRUCTURAL SETTING OF THE DISCOVERY

Presalt exploration in the Brazil offshore suffers from a generalized handicap related to the inadequacy of seismic imaging. Most of the surveys used to place presalt exploration wells were acquired for postsalt target imaging and therefore provide elusive images of the subsalt structural patterns.

BM-C-33 Seismic Imaging

The first exploration wells drilled by BM-C-33 consortium (Seat and Gávea) were positioned using legacy seismic data (Figure 5A). At that time, the seismic data available in BM-C-33 were a depth processing of a three-dimensional volume resulting from merging two different three-dimensional surveys. It is worth mentioning that none of these surveys were designed for presalt targets and all had significant limitations related to short cable and source characteristics. The well results brought to light significant misties in the postsalt section, particularly in Albian–Cenomanian strata. As a consequence, the well to seismic tie in the presalt section was also compromised.

Accordingly, in 2011 and 2012, it was decided to conduct in-house pre-stack depth migration (PSDM) processing (Figure 5B) using as input data that enhanced and matched gathers from the original processing. Analyses reveal that there was room

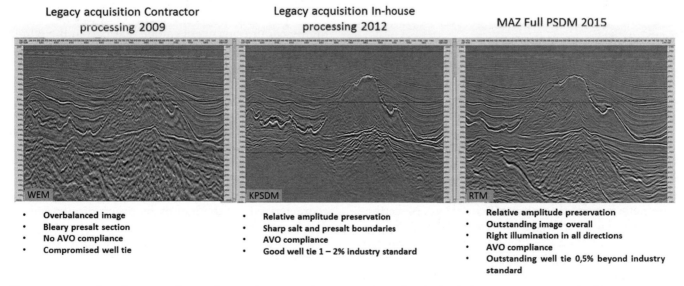

Figure 5. Comparison between A) 2009 legacy data, WEM (wave equation migration); B) the 2012 reprocessed cube, KPSDM (Kirchoff migration); and C) 2014 HD-HR MAZ (high-density–high-resolution multiazimuth) three-dimensional seismic data quality RTM (reverse time migration). PSDM = pre-stack depth migration; AVO = amplitude versus offset.

for velocity model improvement. A total of 24 iterations of anisotropic model updating and remigration were performed through the course of the project. The detailed anisotropic modeling resulted in a significant improvement of subsalt imaging that completely rearranged the structural and faulting framework and minimized well tying shortcomings. Consequently, the prospectivity of the area had to be fully reevaluated. Nevertheless, despite the fact that results from this in-house PSDM showed significant improvement of the presalt image, it was clear that PdA structure complexity required a special acquisition design followed by a tailor-made processing flow.

Starting in 2012, a three-dimensional HD-HR MAZ (high-density–high-resolution multiazimuth) acquisition design with full illumination study was set up by an in-house integrated team. Given the importance of having the most accurate and geologically sound velocity model, the well logging program was adjusted to accommodate velocity measurements at every step. Moreover, a walkaway VSP (vertical seismic profile), designed to provide a reliable anisotropy estimation, together with extended zero-offset VSP data were performed using state-of-the-art equipment and then adapted to a geological complexity processing workflow. Final acquisition and processed cubes were delivered in early 2015 and were of excellent quality (Figure 5C). The unprecedented presalt image allowed detailed structural and stratigraphic interpretation of PdA and also provided the desired dataset for a seismically driven reservoir characterization of this complex reservoir.

Seismic Interpretation

The PdA discovery can be described as a lacustrine isolated carbonate platform deposited in Barremian–Aptian times on top of a volcanic paleohigh of Cabiúnas Formation (Hauterivian). Developing a proper seismic stratigraphic framework of these sequences is a difficult task due to the lack of detailed chronostratigraphic data and the obliteration of original internal seismic facies patterns mainly by tectonic and diagenetic processes (mainly silicification). Nevertheless, the seismic stratigraphic framework of the presalt section allowed the identification of four major sequences overlying the interpreted top of the basement (Figure 4). From this surface to the base of the salt, the identified sequences are rift, Unit B (late rift), and lower and upper Unit A (sag).

The lowermost section of the presalt, interpreted as the acoustic basement, is recognized by weak and chaotic reflectors together with reflection-free zones, and is affected by the faults generated during the main rifting episodes. This section is composed of gneisses and related metamorphic rocks and is bounded by top basement surface (SB-0) (Figure 6). Above this unit, the seismic character changes abruptly to patterns of more continuous, low-frequency, high-amplitude, sometimes chaotic, occasionally oblique, and divergent reflections related to syn-rift deposits of the rift sequence. This interval is strongly affected by normal faulting. The sequence is topped by a boundary (SB-1) (Figure 6) identified by toplaps or truncated reflections and by onlaps of the overlying sediments on top of the volcanic paleohighs.

The first transgressive carbonatic sequence (Unit B) unconformably overlays volcanic rocks, filling half grabens and onlaping the paleohighs generated by the rotated blocks. The seismic internal pattern is characterized by strong and continuous reflectors, sometimes parallel to subparallel, sometimes progradational, showing onlaping and downlaping reflection terminations over the paleohighs or becoming conformable close to the top of the sequence. Laterally, divergent reflection patterns mark a transition to profundal facies. The sequence is interpreted as the start-up of a carbonate platform formation comprising a possible initial phase of backstepping and a late prograding parasequence topped by sequence boundary SB-2 (Figure 6). A possible maximum flooding surface (MFS) has been identified in seismic image and linked in well data to an increase in gamma ray (GR) readings related to a regional uranium anomaly. The marker is also identified in adjacent areas as the surface separating lower Unit B from upper Unit B. This highly continuous event can be mapped in the whole presalt sequence and it is defined by a high-amplitude reflector with toplaps and truncations indicating possible subaereal exposure and erosion.

The lower Unit A sequence is represented by a clear variation of reflection patterns from bench interior areas to platform margin. This sequence is limited by SB-2 at the base and is topped by SB-3 (Figure 6), sequence boundary represented by a high-amplitude very continuous negative reflection. The interval is characterized by an abrupt thickening in the margin characterized predominantly by prograding, moundy, and chaotic reflection patterns.

The top presalt sequence (upper Unit A) displays distinct continuous parallel, high-amplitude reflections comprising profundal lake facies considered to be a sealing unit that locally overlays the presalt reservoirs. The sequence is limited on top by the base of the massive salt of Retiro Formation (SB-4), which effectively seals off the presalt section.

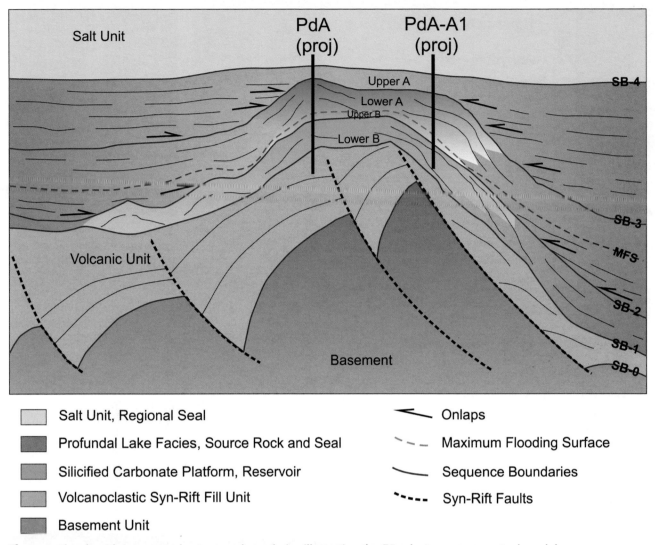

Figure 6. Sketch with interpreted sequence boundaries illustrating the Pão de Açúcar conceptual model.

SEDIMENTOLOGY, DIAGENESIS, AND RESERVOIR PROPERTIES

Sedimentology

A sedimentological and diagenetic study was performed to describe the sedimentary, magmatic, and hydrothermal processes that interacted to create the PdA's unique geological scenario (Figure 7). To achieve these goals, state-of-the-art techniques—including optical and UV petrology, scanning electron microscophy-energy dispersive spectroscopy (SEM-EDS), field emission scanning electron microscope (FESEM), electron probe micro analysis (EPMA), micro X-ray fluorescence (μ-XRF), carbon–oxygen (C-O) stable isotopes, argon–argon (Ar–Ar) (step heating) absolute dating, fluid inclusions studies (fluid inclusions

petrology, microthermometry, confocal laser scanning microscopy [CLSM], micro Fourier transform infra-red spectroscopy [μ-FTIR], μ-Raman spectroscopy), and Pressure–volume–temperature-composition (PVTx) hydrocarbon-bearing fluid inclusion modeling—were applied to unravel a very complex geological and fluid history.

- Volcanic rocks: The oldest unit drilled in PdA well correspond to sublacustrine, glass-rich, hydrothermally altered basalts. This volcanic sequence characterized by pillow-lavas, pillow breccias, hyaloclastites, and laminated surge deposits, suggests that tholeiitic basaltic volcanism took place in a sublacustrine shallow environment (Figures 8 and 9). Recovered volcanics are highly vesicular and rich in glass and plagioclase glomerocrysts, providing an overall glomeroporphyritic texture with minor

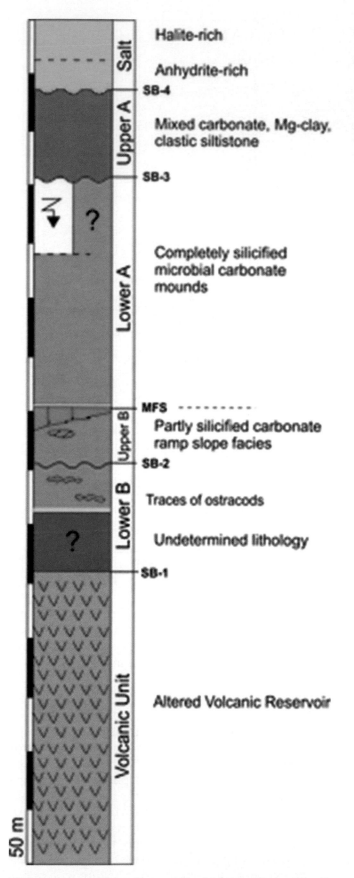

Figure 7. Stratigraphic column of Pão de Açucar discovery well.

Figure 8. Volcanic facies observed in formation micro-imaging (FMI) image log. A) Amalgamated pillow-lava. B) Pillow-breccia to hyaloclastite succession, topped by a highly laminated ash-fall.

clynopyroxene (titanoaugite) and accessory ilmenite/titanomagnetite. Early deuteric alteration is represented by the palagonitization of the pillow-lava glass-rich outer shells. Primary porosity is preserved in the pillow-lava horizons, represented by interconnected interpillow tetrahedral megapore space. Vesicles are empty or otherwise filled up by late secondary alteration minerals such as chlorite, blocky calcite, and low-temperature K-feldspar.

- Lake sediments: Depositional fabrics are poorly preserved due to the intense silicification overprinting. Only the comparison with other less silicified cores in presalt Brazil (mainly Santos Basin) allowed the reconstruction of the sedimentary sequence. These lake sediments are considered to be Barremian–Aptian in age, but no age-diagnostic fossils have been encountered in PdA. Two sedimentary units, defined on the basis of well logs, onlap the underlying volcanic unit; from bottom to top, their lithology is summarized as follows (Figure 9).

  ○ B unit. Well log patterns differentiate a lower B package with a basal, undetermined laminated lithology (resedimented ash falls?) and partly silicified, brecciated microbialitic carbonates, with relicts of spheruliths, shrubs, and ostracods. The base of the lower B package in contact with the volcanics is poorly understood in terms of lithologies and depositional geometries. The upper B unit is also made up of partly

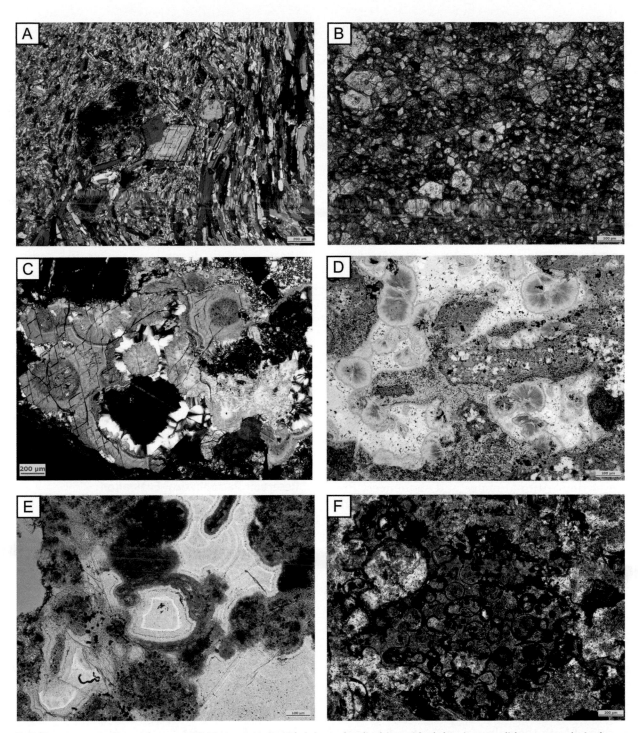

Figure 9. PdA representative rock types. A) Upper A Unit with injected anhydrite with dolomite xenoliths, crossed nicols.
B) Upper A Unit with deep lake/profundal facies with calcitic microspheruliths and euhedral planar dolomite (methanogenic?).
C) Upper A Unit, healing phase with hydrothermally metamorphosed alkaline lake profundal facies, heavy recrystallized former microbial spherulites partially replaced by chalcedony, primary lacustrine kerolite partially preserved, and crossed nicols.
D) Lower A Unit with heavily silicified microbial carbonate with some recrystallized still recognizable carbonate remnants, an open space vug fully cemented by opal globules and late megaquartz while others remain partially cemented, opal now inverted to microquartz with a net microporosity gain, and plain polarized light. E) Lower B Unit with completely silicified ostracod rich horizon and plane polarized light. F) Basalt, glass shard with perlitic texture within an altered glassy matrix, and plain polarized light.

silicified carbonates, mostly coarse and fine-grained doloclastic/calciclastic deposits mixed with fine-grained siliciclastics and volcaniclastics. Lower B has been interpreted as a transgressive system tract (TST) separated from the highstand system tract (HST) (upper B) by an MFS related to the uranium anomaly observed in log data.

o   A unit. This informal unit has two packages based on well logs. The lower A package is made up of extensively dolomitized microbial carbonate buildups (traces of shrubs and spheruliths) that are presently silicified with important vuggy-cavernous and breccia porosity. The upper A package consists of kerolite/talc-rich, fine-grained calciclastic/doloclastic/siliciclastic profundal facies, with debris of spheruliths and locally highly recrystallized. As seen on seismic records, the upper A onlaps the sequence boundary at the top of the lower A. The upper A profundal facies at the well location appear to be laterally grading into a carbonate mound at the top of the structure.

Both A and B units are presently highly brecciated and silicified by the late hydrothermal system. This intense hydrothermal alteration coupled with limited rock sampling prevented the exact determination of depositional facies and sequences. Presilicification porosity is found in only some scarce nonsilicified resisters, mainly as intercrystalline porosity in dolomite-rich rocks. Main reservoir porosity is largely found in the highly brecciated and silicified vuggy-cavernous and microporous lower A and B packages.

Diagenesis

Hydrothermal overprinting and reservoir formation:
A hydrothermal system focused by deep rooted faults affected the whole presalt column, including the volcanic unit, and produced (1) hydraulic fracturing of both the volcanic and sedimentary column; (2) hydrothermal alteration of basalt; (3) almost complete replacement of clean microbial carbonates by silica, enhancing overall porosity; and (4) hydrothermal metamorphism of the upper A kerolite-rich profundal lake facies (Figure 10). It cannot be discarded that early phases of hydrothermalism took place during carbonate deposition, but most of the intense alteration clearly postdates carbonate deposition and early diagenesis.

Hydrothermal basalt alteration:
PdA basalts were affected by a pervasive hydrothermal event. This hydrothermal fluid circulation, triggered by a high geothermal gradient, was prolonged enough to alter silicate minerals formed at magmatic temperatures, leaching silica to the hydrothermal fluid and originating new, hydrous minerals more stable under the new hydrothermal conditions (chlorite, dolomite, calcite, quartz, adularia) (Figure 10).

Hydrothermal alteration of lake sediments:
Hydrothermal corrosion, porosity formation, and silica precipitation have a major impact on the PdA's present-day reservoir properties. The intensity of silicification greatly depends on the original composition of the sedimentary rock. The entire lacustrine unit is cross-cut by a network of millimeter- to decimeter-thick quartz veinlets (stockwork, boxwork) generated after hydraulic fracturing of the enclosing rock (Figure 10). These fractures were probably the main conduits for the hydrothermal fluids and thus controlled the flow of the silica-rich hydrothermal solutions into the former sedimentary rocks. The sum of all the hydrothermal features created the present-day PdA siliceous reservoir, with abundant vugs, fractures, caverns, and patches of microporosity.

Reservoir Petrophysical Evaluation

An extensive wireline (WL) program, composed by logs such as nuclear magnetic resonance (NMR), lateral log resistivity, spectral gamma ray, elemental capture spectroscopy (ECS), resistivity image (FMI), sonic scanner, sidewall core (SWC), and wireline formation testing (MDT), has been run in the PdA well. These data together with logging while drilling (LWD) logs, petrographic and petrological studies, digital rock physics (high-resolution tomography), conventional lab measurements, and cuttings evaluation form the basis of PdA petrophysical interpretation.

Porosity Assessment

PdA porosity assessment is based mainly on NMR, neutron-density and sonic data, and SWC analyses (both digital and conventional). Additional studies have been performed with image logs in order to characterize the secondary porosity. The quantification of porosity is relatively well controlled in the PdA well. Different methods give similar results, and the uncertainty associated with it is very low when compared to

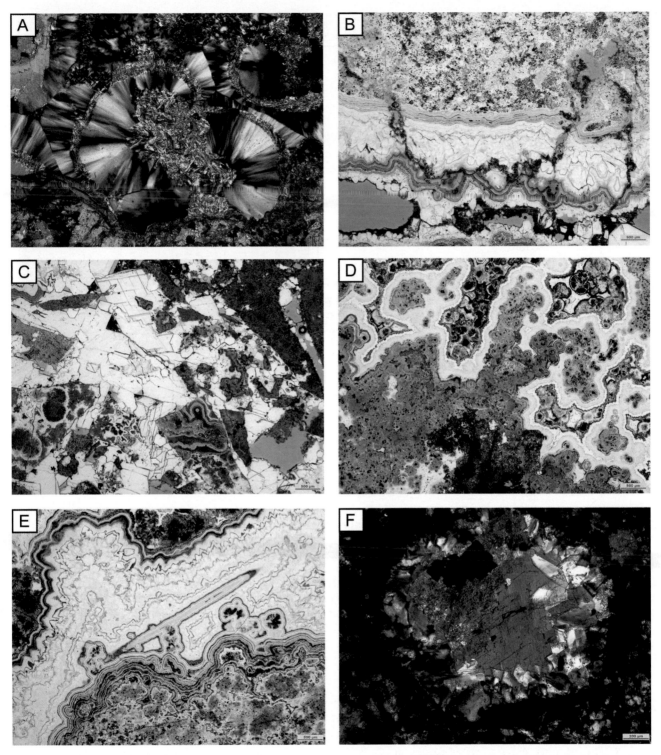

Figure 10. PdA hydrothermal rock features. A) Hydrothermally metamorphosed alkaline lake profundal facies, former microbial spherulites replaced by radiated chalcedony, primary lacustrine kerolite recrystallized to talc flakes, and crossed nicols. B) Silicified carbonate cross-cut by hydrothermally induced (hydraulic) vein, encrusted by several generations of silica (opal-chalcedony-quartz), porosity is represented by vugs along a corroded stylolite and in-vein vugs, and plane polarized light. C) Polimictic, mixed hydraulic/collapse breccia composed of a jigsaw of angular silicified and chalcedonic fragments partially cemented by late dolomite with remnant micro-vuggy to vuggy porosity (blue), and plane polarized light. D) Heavily silicified microbial carbonate, some recrystallized and corroded nonsilicified remnants surrounded by former opal and chalcedony, opal is now inverted to microquartz with a net microporosity (greenish to bluish colors) gain, and plain polarized light. E) Detail of a partially cemented vug, bladed calcite pseudomorphosed by silica encrusted by several chalcedony generations, and plain polarized light. F) Basalt, euhedral adularia crystals (bluish color) rimming a volcanic vesicle, remaining porosity is filled blocky calcite and pyrite, and crossed nicols.

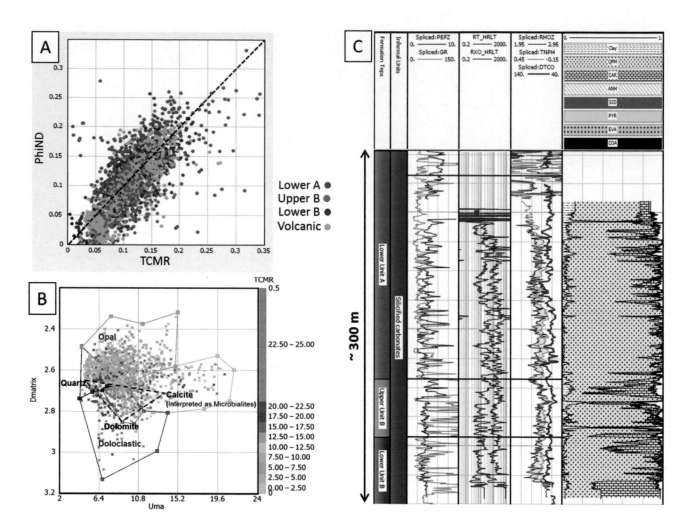

Figure 11. A) Cross-plot between nuclear magnetic resonance NMR and neutron-density total porosity presenting excellent match of different porosity estimation methods. B) Matrix identification cross-plot (apparent volumetric cross section [UMA] vs. apparent matrix grain density [Dmatrix] showing the influence of quartz and opal in the rock composition). C) Composity log for the silicified carbonate reservoir displaying formation tops in Tracks 1 and 2, gamma ray and photoelectrical factor (PEFZ) in Track 3, deep and invaded zone resistivities (RT and RXO) in Track 4; density (RHOZ), neutron (TNPH), and compressional sonic slowness (DTCO) in Track 5; and spectroscopy log (ECS) converted lithology in Track 6 (Clay). QFM = quartz, mica, and feldspar; Car = carbonate; ANH = anhydrite; SID = siderite; PYR = pyrite; EVA = evaporite; COA = coal.

other parameters such as water saturation and permeability (Figure 11A).

Silicified Carbonates Reservoir Porosity Assessment

Silicified carbonates constitute the main reservoir of PdA. Due to the intensity of hydrothermal events that acted in PdA, the log response no longer corresponds to the initial host rock characteristics but to the resulting silicified carbonate rock (Figure 11B). Estimates done using spectroscopy logs (ECS), cuttings, and sidewall cores indicated that the actual reservoir of PdA is comprised of approximately 90% of silica (quartz, chert, chalcedony, and opal) (Figure 11C).

Primary depositional porosity is practically absent in the calciclastic/doloclastic rocks. Porosity in the preserved carbonatic matrix section is mainly intercrystalline and vuggy and is usually enhanced by corrosion. In the silicified units, the porosity system is controlled by the intense hydrothermal events. Multiple events of carbonate dissolution, silica replacement and precipitation, fracturing, and vug generation of the silicified reservoir of PdA resulted in a complex porous reservoir. Silicified carbonates present four scales of porosity (micro, meso, macro, and mega), which can coexist at the same reservoir interval.

Microporosity is pervasive and, locally, can be very important. This sort of porosity can occur disseminated in the matrix or along chalcedony-opal-microquartz

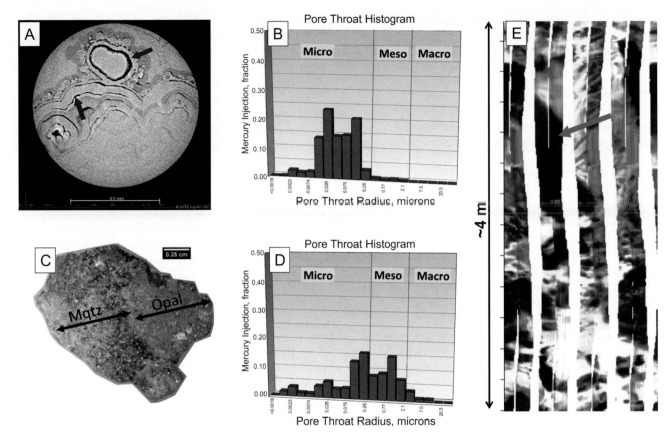

Figure 12. A) Sidewall core tomography showing chalcedony-opal-microquartz layering. Black layers (red arrows) represent micropore bands generated by opal dehydration processing (opal aging process). B) Pore throat radius distribution of sidewall core sample presented in Figure 12A. C) "Pseudo vug" porosity formed by the coalescence of micropores (opal aging) generating a "floating rock" texture (Mqtz = microquartz). D) Pore throat radius distribution of sidewall core sample presented in Figure 12C showing porosity ranging from micro to macro and predominance of mesopores. E) Megaporosity observed on resistivity borehole image.

(Figure 12A, B). Mesopores are observed in most of the SWC and are closely related to micropores; they result from the coalescence of micropores, which forms patches of high connectivity. Occasionally, this process is very intense and the merging of microporosity produces the generation of secondary "pseudo-vugs" (Figure 12C, D).

Macropores are not observed in all SWC samples, although they are consistently observed in NMR porosity and inferred from borehole resistive image logs. This sort of porosity results mainly from dissolution processes, which have generated vugs with different sizes, varying from a few millimeters to a few centimeters. Frequently, vuggy porosity is observed along fractures planes, indicating that dissolution processes are associated with the fracture network. In general, macroporosity occurs with micro and meso and might have an important role in the permeability of the reservoir. Megapores are genetically related to macropores; they occur in some preferential zones and can be

observed only in borehole resistivity images as cavernous porosity (Figure 12E).

Despite the complexity of the pore system, different porosity estimation methods are consistent and converge to provide similar results. Petrophysical interpretation of this reservoir shows a very high net-to-gross (NTG), between 85 and 95%, with average porosity around 13%.

Volcanic Reservoir Porosity Assessment

Most of the porosity found in the volcanic reservoir is related to the primary textures/structures of the volcanic sequence. Interpillow tetrahedral space, vesicles, and irregular breccia interparticle porosity constitute most of the porous space of the volcanic reservoir.

Secondary porosity is observed mainly in the fractures, which are very common in the volcanic section. In some intervals, fractures planes are conjugated, generating a complex interconnected porous system. Possible vugs are observed in the resistivity images, although they are uncommon.

Reservoir Deliverability

The heterogeneity of the porosity system reflects a complex pore–perm relationship that provides uncertainty related to the permeability assessment and the reservoir's deliverability modeling. Distinct permeability estimation methods derived from core, logging, and well testing provide different results.

A well testing was performed in a 218-m thick interval, including the three silicified carbonate reservoir units: lower A, upper B, and lower B. Although drill-stem test (DST) results are not entirely conclusive due to operational problems, first estimations of the average permeability are between 100 and –200 mD, which proved to be much more optimistic than WL- and SWC-derived permeability measurements. The difference between each method is related to the magnitude of each measurement. Due to the scale of the well test analysis, it was possible to characterize the permeability of the whole perm–pores systems, including the main vuggy/cavy/fractured systems, which were not properly investigated by the other methods.

Volcanics were not tested, and the permeability was estimated with well logs. The permeability obtained from well logs for this section is very variable; in the most permeable zones, log permeabilities estimated values up to 560 mD. However, as observed in the silicified carbonate section and other vuggy and fractured systems, well log permeabilities seems to be pessimistic and do not represent the real reservoir deliverability. Although they do not share exactly the same properties, volcanic reservoirs of Cabiúnas Formation have already proved their capability to produce. Badejo and Linguado fields, both from Campos Basin, have already produced from this formation (Reis et al., 2014). Similar to PdA volcanic rocks, fractures and primary porosity (vesicles) have an important role in the porous system of Badejo and Linguado volcanic reservoirs (Mizusaki, 1986).

DISCUSSION OF RESULTS AND EXPLORATORY/ DEVELOPMENT IMPLICATIONS

Proposed Analogs

Due to its complex geological history, comprehensive PdA analogs are not found or recognized in the literature. PdA geological history can be split into three episodes: (1) volcanism, (2) lacustrine deposition, and (3) hydrothermalism. Volcanism in PdA must be thoroughly compared with coeval volcanism occurring throughout the Brazilian Atlantic margin (Mizusaki et al., 1992, 2002, for instance) or even with mid-Atlantic hydrothermal mounds (TAG geothermal system) (Knott et al., 1998; Kelley et al., 2007), which are not the subject of this paper. Also, presalt, lacustrine sediments have a plethora of papers devoted to present-day alkaline carbonates (Bertani and Carozzi, 1985; Guardado et al., 2000; Spadini, 2008; Terra et al., 2010, among others). Consequently, the most differential and outstanding feature for petroleum exploration in the region is to unravel how an off-axis, sublacustrine hydrothermal system originated, evolved, and contributed to PdA reservoir formation and enhancement.

Strictly speaking, high-temperature, hydrothermally mediated petroleum reservoirs are poorly documented. Probable relevant examples are the Parkland oil field (Packard et al., 2001) and Blackburn, Grant Canyon and Bacon Flat oil fields (Hulen et al., 1990, 1994). In Parkland, a hydrothermal system was focused through fractures and scavenged silica from the granitic basement. This fluid ascended through deep faults, boiled-off, and silicified the tight Wabamun limestone, creating a net porosity gain. Likewise, Hulen et al. (1990, 1994) proposed a similar reservoir origin for the Blackburn, Grant Canyon, and Bacon Flat oil fields (United States), although silica is not as abundant as in PdA. In these oil field examples, meteoric waters percolated through deep, listric faults, mobilized, and rose by buoyancy under an extensional regime, with enhanced thermal flow. The PdA reservoir also presents striking similarities to Au–Ag-bearing low-sulfidation epithermal systems (Buchanan, 1981; Hedenquist et al., 1992; Sillitoe, 1993).

The PdA reservoir records a very complex history that started with an off-axis volcanic episode followed by the development of an alkaline, lacustrine, carbonate succession. Later, an intense hydrothermal system affected the entire presalt section, altering volcanics, scavenging silica, and silicifying the microbial carbonate platform. Silicification was extensive (although not 100%) and represented a net porosity gain. Main oil migration took place after intense silicification. These are the main elements of a new conceptual reservoir model that could be a predictable geological tool in the Brazil and Angola offshore basins.

Exploration Implications and Lessons Learned

Within the dozen ultradeep water operations being developed in the Brazil presalt, PdA exploration and appraisal activities occupy a preeminent place in terms of both operational and geological complexity.

Being successful in operations that involve drilling wells in more than 2800 m (9186 ft) of water, through several kilometers of salt, as well as penetrating and properly characterizing an unprecedented reservoir required an enormous effort from multidisciplinary teams integrated by the operator and partner's staff. Because of the high cost of these operations, extremely good planning and continuous optimization were required.

One of the keys in PdA success has been the innovative seismic acquisition and processing that allowed us to obtain extraordinary seismic-quality imaging of the base of the salt and presalt sections. The results of this work resulted in a profound reevaluation of the hydrocarbon potential of the area, thus reorienting further exploration and appraisal activities. Only through the incorporation of the most advanced and at times not yet commercially available technologies in the process, it was possible to obtain a reliable and consistent image, with direct impact on PdA target illumination allowing a continued detailed characterization of this complex reservoir. The HD-HR MAZ PSDM processing was performed with close collaboration between BM-C-33 consortium members, adding experience and knowledge at every step. Interpreters were also fully involved, as were petrophysicists. Valuable support came from the management side.

Of paramount importance has been the fluent interaction between geological and geophysical (G&G) multidisciplinary teams consisting of geologists, geophysicists, petrophysicists, reservoir engineers, sedimentologists, and other high-profile experts who describe the complex and—in some cases—completely unknown processes that have led to the unique PdA reservoir architecture. This understanding allowed rapid introduction of modifications in data acquisition for reservoir characterization and drilling programs.

One of the main challenges the industry is facing are the onerous costs of ultradeep-water operations. As part of the effort to implement cost-reduction initiatives, a reevaluation of data acquisition programs was undertaken with the goal of optimizing WL logging operations, maximizing efforts in logging while drilling (LWD), and avoiding data duplication. For this purpose, a careful comparison of results of WL and LWD tools in terms of data quality, reliability, impact on reservoir characterization, response against unprecedented reservoirs, and costs has been carried out. A milestone in this process has been using new technologies and methodologies in mud logging data acquisition and interpretation. X-ray diffraction together with X-ray fluorescence (XRD/XRF) of drill cuttings and advanced mud gas analyses techniques are now used in the rig and in real time to decrypt complex lithologies and characterize the hydrocarbon fluids' properties. Advanced mud gas analysis (in-house

model) has proved to be capable of providing API and GOR values in real time and continuously across the reservoir section. The results obtained represent an excellent approximation of the hydrocarbon PVT composition from offset wells. Moreover, new methodologies for fluid contact determination allowed important savings in WL fluid sampling.

It is worth noting the significant improvement in drilling efficiency obtained from including highly experienced specialists from Statoil and Petrobras on the operational teams. The partners' alignment of efforts in such a complex operational environment has shown to be extremely productive, indicating the right way of working in this kind of megaproject.

ACKNOWLEDGMENTS

The authors thank the members of the BM-C-33 appraisal team for their insightful discussions and efforts throughout this project, primarily, Alexandre Mattos, Tacilaine Saciloto, Carolina Torres, Gustavo Torres, Eric Cayo, Luis Escalona, Leonardo Legarreta, Sánchez-Pérez-Cejuela, and Didier Wlozsowsky, and also Patrick Calvano for producing some of the artwork herein presented. Likewise, we would like to thank all the editors, coordinators, and reviewers for their time, support, and valuable remarks, in particular Claudio Bartolini, Beverly Molyneux, Kelsy Taylor, Robert Merrill, and Charles Sternbach. The authors are especially grateful to Repsol Sinopec, Statoil, and Petrobras for allowing publication of these results and constructive criticism in reviewing the paper. The authors would like to thank the subsurface imaging team in Houston for their innovative ideas and continuous support.

REFERENCES CITED

ANP (National Agency for Petroleum, Natural Gas and Biofuels), 2015, Boletim da Produção de Petróleo e Gás Natural: no. 58, Junho, p. 15.

Bertani, R. T., and A. V. Carozzi, 1985, Lagoa Feia formation (lower Cretaceous), Campos basin, offshore Brazil: Rift valley stage Lacustrine carbonate reservoirs: Journal of Petroleum Geology, v. 8, no. 1, p. 37–58.

Buchanan, L. J., 1981, Precious metal deposits associated with volcanic environments in the southwest: Arizona Geological Society Digest, v. 14, p. 237–262.

Carvalho, M. D., U. M. Praça, A. C. Silva-Telles Jr., R. J. Jahnert, and J. L. Dias, 2000, Bioclastic carbonate lacustrine facies models in the Campos basin (lower Cretaceous), Brazil, in E. H. Gierlowski-Kordesch and K. R. Kelts, eds., Lake basins through space and time: AAPG Studies in Geology 46, p. 245–256.

Dewey, F., M. Meulen, and P. Whitfield, 2006, Using dual-azimuth data to image below salt domes: First Break, v. 24, p. 55–59.

Dias, J. L., 2005, Tectônica, estratigráfia e sedimentação no Andar Aptiano da margem este Brasileira: Boletim de Geociências da Petrobrás, v. 13, p. 7–25.

Gibbs, P. B., E. R. Brush, and J. C. Fiduk, 2003, The evolution of the syn-rift and transition phases of the central/southern Brazilian and West African conjugate margins: The implications for source rock distribution in time and space, and their recognition on seismic data: Rio de Janeiro, Brazil, 8th International Congress of the Brazilian Geophysical Society, September 14–18, 6 p.

Guardado, L. R., L. A. P. Gamboa, and C. F. Lucchesi, 1989, Petroleum geology of the Campos basin, Brazil: A model for a producing Atlantic-type basin, in J. D. Edwards and A. Santogrossi, eds., Divergent/passive margin basins: AAPG Memoir 48, p. 3–79.

Guardado, L. R., A. R. Spadini, J. S. L. Brandão, and M. R. Mello, 2000, Petroleum system of the Campos basin, Brazil, in M. R. Mello and B. J. Katz, eds., Petroleum systems of the South Atlantic margins: AAPG Memoir 73, p. 317–324.

Hawkesworth, C. J., 1992, Paraná magmatism and the opening of the South Atlantic, in B. C. Storey, ed., Magmatism and the causes of continental break-up: Geological Society Special Publication 68, p. 293–302.

Hedenquist, J. W., A. G. Reyes, S. F. Simmons, and S. Taguchi, 1992, The thermal and geochemical structure of geothermal and epithermal systems: A framework for interpreting fluid inclusion data: European Journal of Mineralogy, v. 4, no. 5, p. 989–1015.

Huang, T., S. Xu, J. Wang, and G. Ionescu, 2008, The benefit of TTI tomography for dual azimuth data in Gulf of Mexico: SEG Technical Program Expanded Abstracts 2008, p. 222–226.

Huang, T., H. Zhang, and J. Young, 2009, Subsalt imaging using TTI reverse time migration: Leading Edge SEG, v. 28, no. 4, p. 448–452.

Hulen, J. B., S. R. Bereskin, and L. C. Bortz, 1990, High-temperature hydrothermal origin for fractured carbonate reservoirs in the Blackburn oil field, Nevada: Geologic Note: AAPG Bulletin, v. 74, no. 8, p. 1262–1272.

Hulen, J. B., F. Goff, J. R. Ross, L. C. Bortz, and S. R. Bereskin, 1994, Geology and geothermal origin of Grant Canyon and Bacon Flat oil fields, Railroad valley, Nevada: AAPG Bulletin, v. 78, no. 4, p. 596–623.

Kelley, D. S., G. L. Fruh-Green, J. A. Karson, and K. A. Ludwig, 2007, The Lost City hydrothermal field revisited: Oceanography, v. 20, no. 4, p. 90–99.

Kenyon, W. E., P. I. Day, C. Straley, and J. F. Willemsen, 1988, A three-part study of NMR longitudinal relaxation properties of water-saturated sandstones: SPE Formation Evaluation, v. 3, no. 3, p. 622–636.

Knott, R., Y. Fouquet, J. Honnorez, S. Petersen, and M. Bohn, 1998, Petrology of hydrothermal mineralization: A vertical section through the TAG mound, in Proceedings of the Ocean Drilling Program: Scientific Results, v. 158, p. 5–26.

Kumar, N., A. Danforth, P. Nuttall, J. Helwig, D. E. Bird, and S. Venkatraman, 2012, From oceanic crust to exhumed mantle: A 40 year (1970–2010) perspective on the nature of crust under the Santos basin, SE Brazil, in W. U. Mohriak, A. Danforth, P. J. Post, D. E. Brown, G. C. Tari, M. Nemčok, et al., eds., Conjugate divergent margins: London, Geological Society, Special Publications, v. 369, DOI:10.1144/SP369.16

Matias, H., 2015, Freakonomics of the pre-salt (offshore Brazil): A perspective of 10 years of exploration: Lisbon, AAPG European Regional Conference & Exhibition, accessed January 17, 2017, https://europeevents.aapg.org/ehome/lisbon2015/programmeday1/.

Matias, H., B. Ninci, R. Margem. F. Mattos, X. Guangsheng, R. Loma, et al., 2015, Unlocking Pandora: Insights from pre-salt reservoirs in Campos and Santos (offshore Brazil): Madrid, Spain, Proceedings of the 77th EAGE International Conference and Exhibition, 5 p.

Meisling, K. E., P. R. Cobbold, and V. S. Mount, 2001, Segmentation of an obliquely rifted margin, Campos and Santos basins, southeastern Brazil: AAPG Bulletin, v. 85, no. 11, p. 1903–1924.

Mello, M. R., W. U. Mohriak, E. A. M. Koutsoukos, and G. Bacoccoli, 1994, Selected petroleum systems in Brazil, in L. B. Magoon and W. G. Dow, eds., The petroleum system: From source to trap: AAPG Memoir 60, p. 499–512.

Mizusaki, A. M. P., 1986, Rochas ígneo-básicas do Neocomiano da Bacia de Campos: Caracterização e comportamento como reservatório de hidrocarbonetos: M.S. thesis, Federal University of Rio de Janeiro (UFRJ), 104 p.

Mizusaki, A. M. P., R. Petrini, P. Bellieni, P. Comin-Chiaramonti, J. Dias, A De Min, et al., 1992, Basalt magmatism along the passive continental margin of SE Brazil (Campos basin) : Contributions to Mineralogy and Petrology, v. 111, no. 2, p. 143–160.

Mizusaki, A. M. P., A. Thomaz-Filho, E. J. Milani, and P. De Césero, 2002, Mesozoic and Cenozoic igneous activity and its tectonic control in northeastern Brazil: Journal of South American Earth Sciences, v. 15, no. 2, p. 183–198.

Mohriak, W. U., 2005, Salt tectonics in Atlantic-type sedimentary basins: Brazilian and West African perspectives applied to the North Atlantic margin, in P. Post and N. Rosen, eds., Petroleum systems of divergent continental margin basins: Proceedings of the 25th Annual Bob F. Perkins Research Conference, Gulf Coast Section: SEPM, p. 375–413.

Mohriak, W. U., D. E. Brown, and G. Tari, 2008, Sedimentary basins in the central and south Atlantic conjugate margins: Deep structures and salt tectonics, in D.E. Brown and N. Watson, eds., Proceedings of the Central Atlantic Conjugate Margins Conference (Halifax), p. 89–102.

Packard, J. J., I. Al-Aasm, I. Samson, Z. Berger, and J. Davies, 2001, A Devonian hydrothermal chert reservoir: The 225 bcf Parkland field, British Columbia, Canada: AAPG Bulletin, v. 85, no. 1, p. 51–84.

Pimentel, G., H. Matias, B. Ninci, R. Loma, M. Esteban, J. Trilla, et al., 2014, New developments in the understanding of pre-salt reservoirs (offshore Brazil): Istanbul, Proceedings AAPG International Conference and

Exhibition, accessed October 25, 2016, http://www.searchanddiscovery.com/abstracts/html/2014/90194ice/abstracts/1948759.html.

Pontet, M., and S. Sciamanna, 2012, Source-rock contribution and petroleum system efficiency: Presalt cluster area, Santos basin, offshore Brazil: Nice, France, AAPG Hedberg Conference, Petroleum Systems, October 1–5, accessed October 25, 2016, http://www.searchanddiscovery.com/abstracts/html/2013/120098hedberg/abstracts/pont.htm.

Pontet, M., and D. Merino, 2013, Petroleum system applied from basin to reservoir scale: An application for the charge timing of the pre-salt cluster area, Santos basin, Brazil: Cartagena, Colombia, AAPG ICE 2013, September 9–11, accessed October 25, 2016, http://www.searchanddiscovery.com/abstracts/html/2013/90166ice/abstracts/pont.htm.

Pontet, M., G. Pimentel, and H. Matias, 2014, Assessment of the pore pressure distribution in the presalt Santos basin, Brazil: A regional approach for prospect de-risking: Istanbul, Proceedings AAPG International Conference and Exhibition, accessed October 25, 2016, http://www.searchanddiscovery.com/abstracts/html/2014/90194ice/abstracts/1948619.html.

Rangel, H. D., P. T. Guimarães, and A. R. Spadini, 2003, Barracuda and Roncador giant oil fields, deep-water Campos basin, Brazil, in M. T. Halbouty, ed., Giant oil and gas fields of the decade, 1990–1999: AAPG Memoir 78, p. 123–137.

Reis, G. S., A. M. Mizusaki, A. Roisenberg, and R. R. Rubert, 2014, Formação Serra Geral (Cretáceo da Bacia do Paraná): um análogo para os reservatórios ígneo-básicos da margem continental brasileira: Pesquisas em Geociências, v. 41, no. 2, p. 155–168.

Sillitoe, R. H., 1993, Epithermal models: Genetic types, geometrical controls and shallow features, in R. V. Kirkham, W. D. Sinclair, R. I. Thorpe, and J. M. Duke, eds., Mineral deposit modeling: Geological Association of Canada, Special Paper 40, p. 403–417.

Simmons, S. F., and B. W. Christenson, 1994, Origins of calcite in a boiling geothermal system: American Journal of Science, v. 294, no. 3, p. 361–400.

Sheriff, R. E., 1991, Encyclopedic dictionary of exploration geophysics: Society of Exploration Geophysicists, p. 384.

Spadini, A., 2008, Carbonate reservoirs in Brazilian sedimentary basins: 19th World Petroleum Congress, p. 1–16.

Szatmari, P., 2000. Habitat of Petroleum along the South Atlantic Margins, in M. R. Mello, B. J. Katz, eds., Petroleum Systems of South Atlantic Margins, AAPG Memoir, v. 73: Tulsa, Oklahoma, American Association of Petroleum Geologists, pp. 69–75.

Terra, G. G. S., A. R. Spadini, A. B. Franca, and C. L. Sombra, 2010, Carbonate rock classification applied to Brazilian sedimentary basins: Boletin Geociencias Petrobras, v. 18, p. 9–29.

Thompson, K., 2004, Interpretation of charging phenomona based on reservoir fluid (PVT) data, in J. M. Cubitt, W. A. England, and S. Larter, eds., Understanding petroleum reservoirs: Towards an integrated reservoir engineering and geochemical approach: Geological Society, London, Special Publications, 237, p. 7–26.

Thompson, D. L., J. Stilwell, and M. Hall, 2015, Lacustrine carbonate reservoirs from early Cretaceous rift lakes of western Gondwana: Pre-salt coquinas of Brazil and West Africa: Gondwana Research, http://dx.doi.org/10.1016/j.gr.2014.12.005.

Thomsen, L., 1986, Weak elastic anisotropy: Geophysics, Society of Exploration Geophysicists, v. 51, p. 1954–1966.

Thomsen, L., 2002, Understanding seismic anisotropy in exploration and exploitation: Society of Exploration Geophysicists, EAGE 2002 Distinguished Instructor Short Course. p. 253, DOI:10.1190/1.9781560801986.

Tritlla, J., R. Loma, V. Sánchez-Pérez-Cejuela, M. Esteban, D. Wloszczowski, R. Perona, J. L. Algibez, M. A. Caja, G. Levresse, P. Bonillo, and D. Tiwary, 2014, Volcanism, alkalinity and hydrothermalism in offshore Brazil: Unraveling the Päo de Açúcar reservoir: Repsol KH Journal, V. 302, p. 65–70.

Winter, W. R., R. J. Jahnert, and A. B. França, 2007, Bacia de Campos: Boletim de Geociêncis da Petrobras, Rio de Janeiro, v 15, no. 2, p. 511–529.

Zhou, R., D. McAdow, C. Barberan, D. Dushman, and F. Doherty, 2004, Seismic anisotropy estimation in TTI media using walkaway VSP data: SEG Technical Program Expanded Abstracts 2004, p. 2525–2528.

12

Rønnevik, Hans Chr, Arild Jørstad, and Jan Erik Lie, 2017, The discovery process behind the giant Johan Sverdrup field, *in* R. K. Merrill and C. A. Sternbach, eds., Giant fields of the decade 2000–2010: AAPG Memoir 113, p. 195–220.

The Discovery Process behind the Giant Johan Sverdrup Field

Hans Chr Rønnevik, Arild Jørstad, and Jan Erik Lie

Lundin Norway AS, Strandveien 4, Lysaker, Norway (e-mails: hans.ronnevik@lundin-norway.no, arild .jorstad@lundin-norway.no, jan-erik.lie@lundin-norway.no)

ABSTRACT

The giant Johan Sverdrup field was discovered in 2010 by well 16/2-6 drilled on the Utsira high, in the central part of the Norwegian North Sea. This area was considered exhausted after more than 40 years of disappointing on-and-off exploration drilling. The discovery of the significant Edvard Grieg field by well 16/1-8 in 2007 converted the Johan Sverdrup prospect to a high probability prospect. The predrill hypothesis was that the two prospects could be part of one large deposit with a 40 to 50 m (131 to 164 ft) saturated oil leg beneath a gas cap and a common oil–water contact (OWC) shallower than 1950 m (6398 ft) mean sea level (MSL). The exploration wells unfolded two normal pressured discoveries with undersaturated nonbiodegraded oil on the flank of a saturated system with biodegraded oil and 6 bar overpressure.

The Edvard Grieg discovery well proved a 40 m (131 ft) oil column above 1939 m (6362 ft) MSL on the west side of the high. The reserves in the plan for development and operations (PDO) were estimated to be 186 million BOE. This number has later been adjusted upward. The predrill estimate was 250 BOE. The reservoir sand was potassium rich and was indicated as shale and water bearing on the wireline logs. Without coring, the reservoir could have been overlooked. The reservoir is proximal Jurassic–Triassic deposits consisting of aeolian, braided river, and alluvial facies. Reservoir quality is also documented in Valanginian bioclastic sandstone and weathered basement.

The Johan Sverdrup discovery well was located to obtain maximum sequence stratigraphic information above the potential OWC at 1939 m (6362 ft) MSL on the east side of the high. The well proved an oil–water contact at 1922.5 m (6307 ft) MSL and showed that the discovery extended into the neighboring license to the west. The main reservoir in Johan Sverdrup is locally derived shallow marine transgressive Volgian sand, overlying reservoir rocks from Zechstein carbonates, lower and upper Jurassic continental to shallow marine sandstones separated by several unconformities. The PDO for the unitized field was issued in February 2015 with a reserve range of 1.7 to 3.0 billion bbl. The main reserve uncertainties are related to recovery factor, oil saturation, time–depth conversion variations, reservoir thickness estimation, and sequence resolution. The oil is nonbiodegraded and heavily undersaturated,

---

DOI:10.1306/13572008M1133687

and has low varying gas–oil ratio (GOR) and OWC varying from 1922 to 1935 m (6306 to 6348 ft) MSL with a substantial residual oil zone below the current free water level (FWL). This reflects the glacial-induced isostasy effects on FWL during Pleistocene.

The Edvard Grieg and Johan Sverdrup fields are situated on the southern part of the Utsira high referred to as the Haugaland High. This high is situated where the northwest extension of the Paleozoic to recent Tornquist wrench zone meets the Caledonian front between Scotland and Norway. In early mid-Jurassic the Haugaland High was part of a regional thermal inversion doming in the central North Sea. Several significant erosional and transgressive events determined the distribution of high-quality condensed Jurassic reservoir sequences from early to late Jurassic.

Late Pliocene and Pleistocene subsidence, including tilting toward the southwest and uplift in the northeast, brought the Johan Sverdrup field into its current structural position. The late structural formation implies late and ongoing migration into the reservoirs. Regional mapping of the shallow Miocene sands in the Utsira Formation showed seismic hydrocarbon indicators of petroleum migration from east to west, sourced by vertical leakage from the Johan Sverdrup field at Jurassic level. The westward migration ends in a glacial tunnel valley that cut into the Miocene sand. Gas flares at sea bottom consisting of gas derived from biodegraded oil have been sampled. This gas leakage has resulted in the formation of patchy carbonate crusts, a process that has been ongoing since the last glaciation.

Coring and production testing have been instrumental for the unfolding of the Edvard Grieg and Johan Sverdrup fields. Improved wireline logging procedures have been used in formation evaluation. The acquisition of 3-D ocean bottom seismic (OBS) and broadband seismic surveys in 2009 and 2012 has also been a catalyst for the unfolding process.

THE EXPLORATION HISTORY OF THE SOUTHERN UTSIRA HIGH

The southern part of the Utsira high, referred to as the Haugaland High, was explored on and off for 40 years before the breakthrough discovery of the Edvard Grieg field in 2007 by well 16/1-8. This discovery opened up for the Johan Sverdrup discovery 3 years later in 2010 by the 16/2-6 well (Figure 1).

Seventeen wells were drilled within the Haugaland High area between 1967 and 2007 prior to the Edvard Grieg discovery. The predrill play concept of the Edvard Grieg and subsequent Johan Sverdrup discoveries was primarily based on five key wells—16/2-1, 16/3-2, 16/1-4, 16/1-5, and 16/1-5A—and available vintage 2- and 3-D seismic data (Figure 2).

The first exploration well drilled on the Haugaland High was Esso's 16/2-1 in 1967. This well was drilled as the third exploration well on the Norwegian continental shelf on the northern part of the high and found good oil shows in Cretaceous chalk and basement.

Well 16/3-2 (Elf) was drilled on the east flank of the high in 1976 and encountered 31 m (102 ft) of Volgian coarse-grained, transgressive marine sandstone from 1951 to 1982 m (6401 to 6503 ft) MSL overlying weathered basement. The sand was overlaid by 20 m (66 ft) of Draupne shale. This well was drilled only a few hundred meters east of the Johan Sverdrup field closure and hit the reservoir sequence some 10 to 15 m (33 to 49 ft) deeper than the deepest paleo oil–water contact.

Well 16/1-4 (Statoil) was drilled in 1993 due northeast of the current Edvard Grieg field and was interpreted to contain wet gas/condensate in basement. This was the primary reason for having a saturated oil system as the predrill model.

Wells 16/1-5 and 16/1-5A (Statoil), drilled southwest of the Edvard Grieg field in 1998, demonstrated more than 200 m (656 ft) of porous shallow marine sandstone with shows in the upper 3 to 8 m (10 to 26 ft). The top of the sand was at 1954 m (6411 ft) MSL and was used as the deepest possible OWC for the Edvard Grieg predrill prospect model.

The last exploration effort before the discovery phase was an area of mutual interest (AMI) cooperation between Statoil, Mobil, and Saga. This resulted in the production license (PL) 265 award in 2001 to Statoil, Esso, and Enterprise due to the mergers of Saga with Statoil and Mobil with Esso (Figure 3). The eastern 709.4 km^2 (274 mi^2) of PL 265 was subsequently relinquished at the end of 2006 due to limited exploration success. The acreage was reawarded as PL 501 in the 2008 annual award in predefined area (APA) licensing round with Lundin as the operator with a 40% share and with Statoil and Maersk Oil as partners.

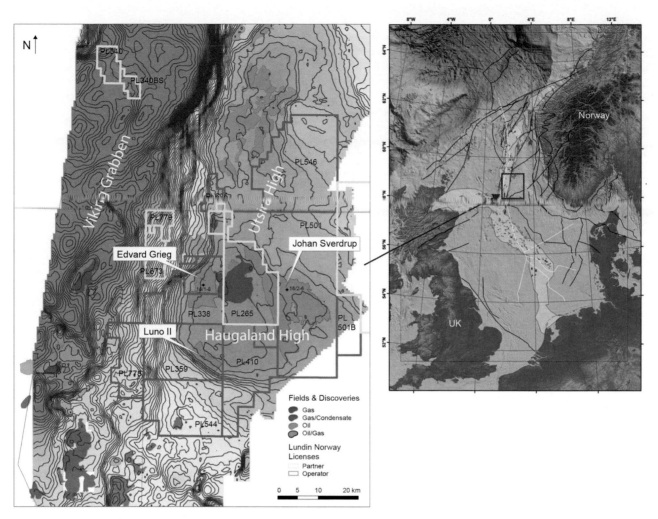

Figure 1. The Johan Sverdrup and Edvard Grieg Fields are located on the Southern Utsira high, called the Haugaland High, in the North Sea on the Norwegian Continental Shelf.

The predrill concept at the time of the Edvard Grieg license application in 2004 was that the Edvard Grieg and Johan Sverdrup prospects could be the northwestern and eastern parts of a large saturated oil accumulation with an oil column between 40 and 50 m (131 and 164 ft) above 1950 m (6398 ft) MSL. The main potential reservoirs were onlapping upper Jurassic shallow marine sands and older Jurassic–Triassic sediments from inlier basins. This model was the basis for Lundin's 100% license applications in the APA licensing rounds during 2004, 2005, 2007, and 2008 and a farm into PL 265 (Figures 2 and 3).

The Edvard Grieg field license (PL 338) was awarded 100% to Lundin in 2004 with a firm well commitment. Lundin farmed down to 50% prior to the first exploration well (16/1-8) (Figures 3 and 4). Although there was a general low interest for farming in, Revus and RWE Dea shared Lundin's positive view

on the prospect and entered the license with 30% and 20% equity, respectively. Edvard Grieg discovery well 16/1-8 demonstrated undersaturated nonbiodegraded oil with a GOR of 125 Sm^3/Sm^3 (786.25 bbl/bbl) and a specific gravity of 0.850 g/cc. The OWC was found at 1939 m (6362 ft) MSL.

The Edvard Grieg delineation program included the 16/1-12 well (2009), which was drilled south of the main discovery inlier basin (Figure 3). The well proved an undersaturated oil column of 42 m (138 ft) with an OWC at 1929 m (6329 ft) MSL oil in weathered and faulted/fractured granitic basement beneath a thin, 20 to 30 cm (8 to 12 in.), early Cretaceous conglomerate. The oil density and type were similar to Edvard Grieg with a GOR of 142 m^3/m^3. Three mini-drill stem tests showed permeability ranges of 2 to 30, 5 to 100, and approximately 700 mD. One vertical interference test verified good vertical communication.

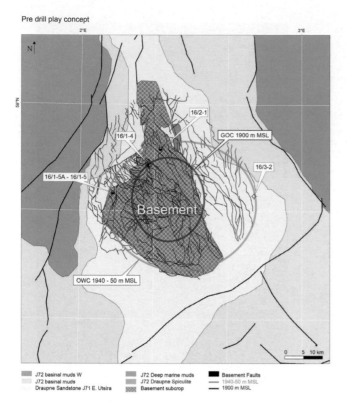

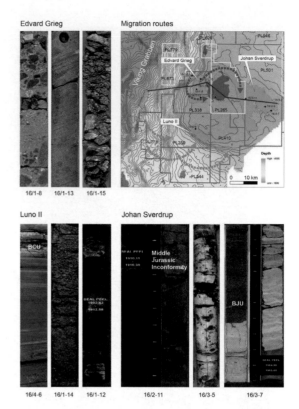

Figure 2. The predrill play concept was that the Edvard Grieg and Johan Sverdrup prospects were part of one large petroleum accumulation with a 40–50 m (131–164 ft) saturated oil leg beneath a gas cap and an oil–water contact shallower than 1950 m (6398 ft) mean sea level.

Figure 3. The reservoir facies on the Haugaland High are new to the Norwegian Continental Shelf except for the Volgian sand sequence in well 16/3-2. The low maturity oils in Edvard Grieg and Johan Sverdrup are nonbiodegraded and under-saturated. The oil in Luno 2 is saturated with a very low maturity.

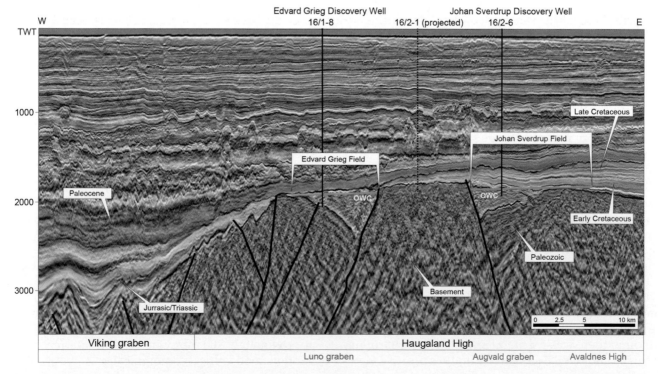

Figure 4. The cross section shows the Edvard Grieg and Johan Sverdrup fields on the flanks of Haugaland High east of the Viking Graben. Location of this section is shown in Figure 3.

Exploration well 16/2-5 in PL 265 was drilled in 2009 to investigate a potential eastern extension of the Edvard Grieg discovery. The well was drilled in a graben in the extension of the Edvard Grieg inlier basin close to the center of the Haugaland High. The well proved a saturated hydrocarbon system with biodegraded oil beneath a gas cap in a poor conglomeratic reservoir. The pressure in this discovery was 6 bar higher than the hydrostatic pressure observed in Edvard Grieg.

The Johan Sverdrup prospect was awarded as PL 501 in January 2009 with a firm well commitment. The Edvard Grieg discovery in 2007 had increased the probability for success for the 200 km² (77 mi²) prospect located on the eastern flank of the Haugaland High (Figures 3 and 4). At the time of license application in APA 2008, the prospect was evaluated to be a part of the Haugaland High structural megaclosure with an OWC at 1939 m (6362 ft) MSL or shallower (Figure 2). The discovery was made by well 16/2-6 in 2010. A 19 m (62 ft) oil column in a 22-m (72-ft)-thick Volgian to lower Jurassic clastic sequence was penetrated. The OWC was proven to be 1922.5 m (6307 ft) MSL. The oil density in the discovery well is 0.89 g/cc, and the GOR is 40 m³/m³. The oil is nonbiodegraded and heavily undersaturated. The water depth in the area is approximately 115 m (377 ft).

The Luno 2 discovery (Figure 3) was made south of the Edvard Grieg field in 2013 by well 16/4-6. This discovery had low-maturity, nonbiodegraded saturated oil with high asphalthene content in Jurassic–Triassic clastic sediments. The OWC was at 1950 m (6398 ft), the GOC was at 1910 m (6266 ft) MSL, and the reservoir pressure was 4 bars lower than hydrostatic. Disappointing delineation wells in 2013 and 2014 (16/5-5 and 16/4-8) have limited the reserve potential, and further delineation is required to evaluate the commercial potential.

The discovery history from the breakthrough in 2007 proved the prolific nature of the Haugaland High. The predrill conceptual model was generally correct in relation to OWC, as well as late and ongoing oil migration and the presence of Volgian reservoir sand. The other reservoirs on the Haugaland High from basement to Valangian are, however, new to the Norwegian continental shelf.

The Edvard Grieg, Johan Sverdrup, and 16/1-12 discoveries constitute a northern undersaturated oil fill spill system instead of one common saturated system. The oil generation and migration is from anoxic Volgian source rocks in the east flank of the Viking graben. The oil types in the Luno 2 are saturated and less mature than the Edvard Grieg and Johan Sverdrup oils.

The exploration leading to the discoveries on the Haugaland High was based on regional 1990s vintage 3-D seismic surveys (Figure 5). The quality was

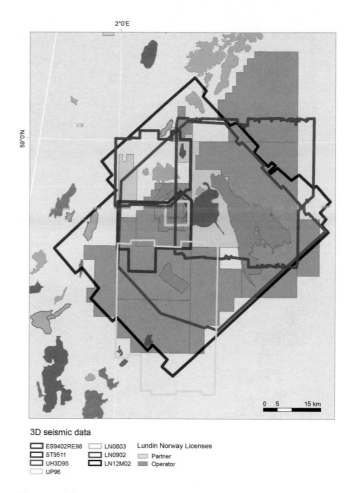

3D seismic data

		Lundin Norway Licenses
ES9402RE98	LN0803	
ST9511	LN0902	Partner
UH3D95	LN12M02	Operator
UP96		

Figure 5. The vintage 3-D seismic data that was used in the initial exploration phase covers most of the map area. A 3-D survey (LN0803) was acquired over Edvard Grieg after the discovery to improve the pre-Chalk imaging. Two large broadband surveys LN0902; 1675 km² (647 mi²) and LN12M02; 2600 km² (1004 mi²) were acquired in 2009 and 2011–2012.

marginal but improved during interpretation by applying a 25 Hz high-cut filter and interpreting on arbitrary dip lines to distinguish primaries from multiples.

The seismic imaging challenges of the sub-Cretaceous reservoir levels on the Haugaland High have been improved by new 3-D acquisitions and processing techniques. Top chalk represents a very large increase in velocity. The seismic waves go critical at short offsets, and only a relatively narrow beam of transmitted energy illuminates the reservoir level. The Edvard Grieg discovery triggered an effort to properly address the seismic imaging challenge. A diagnostic 50 km² (19 mi²) 3-D OBC was acquired in 2008. The richer low-frequency content of the OBC gave a major uplift of the seismic imaging. The knowledge gained from the OBC survey inspired

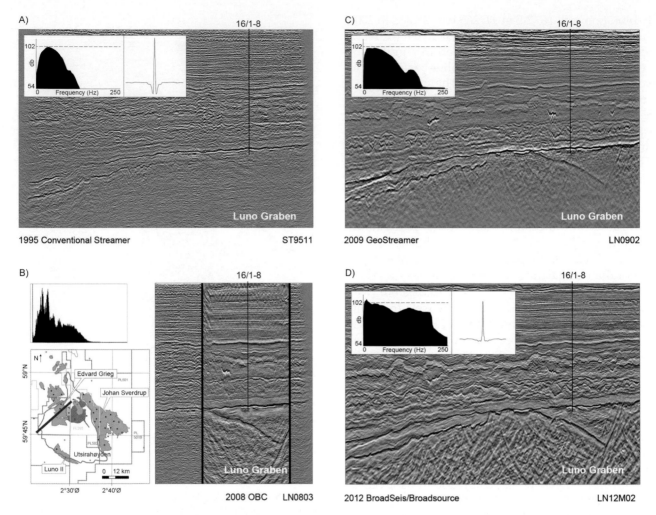

Figure 6. The increased seismic bandwidth improves the shallow and deep imaging simultaneously. A) shows a version of the vintage 3-D seismic data at the time of application in 2004. The Luno graben, containing the Edvard Grieg Field, is barely visible on the vintage data. Marked improvements of the seismic image and bandwidth are seen on the OBC (B) and the following Broadband 3-D seismic surveys (C) (D).

the acquisition of a 1675 km² (647 mi²) broadband Geostreamer® 3-D seismic survey over the entire Haugaland High in 2009. This survey was used to position the Johan Sverdrup 16/2-6 discovery well in 2010. Following the Johan Sverdrup discovery, a new 2600 km² (1004 mi²) BroadSeis™ 3-D seismic survey was acquired over the high in 2011 and 2012 with the aim to further extend the bandwidth and improve resolution. Figure 6 illustrates the improvement in seismic resolution and bandwidth as well as holistic imaging. A profile across the northern Haugaland High, including the Edvard Grieg field, has been used to test and benchmark various seismic broadband acquisition and processing technologies during its rapid development between 2010 and 2015. This includes Geostreamer, BroadSeis, Isometrix™, P-Cable™, and a series of variable 2-D cable geometries.

The low-frequency richness of broadband seismic data encouraged further development of the full waveform inversion (FWI) methods to map out shallow lateral velocity variations to a higher level of detail (Figure 7). The broadband high-resolution shallow image together with the detailed shallow FWI velocities has added to the understanding and mapping of the Pliocene–Pleistocene sequence in the area, which is crucial due to the very late petroleum migration into the Johan Sverdrup field.

STRUCTURAL SETTING OF THE HAUGALAND HIGH

The Haugaland High is situated where the northwest extension of the Paleozoic to recent Tornquist wrench zone meets the Caledonian front between Scotland

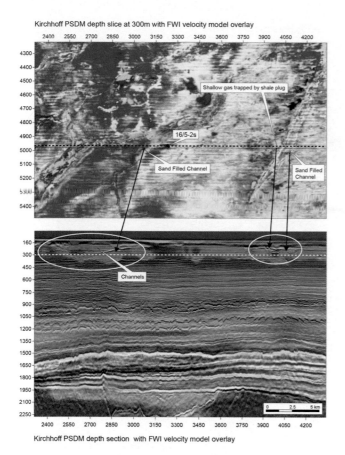

Kirchhoff PSDM depth slice at 300m with FWI velocity model overlay

Kirchhoff PSDM depth section with FWI velocity model overlay

Figure 7. Full-Waveform-Inversion (FWI) identifies the large lateral velocity variations in the shallow Pleistocene and Holocene sequences down to approximately 500 milliseconds (ms). These variations are not detected in conventional stacking velocity analysis. FWI velocity input has improved the prestack depth migration image of the underlying reservoir section. Cool and warm colors represent low and high velocities, respectively.

and Norway (Figure 8). Repeated sinistral and dextral shear movements along the Tornquist line have strongly influenced the depositional and erosional phases on the high.

The dynamic tectonic character of the high is documented by the numerous hiatuses from the Cambro–Silurian to Pleistocene (Figure 9). The wrench movements with alternating shear directions have resulted in the repeated formation of basins followed by intervening inversion and erosion. All these kinematic events have influenced the hydrocarbon habitat of the area.

The earliest post-Caledonian deposits in the area are related to regional deposition of Devonian continental rocks over a peneplain on top basement. During the Carboniferous, largescale rifting created northwest–southeast half grabens separated by the Stephanian

unconformity from the younger sequences (Figure 10). The Caledonian front developed into the Ling graben to south of the high. This area acted as a hinge zone during Permian and lower Triassic (Figure 11). In upper Triassic and lower Jurassic, regional epeirogenic basin formation occurred over the entire high (Figure 12).

A regional early mid-Jurassic thermal doming event uplifted the central part of the North Sea, including the Haugaland High, to a major erosional provenance area (Figures 10 and 13). Erosion reached basement over a large part of the high. Pre-mid-Jurassic sequences are preserved locally in inlier basins and form reservoir sequences in the Edvard Grieg, Johan Sverdrup, and Luno 2 discoveries. The high underwent regional subsidence with deposition periods during middle to upper Jurassic interrupted by regional uplifts and erosion.

The base of the Volgian is a major tectonic event that created local provenances to the west and south of the current high for the main transgressive Johan Sverdrup reservoir sand (Figure 12). The shallow marine sand is locally derived from both Triassic sediments and weathered basement. This is documented by reworked palynomorphs and by petrographic composition analysis. The provenance areas are interpreted to be located to the south, west, and east of the field. The Volgian sand was deposited on an epeirogenic subsiding area. Postdepositional faulting took place in the earliest lower Cretaceous.

During the lower Cretaceous, the Haugaland High subsided in the east–northeast, while the western areas remained high and acted as provenance areas for clastic deposition toward the west (Figure 13). The high was submerged during the upper Cretaceous with deposition of thick chalk that was subsequently uplifted and eroded by marine abrasion and fluvial erosion during earliest Tertiary. Karstification occurred in the high areas of the chalk.

The chalk erosion was terminated by rapid regional subsidence and the deposition of deep marine Paleocene sediments. The main source areas for the Paleocene turbidities were the Shetland platform to the west and reworked chalk from the Utsira high (Figures 10 and 13). A late Paleocene–Eocene wrench movement structured and uplifted the high before the deposition of major sand lobes from the west in Eocene to Miocene times. These depositional systems become shallower marine with age.

A major inversion of the Haugaland High occurred in late Miocene times in response to a new phase of largescale wrenching (Figure 14). This resulted in a structural nose dipping from the northwest toward the southeast at top Utsira sand level over the high. The

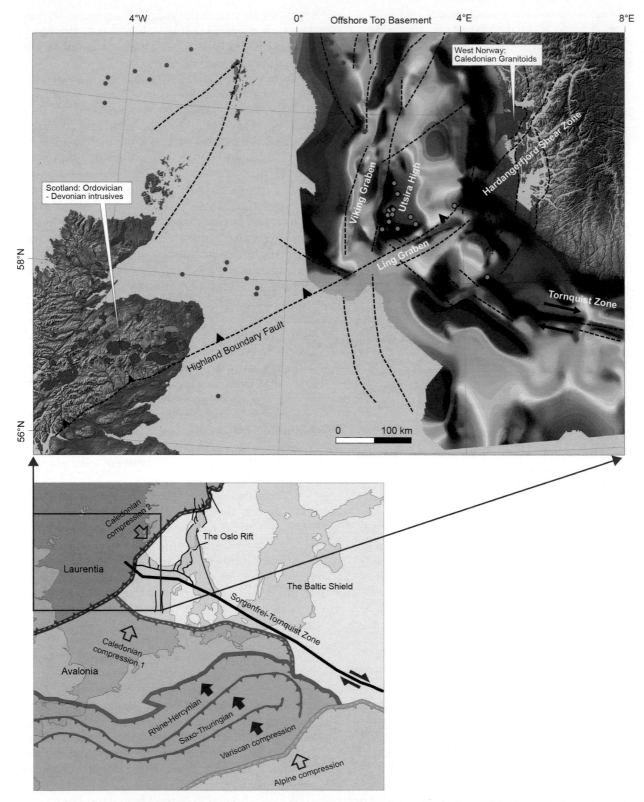

Figure 8. The Utsira high is situated where the Tornquist wrench system crosses the Caledonian front between Norway and United Kingdom. The green dots mark show location of wells that penetrate Caledonian basement consisting of metamorphic and Ordovician and Silurian intrusive rocks.

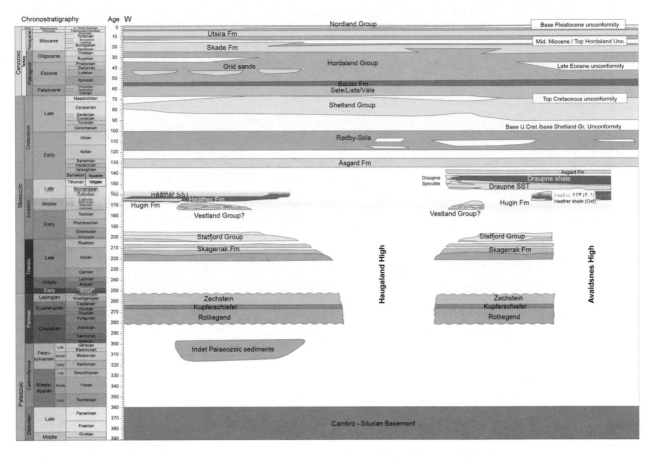

Figure 9. The Wheeler diagram illustrates several hiatuses on the Haugaland High. The kinematic events from Cambro–Silurian to Pleistocene influences the petroleum habitat of the Haugaland High.

inversion resulted in sealing of some pre-Cretaceous chalk faults at the crest of the high. This sealing effect sheltered the late nonbiodegraded undersaturated oil from earlier migrated biodegraded saturated oil. During Eocene and Oligocene times, the basin center was over the eastern part of the Haugaland High. The regional basin axis shifted to the southwest during the Pliocene and Pleistocene, causing renewed petroleum migration and remigration. During the last Pleistocene glaciation, a major tunnel valley was cut into the Miocene Utsira formation.

THE PETROLEUM FILLING HISTORY

The Haugaland High obtained a favorable structural position in relation to migration of oil from the prolific Draupne and Heather source rocks in the Viking Graben in the west during the last 1.5 to 2 million years (Figure 15). The burial history illustrates rapid subsidence in early Tertiary with an accelerated subsidence in Pliocene and Pleistocene. There are marked

and important changes in subsidence and migration directions between these two episodes of subsidence. The rapid late subsidence brought the reservoirs in to a temperature regime around 80 °C, hindering biodegradation.

The Haugaland High obtained its current favorable position for accumulation of petroleum in late Pliocene. This was the result of Pliocene to Pleistocene tilting with relative uplift in the northeast and associated subsidence toward the southwest. The late subsidence events were interrupted by a significant erosion phase close to the top of the Pliocene (Figure 16). The subsidence phases followed a regional late Miocene wrench-induced inversion.

The filling of the prospective traps on the Haugaland High depended on efficient late oil filling. The area is an inverted high where petroleum cannot spill further laterally; rather, it can only leak vertically. Both the 1990s vintage and new broadband 3-D seismic data show good hydrocarbon indicators of petroleum migration from east to west in the Miocene Utsira formation (Figure 16). This was interpreted predrill

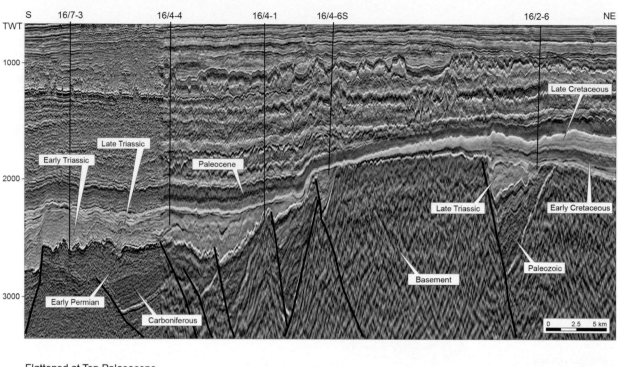

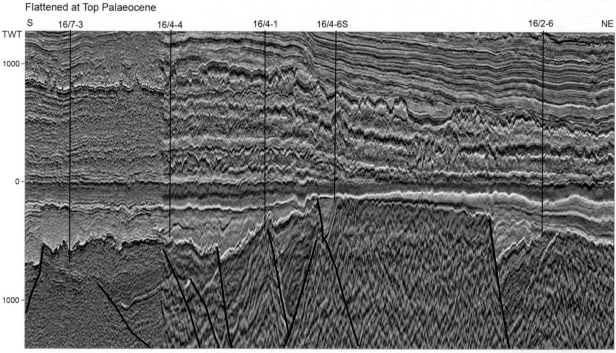

Figure 10. The southwest–northeast cross section over the Haugaland High shows the effect of the late Paleocene wrenching and later subsidence, the early Tertiary sub aerial erosion of the chalk, the effect of Mesozoic wrenching on deposition and erosion reservoir preservation and Paleozoic kinematic development.

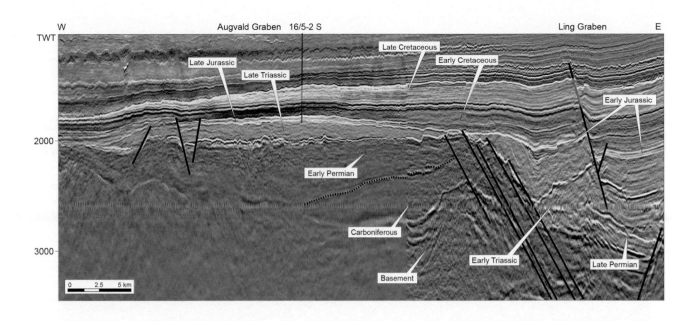

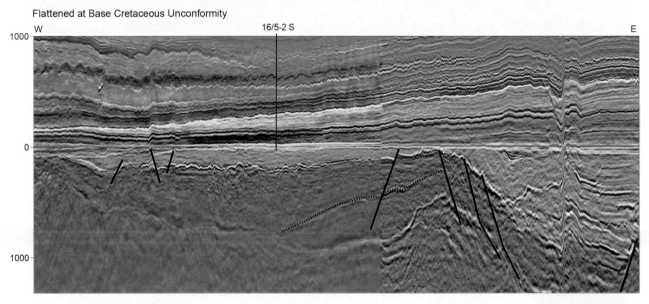

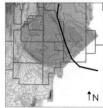

Figure 11. The north–south section along the axis of the Augvald Graben shows the deposition of Zechstein salt and lower Triassic formations in the Ling Graben. The Late Triassic and lower Jurassic sequences are eroded in the southern part of the graben. The Late Jurassic Draupne sand and marine shale is deposited above the base Volgian unconformity.

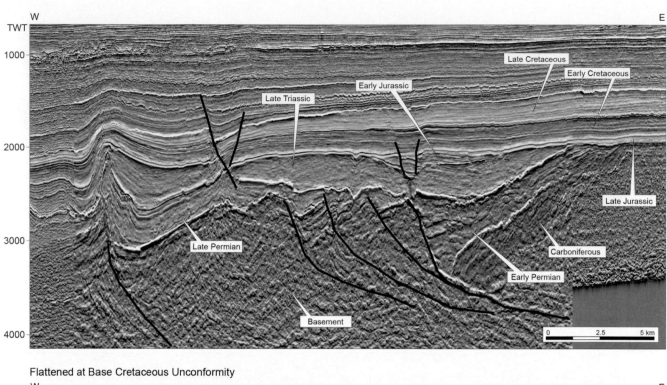

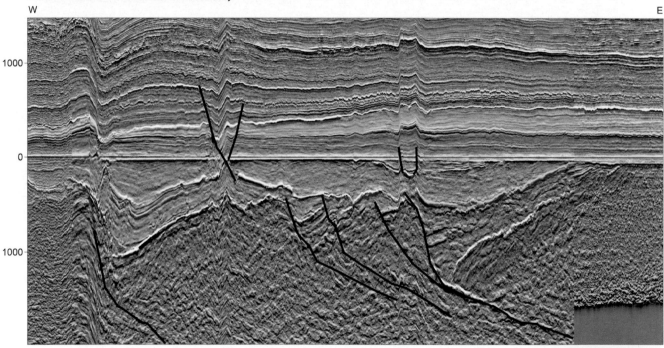

Flattened at Base Cretaceous Unconformity

Figure 12. The east–west section in the transition zone between Haugaland High and the Ling Graben demonstrate how the high was a part of regional epeirogenic basin in upper Triassic and lower Jurassic cut by a marked pre-Volgian unconformity. Transgressive sand and marine shale are deposited above this unconformity in a tectonically passive setting followed by earliest Cretaceous faulting.

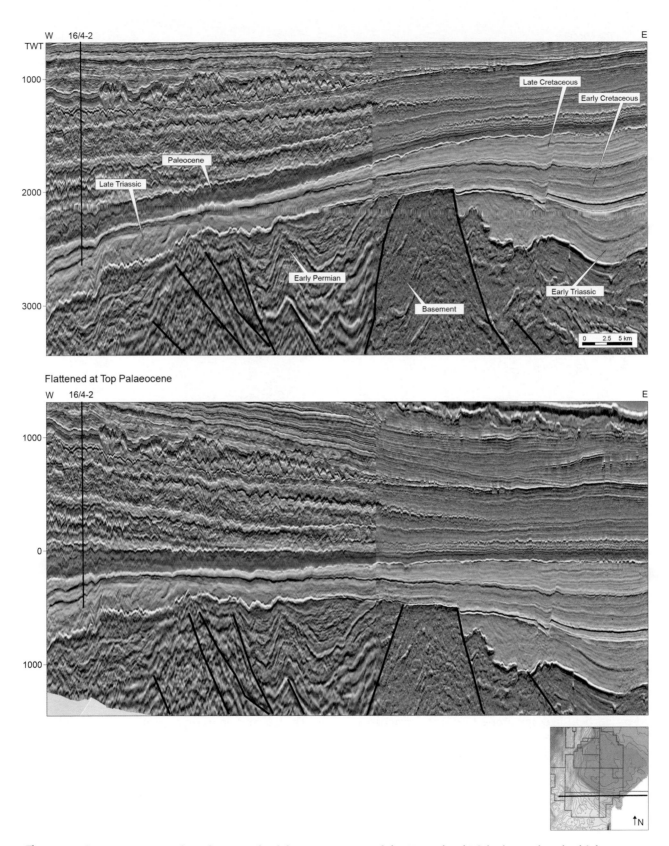

Figure 13. The east–west section along south of the western part of the Haugaland High shows that the high was part of a larger area that subsided to the east, while the western areas remained high and acted as provenance for clastic deposition toward the west during lower Cretaceous. Following the post-Chalk erosion the subsidence occurred in the west–southwest with uplift in the east.

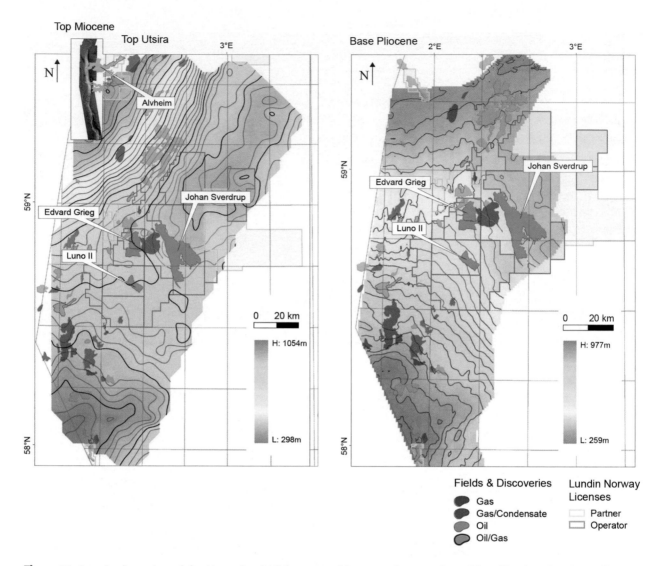

Figure 14. A major inversion of the Haugaland High occurred in post-Miocene. The regional basin axis migrated to the southwest during the Pliocene and Pleistocene causing renewed petroleum migration and remigration. A tunnel valley cuts into the Miocene Utsira formation to the northwest in the Alvheim field area.

to reflect that the whole Haugaland High was filled above a common level shallower than 1940 to 1950 m (6365 to 6398 ft) MSL at the base Cretaceous unconformity (BCU). The hydrocarbon fill column is determined by vertical leakage along faults and fractures, especially during the Pleistocene ice ages due to increased overburden pressure. The bubble point of the Johan Sverdrup oil is between 62 and 69 bars, and the seismic hydrocarbon indicators can reflect oil. Rock physics studies are ambiguous in this respect.

The Utsira formation shallows westward (Figure 14). A glacial tunnel valley cuts into the Miocene west–southwest of the Alvheim field, and significant gas flares and associated algal carbonate mat formation occur around the valley (Figure 17). Analysis of samples

from the flares shows gas from biodegraded oil and supports the likelihood of recent and late migration in line with the hypothesis that was formulated in 2006 prior the discoveries.

The late and ongoing migration is reflected in a fresh oil population cluster marked by the yellow dots at the northern part of the Haugaland High in Figure 18. Along the south flank of the high in the Luno II area a different, very early, mature oil population is marked by a pink dot. The low-maturity oils in the Edvard Grieg, Johan Sverdrup, and Luno 2 discoveries are in line with the late formation of the structures in Pliocene–Pleistocene.

Fresh oil is found below the FWL in the fields. The residual zones vary and are observed down to

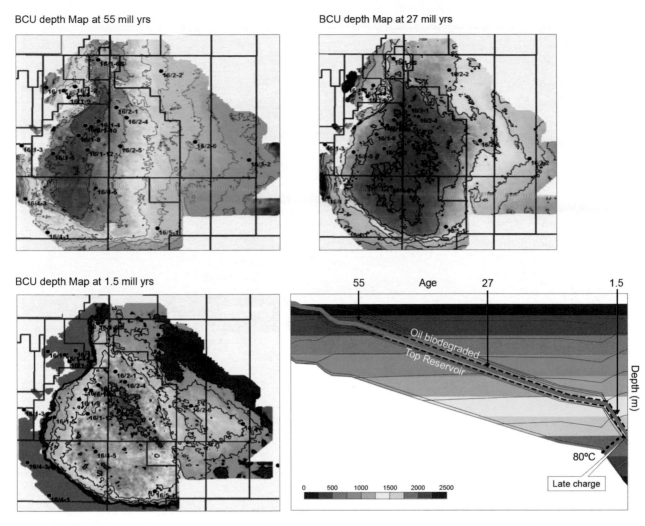

Figure 15. The current structural setting at the Haugaland High was established as late as 1.5 million years ago. Prior to this uplift the Johan Sverdrup field was in the migration shadow. The reservoir temperature at Jurassic level reached above 80 °C (176 °F) at the same time.

approximately 1960 m (6430 ft) MSL. These observations can be related to glacial isostasy related to downwarp during the glaciations and uplifts following the deglaciation phases.

THE EDVARD GRIEG FIELD

The Prospect

The Edvard Grieg field is located in PL338 on the western flank of the Haugaland High (Figure 19). The prospect was defined in relation to an inlier basin limited to the south by a marked east–west-oriented cuesta and to the east by a basement fault. The reservoir and basin fill was predicted to be marine Jurassic over continental Triassic sands. The cap rock was assumed to be a deeply eroded upper Cretaceous chalk that is locally missing along the west flank of the prospect where Paleocene shale can constitute the seal.

The 16/1-8 discovery well was positioned to penetrate a 40- to 50-m (131- to 164-ft)-thick saturated oil leg updip from the shows found in wells 16/1-5 and 16/1-5A and downdip from the possible gas column identified in well 16/1-4. The drilling of the well took place during the autumn of 2007.

The Discovery Well

Well 16/1-8 proved undersaturated oil in proximal Jurassic-to-Triassic coarse clastic reservoirs (Figures 19

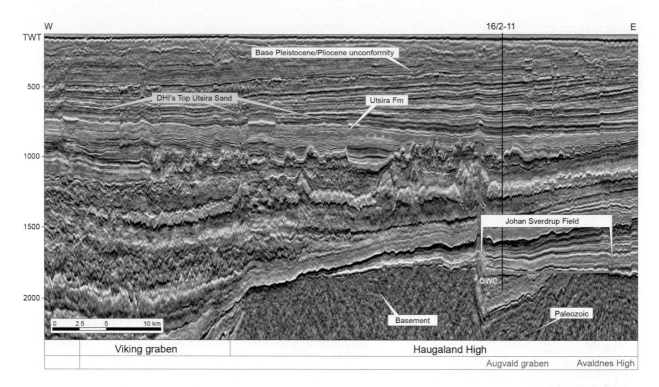

Figure 16. Vertical hydrocarbon migration along the boundary fault of the Augvald Graben and up into the sand prone sequences of Miocene age (Utsira formation) is indicated by direct hydrocarbon indicators (DHI) on the seismic section.

and 20) deposited in alluvial to fluvial environments with marine incursions. The sand and sand matrix are arkosic, and the conglomerate pebbles are granodioritic. The pebbles and boulders are subrounded to angular. The proximal continental deposited sequences are lean in paleo, and the stratigraphic breakdown is challenging. The oil-bearing sequence between 1900 and 1939 m (6234 and 6362 ft) MSL is referred to as upper–lower Jurassic. The 60 m (197 ft) sequence below the OWC is dated to be Hettangian to Norian age.

The K-feldspar-rich reservoir in the Edvard Grieg field could easily have been overlooked without coring since it appears as shale and nonhydrocarbon bearing on standard wireline (Figure 20). The oil-bearing sequence shows up yellow in ultraviolet (UV) light. To compensate for the mineralogical challenge, continuous microscopic and X-ray diffraction (XRD) analyses of cuttings have been introduced as standard tools in the exploration and delineation wells.

The sampled oil gravity is 0.85 g/cc, and GOR is 125 m³/m³. The bubble point pressure is 156.4 bars, and the oil is 30 bars undersaturated in the reservoir. The oil composition shows charging from a source rock deposited in an open marine anoxic environment and at peak oil generation from Volgian–Valanginian Draupne source rocks.

Discovery well 16/1-8 was temporarily abandoned in 2007 and was production tested later in 2009. The recoverable reserves were estimated to 65 to 190 million bbl after the discovery well.

Appraisal Activities

The first appraisal well (16/1-10) was drilled in 2009 and proved the same oil type and OWC as the discovery well (Figure 21). Ten meters (33 ft) of highly productive sandstones overlying thick conglomeratic

A)

B)

C)

Figure 17. A glacial tunnel valley cuts into the Miocene Utsira sand formation. Significant gas flares and associated algal mat carbonate formation occur in the valley. Analysis of samples from the gas flares shows that the gas originates from biodegraded oil. See Figure 14 for location.

sandstones with low flow potential was demonstrated in the well. The two zones were DST-tested comingled. The test showed clear evidence of an increase in permeability thickness of the upper sand away from the well position in all directions. An increase in thickness of the upper sand from 10 to 50 m (33 to 164 ft) and more than 2 Darcy permeability was indicated. The 3-D OBS seismic data also indicated thickening of good sand away from the well. The thickness increase was subsequently confirmed by the 16/1-13 drilled 1.2 km (0.7 mi) to the west. This well encountered a 47 m (154 ft) thick interval of clean aeolian sandstones with

excellent reservoir properties of 30% porosity and 8 to 12 Darcy permeability.

The Edvard Grieg wells have defined six different reservoir facies with a common OWC (Figure 22). The four DSTs that have been performed to date (16/1-8, 10, 15, and 18) demonstrate good communication between the various continental facies in the field. The prime reservoir quality is related to the multi-Darcy aeolian sand. There is, however, also good permeability (hundreds of mD) in the matrix in the fluvial deposits.

The northern extension of the field (Tellus prospect) was appraised by the 16/1-15 well in 2011. The well

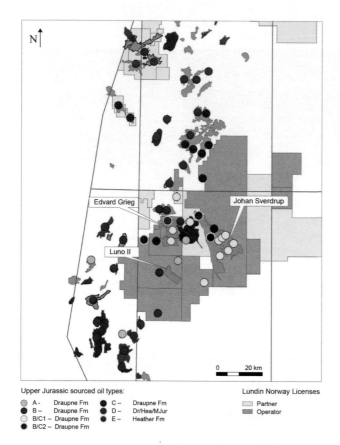

Figure 18. Migration the last 1.5 million years provided fresh nonbiodegraded oil (yellow dots) into the Edvard Grieg and Johan Sverdrup discoveries. The oil type found in Luno 2 (pink) is also late generated and migrated oil, but is of a different type.

encountered 3 m (10 ft) of bioclastic Valanginian sand directly overlying a weathered basement wash. Oil and pressure sampling demonstrated communication with the main Jurassic–Triassic reservoirs to the southeast. The comingled DSTs demonstrated commercial rates in both these reservoirs.

The reason for an OWC of 1939 m (6362 ft) MSL is unclear. The oil can spill toward Johan Sverdrup in the east through the bioclastic Valanginian sand. The OWC can be controlled by the fault leakage and ongoing fill as indicated by the regional petroleum system analysis, the seismic data and gas flares in the tunnel valley in the Alvheim field area.

The PDO was delivered in 2012 based on the 16/1-8, 10, 13, and 15 wells. Both the 3-D OBC (2008) and 3-D broadband seismic data (2009) were used (Figure 5). The recoverable reserves in PDO were estimated to 186 million BOE. Approximately 60% of the reserves are contained in the aeolian sand (Figure 23). Two additional delineation wells and two pilot production

wells have been drilled to refine the stochastic PDO model and provide a more refined deterministic drainage model for the location of the production wells. The first horizontal production well was drilled with 100% net-to-gross and a minimum porosity of 24% (Figure 23). The development of the field was completed in 2015, which is 8 years after the discovery.

JOHAN SVERDRUP DISCOVERY

Prospect

The Johan Sverdrup prospect covered a large area in PL 501 and PL 265 as seen in Figure 24. The structural closure to the east is marked with the stippled line on the base Cretaceous map. Top reservoir is determined by subtracting the varying Volgian shale thickness from BCU. The prospect was initially defined as a part of the large Haugaland High megaclosure with similar oil–water contact as in the Edvard Grieg field. This was the basis for the license application in APA 2008.

The Johan Sverdrup prospect was defined as a 200 km^2 (77 mi^2) three-way dip closure limited by a major fault in the west (Figure 25). The seismic resolution was too low to discriminate between sand and shale over subcropping sequences in the eastern crest of the prospect. The delineation wells and production tests demonstrate a continuous reservoir. The reservoir targets in the prospect were the shallow marine Volgian sand proven in the nearby 16/3-2 well in 1976 and earlier Jurassic and older sequences in the Augvald Graben (Figure 26).

The major predrill uncertainty in relation to the prospect was the migration of oil from the Viking graben in the west. The Haugaland High and Johan Sverdrup prospect obtained the current structural setting in Pliocene–Pleistocene due to increased subsidence and southwestward differential tilting. The hydrocarbon fill was thought to be controlled by the fault seal capacity for vertical leakage through the western boundary fault of the prospect and the compensating late and ongoing migration. Seismic data (Figure 16) show a major erosional event related to a late uplift of the Haugaland High at the Pliocene–Pleistocene boundary. The predrill assessment was that the Johan Sverdrup prospect needed very late oil fills to become successful.

The Discovery Well

Johan Sverdrup discovery well 16/2-6 was drilled in 2010 in PL 501 (Figure 26). The location was selected over the graben to obtain maximum

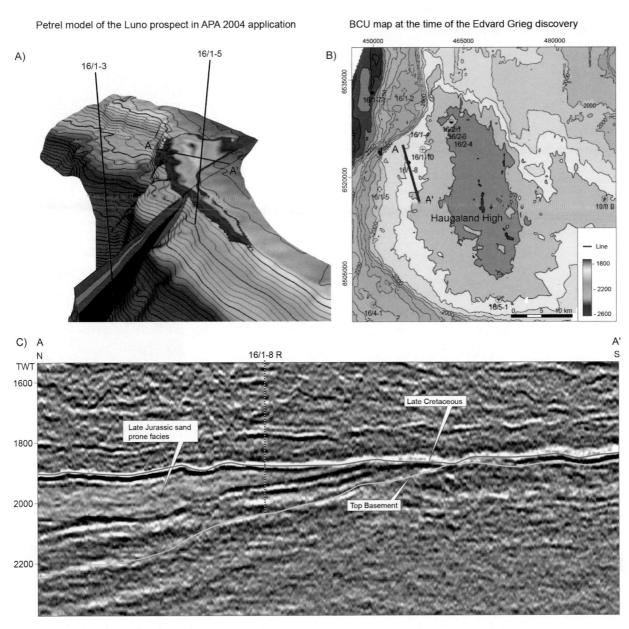

Figure 19. The Edvard Grieg prospect model at time of application in 2004 was an inlier basin containing Late Jurassic sand prone facies. The whole Haugaland High had the potential to be one oil accumulation. The seismic 3-D data quality at the time was not optimal, but selecting the right line direction made it possible to separate dipping layers from multiples.

reservoir sequence information and above the level of the regional OWC hypothesis. The top Jurassic was encountered within 2 m of depth prognosis. A 22-m (72-ft)-thick Jurassic reservoir sequence was penetrated. The top of the reservoir in 16/2-6 consists of a 5.5-m (18-ft)-thick coarse- to very coarse-grained Volgian sand. This sand lies unconformable on a condensed sequence of finer-grained sand of estuarine to continental lower Jurassic age separated by a middle Jurassic unconformity.

The discovery well has total depth in Permian Zechstein carbonates where significant drilling mud losses occurred. The loss was cured with lost circulation material (LCM), and a technical sidetrack 20 m (66 ft) from the main bore hole was drilled to secure proper data quality during wireline logging.

The discovery well demonstrated a hydrostatic pressure regime with a water gradient of 1.02 g/cc and an oil gradient of 0.82 g/cc. The pressure measurements and sampling showed an OWC at 1922.5 m

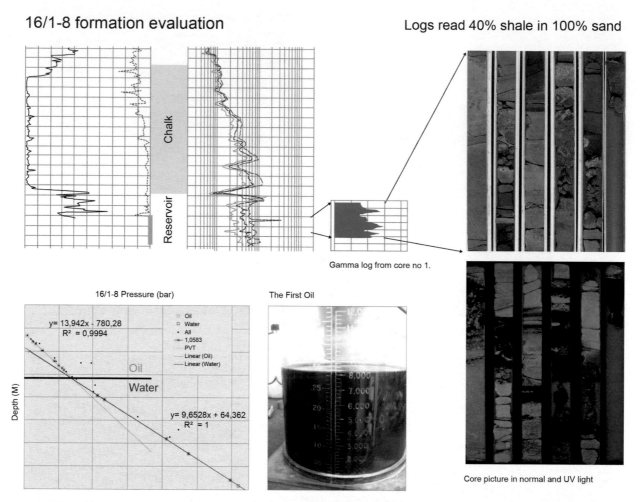

Figure 20. The Edvard Grieg discovery well 16/1-8 shows the K-feldspar-rich reservoir that could easily have been overlooked without coring. The oil-bearing sequence has yellow fluorescence in ultraviolet light. The sampling demonstrated a good light oil gradient and marked oil–water contact at 1939 m (6362 ft) mean sea level.

(6307 ft) MSL and an oil column of approximately 19 m (62 ft) in the well. The oil density in the discovery well is 0.89 g/cc, and the GOR is 40 m³/m³.

The oil is nonbiodegraded fresh oil derived from an anoxic Draupne formation and belongs to the same oil populations as in the Edvard Grieg field.

The upper Jurassic Draupne sand was production tested (DST) at rig-restricted rates of 780 Sm³ oil/day through a 52/64-in. choke. The production index (PI) was extremely high, at 360 m³/d/bar. The test proved excellent reservoir properties, good lateral continuity, and no boundaries within a 2 to 3 km (1 to 2 mi) radius. The 16/2-6 discovery well unfolded a new major gigantic field in line with the predrill hypothesis (Figure 25).

Live fresh oil was observed 12 m (39 ft) below the FWL in Triassic caliche at 1935 m (6348 ft) MSL and

indicted a deeper paleo contact. Similar live oil has been encountered in several of the subsequent appraisal wells. This can be related to glacial-induced isostasy movements.

Delineation Wells

The Johan Sverdrup field is in line with the predrill prospect outline and covers approximately 200 km² (77 mi²) with a maximum hydrocarbon column of approximately 90 m (Figure 27). The Volgian-age Draupne sandstone sequence cannot be seismically distinguished from the Statfjord group in the west and is in seismic tuning with the eastward older subcropping sequences. This makes reliable Draupne sandstone thickness estimation from seismic data difficult,

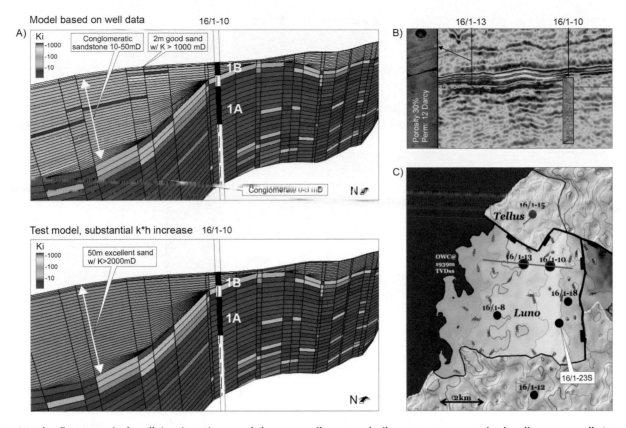

Figure 21. The first appraisal well (16/1-10) proved the same oil type and oil–water contact as in the discovery well. A production test showed clear evidence of an increase in permeability thickness of the upper sand away from the well position. The thickness increase was subsequently confirmed by the 16/1-13 well drilled 1.2 km (0.7 mi) to the west.

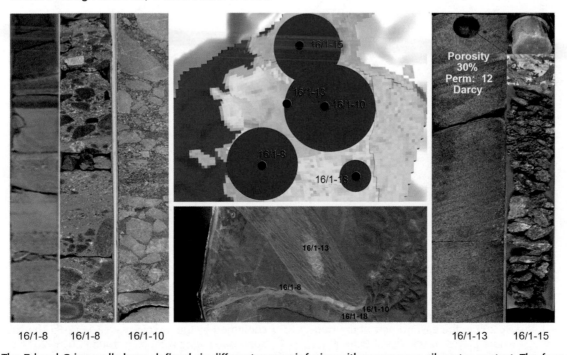

Figure 22. The Edvard Grieg wells have defined six different reservoir facies with a common oil–water contact. The four drill-stem tests performed to date (16/1-8, 16/1-10, 16/1-15, and 16/1-18) demonstrate good communication between the various continental facies in the field. The prime reservoir quality is related to the multi-Darcy aeolian sand (16/1-13). A recent analog from Baja California is shown as reference.

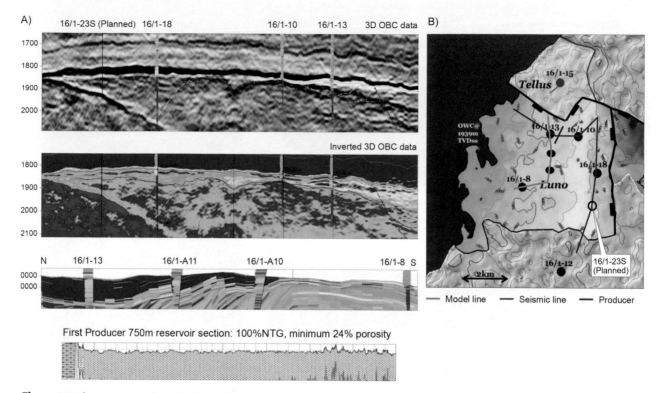

Figure 23. The 3-D OBC (2008) is used for detailed reservoir characterization and well positioning on the Edvard Grieg field. Approximately 60% of the reserves are contained within the aeolian sand seen as low impedance (red/green) on the inverted OBC data and red color in the geological model. The first horizontal production well was drilled with 100% net-to-gross and minimum porosity of 24%.

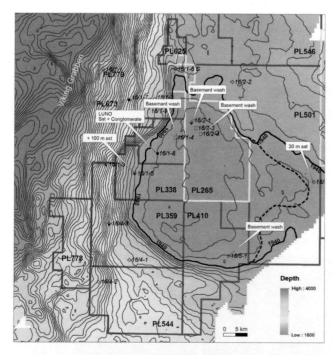

Figure 24. The Johan Sverdrup prospect covered a large area in PL 501 and PL 265 in the eastern part of the Haugaland High megaclosure play concept. The structural closure to the east is marked with the stippled line on the base Cretaceous map.

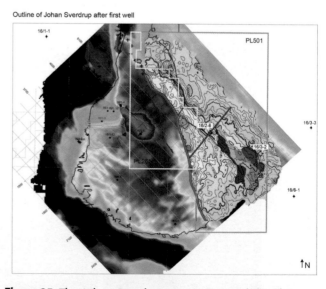

Figure 25. The Johan Sverdrup prospect was defined as a 200 km² (77 mi²) three-way dip closure bounded by a major fault to the west (red outline). The initial model was confirmed by the discovery well 16/2-6. The subsequent appraisal drilling campaign during 2011–2014 confirmed a continuous Volgian sand drape over the Avaldsnes High in the eastern part. Seismic profile in Figure 26 indicated.

Pre-drill play concept sketch

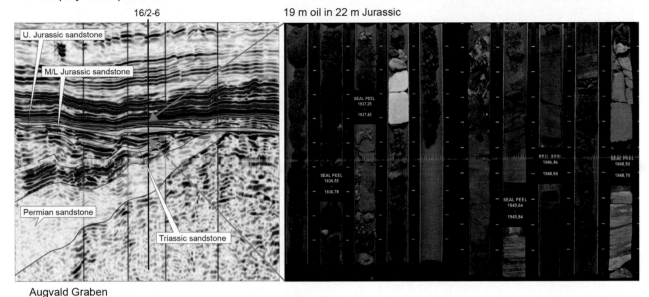

Augvald Graben

Figure 26. The Johan Sverdrup discovery well, 16/2-6, was positioned to penetrate a diversity of potential reservoir sequences in the previously undrilled Augvald Graben above 1940 m (6365 ft) mean sea level (MSL). The well found 5.5 m (18 ft) of shallow marine Late Jurassic Draupne sand of excellent quality above 16 m (52 ft) of lower Jurassic estuarine and continental reservoir facies of good quality. The oil column was 19 m (62 ft) and oil–water contact 1922.5 m (6307 ft) MSL. See Figure 25 for location.

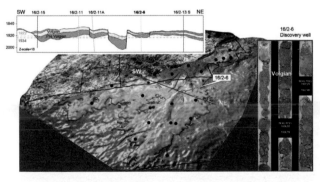

Figure 27. The Johan Sverdrup discovery outline is in line with the predrill prospect and is covering approximately 200 km² (77 mi²) with a maximum hydrocarbon column of approximately 90 m (295 ft). The reservoir quality was significantly better than expected. The Volgian age Draupne sand is holding 75–80% of the reserves in the discovery. A total of 28 delineation wells including eight sidetracks were drilled between 2011 and 2014.

which is crucial as 75 to 80% of the in-place oil volume sits within this sequence.

The large areal extent, flat structure, and reservoir mapping challenges motivated a comprehensive appraisal program and data acquisition strategy. A total of 28 delineation wells, including eight sidetracks, were drilled between 2011 and 2014. All wells gave significant necessary new information in relation to the assessments of volumes in place, drainage strategy, and field development. Even the last two wells provided significant new geological understanding and revisions of the reservoir models.

The Johan Sverdrup exploration and delineation wells provide a unique dataset with fully cored reservoir sections and seven full drill stem tests (DSTs) (Figure 28). Five of the DSTs have been carried out in the upper Jurassic Draupne sand and two in the lower Jurassic Statfjord sediments. Four of the Draupne sand DSTs have been acquired over the eastern part of the field. These tests have overlapping investigation radii (2800 to 3600 m [9186 to 11,811 ft]) and prove continuous high permeability (35 to 70 Darcy) Draupne sands with average thicknesses of approximately 15 m (49 ft). The DST pressure data are used to calibrate the reservoir sand thickness estimation and reservoir continuity, and to optimize the drainage strategy for the area. Measured productivity indexes of between 390 and 1190 Sm³/d/bar are extreme and point to excellent production properties. The 16/2-11 A DST in the Augvald Graben showed good continuity between the Volgian and pre-Volgian sequences.

The first Johan Sverdrup appraisal well (2011; 16/3-4) is located 6.5 km (4 mi) southeast of the

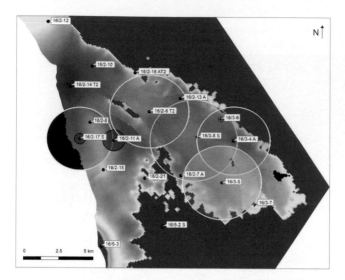

Figure 28. The Johan Sverdrup exploration and delineation wells provide a unique dataset with fully cored reservoir sections and seven full drill stem tests (DSTs). Five of the DSTs have been carried out in the upper Jurassic Draupne sand and two in the lower Jurassic Statfjord sediments. The tests have overlapping investigation radii (2800–3600 m [9186–11,811 ft]) and measured productivity indexes between 390 and 1190 Sm³/d/bar pointing to excellent production properties.

discovery well 16/2-6, and the dry well 16/3-2 from 1976, which found 31 m (102 ft) Volgian sandstone (Figure 29). The main aim was to calibrate the reservoir thickness and Jurassic zonation. The well encountered 13.5 m (44 ft) of excellent Volgian sand directly on fragile tight weathered granodiorittic basement, in an oil down to situation.

The basal part of the Draupne sand in the 16/3-4 well includes an interval with well-rounded sand granules, indicating shallow marine reworking and rapid transgression over a weathered basement. The composition of the sand is very similar to the underlying basement, demonstrating a local intrabasin sediment source.

The well was production tested to provide additional information on sand continuity and thickness variations. In contrast to the discovery well, the DST pressure response was characterized by an increasing derivative (possible thinning) followed by an even larger decrease. Hence, the 16/3-4 A well was sidetracked updip to investigate the local flow limitation indicated by the DST and to provide information on local thickness variability. The sidetrack well penetrated 4.5 m (15 ft) of Volgian sand directly overlying fresh unweathered basement. The sidetrack was drilled in

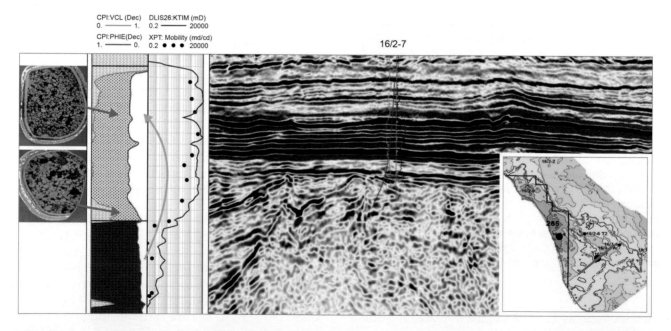

Figure 29. The first Johan Sverdrup appraisal well in 2011 (16/3-4) is located 6.5 km (4 mi) southeast of the discovery between 16/2-6 and 16/3-2. The well encountered 13.5 m (44 ft) of excellent Volgian sand directly on tight kaolinite-rich weathered granodiorittic basement. The rounded granules in the basal part of the Draupne sand indicate a rapid marine transgression. The composition of the sand is very similar to the underlying basement demonstrating a local intrabasin sediment source.

an upper Jurassic paleo-high setting. This sidetrack well and later crest wells demonstrate that the Volgian sand drapes the underlying paleo landscape, thickening into the lows and thinning over the highs.

The third delineation well (16/2-7) was located in the east flank of the Augvald graben. The top reservoir came in 17 m (56 ft) deeper than the prognosis (Figure 30). Online seismic reprocessing during drilling showed that the well was drilled on the low side of a postdepositional lower Cretaceous fault. This was confirmed by sidetrack well 16/2-7A.

These 16/2-7/7A reservoir penetrations demonstrate that the Volgian sand has been deposited in an epeirogenic subsiding basin over an erosional base Volgian unconformity, which also cuts into the regional base middle Jurassic unconformity.

The first well in PL 265 (16/2-8) was drilled in parallel with the fourth reservoir penetration in PL501 (16/2-7A) during the summer of 2011 (Figure 28). The

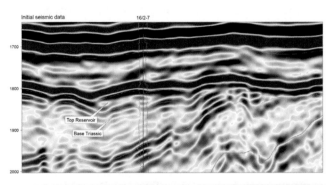

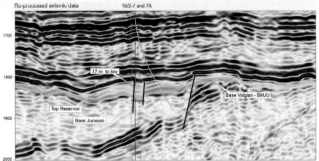

Figure 30. The third delineation well 16/2-7 was located in the east flank of the Augvald Graben. The top reservoir came in 17 m (56 ft) deeper than prognosis. Online seismic reprocessing showed that the well was drilled on the low side of a small postdepositional lower Cretaceous fault that was not visible on the initial seismic data. The sidetrack well 16/2-7A proved the correctness of the initial prognosis.

16/2-8 well proved the existence of a 70 m (230 ft) oil column on the western part of the field in Volgian sand and lower Jurassic with the same OWC and pressure as in discovery well 16/2-6.

The last appraisal wells were drilled during early 2014 (Figure 27). The 16/2-19 well demonstrated a rapid lateral facies change from upper Jurassic shallow marine to poor-quality spiculite facies in the north. This can be related to limited sediment supply from a smaller provenance area to the north on the Haugaland High.

The last delineation well, 16/3-8S (Figure 27), was drilled close to the crest of the Avaldsnes high and penetrated 14 m (46 ft) of Volgian sand of extremely high quality. The well was sidetracked for fresh logging while drilling (LWD). The resistivity logging proved deep mud filtrate invasion in these ultrahigh-permeability sands.

One of the major uncertainties relating to the top reservoir definition in depth is related to overburden velocity variation. This was demonstrated in the 16/5-2 well (Figure 27), where the top reservoir came in 3 to 7 m (10 to 23 ft) below the FWL with the same seismic travel-time as in well 16/2-8, indicating a time-to-depth variation up to 80 m (262 ft) across the field before well calibration. Ongoing FWI processing of the broadband data can compensate for such velocity variations.

The PDO was issued in February 2015 (Figure 27). The recoverable reserve range in the PDO is 1.7 to 3.0 billion bbl. The bulk of the reserves (75 to 80%) are in the extremely good Volgian sandstone reservoir, with 28% porosity and 2 to 70 Darcy permeability. The seismic mapping is based on two generations of broadband seismic data acquired in 2009 and 2012. The key uncertainties for the PDO are recovery factors, initial and irreducible oil saturation, reservoir sequence thickness and resolution, facies distribution, and depth conversion. There are differences in the OWC across the field from 1922.5 m MSL (6307 ft) in the first well to 1925 m MSL (6316 ft) in 16/3-6 and 1935 m MSL (6348 ft) in 16/2-16. There is also a residual oil zone of varying thickness below the various FWL levels. This residual oil zone is mobile as demonstrated by sampling.

The oil is heavily undersaturated, with varying GOR from 25 to 40 m^3/m^3. The oil shows no signs of biodegradation.

SUMMARY

The successful activation of the discovery phase on the Haugaland High was triggered by the discovery of the Edvard Grieg field in 2007 and continued by the discovery of the giant Johan Sverdrup field in 2010.

The discovery breakthrough on the Haugaland High is the result of systematic, data-focused geological and geophysical work backed up by petrographic logging, coring, and production testing during drilling of the concepts. Continuously better technology and methods have been applied in parallel with traditional methods like coring and testing that cannot be replaced by more indirect data types. Wireline logging in potassium-rich reservoirs and extremely porous and permeable sandstones are challenges beyond standard best practice.

The broadband 3-D techniques are major breakthroughs in relation to a holistic subsurface approach. The new broadband seismic surveys have improved reservoir definition and field delineation. The data have also allowed detailed reinterpretation of the shallow overburden, which has provided understanding of recent structural movements and their importance for very late generation, migration, and remigration of hydrocarbons.

The predrill concept for the Haugaland High took into account the results of all 17 of the exploration wells drilled in the area between 1967 and 2004. The wells were reanalyzed into a consistent stratigraphic framework. Together with regional mapping based on merged and reprocessed 1990s vintage 3-D seismic data, a kinematic development of the area from the Caledonian orogeny to Pleistocene was constructed as a basis for an updated petroleum habitat model.

The predrill analyses led to the development of a concept that included a giant saturated oil accumulation around the high with a potential oil column of up to 40 to 50 m (131 to 164 ft) above 1950 m (6398 ft) MSL. Reservoir uncertainty was substantial, but on lapping upper Jurassic shallow marine sands and older Jurassic–Triassic sediments in inlier basins provided significant potential, which could be unwrapped only by drilling.

The Haugaland High is at the current base Cretaceous level, an inverted high end of a spill fill route where petroleum can spill only by vertical leakage into shallower layers. The 3-D seismic data indicated such a situation, leading to a regional migration model where the spill ends up as gas flares at the seafloor in a tunnel valley northwest of the high. Sampling of the gas flares has shown their genetic relationship to biodegraded oil. The key success factor was recognition of the very late Pliocene–Pleistocene structure formation and necessary late and ongoing oil migration.

The predrill overall conceptual model was verified in relation to OWC, late and ongoing oil migration, and the presence of Volgian and older Jurassic reservoir sands. The oil systems were, however, different and more varied than a single common saturated system. The existence of a northern undersaturated fill-spill system and southern saturated system of very low maturity demonstrates the variability in the generation and migration of petroleum. These are in line with the late kinematic movements. Updated petroleum system analyses have been based on continuous updating of oil types.

The comprehensive data acquisition during the exploration and delineation phases has allowed for a continuous upgrading of the models from play concepts to reservoir models as the basis of robust field development plans. The Edvard Grieg model has been upgraded from the stochastic to the deterministic domain by the drilling of two delineation and two to three pilot wells in the development phase.

ACKNOWLEDGEMENTS

The knowledge creation related to the unfolding of the subsurface potential of the Haugaland High relies on the skills of several specialists in geophysics, sequence stratigraphy, petroleum system analysis, petrophysics, and testing in the Lundin subsurface team. The vendors have also been important in improving tools necessary for continuous better practice in unfolding the subsurface reality. In producing this chapter, contributions from Alaistar McDonald, Geir Samuelsen, Els van Weum, and Ingar Trondsen have been crucial.

13

Needham, Daniel L., Henry S. Pettingill, Christopher J. Christensen, Jonathan ffrench, and Zvi (Kul) Karcz, 2017, The Tamar Giant Gas Field: Opening the Subsalt Miocene Gas Play in the Levant Basin, *in* R. K. Merrill and C. A. Sternbach, eds., Giant Fields of the Decade 2000–2010: AAPG Memoir 113, p. 221–256.

The Tamar Giant Gas Field: Opening the Subsalt Miocene Gas Play in the Levant Basin

Daniel L. Needham, Henry S. Pettingill, and Christopher J. Christensen

Noble Energy Inc., Houston, Texas, U.S.A. (e-mails: Dan.Needham@nblenergy.com, Henry.Pettingill @nblenergy.com, Christopher.Christensen@nblenergy.com)

Jonathan ffrench

Noble Energy, Sevenoaks, United Kingdom (e-mail: Jonathan.ffrench@nblenergy.com)

Zvi (Kul) Karcz

Delek Drilling and Avner Oil Exploration, Herzilya, Israel (e-mail: kulk@delekng.co.il)

ABSTRACT

The Tamar gas field, discovered in 2009 by Noble Energy, Delek, and partners, paved the way for a series of presalt discoveries that expanded our understanding of the petroleum systems in the east Mediterranean and the region's hydrocarbon prospectivity. Approximately 40 tcf of natural gas has been discovered in the Oligocene–Miocene so-called Tamar sands play offshore Israel and Cyprus, which includes some of the largest deep-sea gas discoveries in the world over the last decade. The Tamar field development was expedited such that first gas occurred by March 2013, a mere 51 months following drilling of the wildcat well.

Deep-water presalt exploration offshore Israel began in 2003 with the Hannah-1 dry hole. Following a 5-year hiatus, a new subsalt exploration and drilling program began in earnest in 2008, resulting in gas discoveries at Tamar, Dalit, Leviathan, Dolphin, Tanin, Aphrodite, Karish, and Tamar Southwest. The main presalt play area likely extends nearly 30,000 km² (11,583 mi²) in water depths of approximately 1300 to 1700 m (4265 to 5577 ft), in the exclusive economic zones of Egypt, Israel, Cyprus, Lebanon, and Syria.

The Tamar sands reservoir section is comprised of deep-sea floor fan sandstones punctuated by relatively thin beds of silts and mudstones. The accumulations are characterized by thick deposits, over 250 m (820 ft) of gross pay at Tamar, of high-quality reservoir with >20% porosity and >500 mD permeability. The lean gas (over 98% methane) is thought to be biogenic and sourced from the interbedded shaley units, whereas the seal is the regionally extensive early Miocene silty-shaley unit termed the Ng10 shale. Traps are faulted, four-way closures reaching over 100 km² (39 mi²) at Tamar and approximately 330 km² (127 mi²) at Leviathan, the largest discovery to date.

Over 140 m (459 ft) of conventional core has been collected from one appraisal and two development wells at Tamar, and an extensive suite of side-wall cores were taken in the other wells. Core calibration has proven critical to petrophysical evaluation, resource assessment, and completion design.

The Tamar field was developed in under 51 months from discovery to first gas for $3.25 billion in gross development capital. Current production at Tamar is accomplished from five subsea wells, each capable of producing over 250 MMSCF/day and tied back through a subsea manifold to a fixed-leg processing platform located some 150 km (93 mi) south of the field. At the time of development, this was the longest deep-sea tieback in the world. From there, the treated gas is flowed to an onshore terminal in the coastal city of Ashdod. Tamar is currently the only significant provider of natural gas to Israel and has supplied nearly 1.0 tcf of gas as of year end 2016, which fuels over 50% of the local market's power generation needs. The discovery and development of Tamar opened a new chapter for the eastern Mediterranean oil and natural gas industry.

INTRODUCTION

The Tamar gas field, discovered in 2009 by Noble Energy, Delek, and partners, was the first deep-water discovery and the first commercial presalt discovery made offshore Israel. Over 37 tcf of natural gas from eight discoveries have been found to date in the Oligo-Miocene Tamar sands play of the Levant Basin. To date, the Tamar field is the only producing field of this play in the Levant Basin.

The Levant Basin[1] of the eastern Mediterranean is situated in the offshore sectors of Egypt, Israel, Lebanon, Syria, and Cyprus at the confluence of the Arabian, African, and Sinai plates (Figure 1). It is bounded by the shoreline to the east, the stable African craton to the south, the Eurasian plate and Cyprus trench to the north, and the Eratosthenes seamount to the west. Other than the wide shelf in the southern portion of the basin near the northeast portion of the

[1]The basin that occupies the eastern Mediterranean from the Eratosthenes high to the eastern shoreline is referred to in the literature as both the Levant and Levantine. We prefer to use Levant, as it is a geographic term defined in 1497 as the "Mediterranean lands east of Italy," specifically the present-day countries of Egypt, Israel, Lebanon, Syria, and Cyprus, all of which bound the basin.

Nile delta, most of the basin lies in water depths exceeding 1000 m (3281 ft).

The offshore Levant Basin is a polyphase basin that was shaped through four main tectono-sedimentological stages (Figure 2): (1) deep normal faulting in the Mesozoic toward the basin associated with the rifting of the neo-Tethys, progressively transitioning to (2) the contractual Syrian arc regime toward the shoreward southwest direction, associated with the collision of the Arabian and African plates with Eurasia, (3) the overlying sag and passive margin phases in the upper Cretaceous to present, and finally, (4) the evaporate Messinian sequence, caused by the near-complete desiccation of the Mediterranean in the late Miocene.

PRESALT EXPLORATION

The roots of the Tamar discovery can be traced back to the partnership's offshore exploration campaign a decade earlier, which focused on postsalt plays in the Pliocene–Pleistocene-aged Yafo Formation in the south of the Israeli Exclusive Economic Zone. This campaign resulted in the discovery of two offshore postsalt

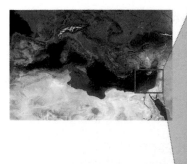
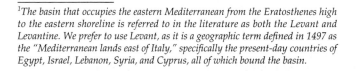
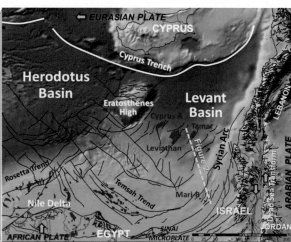

Figure 1. Regional setting of the Levant Basin, offshore Israel (Medimap Group, Loubrieu and Mascle, 2005).

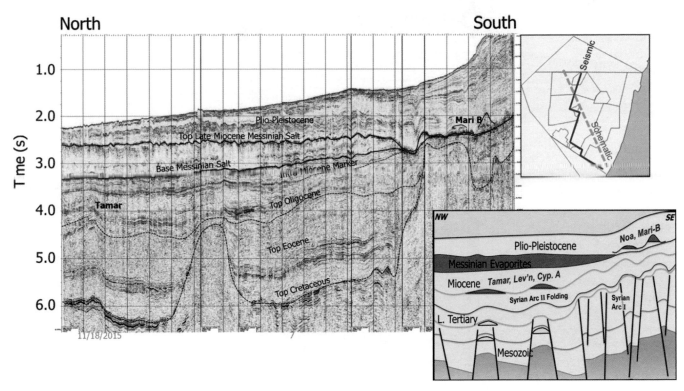

Figure 2. Two-dimensional seismic line and cross-section showing structural configuration and play types. (Two-dimensional seismic profile courtesy of TGS.) See Figure 1 for location.

reservoirs named Noa (1999) and Mari-B (2000), which provided the "steam" and insight for further and deeper offshore exploration. The presalt section of the deep Levant Basin offshore Israel remained undrilled until 2003, when Noble and Delek drilled the first presalt well off the Israeli shelf, Hannah-1 (Figures 3 and 4). Shortly thereafter, Shell and partners drilled the first subsalt well in the deep-water Egyptian Levant, but without commercial success.

The Hannah-1 well targeted two Cenozoic objectives within the fill sequences of two vertically stacked canyons (Figures 3 and 4). Though Hannah-1 failed to find reservoir-quality sands or significant hydrocarbon shows, when placed in a seismic stratigraphic framework, it provided critical age correlation and other clues to the possible prospectivity of Oligocene–Miocene objectives in the deeper basin. While evidence strongly supports a southerly cratonic source for Miocene deep-water sands, Hannah-1 showed that this canyon could capture any Oligocene–Miocene sands that moved by longshore drift along the broad oversupplied shelf to the south, and hence could be a local contributor of sands into deep water. It also provided key data for future well design, as will be discussed below.

The history of exploratory drilling offshore Israel was shaped by advancement in play concepts, available technology, and regulation. Until 2003, the two main plays explored were Mesozoic shelf targets, which yielded some hydrocarbon shows but no commercial developments, and the aforementioned postsalt Pliocene–Pleistocene targets. All of these were drilled in relatively shallow waters (Noa, in the deepest water, was drilled in approximately 800 m [2625 ft]). After the drilling of Hannah-1, there was a drilling hiatus extending 5 years, related to reevaluation of exploration strategies by both oil companies and the Israeli government.

The original Gal licenses (one of which covered Tamar) were awarded to BG in 2000 where the Tamar structure was recognized on older vintage 2-D seismic lines. The BG group acquired a 3-D seismic survey in 2001, which confirmed the Tamar structure and revealed potential hydrocarbon indicators. BG and partners sought a farmout in 2003, eventually leading to the current partner group.

Figure 5 shows a representative 2-D seismic profile that was available predrill Tamar and was sufficient to map out the major tectonic lineaments of the basin, as well as to identify the Tamar structure itself. Also

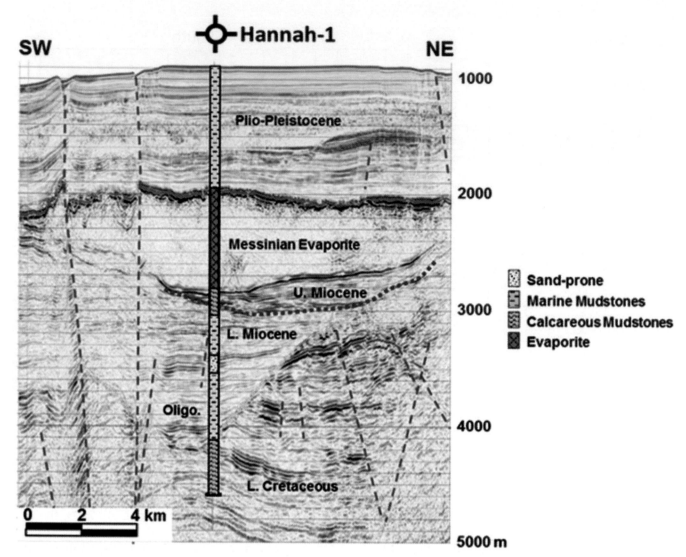

Figure 3. Noble Energy's Hannah-1 exploration well, drilled by Noble Energy Inc. and partners in 2003. See Figure 4 for location. While this well failed to find reservoir-quality sands in the Oligocene–Miocene, it provided critical age correlation to the Tamar area, where Miocene sands were expected. (Two-dimensional seismic profile courtesy of TGS.)

shown in Figure 5 is a profile from a 3-D survey acquired over the prospect in 2003.

Three geological risks received the greatest focus during the evaluation: presence and quality of reservoir, hydrocarbon containment related to the crestal faulting of the anticline, and the validity of the seismic flat spot.

Prior evaluations had expressed uncertainty regarding reservoir presence and quality due to (1) a large distance from the stable passive-margin shelfal depocenters of the African-Sinai terrain; (2) the adjacent Israeli coast, which had been a folded margin during the Cretaceous and consequently a poor Miocene sediment source; and finally, (3) the negative reservoir result of the Hannah-1 well, which had been hypothesized by some to be the primary feeder conduit

for deep-water sands. However, a depositional model was proposed that included a significant deep-water depositional system set up by the stable passive margin to the south and southeast from the craton and the idea that clean reservoir sands could be fed into deep water either from the south or by longshore current along the shelf, where they could be swept into the Afiq Canyon. Furthermore, when put in a sequence stratigraphy context, even if the canyon sequence drilled by Hannah was genetically related to the Tamar objective, the canyon fill at Hannah would have been deposited during the time period following deep-water lowstand deposition as a landward-stepping system shut off deep-water deposition and backfilled the canyon.

The risks associated with seal-breaching faults were mitigated by detailed mapping, including

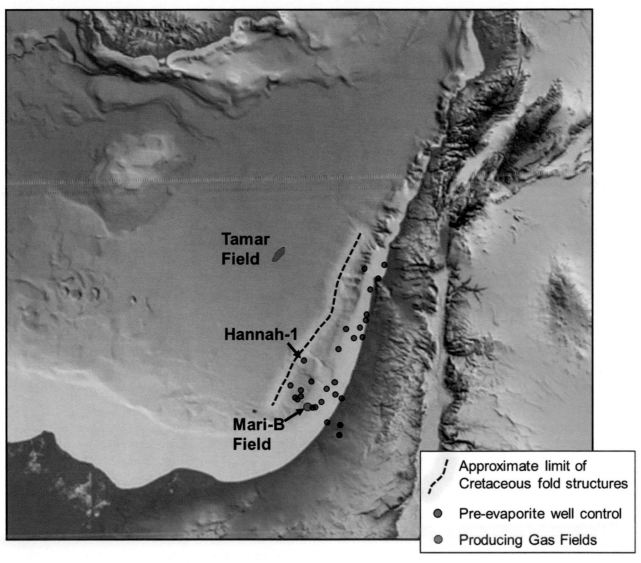

Figure 4. Map showing the pre-evaporite well penetrations in Israel that existed at the time of Tamar licensing. Also shown is the limit of the Cretaceous anticlinal folding related to the Syrian arc events, including the anticline of the Hannah-1 well, which is predominant underneath the present-day shelf. Note that at the time Tamar was licensed, offshore Levant pre-evaporite exploration in Israeli waters was limited to this folded area.

observations of the up-section fault termini. With one exception, the faults died out in the overlying clastic (presumably mudstone) package immediately above the objective, far below the Messinian salt. Pore pressure predictions, based primarily on seismic data, supported the capacity of the seal, assuming a column height as suggested by the flat spot.

The validity of the seismic flat spot was the final geotechnical risk to be addressed. In addition to a thorough evaluation of the aspects of the direct hydrocarbon indicator (DHI) from both seismic mapping and rock properties perspectives, several common flat spot pitfall scenarios were investigated, such as seismic multiples, stratigraphic artifacts, diagenetic

surface, nonhydrocarbon gas, and low-saturation gas, with the conclusion being that all except low-saturation gas were unlikely. It is important to note that for flat spot DHIs in the basin, no false positives were known; however, several true positives, primarily Noa and Mari-B, were recorded.

There was a large uncertainty over the resource estimate at Tamar predrill due to lack of relevant well control and the inherent uncertainty in the available seismic data. Noble's predrill probabilistic calculations yielded a mean recoverable resource of approximately 3 tcf, which proved to be conservative (compare this to current estimates for Tamar of approximately 10 tcf).

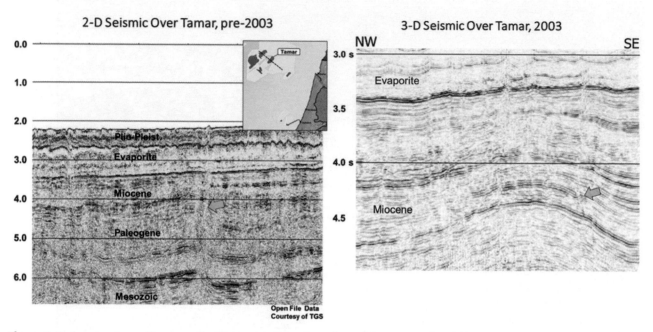

Figure 5. Early seismic profiles over the Tamar structure. Location of the 3-D to the right is essentially identical to a portion of the 2-D line to the left. Green arrow denotes the location of the Tamar anticline. Note the seismic flat spot is clearly visible on the 3-D, and a hint of it is present on the 2-D. (Open file seismic data courtesy of TGS.)

The Tamar prospect had two additional, nongeological, risks: that associated with the actual drilling of a wildcat in 1690 m (5545 ft) water depth through a 1.5-km (0.9-mi)-thick salt column and into a presumably overpressured reservoir section; the other, in a success case, was associated with market. The first risk was mitigated through comprehensive analysis of available data and a robust well design with adequate contingencies. The second was mitigated through market analysis, based on a calculated risk of demand growth in the fledgling local market, following its establishment in 2004 after Mari-B came online.

These technical uncertainties were either overcome or mitigated to the satisfaction of the partners and in late 2008, the Tamar 1 well was spud. In January 2009, the Tamar partners announced a significant discovery, essentially proving up the geological and geophysical models (Figure 6).

REGIONAL GEOLOGICAL FRAMEWORK AND PETROLEUM SYSTEM

Basin Evolution and Regional Structural Setting

The southeastern Mediterranean Basin has a richly documented tectono-stratigraphic history, stretching to late Paleozoic, and has been extensively studied.

Here we provide but a brief setting of the stage and refer the reader to excellent reviews by Garfunkel (1998, 2004), Gardosh et al. (2008), Robertson et al. (2012), Bar et al. (2013), and others.

The offshore Levant Basin is a polyphase basin with a complex geological history in terms of both tectonic evolution and stratigraphic fill. The major tectonic events along with unconformities are shown in Figure 7.

For the purpose of this chapter, which focuses on a Miocene gas play of the Levant Basin, we are primarily interested in the Oligocene bathymetry and subsequent deposition and deformation.

The southern Levant continental margin, a relic of the ancient neo-Tethys ocean, was formed through a series of rifting phases extending from the Permian to the middle Jurassic. The primary axis of these rifting events was northeast–southwest, parallel to the current Israeli coastline, and they left a faulted basement exhibiting a tilted block pattern with pronounced highs (e.g., Leviathan, Jonah) and lows. As the early Mesozoic rifting came to an end, a passive margin formed with the basement subsiding primarily through thermal relaxation. The margin was flooded and exposed intermittently through several transgressions and regressions all the way through the middle Eocene. This phase ended in a transgressive crescendo in the Senonian to middle Eocene, when pelagic sedimentation reached as far "southeast" as Saudi Arabia.

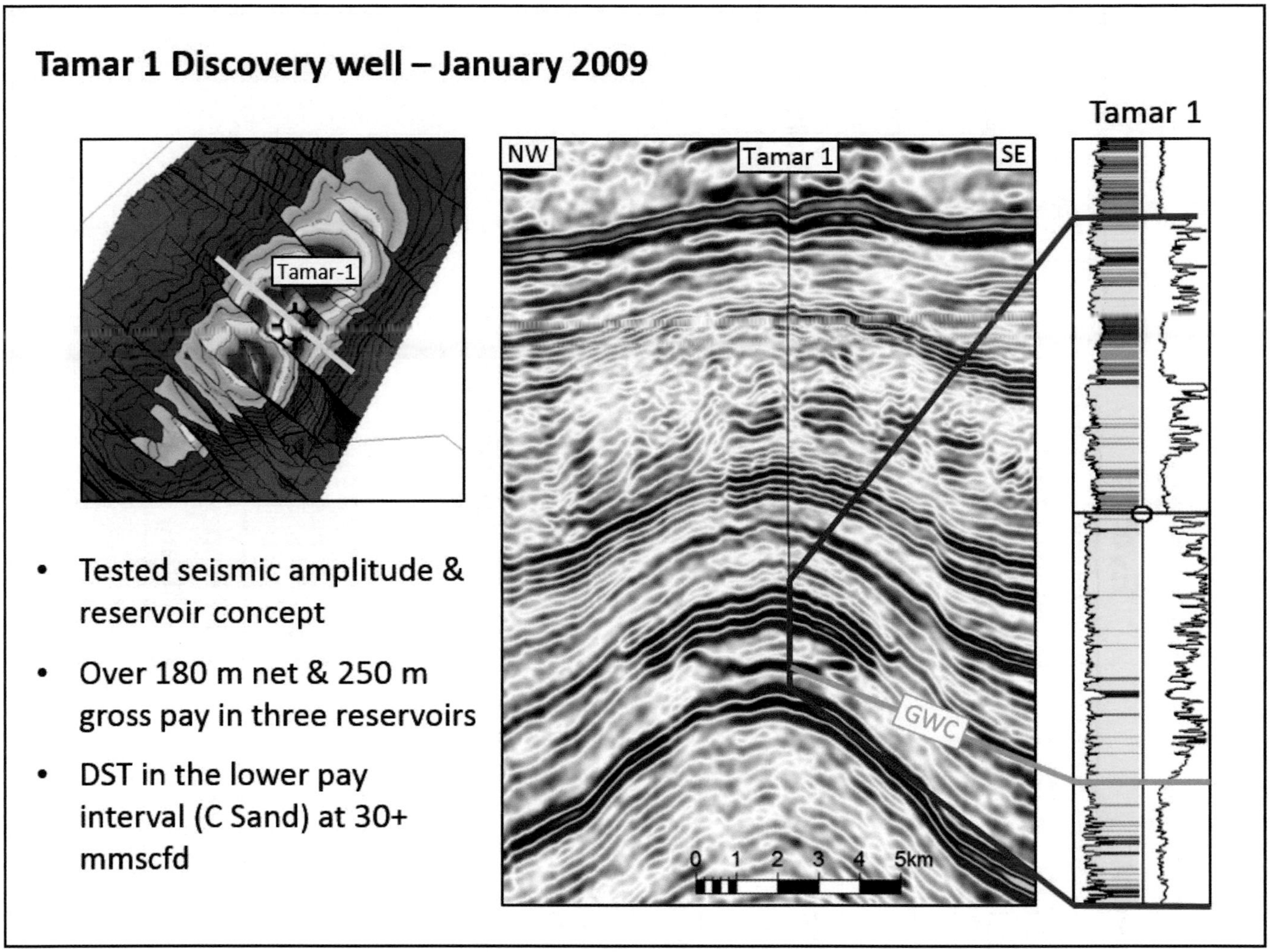

Tamar 1 Discovery well – January 2009

- Tested seismic amplitude & reservoir concept
- Over 180 m net & 250 m gross pay in three reservoirs
- DST in the lower pay interval (C Sand) at 30+ mmscfd

Figure 6. Tamar 1 discovery well, shown on seismic line, which was reprocessed after the discovery. The post discovery resource estimate was approximately 5 tcf mean recoverable.

The closure of the neo-Tethys in the late Cretaceous resulted in horizontal compression and formation of the so-called Syrian Arc fold belt along the northwest margin of the Arabian platform. The axes of these folds vary systematically from east to west in the Sinai, through north–south in Israel, to northeast–southwest in Syria, thus forming a broad *S* shape in map view. The anticlines of the Syrian Arc are thought to have formed through the reactivation in reverse motion of deep-seated Mesozoic rift-related normal faults. The deep-seat fault reactivation created the folds in the upper part of the stratigraphic column. There is substantial evidence from onshore Israel and Lebanon to suggest that the Syrian Arc deformation occurred fairly continuously from late Cretaceous to the Late Tertiary and migrated from south to north; however, two "peaks" seem to stand out: one during the Coniacian–Santonian, the

other during Eocene–Early Miocene. These peaks are often referred to as Syrian Arc I and Syrian Arc II. The current Tamar anticlinal structure formed as the Syrian Arc II pulse was dying out, in the Early Miocene.

The formation of the Syrian Arc folds during primarily pelagic deposition resulted in characteristic thickness and facies variations between fold crests and valleys.

In the late Eocene, the continental margin was reactivated due to the breakup of the Arabian and African plates, which caused a dramatic change in both deposition and deformation. The previously slow rates of pelagic deposition were now significantly accelerated and dominated by siliciclastic sedimentation (Steinberg et al., 2011). The gently dipping shelf was broken up into three distinct morpho-tectonic steps, underlying the current (from east to west) Judean

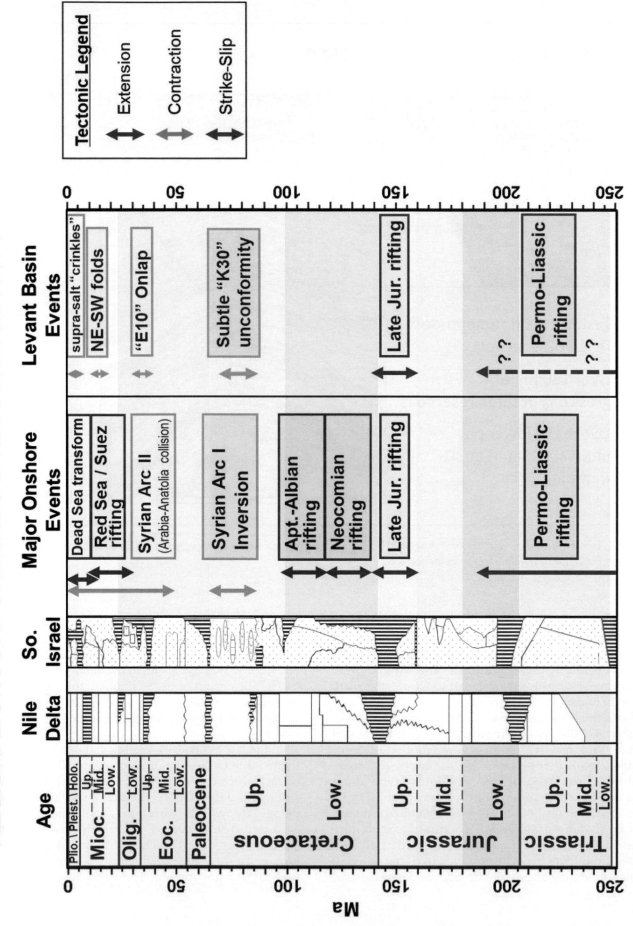

Figure 7. Major basin evolution events for the offshore Levant (right) and onshore Israel (left), along with generalized chronostratigraphic columns from the onshore Nile delta and southern Israel. Modified from George et al. (2013), after Guiraud et al. (2005) and Gardosh et al. (2001).

hills, coastal plains, and continental slope. These steps were deeply incised by submarine canyons (Bar et al., 2013), but later, during the Oligocene–Miocene, they attenuated through rapid sedimentation. Submarine canyons incised the shelf again, though not as deeply, during the Messinian salinity crisis (MSC) caused by the dramatic drop in sea level of the Mediterranean.

The MSC is thought to have had another effect on the structural fabric of the basin (e.g., Ghalayini et al., 2014) by forming a system of prominent northwest–southeast striking normal faults, which die out both downward (most commonly in the Paleogene) and upward (usually near the base of Messinian salt). This vertically bounded normal fault system, termed "piano key" by some (e.g., Kosi et al., 2012), is pronounced at Tamar, yet does not seem to breach the seal.

Finally, during the Pliocene, Nile-derived sediments buried the coastal plain step (Bar et al., 2013) and caused the westward extension of the continental shelf and the formation of the present-day continental slope.

Petroleum System

The petroleum systems of the Levant region can be generally divided into thermal and biogenic.

Thermogenic petroleum systems: Several hydro-carbon-bearing provinces surround the Levant Basin (Figure 8), of which the following source rocks are documented:

Jurassic: Proven oil source rocks in the western desert and throughout the Neotethys ocean realm (Klemme and Ulmishek, 1991; Dolson et al., 2001, 2014). Source of commercial oil production of onshore Israel (Gardosh and Tannenbaum, 2014).

Cretaceous: Proven oil and gas source rocks in the western desert, Gulf of Suez, Lebanon, and Syria (Dolson et al., 2001,

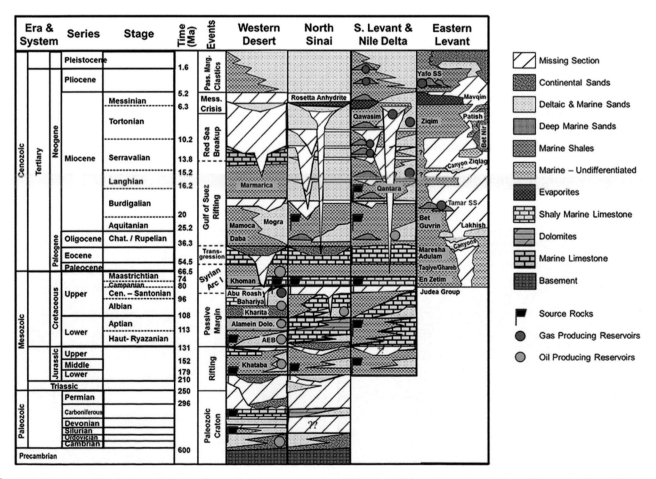

Figure 8. Stratigraphic chart and regional petroleum occurrences within the offshore Levant and the adjacent basins of Egypt. (Egyptian basins modified from Dolson et al., 2001; Levant Basin stratigraphy based on this study and Steinberg et al., 2011; Gardosh et al. 2008.) The producing interval of Israel's two offshore fields are annotated: Mari-B (Pliocene Yafo sands) and Tamar (lower Miocene Tamar sands).

2014; Barrier et al., 2014; Bou Daher et al., 2014). Source of oils recovered onshore Israel (Feinstein et al., 2002; Gardosh and Tennenbaum, 2014).

Paleogene: Proven oil source rocks in the Gulf of Suez (Eocene) and onshore Nile delta (Oligocene) (Dolson et al., 2001, 2014).

Miocene: Proven oil source rocks in the Gulf of Suez and as a source of thermal gas in the Nile delta onshore (Dolson et al., 2001, 2014).

Biogenic petroleum systems: Dry bacterial gas (also referred to as biogenic) was encountered within the Pliocene Yafo sand member in the shelf waters of Israel at Noa-1, Mari-B, and offshore Gaza in Gaza Marine-1. This gas was interpreted as bacterial based on its high methane content and isotopic composition (Feinstein et al., 2002). In addition, many of the Pliocene fields, as well as recent Oligocene–Miocene discoveries offshore Nile delta in Egypt, are attributed to bacterial gas (Dolson et al., 2001; Nassar et al., 2012). The Tamar gas seems to be dominated by an extension of this bacterial gas system into the deep-water, presalt region of the Levant.

Regional Tectono-Stratigraphic History and Depositional Setting of the Tamar Sands

Paleogeographic setting and basin fill: During the upper Paleogene and early Neogene, the Levant Basin was a passive margin with a very large continental hinterland along the entire southern and eastern edges of the basin. This hinterland provided ample updip cratonic sources of sediment to supply the Levant shelf and ultimately deep water. The Paleo-Nile river was established by the late Oligocene and as shown in Figure 9, the southeastern Mediterranean was flanked by a very wide shelf from Oligocene onward, a situation that persists today.

Figure 10 shows the chronostratigraphy of the Levant Basin, during which the Tamar sands and overburden were deposited. Biostratigraphic analysis of the Tamar wells, as well as offset wells, indicates that the Tamar reservoir section was deposited in deep water, during major depositional episodes of the latest Oligocene through early Miocene (primarily Burdigalian) (see Figure 10). This is confirmed by yet unpublished quantitative basin analysis studies.

Sediment driving mechanism: While there are multiple cycles of Oligocene and Miocene deposition in the region, and several global eustatic fluctuations documented (Figure 10), two regional tectonic events stand out as candidates to drive sediment delivery into the deep-water Levant: (1) the so-called Syrian Arc II pulse that initiated in the Oligocene and continued through the Neogene and (2) uplift of the Red Sea shoulders during the Burdigalian (Figure 7) (see Bosworth et al., 2005; Macgregor, 2012). Both events would be expected to shed clastic sediments into the basin, although the Red Sea event would have affected a cratonic source of much greater lateral extent and reached its peak at the time of Tamar sand deposition.

End Oligocene (25 Ma)

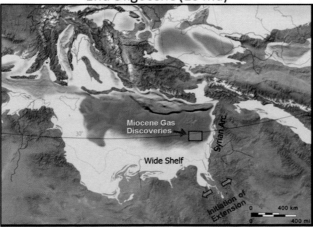

Mid-Miocene (13 Ma)

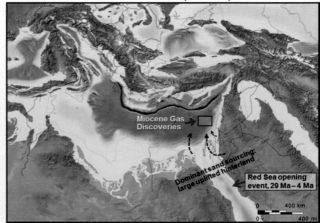

Figure 9. Paleogeography of the Levant and surrounding regions in the late Oligocene (left) and mid-Miocene (right). The area of Tamar and the surrounding discoveries is shown by the red box. (Paleogeographic maps from Ron Blakey/Colorado Plateau Geosystems, 2015.)

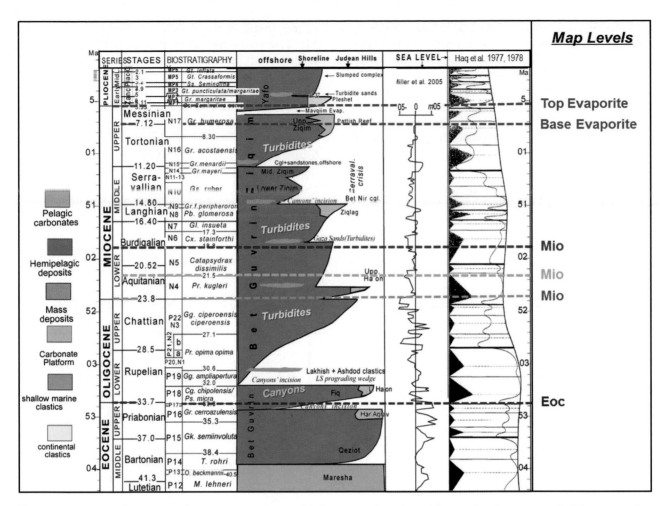

Figure 10. Upper Paleogene and Neogene Levant Basin chronostratigraphy, with map levels annotated. (Chronostratigraphic diagram modified from Gardosh et al., 2008.)

Sediment source: The filling of the basin was almost certainly dominated by the greater paleo-Nile drainage basin, which would encompass both the large paleo-Nile river as well as smaller coastal rivers, in much the same way that the similarly wide shelf of the northern Gulf of Mexico offshore Texas and Louisiana is fed not only by the paleo-Mississippi river and the Rio Grande but also by seven smaller coastal rivers between them. As the southern margin of the Levant is in much the same position today as it was in the Oligocene, it is important to note that a majority of the African craton has been drained in recent history by the Niger and Nile rivers, the latter delivering its entire sediment load into the Levant Basin (Macgregor, 2011). The present-day Nile is the world's fourth largest in terms of annual sediment delivery into the ocean, and studies document the vast effect of the present-day Nile on deep-water deposition. Sr and Nd isotope source tracing by Krom et al. (1999)

and Weldeab et al. (2002) demonstrate that 60 to 80% of the modern Israeli Levant particulate matter is derived from the Nile river, with most of the remainder from aeolian dust of Saharan origin. Venkatarathnam and Ryan (1971) used mineralogy from piston cores to demonstrate the Nile as the dominant detrital source during Pleistocene and recent throughout the eastern Levant, as far north as Turkey. One can only speculate about the robustness of that drainage system in the mid-Miocene; however, with widespread depositional packages through the Paleogene and Neogene, there is no reason to believe the sediment machine was materially less robust than today. In addition to the thick Neogene deposits of the Nile delta region, the slope in front of the narrow Sinai shelf protrudes seaward toward the deep-water Levant.

Some debate over the possible geographic extent of the updip source of Oligocene–Miocene siliciclastics and specifically the Tamar sands still ensues, and it is likely to be pursued further utilizing various techniques. However, it is the authors' opinion that while a contribution from the coastal hills of Israel cannot be ruled out, the overwhelming source volumetrically would be the vast cratonic areas to the south and its wide shelf, as with other major cratons and paleo river systems of the world. In addition to the regional evidence cited above and the sedimentological evidence from cores (see section below), two recent publications promote the aforementioned southern source for the Oligocene–Miocene sandstones as seen at Tamar: Macgregor (2011, 2012) presents a source-to-sink evaluation that correlates the aforementioned rise of the Red Sea shoulders to a pronounced depocenter

to the north, in the deep basin of the Levant (Figure 11). The two are connected through the proto-Nile river. Gvirtzman et al. (2014) utilized 3-D numerical stratigraphic modeling to argue that, given the morphology of the Israeli continental shelf during the Oligocene–Miocene, a dominant Arabian source is implausible.

Slope delivery mechanisms: Several slope canyons have been documented in the adjacent Israeli shelf (summarized by Gardosh et al., 2008). Like most submarine canyons, these probably started their existence by retrograde slumping, ultimately capturing sediment sources as they intersected the shelf updip. Such

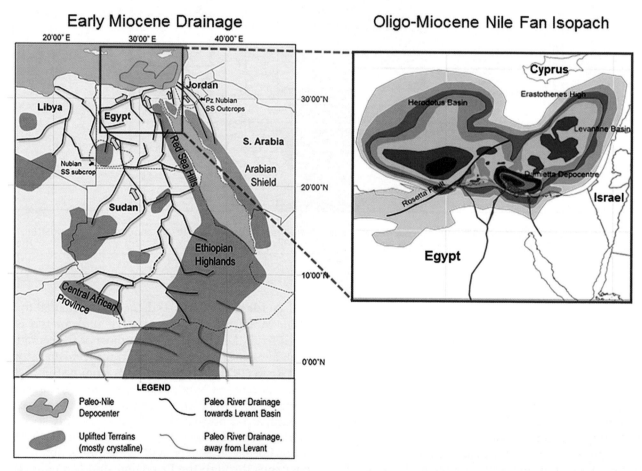

Figure 11. Oligo-Miocene hinterland drainage shown on present-day geography. Yellow arrows indicate principle sediment sourcing hypothesized for the deep-water Levant. Tamar sand lithologies generally agree with the gross components that could be sourced from either the granitic craton of the African–Arabian plate or additionally the Cambrian to Cretaceous Nubian sandstones in southern Egypt, the Red Sea hills, and possibly southern Jordan, as shown here. This may explain the bimodal nature of the sands: highly quartzose medium- to fine-grained subrounded grains (second-cycle, reworked from fluvial and shelfal areas), mixed with less quartzose fine-grained, subangular grains. (Map to the left based on Macgregor, 2011, 2012; this study. Map on the right from Macgregor, 2011, whose permission is required for further use.)

canyons are less documented in the Sinai and paleo-Nile, the latter possibly owing to deep burial below the Pliocene to recent delta. At this time, it is unknown which canyon(s) would have delivered sands into the Tamar area at the time of reservoir deposition, nor the exact path of channelization from slope canyons to Tamar. It is also possible that some sediments accumulated on the Miocene shelf and were transported by counterclockwise ocean currents to the entry point of canyons.

Sand presence in the Tamar area: Given these tectonic and paleogeographic factors, the partnership was optimistic about reservoir-quality sand presence at Tamar. The analogy invoked for sand presence and thickness was the deep-water Paleogene Wilcox Formation of the deep-water Gulf of Mexico, which, like the Levant, was deposited downdip of a broad cratonic hinterland at the time of a major tectonic event (Laramide Orogeny), resulting in widespread and thick sheet-like sands hundreds of kilometers downdip of the contemporaneous shelf margin (Figure 12).

A similar sheet-like nature was supported by the seismic geometries observed in the 3-D seismic data. While the reservoir quality of the Wilcox is variable, it

is buried much deeper than Tamar; hence, the risk of tight sands was deemed to be low.

Tamar sands are encompassed within a seismic package of reflectors that does not change its overall thickness rapidly, as shown in Figures 13 and 14. The reflections themselves are of variable strength (acoustic impedance magnitude) and relatively continuous. Both of these observations led to the conclusion that the Tamar reservoirs are very continuous as sand packages and probably deposited in a relatively unconfined setting, in a fan position that is downdip from the large channelized delivery system(s), where deposition occurred over a relatively unconfined area.

As observed in Figure 13, the Tamar interval fills an elongate northeast to southwest trough, following the major anticlinal axes inherited from the underlying deep-rooted faults and Syrian Arc II folds. The interval has a maximum thickness of 320 m (1050 ft) south of Tamar and thins gradually toward the limits of the deep-water depocenter, maintaining a thickness above 200 m (656 ft) until it approaches the Eratosthenes high to the northwest and the Israeli shelf to the east, at which point it thins rapidly to near zero. The lateral extent of this thick sheet-like unit is world-class in scale, exceeding 140 km (87 mi)

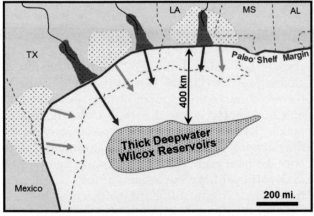

Paleogene Paleogeography (Wilcox Fm.):
Large distance, shelf edge to downdip deepwater play

Comparison of U.S. Gulf Coast Paleogene with Levant Basin

▶ Both had large stable craton feeding passive margin basin, with broad shelf to allow sediment accumulation and sediment re-working.

▶ Both have 100s of km from paleo-coastline to deepwater bathymetric lows.

▶ Major tectonic events drive sediment influx:
 Gulf of Mexico Basin: Laramide Orogeny uplifts hinterland
 Levant Basin: Red Sea Event uplifts hinterland

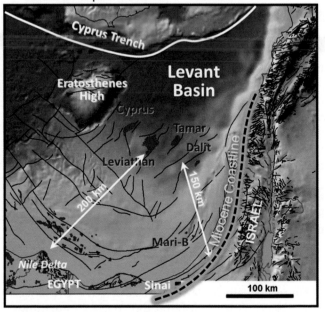

Deepwater Levant (Tamar sands):
Similar transport distances from cratonic sources

Figure 12. Regional paleogeography and depocenter map of the U.S. Gulf of Mexico Paleogene Wilcox Formation compared to the Levant Basin deep-water (present day) with the approximate Miocene coastline added. (From Pettingill et al., 2013; Wilcox Formation modified from Zarra, 2007.)

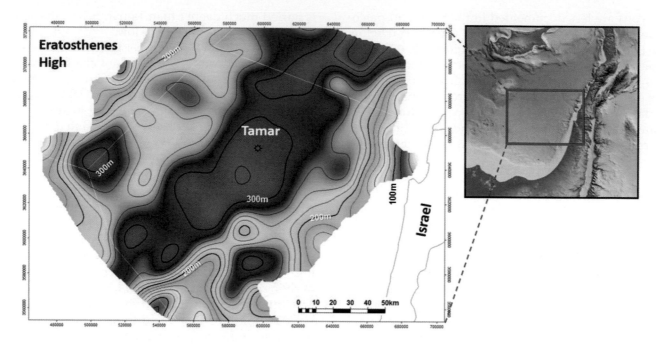

Figure 13. Smoothed seismic isochore map of a gross interval that includes the Tamar reservoirs (contour interval = 20 m [66 ft]), which roughly corresponds to the highlighted interval in Figure 14B. Note the pronounced thick that is oriented northeast–southwest. For most of the area in the deep-water Levant shown, this interval is between 200 and 300 m (656 and 984 ft) thick, before thinning rapidly toward the Israeli coast and the Eratosthenes high.

in width and 200 km (124 mi) or more in length, as shown in Figures 13 and 14.

SEISMIC INTERPRETATION OF THE TAMAR PROSPECT

Tamar Seismic Data

The original 3-D data over Tamar were acquired in 2001 by WesternGeco for British Gas with poststack time migration applied, the final full stack data being quite noisy. A rugose seabed and complex post-Messinian evaporite section due to multiple shallow faulting above a thick evaporite section (approximately 1500 m [4921 ft]) contributed strongly to poor imaging of the deeper presalt Tamar reservoir section. Noble had the 3-D reprocessed by Geotrace in 2006, applying prestack time migration, and the outputs included conditioned gathers and multiple angle stacks. The improvement in data quality at this stage was significant, confirming the presence of the DHI. In 2010, following the successful drilling of Tamar-1 and Tamar-2 (the wildcat and appraisal wells), the 3-D was reprocessed by PGS, this time applying Kirchhoff prestack depth migration, which massively improved the data quality, particularly at

reservoir level. Figure 15 illustrates this succession of improvements.

The Tamar DHI

The Tamar DHI tank is approximately 20 km (12 mi) long, 6 km (4 mi) wide, and 280 m (919 ft) high (Figure 16) and is defined by multiple seismic DHI characteristics (Figure 17). At the base of the tank there is a marked flat spot indicating a single continuous fluid contact across the whole tank. The top of the tank is defined by a weak soft impedance event above the flat spot, which switches to a strong hard impedance event at and below the flat spot. Below the top tank soft event is a succession of four bright amplitude events (hard, soft, hard, soft). These four internal events extend down to the flat spot, where there is a change in amplitude strength as they harden up slightly due to constructive tuning with the flat spot event. Below the flat spot, these events weaken to close to zero impedance. Within the tank below the deepest soft event is a seismically opaque zone down to the flat spot. Observation of the flattened gathers and angle stacks (see Figure 18) indicates a class III amplitude versus offset (AVO) response at the hydrocarbon interfaces with a weak gradient. Water-bearing reservoir interfaces indicate a class I AVO response.

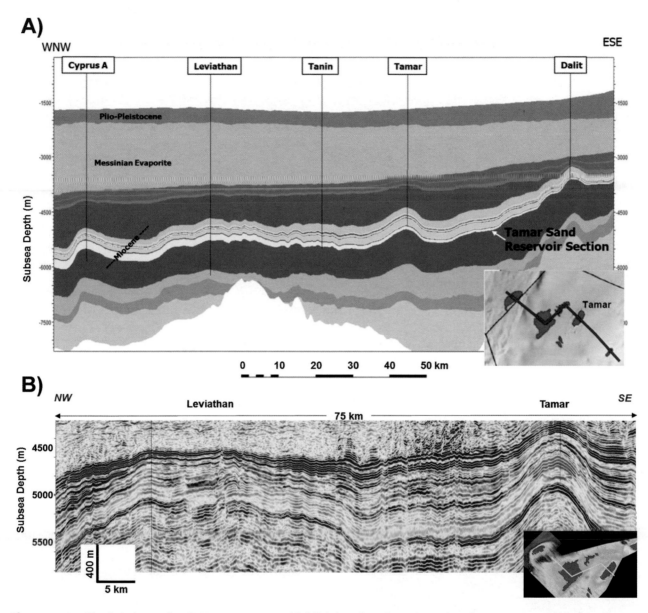

Figure 14. Profile views over the deep-water Levant, highlighting the Miocene section that encompass the Tamar reservoir sands. A) Geoseismic cross-section. B) Detailed seismic profile covering a portion of the geoseismic section (×12 vertical exaggeration; faults not annotated) with the gross interval that includes the A-B-C reservoirs highlighted in yellow. Note that the gross interval extends for over 75 km (47 mi), with minor thickness variation.

Tamar Geophysical Studies Predrill

Noble conducted an in-house pore pressure study in 2007 utilizing well data from the Hannah-1 well drilled 100 km away. Previously, overpressure analogous offshore Nile delta wells had been a concern. The study concluded that pore pressure was estimated to be between 9500 and 10,500 psi at reservoir level (Figure 19). As a result, little or no overpressure was to be expected in the Tamar reservoir.

Also in 2007, Noble conducted an in-house elastic impedance inversion of the 3-D data (Figure 20). The results supported the presence of a fluid anomaly at Tamar.

Noble in conjunction with Ikon Science conducted a rock physics/AVO study of Tamar in 2007, again using the only available relevant well data from Hannah-1. This study concluded that a fluid effect was present within the Tamar tank, though dry gas, wet gas, oil, or low-saturation gas were all possible. Two-dimensional

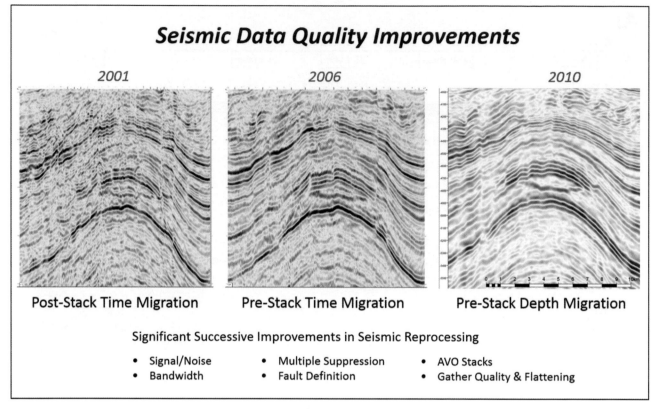

Figure 15. Seismic data improvements—matched amplitude and display color for effective comparison of the three processing vintages.

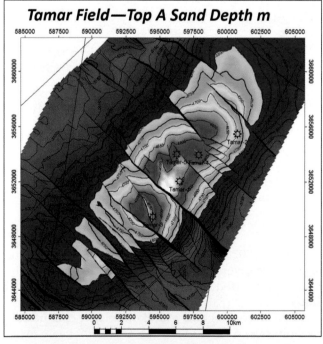

Figure 16. Top Tamar A sand depth map—hydrocarbon-bearing tank in white to light blue, dark blue to magenta is water-bearing below the gas water contact at −4797 m (−15,738 ft) true vertical depth subsea (TVDss).

modeling using the Hannah-1 well rock properties had a good fit to three major sand units separated vertically by major shale units within the fluid anomaly. From top to bottom, the sands were termed the Tamar A sand, B sand, and C sand, which were separated by

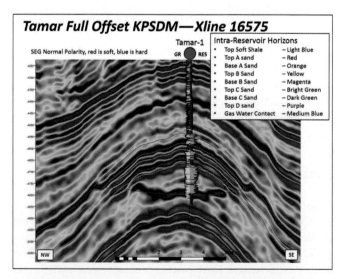

Figure 17. Tamar well tie. Gas-bearing sand in pink at Tamar-3 corresponds to the DHI tank with top reservoir A sand in red down to the gas–water contact in blue.

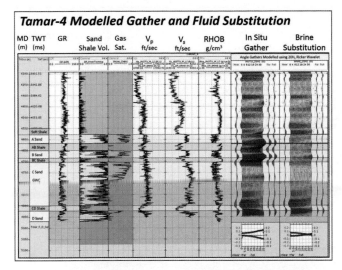

Figure 18. Tamar gather and fluid substitution. Display is from RokDoc® (commercially available modeling software from Ikon Science) showing the modeled gather response at Tamar-4. The Vp (sonic), Vs (shear sonic), RHOB (density) logs, and a 20 Hz (dominant frequency) Ricker wavelet were used in RokDoc® to model the expected seismic response.

the AB and BC shales, respectively. These predicted lithological units were proven correct by the discovery well in January 2009, and the DHI tank proved to be gas bearing. The continuity of the flat spot across the three main reservoir sands and subsequent pressure profiles indicate that the sand units are in pressure communication over geological time, either through the AB and BC shales, and/or through faults. Further shale units were identified by the Tamar-1 well, the NG20 (soft shale) seal above the A sand and the CD shale (NG10 SB) below the C sand, respectively. These shale units were of lower acoustic impedance than the intrareservoir shale units. Below the CD shale, the D sand is locally gas bearing with a deeper gas-water contact (GWC).

Tamar Seismic Interpretation

Interpretation was carried out on the full offset prestack depth-migrated data set (Figure 21). The data have been conditioned to be zero phase using available

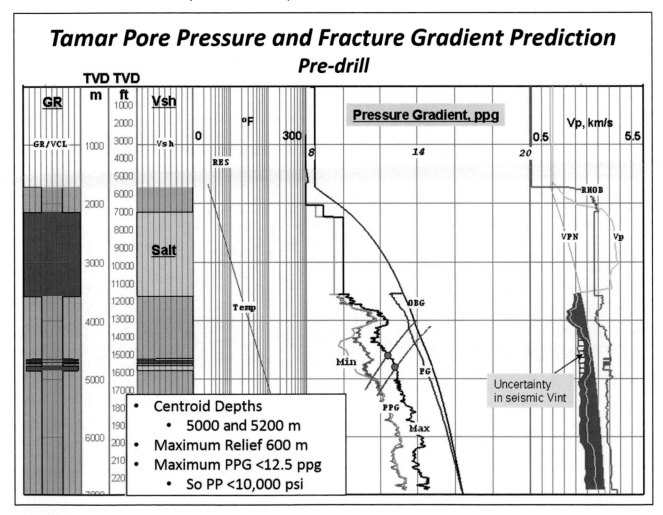

Figure 19. Tamar-1 pore pressure and fracture gradient prediction.

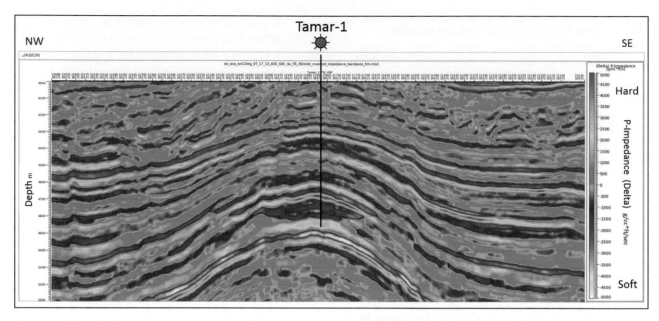

Figure 20. Tamar seismic inversion. The fluid response on the band-limited *p*-impedance is very clear for each of the A, B, and C sands with a consistent single gas–water contact for all three sands.

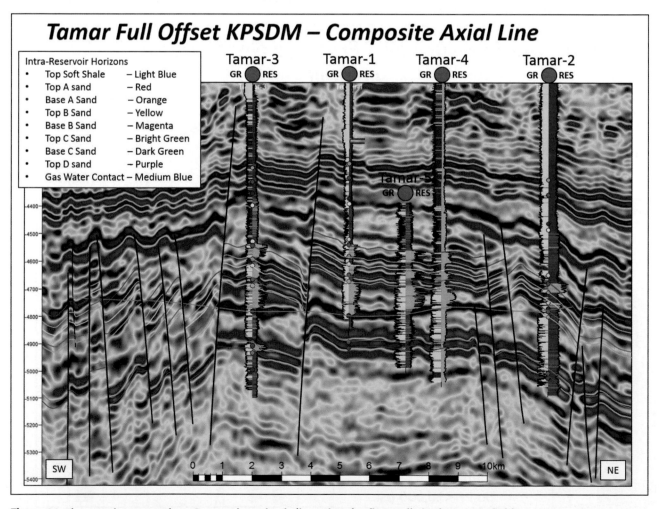

Figure 21. Flat spot interpretation. Composite seismic line tying the five wells in the Tamar field.

well data and displayed as Society of Exploration Geophysicists (SEG) normal polarity such that troughs are soft and peaks are hard. Some horizontal smoothing was also applied to reduce near vertical jitter and enhance the character variation in the seismic data. Several major events were interpreted, including seabed, top Messinian evaporite, base Messinian evaporite, lower/middle Miocene unconformity, top Tamar A sand, flat spot, top CD shale marker, and near base Oligocene. Also, within the Tamar tank only, four further events were mappable at base A sand, top and base B sand, and top C sand.

Tamar is a large inverted hogback anticlinal structure aligned south-southwest to north-northeast and transected by multiple normal faults (Figure 16). These faults strike northwest–southeast with fault planes at 45° to 60° of dip and terminate downward into a relatively mobile pre-Oligocene Tertiary section. As the hogback structure was being formed during a northwest–southeast compressional phase that affected the Tamar area in the middle Miocene, there was associated tension in the orthogonal direction causing this fault movement. There is also a subtle influence on the reservoir section of deep-seated left lateral transform faulting resulting in transtensional lows adjacent to the Tamar structure.

Tamar Well to Seismic Ties

There is a good fit of wells to full-offset zero-phased seismic data with good amplitude preservation (Figures 17 and 20). At the Tamar sand reservoir level, the full-offset data have a dominant frequency of 20 Hz and thus a temporal two-way-time tuning thickness of 25 ms[2]. The average interval velocity through the reservoir is approximately 3200 m/sec, which results in a depth tuning thickness of 40 m[3].

Across the Tamar tank, the A and B sand units are more than 30 m (98 ft) thick, the C sand is more than 200 m (656 ft) thick, and the four major shale units (soft shale, AB, BC, and CD shale) are thinner and vary from 18 to 35 m (59 to 115 ft) thick. The seismic interfaces within the Tamar tank thus have a tuned response and are not fully resolved. However, the lithological units are thick enough such that the tuned interfaces are laterally continuous across the Tamar tank and indicate good continuity of the major sand and shale units.

---

[2]*The reciprocal of two times the dominant frequency.*

[3]*As defined by a quarter wavelength or one quarter of the interval velocity divided by the dominant frequency.*

Horizon Amplitude Extractions

Horizon amplitude extractions demonstrate the consistency of amplitudes at the top of the Tamar tank, within the tank and their downdip conformance to structure (Figure 22). They also illustrate any changes in amplitude at the GWC in the form of hardening tuning rings due to constructive tuning of each seismic interface with the GWC. The extractions also show the change in amplitudes below the GWC, including the amplitude shadow (as exhibited in Figures 17 and 21). At Tamar, all top gas sand events are consistently soft, and all base gas sands are consistently hard. Below the GWC, the wet top A sand is hard, the base C sand is soft, and all other top and base sand interfaces are close to zero impedance. This configuration is due to the fact that the internal shale units (AB and BC shales) are relatively hard such that when the intervening sands are wet, there is little impedance contrast with the shales. Conversely, when the intervening sands are gas bearing, there is a strong impedance contrast with the shales. The soft shale above the A sand is relatively soft, thus a soft shale over a wet A sand is hard while a soft shale over a gas-bearing A sand is a weak soft. The CD shale below the C sand is softer still, and wet base C sand is always a strong soft. The top D sand is a strong hard when wet and a slightly weaker hard when gas bearing such as at Tamar-3 at the south end of the field.

RESERVOIR PREDICTION AND CHARACTERIZATION

Tamar Sand Nomenclature, Correlation, and Gross Geometry

A stratigraphic log correlation section across the Miocene reservoirs of the Tamar field is shown in Figure 23, which shows the productive A, B, and C sands of the Tamar field, as well as the underlying D sand, which has gas pay in some of the other fields in the region. The overall A-B-C package is about 250 m (820 ft) gross thickness. Each of the sand units is relatively high net gross and of constant thickness across the field, and within the sand units, there is a high degree of amalgamation of massive sand beds, as well as occasional thin- or medium-bedded heterolithic zones of sand, silt, and mudstone, interpreted to be distal turbiditic flows.

The three main reservoir units in Figure 23 are separated by intervals that are comprised of mudstones and occasional thin-bedded turbidites. These shale-prone intervals are regarded as hydrocarbon flow boundaries, separating the major sand units into distinct hydrocarbon flow units. However, as evidenced

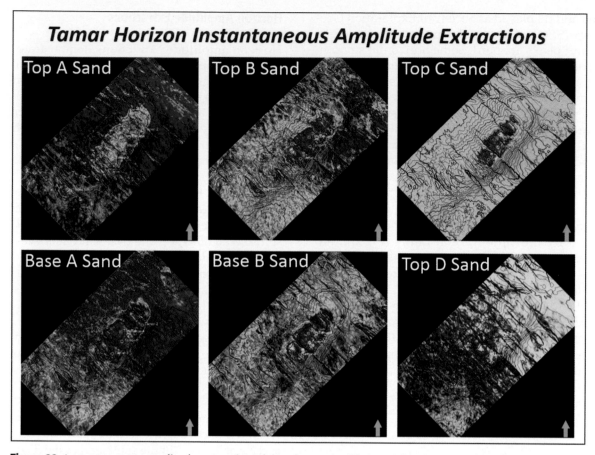

Figure 22. Instantaneous amplitude extractions from the top and base of the three major sand units A, B, and C. Blues are hard, and reds are soft and fit. The amplitude change for each of the major interfaces corresponds closely to the gas-water contact intersection.

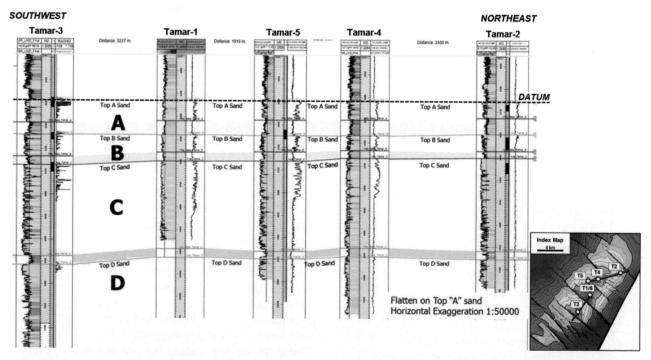

Figure 23. Stratigraphic log correlation section of the Tamar A, B, C, and D sands over the Tamar field. Section datum is the top A sand, which is the uppermost reservoir of the Tamar field. Note the relatively constant thickness of the sand packages over the area of the field.

by a common gas–water contact, identical pressure profiles and gas composition, these flow units were in communication over geologic time, either through the AB and BC shales or through faults.

Reservoir Facies Definition from Core and Logs

The Tamar sands have been characterized based on an extensive suite of logs from five Tamar wells, over 140 m (459 ft) of conventional core taken from three of the wells, and additional side-wall cores. Integrating these data with the 3-D seismic data formed the basis for the characterization of the meso- and flow-unit scale reservoir architecture.

As shown in Figure 24, six distinct facies could be defined within the Tamar reservoir units for reservoir architecture definition. In the broadest sense, these facies can be grouped into four reservoir types:

(1) *Noncohesive sand-rich debris flows (facies 6 in Figure 24).* A sandy or silty matrix with oblate mudstone clasts of variable size suspended throughout. Sorting is very poor, and the units are relatively structureless, other than some compaction or flow

lamination. These are interpreted as being the product of cohesionless mass flows and/or slurry flows (sensu Mutti, 1999).

(2) *Massive sand beds, highly amalgamated, with occasional linked-debrite caps (facies 1 and 2 in Figure 24).* Massive, relatively structureless, and poorly graded or ungraded. Compositionally, these massive beds are quartzarenites, with greater than 90% quartz, with only a small percentage of feldspathic and other minerals, and generally less than 3% clay. The grain size is predominantly fine sand, sorting is predominantly poor, and grains are subrounded to subangular (Christensen and Powers, 2013). Common features observed are dewatering (dish structures, dewatering pipes), load and flames at the base, inverse grading bands (depositional sieving), coarse-tail grading, and mudstone rip-up trains (Figure 24). This facies is interpreted as a hyperconcentrated density flow or a high-density turbidity current, deposited rapidly, with rapid frictional freezing and dewatering. On a meso-scale, these fast depositional events amalgamate to form high net-to-gross units that are tens of meters thick with a "blocky"-shaped gamma-ray (GR) pattern, as seen in Figure 23. These facies

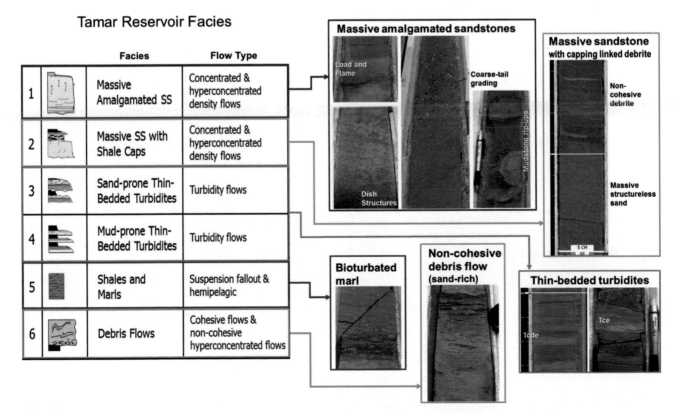

Figure 24. Tamar reservoir facies, based on lithologies observed in core. This facies scheme is simplified from the scheme defined by Mulder and Alexander (2001).

are easily recognized on image logs, as shown in Figure 25.

(3) *Thin- to medium-bedded turbidites, forming packages of variable net-to-gross (facies 3 and 4 in Figure 24; see also Figure 26B).* This facies consists primarily of the typical Bouma sequence. Most commonly, the sand beds contained in this facies are less than a centimeter thick, though occasionally they reach a thickness of a few centimeters. Grain size varies from fine sand to silt and is generally poorly sorted. However, as with the thick-bedded sands, quartz content typically exceeds 90%, such that porosity and permeability remain high. The most common components of the Bouma sequence are Tbcde, Tcde, and Tce, with the cross-laminated Tc unit comprising the volumetrically dominant sand fraction. Occasional flame structures are seen at the base. This facies is interpreted to be a low-density turbidity current, deposited after the aforementioned high concentration flows and often overlying them, and presumably as downdip equivalents, as the flow transforms. As with the massive sands, these facies are easily recognized on image logs (Figure 25).

(4) *Mudstones, varying from silty thin-bedded turbidites to hemipelagic mudstones and marls (facies 5 in Figure 24).* These mudstones are intercalated in the most shale-prone packages. Whereas the silty laminated mudstones are considered the most distal

equivalent of the low-density turbidite facies, the pure mudstone and carbonate-rich marls are interpreted to be deposited during quiescent periods when only hemipelagic activity occurs, with some suspension fallout of mud-sized particles.

It is important to note that in many sections of the Tamar cores, the sand particle size is bimodal, with the coarser fraction slightly more rounded and containing occasional quartzose overgrowths, indicating residence time in a previous environment before being transported to deep water (secondary sourcing). This supports the provenance proposed herein of a mature African–Arabian craton to the south, with local mixing of sands possibly occurring in the intervening continental and shallow marine areas surrounding the deep-water Levant. It is noteworthy that Ryan et al. (1973), in their analyses of Pleistocene to recent piston-core sediments, also found evidence of rounding, as well as grain abrasions normally associated with shallow marine and aeolian environments, and hence also concluded that the deep marine sediments had spent time in an intermediate clastic environment.

Interpretation of Depositional Process and Reservoir Architecture

Using these facies as building blocks, the resulting depositional model is one of an area in front of the main channel delivery systems, where the channels lose their leveed confinement and debouch their load in the channel-lobe transition or proximal lobe setting. Such areas are known worldwide for accumulations of thick massive sandstone units that form aggregated packages of sand beds which extend for thousands of meters (e.g., Chapin et al., 1994; Remacha et al., 2015). As such, based on outcrop analogies, the thicker beds are probably lenticular on a scale of tens to hundreds of meters. In this fan position, lateral offset stacking of beds is common, as one flow deposits its load, often by hydraulic jump, and the next flow often offsets laterally where seafloor topography offers greater accommodation (Straub and Pyles, 2012; Fielder et al., 2013; Remacha et al., 2015). This process of offset stacking and the resulting stacking pattern is shown schematically in Figure 26.

The thicker massive beds concentrate at any one given time in the axial zone of this proximal lobe setting, as shown in Figures 26A and 27. These systems are primarily aggradational; however, within the axial zones where the high-energy flows are concentrating at the mouth of the channel, there is a high degree of

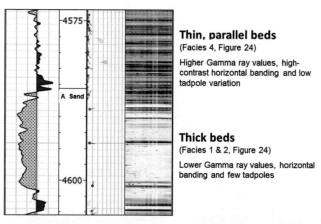

Thin, parallel beds
(Facies 4, Figure 24)

Higher Gamma ray values, high-contrast horizontal banding and low tadpole variation

Thick beds
(Facies 1 & 2, Figure 24)

Lower Gamma ray values, horizontal banding and few tadpoles

Figure 25. Image log showing the parallel bedding of the Tamar A sand reservoir. Note the high degree of planarity (horizontal banding of image and parallelism of dips) within the laminated units, and to some degree within the massive amalgamated sands (mainly horizontal banding). This is believed to be part of the evidence that the Tamar sands generally lack a high degree of channelization or the buildup of confining levees, which would lead to dispersive dip patterns from bed stacking within channels, levee buildup, and resolvable slumping.

Tamar Reservoir Architecture

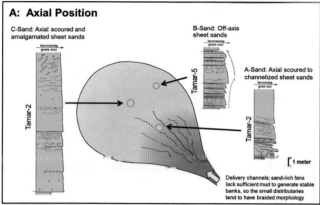

A: Axial Position

C-Sand: Axial scoured and amalgamated sheet sands

B-Sand: Off-axis sheet sands

A-Sand: Axial scoured to channelized sheet sands

Delivery channels: sand-rich fans lack sufficient mud to generate stable banks, so the small distributaries tend to have braided morphology

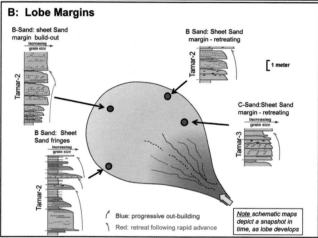

B: Lobe Margins

B-Sand: sheet Sand margin build-out

B Sand: Sheet Sand margin - retreating

B Sand: Sheet Sand fringes

C-Sand:Sheet Sand margin - retreating

Blue: progressive out-building
Red: retreat following rapid advance

Note schematic maps depict a snapshot in time, as lobe develops

Figure 26. Tamar depositional model and reservoir architecture, as observed in core descriptions, image logs, and log correlations. A) Lobe axis. B) Lobe margins ('fringes'), or off-axis areas.

which reach the peripheries of the proximal lobes (Figures 26A and 28), as the high-concentration flows drop their coarse fraction by frictional freezing and give way to the more classical turbidity currents that may continue on to the fringe areas. These heterolithic zones may organize themselves as sanding upward or shaling upward, depending on whether the depositional system is prograding or waning at a given time and location, as shown in Figure 26. The gradual changes in the facies associated with this transformation of flows from axial to distal fringe areas are shown in Figure 28.

It is important to note that the core intervals with less amalgamation are comprised not only of thin- and medium-bedded turbidites (facies 3 and 4 in Figure 24), which are thought to be deposited by the distal flow equivalents of the massive sands. These intervals also contain abundant linked debrites, which occur at the tops of massive sand beds and are often gradational with the underlying massive sand (facies 2 in Figure 24A). The reader is referred to Haughton et al. (2001) for a complete explanation of the genetic origin of these flows, which commonly occur when sediment delivery systems are out of grade, which we expect would have occurred as a result of the Red Sea tectonic event. Such linked debrites have been observed to commonly occur in the fringe areas of inner lobes (Paul Weimer, Personal Communication, 2015), which is consistent with their occurrence within intervals demonstrating less amalgamation and containing thin-bedded turbidites, although it cannot be determined whether this is a function of nondeposition in the axial zone versus lack of preservation due to flow scouring in the axial areas.

The proximal lobe reservoir architecture and its resulting stacking pattern as described herein have many well-documented outcrop analogs around the world. Among the best known are the Permian

vertical amalgamation and minor erosion not resolvable on seismic imaging, yet observed in the core.

The intervening heterolithic units are interpreted to be the continuation of these massive sand flows,

Tamar Reservoir Architecture at sand package scale:
aggrading fan packages with minor channels and scours

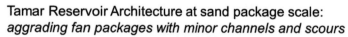

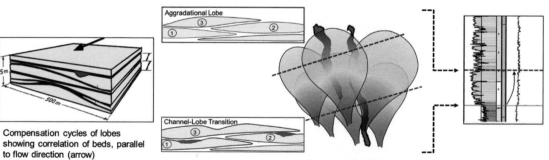

Figure 27. Tamar reservoir architecture. Model of aggrading fan lobes.

Aggradational Lobe

Channel-Lobe Transition

Compensation cycles of lobes showing correlation of beds, parallel to flow direction (arrow)
Modified from Nelson and Nilson (1984)

Typical aggradational package:
• sanding upward as it 'progrades'; shaling upward as it retreats.
• package thins towards lobe peripheries

Lateral and Vertical Transitions of Facies Assemblage

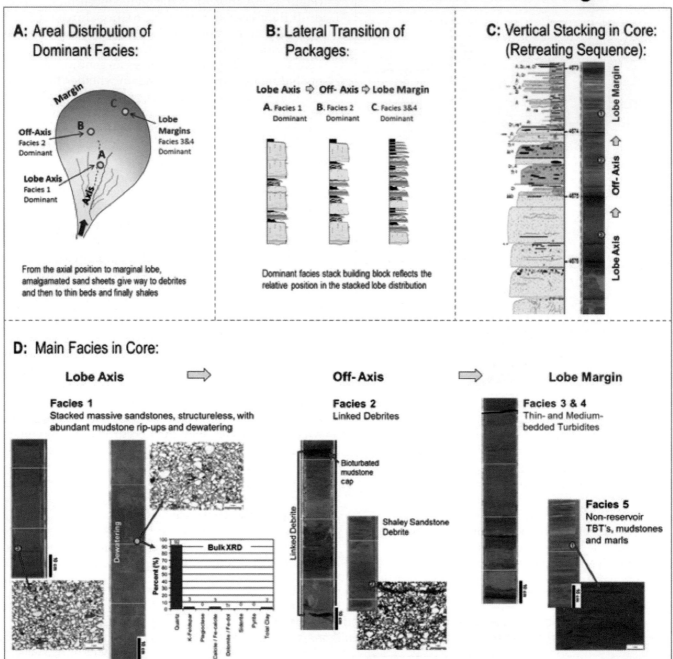

Figure 28. Tamar reservoir architecture: lateral and vertical transitions of facies, within the framework of lobe deposition, based on core and log observations. Facies numbers are as defined in Figure 24. A) Schematic of a single lobe from channel mouth to distal margin, with dominant facies annotated. B) Lateral transition of stacked sand beds, schematically showing the observed changes in the vertical facies packages when moving from the axial position to the margins of a lobe.
C) Typical vertical stacking of facies, for a portion of a reservoir that is retreating through time, such that the lower energy and sand-poor facies cap off the sequence as the axis of deposition migrates away from core location and/or the entire system shuts off, yielding a 'backstepping' of facies. D) Images of the main facies in core and thin section photomicrographs. Typical grain composition measurement shown for the massive sand in the inset. Note the quartz content exceeding 90% and the sub-rounded quartz grains, which reflect a relatively mature provenance.

Skoorsteenburg Formation of South Africa, the Carboniferous Ross sandstone of southern Ireland, and the Eocene Hecho group of Spain. The latter two are shown in Figure 29. The Ross Formation in particular shows a very similar stacking pattern of massive, amalgamated sands with intervening heterolithic zones of medium- to thin-bedded turbidites, with log correlations over kilometers very comparable to the Tamar subsurface data. The critical aspects of these systems for oil and gas prospectivity and production are (1) high net-to-gross packages, with thick aggregate packages of amalgamated beds, which have high internal connectivity and hence high Kv; (2) package continuity of thousands of meters, often exceeding 20 km (12 mi); (3) bed continuities of hundreds to thousands of meters, or even ten-thousands of meters, with excellent Kh; and (4) as net-to-gross diminishes from lobe axis toward the fringes, loss of amalgamation (Kv barriers) but excellent bed continuity and Kh. These characteristics all match the observations of the Tamar data to date.

In summary, the Tamar reservoir is a thick and continuous set of sands deposited hundreds of kilometers downdip of the contemporaneous shelf margin, in a relatively unconfined setting, where large-scale delivery channels debouch their load in an aggrading and laterally offsetting set of proximal lobes (also called channel-lobe transition in the literature). Unique aspects of the Tamar depositional system and the reservoir architecture described herein are:

(1) For sand-rich fans, a world-class areal extent (see scaled comparisons and discussion in Weimer and Pettingill, 2007). Whereas sand-rich fans have been described in the literature primarily in active margins or confined settings with relatively coarse sediment (e.g., Normark, 1970; Barnes and Normark, 1983/1984; Reading and Richards, 1994; Richards

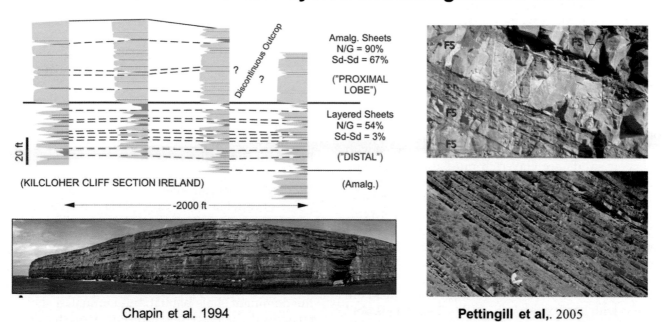

Sub-environments: Layered and amalgamated sheets

Amalg. Sheets
N/G = 90%
Sd-Sd = 67%

("PROXIMAL LOBE")

Layered Sheets
N/G = 54%
Sd-Sd = 3%

("DISTAL")

(Amalg.)

20 ft

(KILCLOHER CLIFF SECTION IRELAND)

-2000 ft

Chapin et al. 1994

Pettingill et al,. 2005

Figure 29. Outcrop analogs for the Tamar sheet sands/stacked lobe complexes. Left: Carboniferous Ross Formation, Ireland, from Chapin et al. (1994). Note the set of massive, amalgamated sand beds in the upper half of the section, overlying medium- to thin-bedded interbeds. While individual bed correlations between measuring stations are difficult in the lower interval and almost impossible in the upper amalgamated zone, the beds in outcrop are highly correlative over the length of this outcrop, which extends over a kilometer in total (not all is shown in this photo). Right: Eocene Hecho group, Spain, from Remacha, Pettingill and Fernandez (2015), courtesy Nautilus, whose permission is required for further use. Note the massive structureless sands in the top of the upper photo (the large prominent bed is about 1.5 m [5 ft] thick) and the rather continuous thin- to medium-bedded sands in the lower photo (sand beds millimeters to decimeters thick).

and Bowman, 1998; Richards et al., 1998; Mattern, 2005), this chapter documents a classic mega-scale passive margin sand-rich fan.

(2) Relatively low confinement, with single-sand packages extending thousands of square kilometers.

(3) A robust depositional system fetching sediments from a supercontinent of vast area, drained by a large river system (analogous to the present-day Amazon, Nile, Niger, or Mississippi). Uplift of this large hinterland during the Red Sea event would drive a large quantity of sediment into the deep basin.

(4) Amalgamated sheet geometries deposited within a proximal lobe environment hundreds of kilometers from the paleo-shelf margin.

(5) Sediment provenance and transport favorable to produce world-class reservoirs, both in terms of reservoir quality (due to high porosity-permeability) and reservoir drainage (due to a sheet-like architecture).

Petrophysical Analysis and Rock Properties

Formation evaluation challenges and core-calibrated log analysis workflow:
Details on Tamar field formation evaluation challenges and core-calibrated log analysis workflows are published in Christensen and Powers (2013). Key points from this previous work are summarized below.

Lithology challenges: The primary lithology-related formation evaluation challenge in Tamar field is variable mudstone lithology. Mudstones interbedded with reservoir sands are clay-rich mudstones, but they are not thick enough to be fully resolved on logs and thus cannot be used for log analysis parameter selection. The bounding units above and below reservoir intervals are carbonate-rich mudstones with distinct petrophysical properties that are not applicable in log analyses of reservoir intervals.

Fluid challenges: Reservoir fluids in Tamar field are dry gas with low condensate yield (<2 stock tank bbl/MMSCF) and low salinity formation water (<20,000 ppm). The primary fluid-related formation evaluation challenges are associated with the use of high-salinity, water-based mud. This mud system creates a host of formation evaluation problems: It limits logging technologies that can be applied in lithology analysis, it complicates fluid corrections to logs used in porosity calculations, and deep invasion prevents resistivity logs from reading true formation resistivity in some reservoir intervals.

Core-calibrated workflow: Application of nuclear magnetic resonance (NMR) logging technology was critical to working around the formation evaluation challenges and is an integral part of the core-calibrated log analysis workflow development for Tamar field:

- *Lithology.* Shale volume calculated from the ratio of NMR clay-bound water volume to gas-corrected, total porosity
  - o Calibrated to core laser particle size analysis measurements with shale volume ($V_{sh\ LPSA}$) defined as the cumulative grain size fraction smaller than coarse silt
- *Porosity.* Total porosity, corrected for fluid effects (gas effects and mud filtrate invasion), calculated using the density/magnetic resonance method (Freedman et al., 1998)
  - o Calibrated to oven-dried core porosity measured at reservoir net-mean-stress
- *Permeability.* Derived from a transformation of NMR log-based porosity
  - o Calibrated to core absolute brine permeability at reservoir net-mean-stress
- *Water saturation.* Capillary pressure-based, saturation/height model used to get around issues with resistivity log-based methods
  - o Calibrated to core air-brine (porous plate) capillary pressure measurements made at reservoir net-mean stress

Output from this formation evaluation workflow for the Tamar-1 discovery well is shown in Figure 30.

Reservoir Properties

Lithology: Reservoir intervals in Tamar field are composed of variable mixtures of two end-member lithologies: unconsolidated, clean sands (quartz arenites) and clay-rich mudstones. The mineralogy of both of these lithology end members does not vary significantly between the A, B, and C sand reservoirs. In shaly-sand portions of the reservoirs, detrital, pore-filling shale is the dominant shale habitat, but laminated shale and structural shale are also present (Christensen and Powers, 2013).

Porosity and permeability: As shown in Figure 31, porosity and permeability for clean end-member sands ($V_{sh\ LPSA}$[4] < 5%) does not vary significantly between the A, B, and C sand reservoir intervals. The

---

[4]*Volume of shale calculated from laser particle size analysis.*

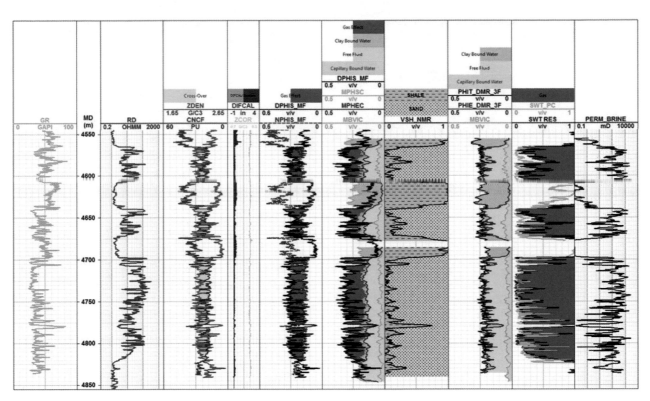

Figure 30. Log display of input wireline logs and output formation evaluation results for the Tamar-1 discovery well. Track 1: gamma ray (GR); Track 2: deep laterolog resistivity (RD); Track 3: bulk density (ZDEN) and neutron porosity (CNCF), as delivered on a sandstone matrix, fresh-water scale; Track 4: differential caliper (DIFCAL) and bulk density correction (ZCORR); Track 5: density porosity (DPHIS_MF) and neutron porosity (NPHIS_MF) recomputed using high-salinity mud filtrate as the fluid and sandstone (quartz) as the matrix; Track 6: recomputed density porosity (DPHIS_MF) overlain with NMR total porosity (MPHSC), NMR effective porosity (MPHEC), and NMR capillary-bound water volume (MBVIC); Track 7: shale volume (VSH_NMR); Track 8: total (PHIT_DMR_3F) and effective porosity (PHIE_DMR_3F) corrected for gas effects and high-salinity mud filtrate invasion; Track 9: comparison of water saturation calculated with resistivity (SWT_RES)- and capillary pressure (SWT_PC)-based methods; Track 10: single-phase, absolute permeability to brine (PERM_BRINE).

relatively low porosity (22 to 28%) for sands with permeabilities greater than 1 Darcy (>1000 mD) is associated with poor grain size sorting in these reservoirs (Figure 32). Although poor sorting negatively impacts porosity, permeability in unconsolidated rocks is less sensitive to sorting and is largely a function of grain size (Beard and Weyl, 1973). The grain size distribution as well as the lack of appreciable cementation are the key reservoir attributes contributing to the high permeability of the Tamar field reservoirs.

Both porosity and permeability decrease rapidly with relatively minor increases in shale volume (Figure 31). This rapid fall-off is associated with the dominant habitat of shale material in reservoir intervals. Most shale is present in the form of detrital, fine-grained material that fills pores and plugs pore throats, destroying both porosity and permeability.

Water saturation and saturation/height modeling:
High in the gas column, above the thin (<2 m) transition zone, water saturation (Sw) in Tamar reservoir sands varies widely from less than 5% in the cleanest sands to over 90% in sands where most of the pore space has been filled with detrital shale (Figure 33).

Capillary pressure (Pc) curves have unimodal pore throat distributions across the full range of reservoir quality and are fit using only three fit parameters: Sw @ Pc = ∞, entry pressure, and curvature. Early versions of the Tamar FE workflow used the Brooks–Corey (Brooks and Corey, 1964) Pc model (Christensen and Powers, 2013), but the Thomeer (1960) model is now being used, as it yields better statistical fits to measured data. Modeled Pc curves, with fit parameters predicted by permeability and porosity, match measured data in an unbiased manner across the full spectrum of equivalent

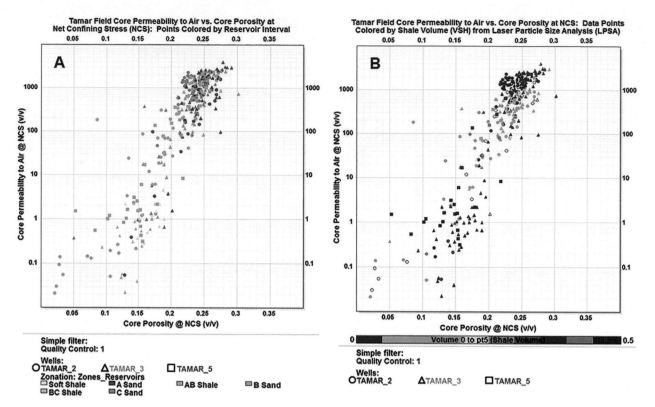

Figure 31. Cross-plots of core permeability to air versus core porosity at reservoir net mean stress. Points in the plot on the left are colored by reservoir interval and points in the plot on the right are colored by core shale volume from laser particle size analysis (cumulative grain size fraction smaller than coarse silt).

column heights and water saturations sampled in laboratory Pc measurements. Using height above free water, porosity, and permeability as input, modeled Sw matches core measured Sw with a relative error (1 SD) of 28%. Relative error is calculated as (measured − predicted) / measured × 100%, yielding the following uncertainty levels at different saturation states:

- At Sw measured = 5%: Sw predicted = 5% +/− 1.4% (5% × 28%)
- At Sw measured = 10%: Sw predicted = 10% +/− 2.8% (10% × 28%)
- At Sw measured = 20%: Sw predicted = 20% +/− 5.6% (20% × 28%) … etc…

The use of a core-calibrated, capillary pressure-based, saturation-height model as a replacement to resistivity log-based saturation estimates generated with resistivity logs of dubious quality results in increased gas saturation estimates high in the gas column. Porosity-weighted, average gas saturation (Sg) in the A and B sands of the Tamar-1 well, near the crest of the structure, increases from Sg ≈ 73% generated using resistivity-based methods to Sg ≈ 82% when the core-calibrated, capillary pressure-based methodology is used.

TAMAR DEVELOPMENT AND PRODUCTION

Tamar Appraisal and Development

After the Tamar 1 discovery well, the Tamar partner group decided to fast-track the development with initial plans for first gas just over 3 years from discovery. This was an enormous challenge for the appraisal and development teams and required clear goals and objectives as well as close coordination and communication. Because Tamar was essentially a gas-to-power project, the overriding development objective was high reliability at 99% uptime. Both the appraisal and development plans were designed to provide such reliability, through an overall redundancy strategy of $n + 1$ on critical production elements.

Appraisal Program

The primary objective of the appraisal program was to reduce uncertainties in resource size and deliverability. The DST in Tamar 1 provided good information on reservoir deliverability; however, there were some uncertainties regarding log response and the

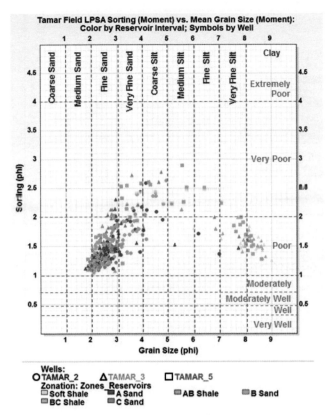

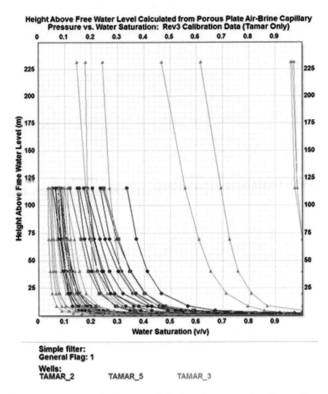

Figure 32. Cross-plot of grain size sorting versus mean grain size on the Φ scale: grain size = $(1/2\text{ mm})^\Phi$. Data are from core laser particle size and method of moments used to calculate both sorting and mean grain size.

Figure 33. Tamar field core air-brine (porous plate) capillary pressure versus water saturation profiles. Laboratory capillary pressure data ($P_{c\,lab}$) have been converted to reservoir conditions ($P_{c\,res}$) and then to height above free water level ($P_{c\,res} = 0$ @ free water level).

petrophysical analysis. Additionally, while pressure data obtained at Tamar 1 indicated that the three main reservoir sands were in communication vertically, lateral connectivity and cross-fault communication remained unconstrained.

The Tamar 2 appraisal well was located 6 km (4 mi) to the north–northwest of Tamar 1 to meet the following objectives and gather critical reservoir information: (1) drill and log the gas–water contact in the intermediate B sand, (2) maintain sufficient height on structure to be retained as an upper A sand producer, (3) drill through the base of the lower water-filled C sand, (4) take pressures in all reservoirs in both the gas and water legs, and (5) take conventional core in all reservoirs and across the gas-water contact on a heads-up basis.

In July 2009, Tamar 2 met all of its objectives, finding 42 m of net pay as predicted, resulting in an upgrade on the estimated mean resources to 6.3 tcf (see Figure 34).

At this point, the partner group was comfortable with the subsurface issues and uncertainties and prepared to move forward with project sanction.

Remaining uncertainties were to be addressed in the development campaign (see Development Approach section below) and during production.

Development Approach

The Tamar development was initially envisioned to be a subsea tieback to an onshore facility in the northern coastal plain. However, the Israeli statutory process for approval of a new onshore entry point required more time, and as a result, the host concept was changed to a shallow-water platform near the existing Mari-B platform, approximately 150 km (93 mi) to the south. Because of the rapid execution time frame, it was critical to establish and lock down the reservoir basis of design early in the front-end process. However, several subsurface uncertainties remained to be addressed, specifically dynamic field performance and reservoir connectivity. The team took on an appraise while developing philosophy to capture essential reservoir data and set up for an appropriate level of

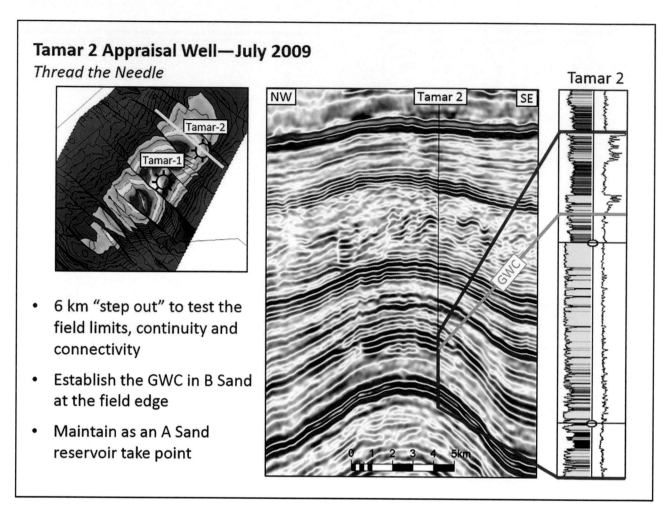

Tamar 2 Appraisal Well—July 2009
Thread the Needle

Tamar 2

NW · Tamar 2 · SE

- 6 km "step out" to test the field limits, continuity and connectivity

- Establish the GWC in B Sand at the field edge

- Maintain as an A Sand reservoir take point

GWC

0 1 2 3 4 5km

Figure 34. Tamar 2 appraisal well.

reservoir monitoring during production to understand dynamic performance characteristics.

A total of five producers were drilled for the Phase 1 production of up to 1.2 BCF per day. To capture critical connectivity issues, each well was set up to be individually metered and pressure monitored. The wells were staggered across multiple fault blocks with three completions in the lower C sand to monitor cross-fault connectivity. In the central fault block, two wells were completed in two different zones to monitor vertical connectivity (see Figure 35).

The location, rates, and objectives for each of the development wells were chosen to balance development cost with reservoir monitoring and appraisal needs.

Development Drilling

Drilling and completion activities were undertaken in batch mode with the Transocean *Sedco Express* from April 2011 to November 2012. With the exception of the Tamar 6 well, which was a twin of Tamar 1, each well was drilled and fully evaluated penetrating the gas–water contact and the base of the C sand. The wells were plugged back, and a sidetrack was drilled for completion. In addition, 143 m (469 ft) of conventional core was taken to ensure reliability of completion design and calibrate the petrophysical model.

All of the wells came in as expected and were completed as planned. In addition, the Tamar 3 well found a small isolated gas accumulation associated with a D sand four-way closure. There was remarkable reservoir continuity exhibited in both stratigraphy and pressure (see Figures 36 and 37).

Well Completion

Each of the Tamar reservoirs is capable of delivering high-rate, long-lived production. To simplify design,

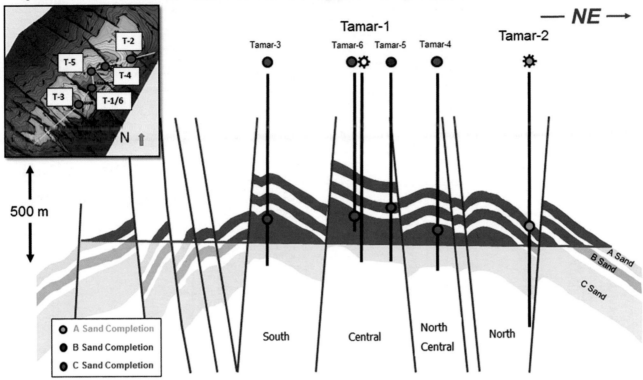

Figure 35. Cross-section through Tamar Phase 1 development wells. Completion intervals and well locations were chosen to balance reservoir monitoring and production performance objectives.

improve reliability, and facilitate reservoir monitoring, single-zone completions were employed. Large-bore, high-rate open-hole gravel pack completions capable of delivering up to 300 MMscfd per well were constructed. A completion design schematic is shown in Figure 38 and more fully described in Healy et al. (2013).

Facilities

The Tamar development was sanctioned in September 2010 and achieved first gas in March 2013, only 51 months after discovery at a development cost of $3.25 billion. The Tamar project was designed with significant redundancy, as it was projected to be the primary, if not the sole, provider of natural gas to the state of Israel. The Tamar field is being produced from five subsea wells tied back to a host platform 150 km (93 mi) south-southwest of the field. The wells are tied to a 12-slot manifold that will support expansion and additional drilling phases (see Figure 39). At the time of installation, the Tamar tieback distance was the longest in the world.

Field Performance

Since startup in March 2013, the Tamar field performance has been outstanding, meeting both reliability and production objectives. Production varies with demand on a daily and seasonal basis (see Figure 40). Daily production in the field peaked at just over 1 BCFD in August 2015. Individual well performance has been outstanding with no loss in productivity over the first 2.5 years of production. The well performance is monitored daily with our proprietary production management system and with pressure transient analysis.

By the end of 2016 Tamar had produced approximately 1.0 tcf of natural gas and more than 0.8 million bbl of condensate. The current estimate of ultimate recoverable resources is approximately 11 tcf (10.1 tcf at Tamar and 0.9 tcf at Tamar SW). Several individual well shut-ins generally confirmed the reservoir models and are currently being analyzed to constrain some of the bigger uncertainties regarding the field, mainly reservoir connectivity (cross-fault communication).

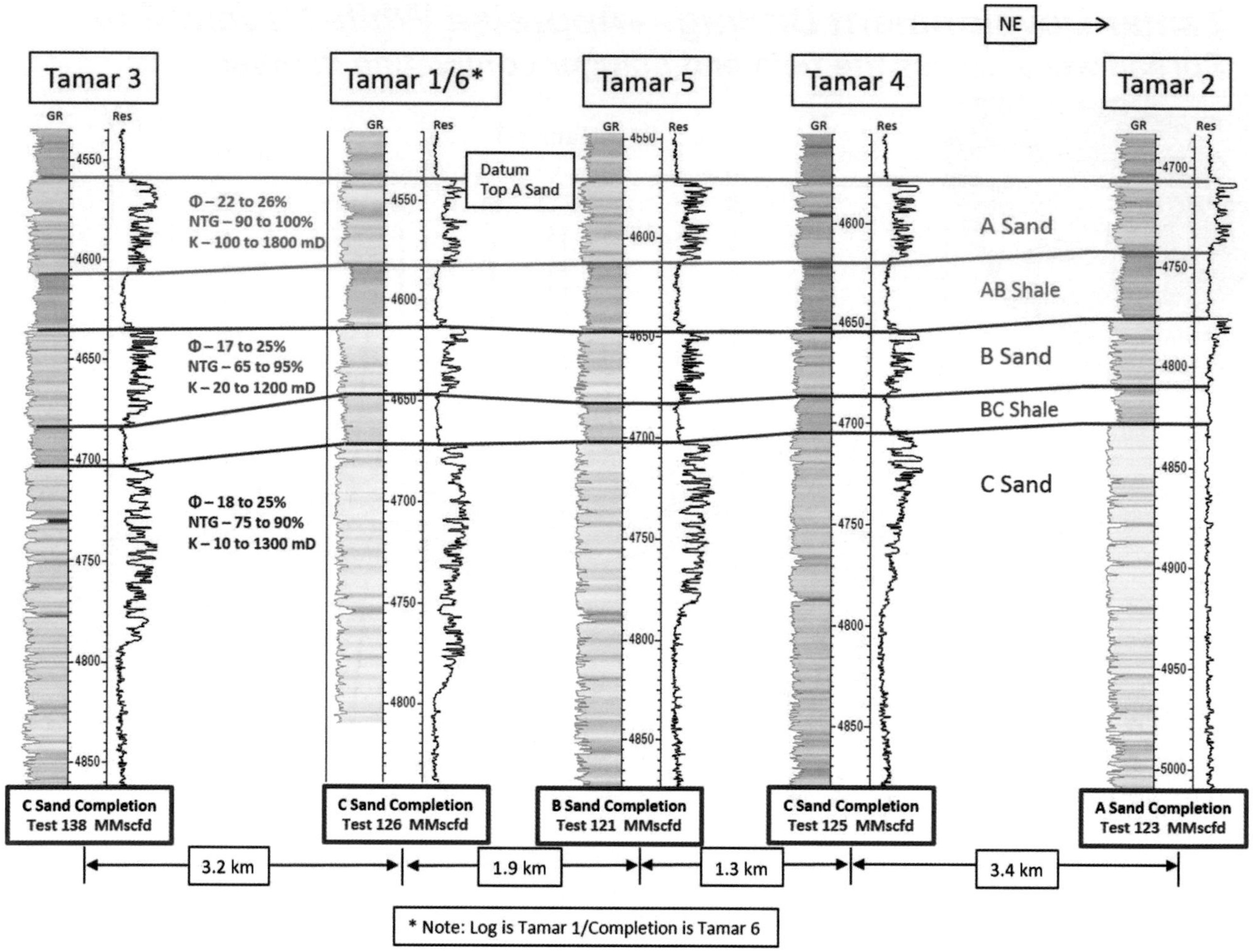

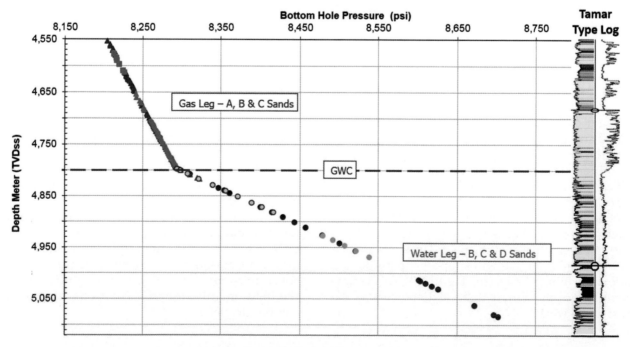

Figure 36. Stratigraphic cross-section through Tamar wells. Completion intervals and cleanup flow rates are noted for each well. Pressure transient analysis was performed during well clean-up, enhancing confidence in the reservoir and well deliverability.

Figure 37. Tamar field pressure data. Pressure data from all five Tamar wells are overlain showing field wide contact and connectivity throughout the reservoir section.

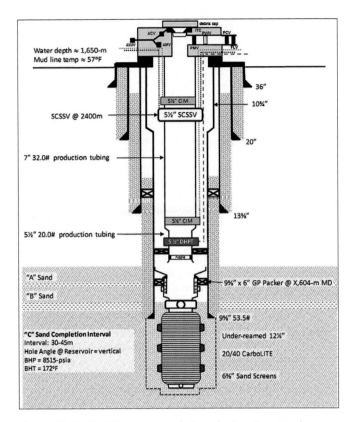

Figure 38. Typical Tamar completion design (see Healy et al., 2013).

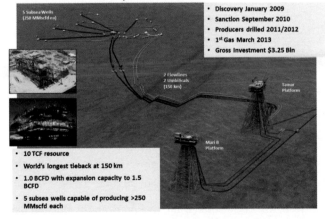

Figure 39. Tamar field Phase 1 development schematic.

Post-Tamar Exploration

Since the Tamar discovery in January 2009, Noble Energy and partners have drilled seven successful exploration wells with approximately 40 tcf of natural gas discovered in Oligocene–Miocene reservoirs in the Levant Basin of the eastern Mediterranean. These discoveries include Dalit, Leviathan, Dolphin, Tanin,

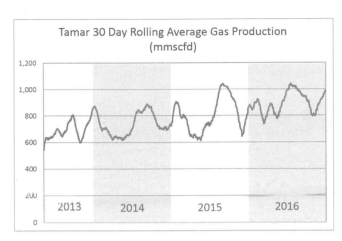

Figure 40. Tamar production from startup through the end of the third quarter, 2016.

Karish, and Tamar SW in Israeli waters and Aphrodite offshore Cyprus.

The Tamar SW satellite was discovered in 2013, southwest of the main Tamar field. Tamar SW-1 discovered pay in the A and B sands, and added 0.9 tcf of reserves to the Tamar project. The development plan calls for tying back TSW-1 to the Tamar project in the near future.

CONCLUSIONS

The Tamar gas field discovery and development represent an incredible full-life cycle achievement from exploration thinking to development execution through to production reliability. Tamar represents not only a critical discovery in the opening of a new play but also provides a reliable source of energy for Israel. Some of the many accomplishments of the Tamar team from exploration to production include the largest gas field discovered in the decade of 2000 to 2009, the longest subsea tieback at the time of development, remarkably short cycle time of 51 months from discovery to first gas, and—finally—production reliability to meet critical energy needs. To accomplish all of these items on a single project, particularly for a project of this scale, is possible only through an integrative, collaborative effort from all partners and stakeholders.

ACKNOWLEDGMENTS

A project of this magnitude involves hundreds of contributors over a 5- to 6-year time frame. The contributors to the ideas and interpretations expressed herein are too numerous to name. The authors would like to thank all of the partners, employees, and contractors that made Tamar possible. In particular, the authors would like to thank Gordon Fielder for his role in furthering our understanding of the reservoir deposition and architecture. The authors would also like to thank the Israeli government, particularly the Ministry of Infrastructures, Energy and Water Resources for their role in Tamar's success. The authors would also like to thank the reviewers for their valuable comments and suggestions that vastly improved the manuscript.

REFERENCES CITED

Alsharhan, A. S., and E. A. Abd El-Gawad, 2008, Geochemical characterization of potential Jurassic/Cretaceous source rocks in the Shushan basin, northern Western desert, Egypt: Journal of Petroleum Geology, v. 31, no. 2, p. 191–212.

Bar, O., Z. Gvirtzman, S. Feinstein, and E. Zilberman, 2013, Accelerated subsidence and sedimentation in the Levant basin during the late Tertiary and concurrent uplift of the Arabian platform: Tectonic versus counteracting sedimentary loading effects: Tectonics, v. 32, p. 334–350.

Barnes, N. E., and W. R. Normark, 1983, Parameters for comparing modern submarine fans and ancient turbidite systems: Geo-Marine Letters, v. 3, doi:10.1007/BF02462472.

Barnes, N. E., and W. R. Normark, 1983/1984, Diagnostic parameters for comparing modern submarine fans and ancient turbidite systems: Geo-Marine Letters, v. 3, enclosed map.

Barrier, E., L. Machour, and M. Blaizot, 2014, Petroleum systems of Syria, in L. Marlow, C. Kendall, and L. Yose, eds., Petroleum systems of the Tethyan region: AAPG Memoir 106, p. 335–378.

Beard, D. C., and P. K. Weyl, 1973, Influence of texture on porosity and permeability of unconsolidated sand: AAPG Bulletin, v. 57, no. 2, p. 349–369.

Blakey, R., 2015, Colorado Plateau Geosystems website, accessed February 6, 2017, https://deeptimemaps.com.

Bosworth, W., P. Huchon, and K. McClay, 2005, The Red Sea and Gulf of Aden basins: Journal of African Earth Sciences, v. 43, p. 334–378.

Bou Daher, S., F. H. Nader, H. Strauss, and R. Littke, 2014, Depositional environment and source rock characterization of organic matter rich upper Santonian–upper Campanian carbonates, northern Lebanon: Journal of Petroleum Geology, v. 37, no. 1, p. 5–24.

Brooks, R. H., and A. T. Corey, 1964, Hydraulic properties of porous media: Colorado State University Hydrology Paper Number 3, 37 p.

Chapin, M. A., P. Davies, J. L. Gibson, and H. S. Pettingill, 1994, Reservoir architecture of turbidite sheet sandstones in laterally extensive outcrops, Ross formation, western Ireland, in P. Weimer, A. H. Bouma, and B. F. Perkins, eds., Submarine fans and turbidite systems: Gulf Coast Section SEPM Foundation 15th Annual Research Conference, p. 53–68.

Christensen, C. J., and G. Powers, 2013, Formation evaluation challenges in Tamar field, offshore Israel: SPWLA 54th Annual Logging Symposium, SPWLA-2013- AAAA, p. 1–12.

Dolson, J. C., M. Atta, D. Blanchard, A. Sehim, J. Villinksi, T. Loutit, et al., 2014, Egypt's future petroleum resources: A revised look into the 21st century, in L. Marlow, C. Kendall, L. Yose, eds., Petroleum systems of the Tethyan region: AAPG Memoir 106, p. 143–178.

Dolson, J. C., P. J. Boucher, S. Siok, and P. D. Heppard, 2005, Key challenges to realizing potential in an emerging giant gas province: Nile Delta/Mediterranean offshore, deep water, Egypt, in A. G. Dore and B. Vining, eds., Petroleum geology: Northwest Europe and global perspective: Proceedings of the 6th Petroleum Geology Conference: Geological Society of London, p. 607–624.

Dolson, J. C., M. V. Shann, S. Matbouly, C. Harwood, R. Rashed, and H. Hammouda, 2001, The petroleum potential of Egypt, in M. W. Downey, J. C. Threet, and W. A. Morgan, eds., Petroleum provinces of the twenty-first century: AAPG Memoir 74, p. 453–482.

Feinstein, S., Z. Aizenshtat, I. Miloslavski, P. Gerling, J. Slager, and J. McQuilken, 2002, Genetic characterization of gas shows in the east Mediterranean offshore of southwestern Israel: Organic Geochemistry, v. 33, p. 1401–1413.

Fielder, G., Pettingill, H.S., Karcz, K., Davis, M.K., Fenton, S., Hosler, J., et al., 2013, The Miocene Tamar Sands: an unconfined submarine fan reservoir: Bat Sheva de Rothschild Seminar, Cesarea, Israel, April 28–30, 2013, Conference Proceedings.

Freedman, R., C. C. Minh, G. Gubelin, J. J. Freeman, T. McGinness, B. Terry, et al., 1998, Combining NMR and density logs for petrophysical analysis in gas-bearing formations: SPWLA 39th Annual Logging Symposium, Paper II, SPWLA-1998-II, p. 1–14.

Gardosh, M., B. Buchbinder, Y. Druckman, and R. Calvo, 2008, The Oligo-Miocene deep-water system of the Levant basin: Geological Survey of Israel, accessed February 6, 2017, http://www.gsi.gov.il/_uploads/ftp/GsiReport/2008/Gardosh-Michael-GSI-33-2008.pdf .

Gardosh, M., Y. Druckman, B. Buchbinder, and M. Rybakov, 2008, The Levant basin offshore Israel: Stratigraphy, structure, tectonic evolution and implications for hydrocarbon exploration: Geological Survey of Israel Report GSI/4/2008, 121 p.

Gardosh, M., Z. Garfunkel, Y. Druckman, and B. Buchbinder, 2010, Tethyean rifting in the Levant region and its role in early Mesozoic crustal evolution: Geological Society of London, Special Publication, v. 341, p. 9–36.

Gardosh, M., and E. Tannenbaum, 2014, Petroleum systems of Israel, in L. Marlow, C. Kendall, and L. Yose, eds., Petroleum systems of the Tethyan region: AAPG Memoir 106, p. 179–216.

Gardosh, M., P. Weimer, and A. Flexer, 2011, The sequence stratigraphy of Mesozoic successions in the Levant margin, southwestern Israel: A model for the evolution of southern Tethys margins: AAPG Bulletin, v. 95, no. 10, p. 1763–1793.

Garfunkel, Z., 1998, Constraints on the origin and history of the eastern Mediterranean basin: Tectonophysics, v. 298, p. 5–35.

Garfunkel, Z., 2004, Origin of the eastern Mediterranean basin: A reevaluation: Tectonophysics, v. 391, p. 11–34.

George, R. P., D. Sanabria, M. Barrett, J. Steinberg, B. Bruce, D. Kendall, et al., 2013, Tectonic evolution of the Levant basin: Bat Sheva de Rothschild Seminar, Cesarea, Israel, April 28–30, Conference Proceedings.

Ghalayini, R., J.-M. Daniel, C. Homberg, F. H. Nader, and J. E. Comstock, 2014, Impact of Cenozoic strike-slip tectonics on the evolution of the northern Levant basin (offshore Lebanon): Tectonics, v. 33, p. 2121–2142, doi:10.1002/2014TC003574.

Guiraud, R., W. Bosworth, J. Thierry, and A. Delplanque, 2005, Phanerozoic geological evolution of northern and central Africa: An overview: Journal of African Earth Sciences, v. 43, no. 103, p. 83–143.

Gvirtzman, Z., I. Csato, and D. Granjeon, 2014, Constraining sediment transport to deep marine basins through submarine channels: The Levant margin in the late Cenozoic: Marine Geology, v. 347, p. 12–26.

Gvirtzman, Z., M. Reshef, O. Buch-Leviatan, G. Groves-Gidney, Z. Karcz, Y. Makovsky, et al., 2015, Bathymetry of the Levant basin: Interaction of salt-tectonics and surficial mass movements: Marine Geology, v. 360, p. 25–39.

Haughton, P. D. W., W. D. McCaffrey, and M. Felix, 2001, Origin and significance of "linked debrites": A key reservoir heterogeneity in sandy turbidite systems: AAPG Convention Abstracts with Program, p. A83.

Healy, J., J. Sanford, K. Dufrene, J. Fink, D. Reeves, and T. Hopper, 2013, Design, installation, and initial performance of ultra-high-rate gas deep-water completions: Tamar field: SPE Annual Technical Conference and Exhibition, New Orleans, Louisiana, September 30–October 2, SPE Paper # 166368.

Klemme, H. D., and G. F. Ulmishek, 1991, Effective source rocks of the world: Stratigraphic distribution and controlling depositional factors: AAPG Bulletin, v. 75, no. 12, p. 1809–1851.

Kosi, W., Tari, G., Nader, F. H., Skiple, C., 2012. Structural analogy between the "piano key faults" of deep-water Lebanon and the extensional faults of the Canyonlands grabens, Utah, United States. The Leading Edge 31.

Krom, M. D., R. A. Cliff, L. M. Eijsink, B. Herut, and R. Chester, 1999, The characterization of Saharan dusts and Nile particulate matter in surface sediments from the Levantine basin using Sr isotopes: Marine Geology, v. 155, p. 319–330.

Macgregor, D., 2011, Rift shoulder source to pro-delta sink: The Cenozoic development of the Nile drainage system: AAPG International Conference and Exhibition, Milano, Italy, October 23–26, Search and Discovery Article 50506, accessed October 25, 2016, http://www.searchanddiscovery.com/abstracts/html/2011/ice/abstracts/abstracts275.html.

Macgregor, D. S., 2012, The development of the Nile drainage system: Integration of onshore and offshore evidence: Petroleum Geoscience, v. 18, p. 417–431.

Mattern, F., 2005, Ancient sand-rich submarine fans, depositional systems, models, identification, and analysis: Earth-Science Reviews, v. 70, p. 167–202.

Medimap Group, Loubrieu, B., and Mascle, J., 2005, Morpho-bathymetry of the Mediterranean Sea, CIESM/Ifremer special publication, Atlases and Maps, Two maps at 1:2,000,000.

Mulder, T., and J. Alexander, 2001, The physical character of subaqueous sedimentary density flows and their deposits: Sedimentology, v. 48, no. 2, p. 269–299.

Mutti, E., R. Tinterri, E. Remacha, N. Mavilla, S. Angella, and I. Fava, 1999, An introduction to the analysis of ancient turbidite basins from an outcrop perspective. AAPG Continuing Education Course Note Series #39, accessed October 26, 2016, http://archives.datapages.com/data/specpubs/cn39/CE-39html/cn39.htm.

Nassar, M., I. Nijenhuis, T. A. Fattah, and A. E. Ramadan, 2012, Occurrence, character and origin of natural gases in the deep-water Nile Delta, Egypt, 2012: North Africa Technical Conference and Exhibition, 20–22 February 2012, Cairo, Egypt, SPE 152891-MS.

Normark, W. R., 1970, Growth patterns of deep-sea fans: AAPG Bulletin, v. 54, p. 2170–2195.

Pettingill, H. S., S. C. Cunningham, D. Needham, J. Vanhorn, and J. Demarest, 2013, Exploration of the deep-water Levant basin: The opening of a new petroleum province: Bat Sheva de Rothschild Seminar, Cesarea, Israel, April 28–30, Conference Proceedings.

Pettingill, H. S., and G. Fielder, 2014, Tamar Sands Core Workshop, oral seminar presentation, February, Hotel Dan Tel Aviv, Conference Proceedings.

Reading, H. G., and M. Richards, 1994. Turbidite systems in deep-water basin margins classified by grain size and feeder system: AAPG Bulletin, v. 78, p. 792–822.

Remacha, E., and L. P. Fernandez, 2003, High-resolution correlation patterns in the turbidite systems of the Hecho group (south-central Pyrenees, Spain): Marine and Petroleum Geology, v. 20 (6-8), p. 711–726.

Remacha, E., H. S. Pettingill, and L. P. Fernandez, 2015, Sand-rich turbidite systems and megaturbidites of the Hecho group from slope to basin plain: Facies, stacking patterns, controlling factors and diagnostic features: Nautilus World Ltd., Course N28 Guidebook, 84 p., Course details on https://www.nautilusworld.com/CourseDetails?coursecode=N028&techtype=ALL).

Richards, M. and M. Bowman, 1998, Submarine fans and related depositional systems II: variability in reservoir architecture and wireline log character: Marine and Petroleum Geology, v. 15, p. 821–839.

Richards, M., M. Bowman, and H. Reading, 1998, Submarine-fan systems I: Characterization and stratigraphic prediction: Marine and Petroleum Geology, v. 15, p. 687–717.

Robertson H. F., O. Parlak, and T. Ustaomer, 2012, Overview of the Palaeozoic-Neogene evolution of Neotethys in the eastern Mediterranean region (southern Turkey, Cyprus, Syria): Petroleum Geoscience, v. 18, p. 381–404.

Ryan, W. B. F, K. Venkatarathnam, and F. C. Wezel, 1973, Mineralogical composition of the Nile cone, Mediterranean ridge and Strabo trench sandstones and clays, *in*

W. B. F. Ryan, K. J. Hsu, Initial reports of the Deep Sea Drilling Project, v. 13: Washington, D.C., U.S. Government Printing Office, p. 731–746.

Steinberg, J., Z. Gvirtzman, Y. Folkman, and Z. Garfunkel, 2011, The origin and nature of the rapid late Tertiary filling of the Levant basin: Geology, v. 39, p. 355–358.

Straub, K. M., and D. R. Pyles, 2012, Quantifying the hierarchical organization of compensation in submarine fans using surface statistics: Journal of Sedimentary Research, v. 82, p. 889–898.

Thomeer, J. H. M., 1960, Introduction of a pore geometrical factor defined by the capillary pressure curve: Journal of Petrology Technology, v. 12, no. 3, p. 73–77.

Venkatarathnam, K., and W. B. F. Ryan, 1971, Dispersal patterns of clay minerals in the sediments of the eastern Mediterranean: Marine Geology, v. 11, p. 261.

Weimer, P., and H. S. Pettingill, 2007, Deep-water exploration and production: A global overview, *in* T. H. Nilsen, R. D. Shew, G. S. Steffens, and J. R. J. Studlick, eds., Atlas of deep-water outcrops: AAPG Studies in Geology 56, CD-ROM, 29 p.

Weldeab, S., K. C. Emeis, C. Hemleben, and W. Siebel, 2002, Provenance of lithogenic surface sediments and pathways of riverine suspended matter in the eastern Mediterranean Sea: Evidence from 143Nd/144Nd and 87Sr/86Sr ratios: Chemical Geology, v. 186, p.139–149.

Williams, G. A., and R. A. Chadwick, 1964, Quantitative seismic analysis of a thin layer of CO_2 in the Sleipner injection plume: British Geological Survey, Keyworth, Nottingham, England Geophysics 2012, SEG Library p. 6.

Zarra, L., 2007, Chronostratigraphic framework for the Wilcox formation (upper Paleocene-lower Eocene) in the deep-water Gulf of Mexico: Biostratigraphy, sequences, and depositional systems: Proceedings, 2007 GCSSEPM Perkins Conference, p. 81–145, http://www.gcssepm .org/conference/2007_conference.htm.

14

Dailly, Paul, Tracey Henderson, Kathy Kanschat, Phil Lowry, and Stephen Sills, 2017, The Jubilee field, Ghana: Opening the late Cretaceous play in the West African transform margin, in R. K. Merrill and C. A. Sternbach, eds., Giant fields of the decade 2000–2010: AAPG Memoir 113, p. 257–272.

The Jubilee Field, Ghana: Opening the Late Cretaceous Play in the West African Transform Margin

Paul Dailly, Tracey Henderson, Kathy Kanschat, Phil Lowry, and Stephen Sills

Kosmos Energy, Dallas, Texas, U.S.A. (e-mails: pdailly@kosmosenergy.com, thenderson@kosmosenergy .com, kkanschat@kosmosenergy.com, Lowryph@gmail.com, ssills@kosmosenergy.com)

ABSTRACT

The discovery of the Jubilee field in the Tano Basin of Ghana opened a new play in the deep water of the Atlantic transform margins. The field is a late Cretaceous combination structural-stratigraphic trap associated with topography created by the transform tectonics during the opening of the Atlantic. Prior to the drilling of the discovery well, the African transform margin had seen very little deep-water exploration with only nine wells drilled over a margin more than 2000 km (1243 mi) long. The field was discovered in June 2007 with the Mahogany 1 well, which encountered 98 m (322 ft) of high-quality oil pay in a Turonian-aged fan sequence trapped in a combination structural-stratigraphic trap. Subsequent to the discovery, accelerated appraisal and phased development resulted in first production in November 2010. The field is currently producing more than 100,000 BOPD and has a planned peak production of 120,000 BOPD. The discovery has resulted in an industry-wide exploration campaign of over 50 wells in the last 8 years. These have resulted in a number of additional discoveries and to date at least one additional development. This chapter describes the exploration play concept and the geology of the field.

INTRODUCTION

The Jubilee field is a Turonian-aged, combination structural-stratigraphic trap located in 1200 to 1500 m (3937 to 4921 ft) of water on the present-day continental slope of the Tano Basin, 60 km (37 mi) off the coast of Ghana (Figure 1). The field was discovered in June 2007 by the drilling of Mahogany 1 exploration well in the West Cape Three Points block operated by Kosmos Energy. Subsequent drilling demonstrated that the field extended into the adjacent Deepwater

Tano block operated by Tullow Oil. Partners in the Jubilee field are Kosmos, Tullow, Anadarko, PetroSA, and GNPC. The field is estimated to contain reserves of more than 600 million barrels. Phase 1 of the development came on-stream in November 2010 and at peak production is expected to produce approximately 120,000 barrels of oil per day. Subsequent to the discovery of Jubilee, additional discoveries were made on the exploration blocks resulting in the ongoing Tweneboa Enyenra Ntomme fields (TEN) development and in the Mahogany East discoveries,

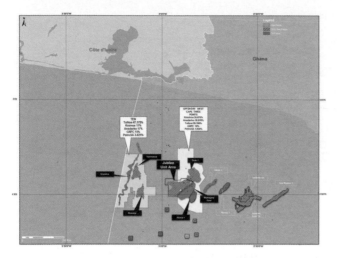

Figure 1. Jubilee field location map. (Data courtesy of IHS.)

Figure 2. Gravity map of the African transform margin showing the location of major fracture zones and adjacent basins. Areas containing deep-water late Cretaceous oil and gas discoveries are shown in green. C/O = Ceiba/Okume; A/O = Aje/Ogo; J/T/S = Jubilee/TEN/Sankofa; B = Boabab; V/M = Venus/Mercury. (Modified from Dailly et al., 2013.)

currently under appraisal. Beyond these licenses, the discovery opened up a program of exploration associated with the new play along the West African transform margin. This exploration program has resulted in the drilling of an additional 50 wells that have yielded a number of additional discoveries, including the Sankofa field currently under development.

WEST AFRICAN TRANSFORM MARGIN: TECTONIC EVOLUTION AND STRATIGRAPHIC SETTING

The West African transform margin tectonic province extends from northern Gabon in the south and east to Sierra Leone in the north and west and is dominated by the presence of a series of northeast–southwest trending crustal scale strike-slip faults (Figures 2 and 3). It is bounded by the St. Paul fracture zone in the north and the Ascension/Kribi fracture zones in the south (see Figure 2), within this province, transform faults dominate the present-day configuration and played a dominant role in structural and basin evolution. To the north and south of these features, extension and oceanic development was largely dominated by dip slip processes. Within this province, however, a more complicated history of rapidly varying extension, transtension, and transpression has led to a mosaic of structural features with rapidly varying chronostratigraphic evolution from subbasin to subbasin.

These transform zones accommodated initial extension of the central Atlantic around late Aptian to early Albian times (120 Ma) (Klitgord and Schouten, 1986) and the subsequent separation of the African and South American plates through the late Cretaceous and Tertiary to the present day. The majority of tectonic activity was completed by Campanian to Maastrichtian times and largely postrift subsidence and deposition occurred

from the Maastrichtian through the Tertiary. These margins are dominated by late Cretaceous sequences except in a number of isolated places where they are overlain by thick Miocene deltaic sequences associated with the Volta, Niger, Rio del Rey, and Sanaga rivers. In a number of places, the late Cretaceous clastic input points may represent precursors to the Miocene to Recent river systems, whose drainage systems were subsequently captured and redirected by Tertiary uplift.

Previous authors have described the tectonic evolution of this transform-dominated system (Basile et al., 1996, 1998; Attoh et al., 2004; Antobreh et al., 2009; Dailly et al., 2013) and in particular the evolution of the Romanche fracture zone and transform fault. This feature coincides with one of the most prominent fracture zones in the equatorial Atlantic, associated with an offset of the mid-Atlantic ridge of approximately 900 km (559 mi) (Attoh et al., 2004). The continental extension of this fracture zone (FZ) is located offshore Ghana and is well described from Ocean Drilling Program (ODP) drilling conducted in 1995 and associated studies (Figure 3) (Mascle et al., 1996). This data set, when combined with the understanding gained from recent oil industry exploration activity immediately to the north in the Tano Basin, allows a more integrated picture of the tectonostratigraphic evolution of this transform-dominated basin to be developed.

Intracontinental transform deformation and rifting was initiated between 140 and 120 Ma in the early Cretaceous (LePichon and Hayes 1971; Klitgord and Schouten, 1986). Apatite fission track analysis (AFTA) data from ODP sites 959 and 960 suggest this rifting was associated with rapid cooling and uplift (in the region of 900 m [2953 ft]) of the ridge relative to the Ivorian Basin between 120 and 115 Ma (Clift et al.,

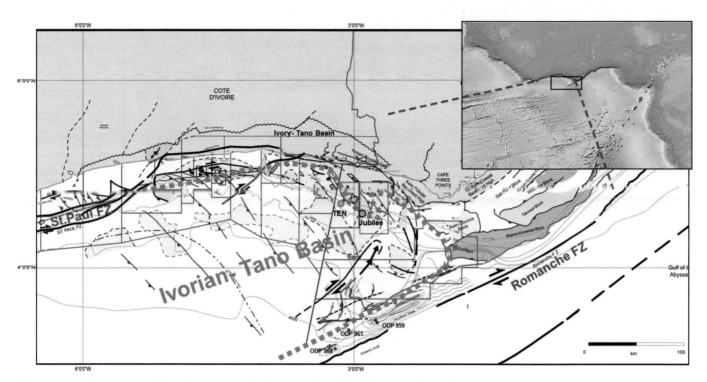

Figure 3. Ivorian–Tano Basin major structural elements. (Modified from Dailly et al., 2013.)

1997). This uplift and cooling is interpreted to be associated with footwall uplift (Basile et al., 1998).

The transition from an intracontinental transform environment to an active ocean–continent transform evolved with the development of a spreading ridge to the south of the Romanche fracture zone (RFZ). This was juxtaposed against continental crust to the north of the RFZ and is estimated to have developed in the mid-Albian (105 Ma) (Clift et al., 1997; Clift and Lorenzo, 1999). This period is associated with the development of compressional structures along the Romanche ridge and in the Tano Basin.

As spreading continued and the spreading ridge moved west relative to the northern, continental, side of the transform, the ridge contacted the continent–ocean boundary to the north and was then juxtaposed against oceanic crust. This was associated with the transition to passive margin subsidence and occurred around 90 to 84 Ma (Klitgord and Schouten, 1986; Attoh et al., 2004; Moulin et al., 2010).

TANO BASIN: STRUCTURAL ARCHITECTURE AND STRATIGRAPHIC EVOLUTION

The tectonic evolution outlined above controlled the basin fill of the Tano–Ivorian Basin and is closely associated with the play elements of the Jubilee play. The basin is located immediately north of the RFZ ridge and is one of the main depocenters located within the transform

margin (see Figure 3). It contains a series of early Cretaceous pull-apart depocenters bounded by releasing bend extensional faults associated with the St. Paul transform fault to the northwest and subdivided by a series of large transpressional arches associated with the Romanche transform movement to the southeast.

Figure 4 shows a chronostratigraphic chart summarizing the stratigraphic and tectonic history of the Tano Basin. Considerable drilling in the shelf area has helped define the deeper stratigraphy of the basin, which consists of a series of Devonian- and Carboniferous-aged sequences that have been penetrated in the deepest exploration wells. These prerift layers are overlain by a thick sequence of Aptian and Albian clastics that are interpreted to be syn-kinematic and associated with the rift/transtensional phase prior to oceanic crust development and subsequent continental separation. This sequence is capped by a Cenomanian flooding event frequently associated with shallow-water carbonate facies on structural highs and with deep-water shales in structural lows. Overlying this Cenomanian flooding sequence is a series of late Cretaceous deep-water clastic sequences that infill the ridge and basin topography created by the initial transform margin development and the inception of an oceanic spreading center on the south side of the Romanche ridge. These sequences were fed by a series of large palaeo-canyons seen in shallow-water 2-D seismic lines. This resulted in thick Cenomanian- to Campanian-aged clastic sequences in

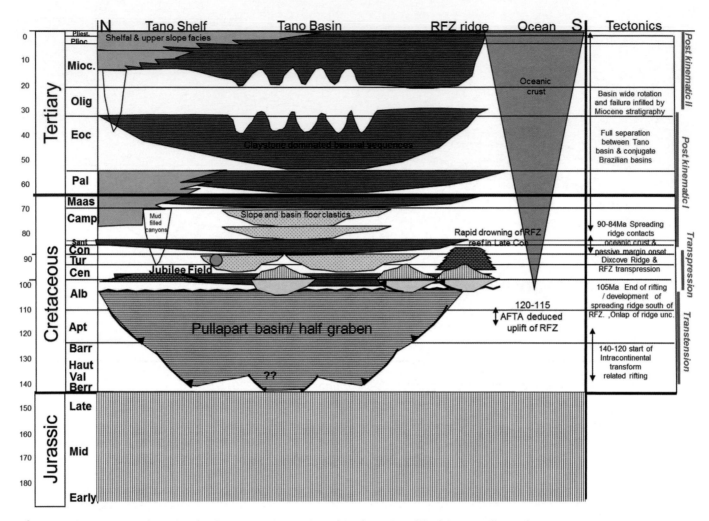

Figure 4. Tano Basin and Romanche fracture zone stratigraphic chart. (Modified from Dailly et al., 2013.)

the deep-water portion of the basin. This sequence is overlain by a moderate thickness (typically 1 to 1.5 km [0.6 to 0.9 mi]) of Maastrichtian and Tertiary stratigraphy, which is largely shale prone due to the cessation of clastic deposition and represents passive infill until the mid-Tertiary (late Eocene to ?Oligocene), when major slumping and possible rotation and uplift in the hinterland to the depocenter occurred. This was infilled by Miocene- to recent-aged stratigraphy.

WEST AFRICA: EXPLORATION TRENDS

The exploration history of the West African margin has evolved over the last 50 years into progressively deeper water and progressively deeper stratigraphy. Figure 5 shows a graph of exploration discovery rates by play since 1950. The graph demonstrates the gradual move from shallow-water Tertiary plays through progressively older shallow-water stratigraphy,

followed by a movement of exploratory drilling out to deep water and the start of a similar trend into progressively deeper stratigraphy.

Exploration of the Cretaceous clastic sequences of West Africa started in 1950s and until the late 1990s was confined to shelfal areas. Although deep-water exploration of the Tertiary sequences in the Niger delta and Congo fan started in the early 1990s, much less exploratory drilling has been focused at the Cretaceous sequences located in deep water until the last decade. This is likely due to the lack of the simple structural closures that are characteristic of the successful exploration of deep-water portions of the Miocene Niger delta and Congo fan basins. In addition, the application of geophysical risk reduction techniques is generally considered to be more robust in reduced burial depths and younger sedimentary sequences that are associated with these Miocene reservoirs. By comparison, these techniques have been viewed as higher risk in older and more deeply buried Cretaceous successions in West Africa.

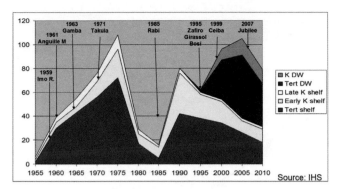

Figure 5. Number of discoveries through time for key plays and key play opening discoveries in West Africa. During the 1990s, the industry moved from shelf plays to Tertiary deep water but was very slow to focus on Cretaceous targets located in deep water. (Data courtesy of IHS.) (Modified from Dailly et al., 2013.)

While the Tertiary depocenters have been the focus of West African exploration by large oil companies, smaller, independent exploration companies pioneered the exploration of higher risk Cretaceous plays in deep-water basins (Dailly, 2000; Morrison et al., 2000; Bird et al., 2001), resulting in a number of Cretaceous discoveries in deep water such as the Ceiba (Dailly et al., 2002) and Okume fields in Equatorial Guinea and the Baobab field in Cote D'Ivoire.

EXPLORATION HISTORY OF THE TANO BASIN AND THE DEVELOPMENT OF THE JUBILEE PLAY ELEMENTS

In the case of the Tano Basin, exploration drilling on the shelf occurred throughout the 1960s until the 1980s and was focused largely at Albian and older sequences where structural trapping geometries could be seen from 2-D seismic data. This phase of exploration resulted in a number of modest-sized oil and gas discoveries, including the Saltpond field (still producing today), and the North and south Tano discoveries. These wells were targeted at structural highs on which late Cretaceous sequences were thin or condensed and therefore no sands of any significance were encountered. Subsequent drilling of the West Tano 1x and WCTP 2x wells in the 1990s in structurally lower positions demonstrated the presence of thin late Cretaceous sands, but these were of insufficient thickness to be commercial. Drilling of these plays slowed by the 1990s due to limited trap size and lack of predictability in reservoir quality; however, the geochemistry of the oils encountered in some of these wells suggested the presence of a deep-water Cretaceous kitchen south and outboard of the south Tano ridge, an Albian structural high that underlies and underpins the present-day shelf (Figures 6 and 7).

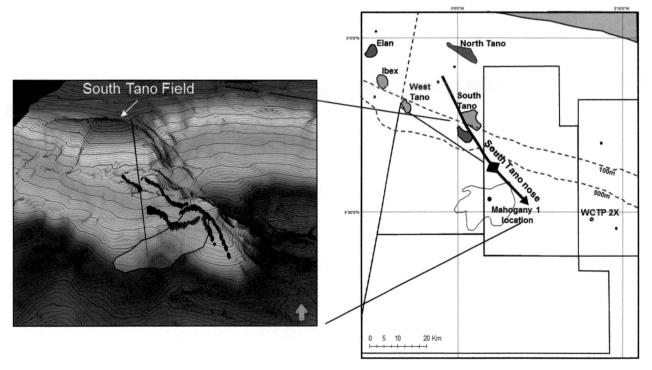

Figure 6. Tano Basin shelf discoveries and structural architecture of the south Tano nose, which plunges southeast toward the late Cretaceous depocenter and likely acts as a major migration focus and assists in trap development. (From Dailly et al., 2013, with permission of Geological Society of London, whose permission is required for further use.)

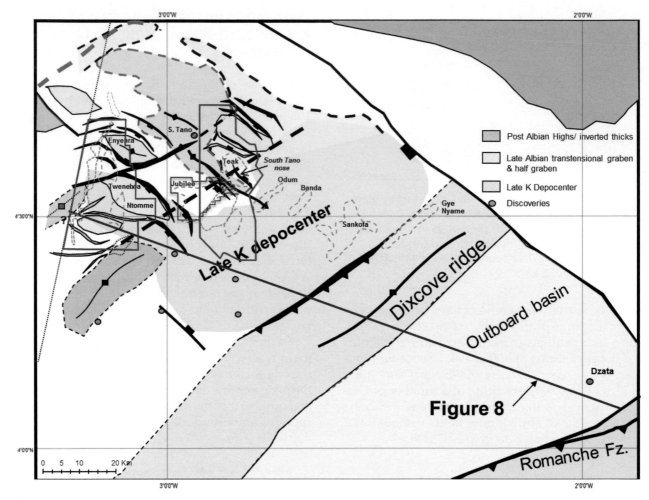

Figure 7. Tano Basin structural elements. (Modified from Dailly et al., 2013.)

The deep-water portion of the Tano Basin consists of two major depocenters that are subdivided by a large transpressional ridge called the Dixcove ridge. This developed in the Cenomanian associated with movement along the Romanche fracture zone and separates a northern depocenter, dominated by a northwest–southeast trending Albian transtensional fabric of which the south Tano ridge is the key feature, from a southern depocenter dominated by Cenomanian transpressional fold and thrust fabric (Figures 7 and 8).

The south Dixcove ridge acted as a barrier to late Cretaceous deep-water clastic sequences emanating from large canyons located in the shelfal area and possibly associated with a palaeo Volta river. This resulted in a thickened and ponded depocenter developing to the north of the ridge. This became the focus of deposition for a series of late Cretaceous fan sequences (Figure 9). This thick late Cretaceous sequence provided sufficient overburden to mature a source kitchen that otherwise would have been marginally mature due to the relatively thin Tertiary overburden.

Although no structural trapping geometries were recognized, the presence of a large unpenetrated canyon fill sequence in the shallow-water portion of the WCTP block seen on 2-D seismic data and the concept of late Cretaceous sands emanating from this canyon and being draped over the deep-water extension of the south Tano nose and charged from a potential deep-water kitchen to the south were the play elements and exploration concept that led Kosmos Energy to license the WCTP block in 2005 with a commitment to acquire a 3-D survey over the deep-water extension of the Tano nose (Figure 10).

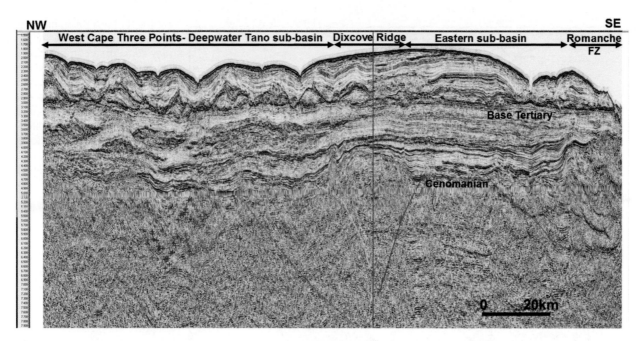

Figure 8. Tano Basin regional seismic line showing that (a) early deformation of the Romanche and Dixcove transpressional anticlines creates depocenters that young to the northwest; (b) the Dixcove ridge funnels late Cretaceous fan systems and creates a thick south of the south Tano high, which is reservoir bearing and sufficiently thick to mature the source kitchen; and (c) this late Cretaceous play is deformed in the Oligocene–Miocene, giving a focus to regional migration. (Modified from Dailly et al., 2013.)

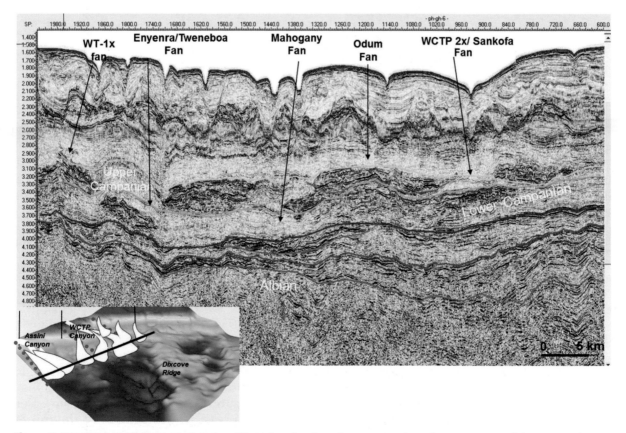

Figure 9. Detail of western part of regional line showing late Cretaceous slope fan geometry of the reservoir targets in the lower slope area of the Tano Basin. (Modified from Dailly et al., 2013.)

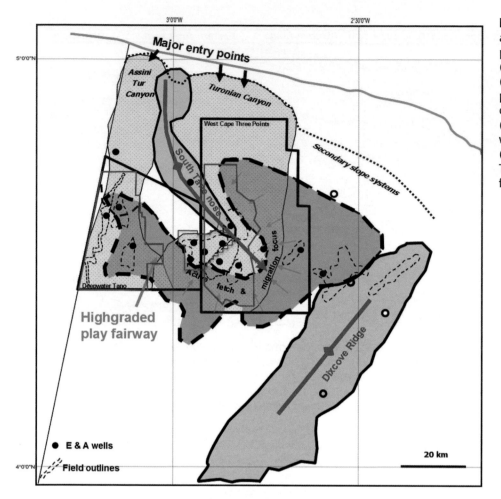

Figure 10. Tano Basin play elements and integration into the Mahogany play concept; a combination of (a) mature basinal oil kitchen, (b) regional charge focus into plunging nose with updip evidence of a working of migration pathway, (c) late Cretaceous turbidite fairway wrapped over structural nose, and (d) focus on sweet-spot in northern Tano Basin deep water. (Modified from Dailly et al., 2013.)

JUBILEE PLAY ELEMENTS AND PETROLEUM GEOLOGY

Reservoir

The Mahogany 1 discovery well was drilled in June 2007 and targeted a Turonian fan that had ponded in a down-dip position off the southwestern flank of the south Tano ridge. Figure 11 shows a seismic line and far amplitude extraction across the Mahogany prospect (subsequently renamed the Jubilee field) as described prior to drilling. The fan forms one of a number of Turonian- to Maastrichtian-aged fans located on the south side of the south Tano nose.

The discovery well was drilled to a depth of 3802 m (12,474 ft) total vertical depth sub-sea (TVDss) and encountered 98 m (322 ft) of oil-bearing high-quality Turonian sandstones over a 271-m (889-ft)-gross section organized into stacked lower slope channelized fan packages (Figure 12). Individual pay sands were up to 35 m (115 ft) thick with porosities greater than 20% and permeabilities generally ranging from 100 to 1000 millidarcies with some permeabilities exceeding 1000 mD. The Hyedua-1 (H-1), Mahogany-2 (M-2), and Hyedua-2 (H-2) appraisal wells were drilled by the end of 2008 and confirmed a 250 m (820 ft) average gross interval of stacked, amalgamated turbidite channel and fan sands with net pay intervals ranging from 20 to100 m total vertical depth (TVD). A subsequent drill stem test (DST) in the Mahogany 1 well flowed oil at a rate of more than 20,000 barrels per day.

The upper and lower Mahogany intervals comprise the two primary hydrocarbon-bearing intervals within the Jubilee field separated by a mappable sealing shale (Figure 12). Pressure data along with fluid samples demonstrated three main pools, UM2, UM3, and LM2, along with a series of secondary pools. Appraisal drilling confirmed that these were in static communication over distances of more than 5 km (3 mi). Figure 13 is an oil excess pressure plot based on MDT pressures from three of the initial wells showing the six oil reservoirs and the two main oil water contacts (OWCs) identified within the field.

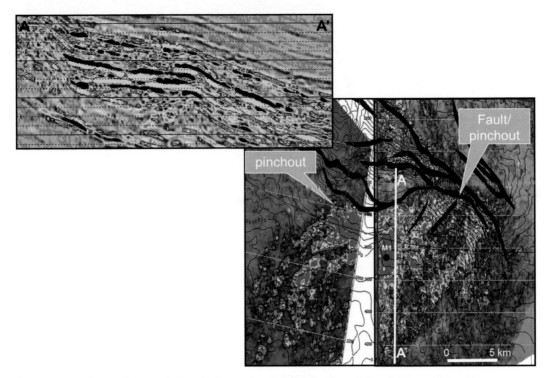

Figure 11. North–south seismic line and RMS far amplitude map of the Mahogany Turonian prospect prior to drilling of Mahogany 1 (Jubilee discovery well) in 2007. The prospect was a combination structural and stratigraphic trap with seismic attribute support. The exploration well was placed several hundred meters downdip from the potentially trapping faults. (From Dailly et al., 2013, with permission of Geological Society of London, whose permission is required for further use.)

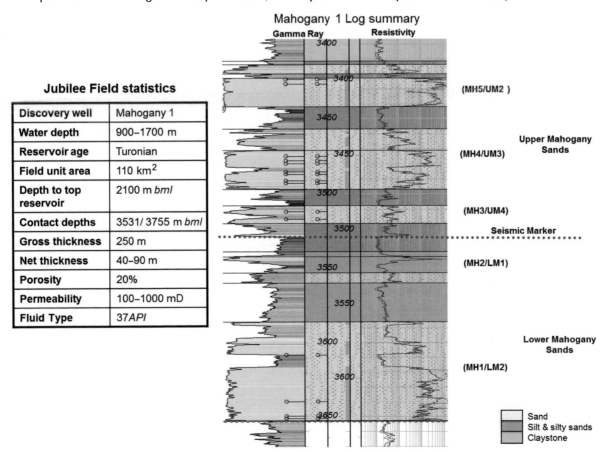

Figure 12. Log of Mahogany 1 reservoir section showing the stacked Turonian oil-bearing interval encountered in the well and summary Jubilee field statistics. (Modified from Dailly et al., 2013.)

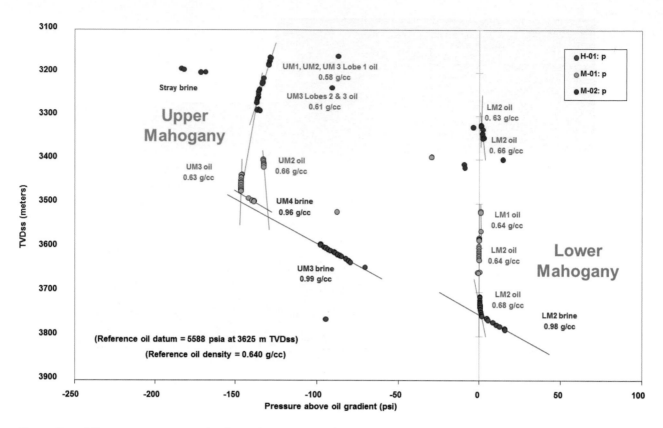

Figure 13. Jubilee excess pressure plot for Mahogany 1, Mahogany 2, and Hyedua 1 wells showing the Mahogany pools and free water levels. (From Sills, 2012, with permission of Offshore Technology Conference, whose permission is required for further use.)

OWCs were penetrated for both the UM3 and LM2 pools, confirming column heights of greater than 400 m (1312 ft) for the main pools.

Rock Properties

A total of 427 m (1401 ft) of whole core was recovered from four cored wells (Figure 14). Core measurements yielded pay interval porosities averaging 21% and permeabilities of several hundred mD (Sills, 2012). Also shown in Figure 14 is a porosity–permeability cross-plot showing the range of core measurements from the Mahogany1 discovery well and the Hyedua1 and Hyedua1BP01 appraisal wells. The formation pore volume compressibility of 1.5 microsips (Msip) obtained from core measurements is consistent with a well-consolidated formation.

The reservoirs are well defined seismically and a series of compensatory, stacked, lower slope, amalgamated channels that entered the basin from the northeast and filled the basin, progressively onlapping the Tano ridge, from southeast to northwest (see Figures 15, 16A, and 16B).

Seal

At the top of the reservoir sequence, a thick shale section is developed that provides an ultimate top-seal to the Jubilee complex (Figure 12). Overlying Campanian fans cut down into the top-seal in particular in the Mahogany East and Teak areas, but over the core Jubilee unit area, the top-seal section is well preserved (Figure 16). A number of well-developed intraformational seals occur within the reservoir sequences, resulting in the development of the separate pools. These include an *extensive shale section* that separates the two intervals with an oil column pressure offset of 150 psi.

Charge

Many of the previous shelf exploration wells encountered hydrocarbons. The oils from some of these Albian reservoirs had a geochemical signature suggestive of a possible deep-water oil kitchen and indicating lateral migration over a large distance due to the immaturity of source rocks in the shelf area. This was confirmed by the presence of oil in the WCTP2X well drilled by Hunt Oil in 1999. The southward plunge of the south

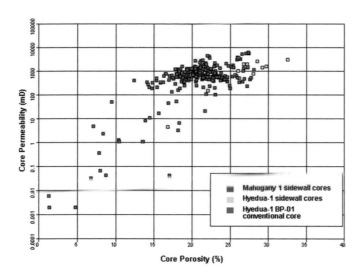

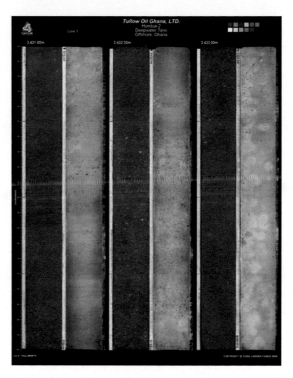

Figure 14. Jubilee rock properties. There was 427 m of whole core gathered from four wells. The photograph shown is from the Hyedua 2 well, upper Mahogany interval. The core-derived porosity/permeability plot shows porosities range from 15 to 30% with an average of 21%. Permeabilities range from hundreds to thousands of mD. Sands are generally well consolidated. (From Sills, 2012, with permission of Offshore Technology Conference, whose permission is required for further use.)

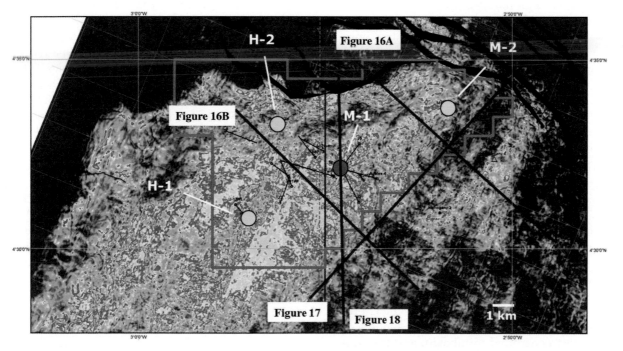

Figure 15. Mahogany fan RMS amplitude extraction showing location of early appraisal wells. Line location for Figures 16–18. (Modified from Sills, 2012.)

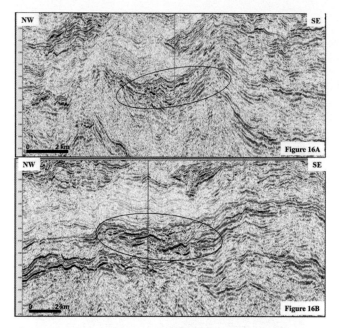

Figure 16A and B. Northwest–southeast two-dimensional strike lines through Jubilee and Mahogany fan sequences showing pinch out to the northwest onto the south Tano high. Circled area shows internal reservoir architecture and progressive younging of fan sequences to the northwest. For location, see Figure 15. (From Dailly et al., 2013, with permission of Geological Society of London, whose permission is required for further use.)

Tano ridge into the deep-water Tano Basin depocenter appears to act as a regional migration focus for generated hydrocarbons (Figure 6). Subsequent discoveries to the south of the West Cape Three Points license confirm the presence of a deep-water kitchen, which is likely the source of the Jubilee oil.

Trap

The south Tano nose is one of a suite of northwest–southeast Albian fault-bounded structural highs associated with transtension on the St. Paul transform fault zone and constitutes part of a sequence of horsetail play extensional faults blocks (Antobreh et al., 2009) (Figures 3 and 7). These faults hold up the present-day shelf along the Ivorian–Tano Basin margin but plunge into the deep-water portion of the basin. The faulting associated with the development of this ridge has created a series of bowl-shaped depocenters that were infilled and onlapped by the deposition of late Cretaceous fan sequences. The Jubilee reservoir sequences infill such a fault-controlled minibasin, and the trap has been formed by a combination of pinch-out, shale-out, and extensional faulting around the margin of the reservoir sequence and depocenter.

In an updip direction (to the northeast), the reservoirs are trapped on the downthrown side of an extensional fault that separate the Jubilee field from the Teak discovery, which contains a separate gas pool reservoired within the same Turonian fan system (Figures 15 and 17). Toward the northwest, the field is trapped by the pinch out onto the south Tano ridge of the entire Turonian fan sequence (Figure 18). To the southeast, a more complicated series of shale-outs are associated with thinning of individual sand bodies moving away from the axial part of the fan system. These sequences contain the Mahogany East and Akasa pools.

These trapping mechanisms have resulted in a field with an approximate area of 110 km² (42 mi²) that has large vertical relief, continuous oil columns in excess of 400 m (1312 ft), and reservoirs with reasonably steep dips of 3 to 5° on the flanks and 10° at the crest as well as estimated ultimate recoverable reserves of more than 600 million bbl.

Reservoir Fluid Properties

Initial reservoir pressure varied across the field from 5000 to 5700 psia as a function of TVD. Initial reservoir temperature varied across the field from 196 to 225° F as a function of TVD, overburden thickness, and water depth (Sills, 2012). The reservoir hydrocarbon fluids are undersaturated, moderately volatile black oils with the degree of initial undersaturation ranging from about 1200 psi near the Lower Mahogany reservoir OWC to bubble-point. Stock tank oil gravities ranging from 36 to 38° API were measured in the lab on uncontaminated reservoir oil samples obtained from DSTs. Corresponding single-stage flash gas-to-oil ratios (GORs) ranged from 1.25 to 1.58 MSCF/stock tank barrel (STB). On initial production, the field produced at an average gas–oil ratio (GOR) of about 1.2 MSCF/STB. Initial formation volume factors ranged from 1.57 to 1.69 barrels (RB)/STB. The uncontaminated reservoir oil viscosity measurements range from 0.16 to 0.3 centipoise (cp) at reservoir conditions and vary with solution GOR and oil gravity. A compositional gradient is evident in the field, with in situ oil densities ranging from 0.68 g/cc near the Lower Mahogany reservoir OWC to 0.58 g/cc in the up-dip regions of the Upper Mahogany reservoir.

JUBILEE FIELD DEVELOPMENT

Following confirmation of the Mahogany 1 discovery by appraisal drilling, an accelerated and phased development was undertaken and an intensive development

SW   **NE**

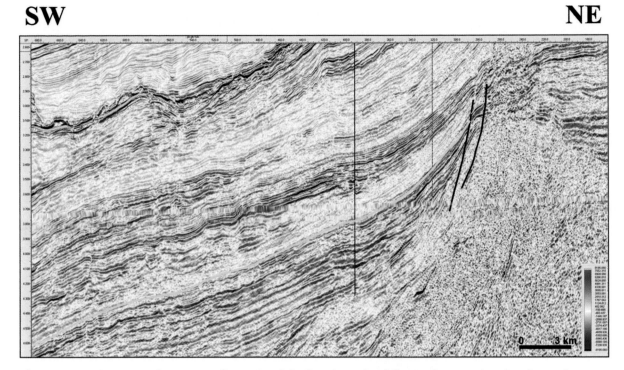

Figure 17. Northeast–southwest two-dimensional dip line through Jubilee/Mahogany showing the updip trapping elements; yellow horizon is top Turonian fan. For location, see Figure 15. (From Dailly et al., 2013, with permission of Geological Society of London, whose permission is required for further use.)

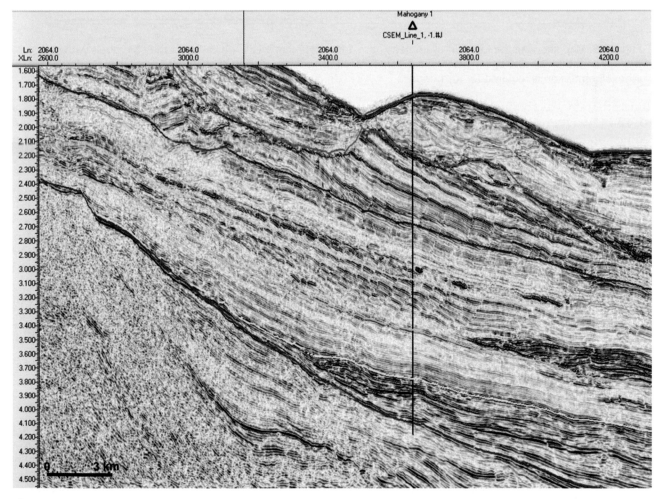

Figure 18. North–south line showing Mahogany 1 location and pinch out of Mahogany fan to the north. (Modified from Jewell, 2011.)

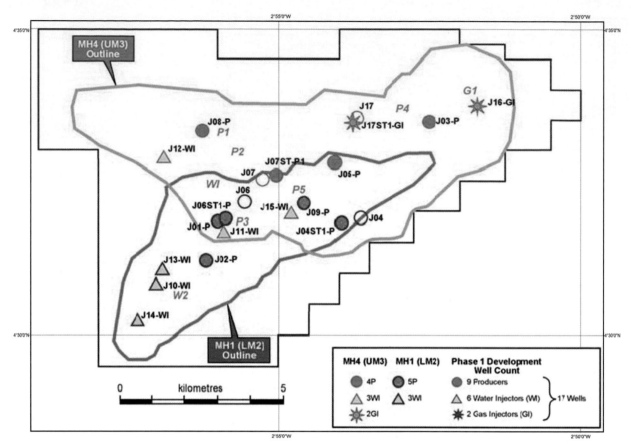

Figure 19. Map showing the location of Jubilee Phase 1 development wells, which target the core pools within the upper and lower Mahogany reservoirs. (From Sills, 2012, with permission of Offshore Technology Conference, whose permission is required for further use.)

drilling program was conducted throughout 2009 and 2010. The 17-well Phase 1 development program targeted just under 300 million bbl in the two most volumetrically significant reservoirs in these intervals, the UM3 and the LM2, and comprises nine producers, six water injectors, and two gas injectors (McLaughlin, 2012). Figure 19 shows the Phase 1 development well locations relative to the Jubilee field unit boundary and the developed reservoir outlines. The Jubilee Phase 1 development program included middip and updip producers supported by downdip water injectors generally over distances of 1 to 5 km (0.6 to 3 mi). The dynamic interwell connectivity and water injectivity levels achievable during waterflood were identified early on as key reservoir uncertainties. A June 2008 DST in the Mahogany 2 appraisal well had indicated potential compartmentalization within the lower Mahogany interval. To reduce these uncertainties, a four well, long-term interference test was initiated in the LM2 reservoir in May 2009, eighteen months prior to field startup. Results from the interference testing established pressure continuity through the reservoir over distances exceeding 5 km (3 mi), reduced the uncertainty in

original oil in place (OOIP), and confirmed pretest water injectivity estimates. Field startup occurred on November 28, 2010, and production has continued to ramp up as additional Phase 1 wells have been brought online. A static and dynamic reservoir model uncertainty analysis constrained with a history match through January 2011 of the interference test pressures, and only the first 2 months of field performance significantly reduced the uncertainty associated with Phase 1 waterflood performance. As of April 2015, the field was producing more than 100,000 barrels of oil per day and is expected to produce 120,000 BOPD once the facility is at peak production. The development was performed by a Kosmos-led multidisciplinary integrated project team (IPT) that included members from Kosmos, Tullow, Anadarko, and GNPC. Tullow is the unit operator.

SUBSEQUENT DISCOVERIES

Following the Jubilee discovery, the Mahogany East, Teak, Odum, and Akasa discoveries were made in the area of the Jubilee fan. To the west in the Deepwater

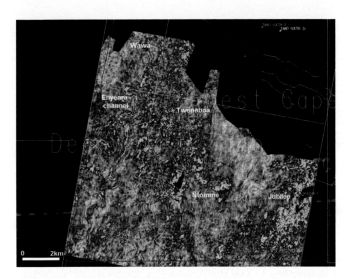

Figure 20. TEN amplitude extraction showing architecture of Tweneboa, Enyenra, and Ntomme reservoirs. (Modified from Jewell, 2011.)

Tano block, the Tweneboa, Enyenra, and Ntomme discoveries were made in a separate Turonian fan, which was also ponded against the south Tano nose (see Figures 1 and 20). Development of these discoveries (the TEN complex) is currently underway and is planned to produce an additional 80,000 BOPD from 2016.

IMPLICATIONS FOR FUTURE ATLANTIC TRANSFORM MARGIN EXPLORATION

Recognition of a successful and repeatable combination trap-dominated petroleum system in the late Cretaceous passive margin sequence along the West African equatorial transform margin has opened up a new play type that may be replicated around the south and central Atlantic margins. Beyond the Jubilee licenses, additional discoveries have been made in the Tano Basin, with the Sankofa discovery now under development. Further afield, a number of discoveries have been made in Cote d'Ivoire, Liberia, and Sierra Leone, although to date, none have been declared commercial. As Figure 2 shows, late Cretaceous stratigraphic oil plays have now been discovered over an area from Sierra Leone to Equatorial Guinea. These discoveries typically are associated with combination structural-stratigraphic traps in late Cretaceous reservoirs that shale or pinch out against underlying syn-rift structural highs developed in association with Gulf of Guinea transform tectonics. Despite these recent technical successes, few development projects are ongoing outside the Tano Basin, and the ability to juxtapose robust reservoir fairways with good trap fairways

remains the key challenge in making commercial-scale discoveries in this and other abrupt margin plays.

ACKNOWLEDGMENTS

Parts of this paper have been modified from Dailly, P., Henderson, T., Hudgens, E., Kanschat K., and Lowry P., 2013, Exploration for Cretaceous stratigraphic traps in the Gulf of Guinea, West Africa and the discovery of the Jubilee field: A play opening discovery in the Tano Basin, Offshore Ghana, in W. U. Mohriak, A. Danforth, P. J. Post, D. E. Brown, G. C. Tari, M. Nemcok, eds., Conjugate divergent margins: London, Geological Society of London, Special Publications, 369, http://dx.doi.org/10.1144/SP369.12 # The Geological Society of London 2013.

The authors would like to thank Ghana National Petroleum Company for original permission to publish the seismic data shown. Thanks also to the Jubilee partners Tullow Oil, Kosmos Energy, Anadarko Petroleum Corporation, and PetroSA.

REFERENCES CITED

Antobreh, A. A., J. Faleide, F. Tsikalas, and S. Planke, 2009, Rift-shear architecture and tectonic development of the Ghana margin deduced from multichannel seismic reflection and potential field data: Marine and Petroleum Geology, v. 26, p. 345–368.

Attoh, K., L. Brown, J. Guo, and J. Heanlein, 2004, Seismic stratigraphic record of transpression and uplift on the Romanche transform margin, offshore Ghana: Tectonophysics, v. 378, p. 1–16.

Basile, C., J. Mascle, J. Benkhelil, and J. Bouillin, 1998, Geodynamic evolution of the Côte D'Ivoire-Ghana transform margin: An overview of Leg 159 results, in J. Mascle, G. P. Lohmann, and M. Moullade, eds., Proceedings of the Ocean Drilling Program: Scientific results, v. 159. Ocean Drilling Program, College Station, Texas, p. 101–110.

Basile, C., J. Mascle, F. Sage, G. Lamarche, and B. Pontoise, 1996, Pre-cruise and site surveys: A synthesis of marine geological and geophysical data on the Côte D'Ivoire-Ghana transform margin, in J. Mascle, G. P. Lohmann, P. D. Clift, et al., Proceedings of the Ocean Drilling Program, Initial Reports, v. 159, p. 47–60.

Bird, S., K. Geno, and G. Enciso, 2001, Potential deep water petroleum system, Ivory Coast, West Africa, in GCSSEPM Foundation 21st Annual Research Conference, Petroleum Systems of Deep-water Basins, p. 539–547.

Clift, P. D., J. Lorenzo, A. Carter, A. J. Hurford, and ODP Leg Scientific Party, 1997, Transform tectonics and thermal rejuvenation on the Côte D'Ivoire-Ghana margin, West Africa: Journal of the Geological Society, London, v. 154, p. 483–489.

Clift, P. D., and J. M. Lorenzo, 1999, Flexural unloading and uplift along the Côte d'Ivoire-Ghana transform margin, equatorial Atlantic: Journal of Geophysical Research, v. 104, no. B11, p. 25,257–25,274.

Dailly, P., 2000, Tectonic and stratigraphic development of the Rio Muni basin, Equatorial Guinea: The role of transform zones in Atlantic basin evolution, *in* W. U. Mohriak and M. Talwani, eds., Atlantic rifts and continental margins: American Geophysical Union Geophysical Monograph, v. 115, p. 105–128.

Dailly, P., T. Henderson, E. Hudgens, K. Kanschat, and P. Lowry, 2013, Exploration for Cretaceous stratigraphic traps in the Gulf of Guinea, West Africa and the discovery of the Jubilee field: A play opening discovery in the Tano basin, offshore Ghana, *in* W. U. Mohriak, A. Danforth, P. J. Post, D. E. Brown, G. C. Tari, M. Nemcok, eds., Conjugate divergent margins: London, Geological Society of London, Special Publication 369, DOI:10.1144/SP369.

Dailly, P., P. Lowry, K. Goh, and G. Monson, 2002, Exploration and development of Ceiba field, Rio Muni basin, southern Guinea: Leading Edge, November, p. 1140–1146.

Jewell, G., 2011, Exploration of the transform margin of West Africa: Discovery thinking; Jubilee and beyond: AAPG Search and Discovery Article 110156 accessed October 27, 2016, http://www.searchanddiscovery.com/pdfz /documents/2011/110156jewel/ndx_jewel.pdf.html.

Klitgord, K. D., and H. Schouten, 1986, Plate kinematics of the central Atlantic, *in* P. R. Vogt and B. E. Tucholke, eds., The Geology of North America: v. M, The western North Atlantic region: Boulder, Colorado, Geological Society of America, p. 351–377.

LePichon, X., and D. E. Hayes, 1971, Marginal offsets, fracture zones and the early opening of the south Atlantic: Journal of Geophysical Research, v. 76, p. 6283–6293.

Mascle, J., G. P. Lohmann, and M. Moullade, eds., 1996, Proceedings of the Ocean Drilling Program: Initial results, v. 159: College Station, Texas, Ocean Drilling Program.

McLaughlin, D., 2012, Jubilee project overview: Offshore Technology Conference 23430, accessed January 17, 2017, www.mdl2179trialdocs.com/releases/.../TREX-232812.pdf.

Morrison, J., C. Burgess, C. Cornford, and B. N. Zalasse, 2000, Hydrocarbon systems of the Abidjan margin, Cote D'Ivoire, *in* Offshore West Africa 2000 Conference Proceedings, p. 1–13.

Moulin, M., D. Aslanian, and P. Unternehr, 2010, A new starting point for the south and equatorial Atlantic Ocean: Earth-Science Reviews, v. 98, p. 1–37.

Sills, S., and D. Agyapong, 2012, Jubilee field reservoir description and waterflood performance overview: Offshore Technology Conference, 23541, accessed January 17, 2017, https://www.itlos.org/fileadmin/itlos/.../S.../OTC-23451-MS.pdf.

Fletcher, Tom, 2017, The Windjammer discovery: Play opener for offshore Mozambique and East Africa, in R. K. Merrill and C. A. Sternbach, eds., Giant fields of the decade 2000–2010: AAPG Memoir 113, p. 273–304.

15

The Windjammer Discovery: Play Opener for Offshore Mozambique and East Africa

Tom Fletcher

Anadarko Petroleum Corporation, 1201 Lake Robbins Drive, The Woodlands, Texas 77380, U.S.A. (e-mail: tom.fletcher@anadarko.com)

ABSTRACT

The Windjammer prospect spud in late 2009, leading to the discovery of 190 trillion cubic feet (tcf) in the offshore region of the Rovuma Basin in northern Mozambique. The key reservoirs are composed of stacked submarine fan complexes from the Oligocene, Eocene, and Paleocene epochs of the lower Tertiary. The submarine fans form traps truncating against the leading edge of the Palma fold and thrust belt. The high-permeability reservoirs are thick, widespread, and very well connected, making them ideally suited for long-term natural gas production and liquid natural gas (LNG) exports. The massive amount of gas found offshore Rovuma has the potential to elevate Mozambique to the world's third-largest exporter of natural gas.

INTRODUCTION

In the Mozambique 2005 bid round, the Rovuma Basin offered one of the last unexplored Tertiary delta systems left in the world. Anadarko Petroleum Corporation identified approximately 100 structural and combination structural-stratigraphic leads in the Area 1 "Offshore" block of the Rovuma in northern Mozambique. This frontier play contained traps associated with growth and extensional faulting in the onshore and shallow-water areas of the block. Farther offshore in deep water, the extensional play was linked by a regional decollement surface to a set of compressional structures associated with several fold and thrust belts. Anadarko recognized that linked extension-compression structural systems in Tertiary deltas have been proven to be hydrocarbon provinces worldwide and home to billions of barrels of oil. The structural system illustrated on seismic data in the Rovuma Basin looked similar to those seen in the world-class petroleum systems of the Niger delta, Mahakam delta, and the Gulf of Mexico. In addition to the Tertiary plays, Anadarko also recognized Mesozoic plays underneath the decollement and older plays associated with rifted and rotated horst blocks. The multiple play types, the presence of surface oil seeps along the east African margin, and the reported oil and gas shows in the two points of well control in the Rovuma Basin encouraged the company to bid aggressively to capture the block. Using a probabilistic system of play analysis, Anadarko estimated as many as 3 billion barrels of oil could be found in Area 1. Our estimates proved to be significantly wrong.

In December 2009, the *Belford Dolphin* sailed to the location of the Windjammer prospect to spud the first deep-water well in the Rovuma Basin. A lost well and mechanical sidetrack later, Windjammer 2 (BP1) logged over 183 m (607 ft) of natural gas pay to open up a new gas province offshore East Africa. Since the initial discovery, Anadarko and its joint venture parties (Mitsui, Empresa Nacional de Hidrocarbonetos LP, Bharat PetroResources, Cove Energy [later purchased by PTTEP in 2012], and Videocon [later purchased by ONGC Videsh & Oil India in 2014; ONGC Videsh also acquired a portion of Anadarko's interest in 2014]) have drilled 51 wellbores and have found over 100 tcf of gas in place in Area 1 of the Rovuma Basin. Chasing the same reservoirs onto the adjacent Area 4 Block, Eni S.p.A. and their joint venture parties (Empresa Nacional de Hidrocarbonetos, LP Galp, Kogas, and CNPC) have drilled 14 additional wells, bringing the total gas discovered initially in place (GIIP) to over 190 tcf between the two blocks. These discoveries have positioned Mozambique on the world stage to become a leading exporter of liquid natural gas (LNG) in the coming decades.

ROVUMA BASIN HISTORY

After nearly five centuries as a colony of Portugal, the Frente de Libertação de Moçambique (FRELIMO) initiated a long war of independence against colonial rule in 1964. In 1974, after a military coup at home, the new Portuguese government became more open to the idea of Mozambican self-rule. FRELIMO and Portugal signed the Lusaka Accord to end the war, and the independent country of Mozambique was created. However, the next few decades proved to be equally difficult for the people of the newly formed country. The transitional government formed by FRELIMO failed to unite the population, and organized resistance from Resistência Nacional Moçambicana (RENAMO) led to a civil war that lasted for nearly 20 years, ending finally in 1992. A United Nations-brokered peace agreement between the two factions led to the first democratic elections in 1994.

While Mozambique was struggling for independence and peace, the rest of the world was experiencing a technology explosion in the search for hydrocarbons. Basins with geology similar to the Rovuma—such as the Campos of Brazil, the Niger Delta, and the Gulf of Mexico—boomed with activity and discoveries in shallow and deep water alike. It was not until 1981 and the formation of Empresa Nacional de Hidrocarbonetos, LP (ENH; National Oil Company of Mozambique) that exploration finally began in the Rovuma

Basin. The Geophysical Company of Norway (Geco) shot the first seismic program in the Rovuma Basin with an offshore 2-D survey totaling less than 500 km (311 mi). That early survey began to highlight the structures offshore and the potential of the Rovuma. However, the first drill bit to dig into the Rovuma Basin was at the Agip Mnazi Bay 1 just north of the Mozambique border in Tanzania. The well drilled into the Cretaceous and found gas-bearing reservoirs in the Tertiary. Even with an early reserve estimates by Agip of 1.1 tcf (Agip, 1983), the gas was left stranded without a market.

Further exploration by the joint venture of Esso and Shell was undertaken in 1984 in the onshore portion of the Rovuma Basin in Mozambique. Acquisition of 1500 km (932 mi) of 2-D seismic data highlighted a complexly growth-faulted tectonic regime and led to the 1986 spud of Mocimboa-1 targeting Cretaceous turbidites. The well was drilled to a total depth of 3493 m (11,463 ft) and encountered positive oil and gas shows but was abandoned as a dry hole. ENH acquired 150 km (93 mi) of 2-D seismic data in the shallow-water bays along the coast that illustrated the continuation of growth-faulted strata offshore, but further exploration ground to a halt until 1996.

Lonropet SARL was awarded a 7-year Production Sharing Agreement (PSA) concession for the land and shallow-water portion of the Rovuma Basin (Figure 1) in 1996 and by 1998 had acquired 3200 km (1988 mi) of

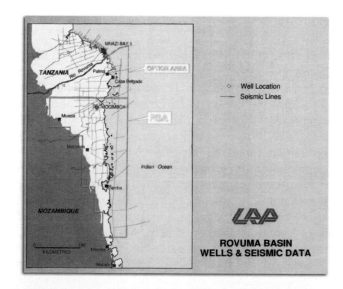

Figure 1. Location of Lonropet 1996 production sharing agreement (PSA). Note location of Mnazi Bay 1 and Mocimboa 1, the only well penetrations in the Rovuma Basin prior to Anadarko entry. (Courtesy of INP, whose permission is required for further use.)

2-D seismic data. The company focused its mapping on the basement rift blocks in the southern portion of the basin while leaving the Tertiary toe-thrusts unmapped, as most of those structures were found in the Option Area of the concession in deep water (Barber, 1997). Lonropet also conducted important field investigations in conjunction with Petroleum Geoservices (PGS) and ENH, sampling oil seeps along the coast, as well as collecting possible source and reservoir rocks for evaluation in the lab. Although this work did not conclusively link a source rock to the seeps, geochemical analysis did seem to indicate an active petroleum system with live Jurassic-aged oil (Lonropet, 2000). Despite Lonropet's concerted efforts to promote the block, the company relinquished the PSA without drilling a well.

ANADARKO ENTRY

Anadarko first became interested in the Rovuma Basin in 2000 when Distinguished Geophysical Advisor Brian Frost convinced his supervisor, Martin Evans, to buy a pair of offshore "zig-zag" regional 2-D seismic lines acquired by Western Geophysical. Those lines provided Frost with enough evidence to believe that the relatively unexplored Tertiary basin offshore Mozambique had the potential to hold vast quantities of oil as had been found in other basins such as the Niger delta of Nigeria and the Campos Basin in Brazil. Working with Vice President of Business Development Ian Cooling in November 2004, Frost convinced Anadarko's management that a trip to a data room in Maputo, Mozambique, was an idea whose time had come. Joined by Project Geologist Andrew Mehlhop, the Anadarko team spent 12 days digesting the complete data set from Lonropet's time in the block, as well as all the older well and seismic data from the Mocimboa and Mnazi Bay exploration campaigns. Frost and Mehlhop highlighted over 100 leads in offshore Area 1 (Figure 2). Their recommendation to pursue this opportunity of many repeatable oil prospects was very well received by executive management. Anadarko submitted an aggressive work program and bid in the 2005 second licensing round for Offshore Area 1. The $465 million bid package, which included both new 3-D seismic data and multiple wells, proved to be the winner, giving Anadarko entry to a new country and a new basin to explore.

Anadarko wasted no time beginning the exploration program for Area 1. The final Exploration and Production Concession Contract (EPCC) did not have an effective date until February 1, 2007. Even while the EPCC was being negotiated and drafted by

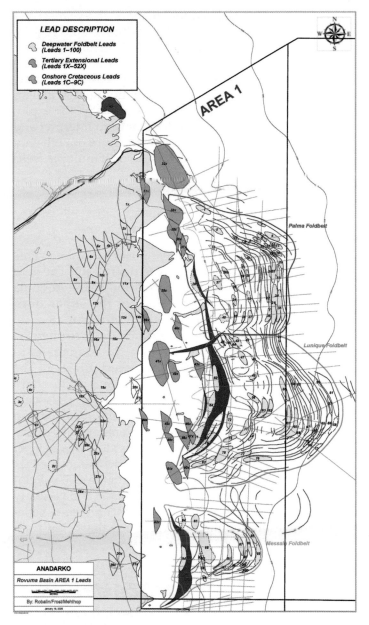

Figure 2. Prebid original lead map generated by Brian Frost and Andrew Mehlhop; used with permission from Anadarko Petroleum, whose permission is required for further use.

Cooling, Land Director, Paul Feldman, and new Country Manager John Peffer of Anadarko, Anadarko's Environmental Health and Safety (EHS) team started the extensive environmental impact assessment (EIA) in late 2006. The EIA laid the groundwork for permitting wells and acquiring 2- and 3-D seismic data offshore. The EIA needed to include permits for both wells and seismic data so the work commitments in the EPCC could be met in a timely manner. The EPCC called for 1000 km (621 mi) of new 2-D data, 3000 km^2 of 3-D seismic data, and seven exploration wells to be drilled within the first 5-year phase of exploration.

The EPCC also allowed for an optional 3-year second phase of exploration to follow, which would require another 2000 km² (722 mi²) of 3-D seismic data and four additional exploration wells. More than a few managers at Anadarko (and later potential partners) cringed at such a heavy work commitment in a high-risk frontier exploration play. Meanwhile, the explorationists were thrilled at the chance to interpret and explore virgin territory while having not only the opportunity, but the commitment, to drill multiple wells in the hunt for hydrocarbons.

REGIONAL GEOLOGY

Many previous authors have postulated the events that led to the modern-day Rovuma Basin. The general consensus is that the formation of the Rovuma Basin began with the breakup of the supercontinent Gondwana in the late Carboniferous to early Jurassic periods. The early intracratonic rifting saw mainland Africa separate from the Madagascar–India–Antarctica plate in an east–west direction. The rifting caused northeast–southwest and north–south trending block-faulted basins to develop that were filled with continental clastics. Thermal subsidence in early Jurassic focused along the eventual East Africa–Madagascar plate margin. This rift valley was a site of lacustrine deposits, which sourced the Bemolanga tar sands of Madagascar (Rusk and Bertange, 2003). Reinitiation of the rift began middle Jurassic and is clearly illustrated on seismic data as an unconformity separating the block-faulted and tilted bedding below from sag-related parallel bedding above. The Madagascar–India–Antarctica land mass separated from East Africa and drifted south along the Davie fracture zone, a right lateral transform fault. Anadarko felt this early drift phase in the middle Jurassic was likely a time of restricted marine source rock deposition along the axis of the Davie fracture. The southward movement of the Madagascar–India–Antarctica land mass relative to the Africa craton ended in the Aptian age of the early Cretaceous. The India-Seychelles plate separated from Madagascar and drifted north in the late Cretaceous, leaving the Rovuma Basin area between Madagascar and Mozambique as a passive margin that filled with late Cretaceous and Tertiary clastic sediments.

Beginning in the early Tertiary, tectonic activity and uplift associated with the modern East African rift shed large volumes of sediment into the Rovuma Basin. The Tertiary section within the Rovuma delta reaches a maximum thickness of approximately 5000 m (16,400 ft). Gravity-driven delta tectonics resulting from both uplift and sediment loading produced a classic, linked system of deformation. The structural geology is characterized by numerous listric growth faults onshore and in shallow water linked by a regional detachment layer downdip to compressional fold and thrust belts in the deep water (Figure 3). The deformation of the Rovuma Basin Tertiary sediments in northern Mozambique continued at least through the end of the Miocene and into the Pliocene, with several catastrophic gravity slides reactivating earlier folds and faults. Several of these folds and faults reached the modern seafloor.

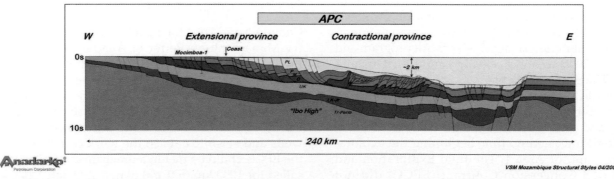

Figure 3. Structural style of Lunique fold and thrust belt. (Courtesy of Van Mount; used with permission from Anadarko Petroleum, whose permission is required for further use.)

PHASE 1 EXPLORATION

At the signing of the EPCC in 2007, Anadarko controlled 85% of Area 1, with ENH as its sole partner. The 15% interest of ENH was to be carried through the exploration phase. The company realized that the Rovuma Basin was a frontier exploration play with great potential but also with a high risk of failure and an expensive work program. Two orders of business were clear to International Exploration Vice President Frank Patterson and the new Exploration Manager, Carol Law: (1) farm down the 85% working interest on a promoted basis to help defray the high exploration costs and (2) reduce the geologic risk by acquiring 3-D seismic data.

A data room was opened in the fall of 2007 staffed by this author, Senior Geophysical Advisor Thad Dunbar, and Feldman. Anadarko was seeking a 2 for 1 carried interest on all capital expenditures associated with the Phase 1 work commitment in the EPCC. The estimated value for the initial 5-year work program that included drilling seven wells, four in deep water and three on the shelf; reprocessing 1000 km (621 mi) of existing 2-D seismic data; and acquiring 3000 km^2 (1158 mi^2) of 3-D seismic data was estimated $268 million in the EPCC. An optional 3-year Phase 2 in the EPCC included four more wells and another 2000 km^2 (772 mi^2) of 3-D seismic data and was valued at $197 million. Over 30 companies visited the data room, with most declining to bid due to the initial seven-well commitment in such a remote frontier exploration play.

The technical team recognized that the key risk to the play was the lack of solid evidence for a robust working source rock. Although several authors, including Chris Machete-Downs, had done an excellent job of documenting oil and gas seeps along the East African margin (Machete-Downs, 2007), only two gas fields had been discovered: Songo Songo off the coast of Tanzania and Mnazi Bay, a stranded gas field also in Tanzania but located in the Rovuma Basin. From the 2-D data available at the time in the Rovuma, the other elements of the petroleum system were readily identifiable, although the late structuring of the fold and thrust belts increased the chances of finding gas, a far less desirable outcome to an oil discovery. The gas risk caused Anadarko to seek out Japan's Mitsui & Co. as an ideal partner based on their LNG expertise. Mitsui became the first party to join the joint venture and obtained a 20% interest. Anadarko also orchestrated a 4-for-1 trade of working interests with the Artumas Group out of Canada. Artumas was the winning bidder and operator of the adjacent Onshore Block in the Rovuma Basin. This trade gave Anadarko multiple opportunities in the Tertiary delta from shallow-water depositional environments all the way to the basin floor, which spread the risk while giving the company the best chance for success across a wide variety of plays. The data room was closed after two Indian companies—Bharat PetroResources Limited (BPRL) and Videocon Industries—made a joint bid for 10% apiece. Bringing in joint venture partners and reducing Anadarko's paying interest served to meet the company's goal of reducing the capital outlay needed for the large exploration program. The joint venture was set to begin exploring with Anadarko at 36.5%, Mitsui at 20%, ENH at 15% (carried), Bharat at 10%, Videocon at 10%, and Artumas at 8.5% (Artumas's interest was later acquired by Cove Energy in 2009, just prior to the Windjammer spud).

Anadarko's Geophysical Technology Team led by Distinguished Geophysical Advisors John O'Brien and John Moran collaborated with Dunbar to lay out the largest 3-D survey ever acquired by Anadarko (at that time). The survey was designed to cover the northern two fold and thrust belts. These two deep-water fold and thrust belts, named Palma and Lunique, contained the majority of the 100 leads identified by Frost and Mehlhop. Additional seismic interpretation by the exploration team recognized deep-water seismic facies on the older 2-D seismic data outboard of the Palma fold belt indicative of submarine fan deposition and reservoir-quality sands. The purpose of the 3-D survey was to confirm that many of the one- and two-line structural leads seen on the older 2-D data were valid anticlinal closures containing deep-water turbidite reservoirs. Should the petroleum system be working, the multiple leads could result in many repeatable prospects for oil within the Palma and Lunique fold and thrust belts. Moran and O'Brien laid out a 3300 km^2 (1274 mi^2) survey to be shot in a pair of north–south race tracks. Data were acquired via a normal 3-D marine survey towed streamer array with twelve 6000-m (19,685-ft)-long cables and a dual source array. Ten streamers were used for steering, with the outer streamers being included in the coverage computations. This strategy successfully reduced infill requirements and allowed for some reconnaissance 2-D lines to be acquired for the same price. Based on the structural trends, an east–west shooting direction would have been preferable, but islands and rapid change in very shallow water made this prohibitively expensive and most likely logistically impossible. The original outline of the survey was notched to avoid the islands but was later adjusted in the final plan to avoid shorter line lengths and multiple line change turns (Figure 4). The final size of the Palma-Lunique 3-D survey was 3370 km^2 (1301 mi^2). Law and Peffer

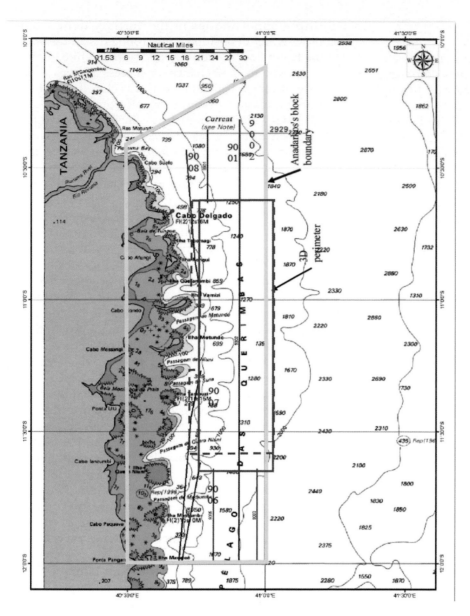

Figure 4. Original Palma-Lunique 3-D outline (dashed red) overlain by final 3-D (purple) outline. Additional 2-D lines were acquired by the 3-D vessel as the 12-line acquisition program minimized the need for infill. The changes to the original planned outline proved fortuitous as the 2-D lines led to the Golfinho prospect and the extension to the south led to the Ironclad prospect. Used with permission from Anadarko Petroleum, whose permission is required for further use.

successfully negotiated with the adjacent Area 4 owners to allow acquisition of a 3-km (1.8-mi)-wide strip in Area 4 to aid in the imaging of Area 1. This 3-km (1.8-mi)-wide strip became important as the key reservoirs discovered at Windjammer extended into Area 4. On January 22, 2008, the CCG Veritas vessel *MV Geo Challenger* began the 3-D acquisition. The 3-D and additional 2-D lines were completed by May 17, 2008, on time and on budget.

Within several weeks of the end of acquisition, the technical team, aided by new Senior Geophysical Advisor Dave Jones, began interpreting the fast-track 3-D data and executing a strategy to fully explore the petroleum system of Area 1. The early focus of the interpretation was on the fold and thrust belts where many of the leads had been identified on the older 2-D data. The Rovuma Basin has three named fold and thrust belts from north to south: Palma, Lunique, and Messalo. Mapping the three fold and thrust belts with modern 3-D seismic data led to a much more complicated story than three simple fold and thrust belts, however. Each fold belt was composed of multiple episodes of failures and mass wasting with detachments occurring at several different stratigraphic levels. In general, the thrusts became steeper and much more complicated westward as later failures slammed into the back of previous thrusts and deformed the faults and rock layers into steeply dipping, complex folds.

The deformation began as early as late Oligocene and continued into the Pliocene with many of the later faults extending to the modern seafloor. The outer portions of the fold and thrust belts in the east are less deformed and could be considered analogous to a small fender bender that occurred at the base of a hill when traffic stopped suddenly. Periodically, later flow of cars and trucks continued to charge forward, causing larger and multiple vehicle wrecks. The process continues with larger and larger pile-ups to the west, up the hill, until traffic finally diverts around the large pile-up. The Lunique fold belt is a diversion around the older Palma fold belt. The southern edge of the Palma fold belt is clipped by the mass movement of the Lunique fold belt as evidenced by a clear cross-cutting relationship. Part of the Palma fold belt is translated eastward and is faulted and further deformed by the Lunique movement. The net result of the complicated structuring in the fold and thrust belts was that most of the 2-D leads did not materialize into valid structural closures, and many of the fault blocks extended to the seafloor with no seal for potential hydrocarbon accumulations.

With the many unknowns concerning the key risks of source and charge, the team needed to test different ideas with each of the first four exploration wells to ensure the best chance for success. The multiwell work commitment and aerially extensive 3-D survey provided just this opportunity. Of course, finding hydrocarbons early in the exploration program was critical not only to answer questions about potential source rocks but also to provide encouragement to the joint venture to continue with the work commitment. The team developed a portfolio of prospects from which four could be chosen, with each testing a different concept and play type. The initial list included (1) Windjammer, a robust anticline on the frontal edge of the Palma fold belt containing a thick Oligocene reservoir section exhibiting a class II amplitude versus offset (AVO) response. Windjammer has additional potential below the anticline because the Oligocene section was repeated in the footwall block, and below that, a Paleocene stratigraphic trap; (2) Collier, also a large anticline but in the Lunique fold belt with class I AVO; (3) Galleon, a Miocene anticline in the Palma fold belt with stacked reservoirs showing flat spots and class III AVO conformance—the Miocene anticline at Galleon sat above an Oligocene footwall trap with class II AVO in addition to a large lower Eocene stratigraphic feature; and (4) Black Pearl, a 2-D defined Cretaceous stratigraphic trap in the southern portion of the block. The strategy and drilling plan rapidly evolved into drilling the four wells consecutively while knowing that the results from early wells would require adjusting the plan on the fly. These four prospects were independent of each other and represented an order of drilling should the wells fail (Figure 5). A portfolio of ready-to-drill wells was imperative to keep the rig on schedule for four consecutive wells, irrespective of the results. Initially, the flat spots and apparent, but uncalibrated, direct hydrocarbon indicators (DHI) at the Galleon prospect provided compelling evidence to drill that well first. Recovering hydrocarbons early in the program was paramount to the strategy, but Anadarko believed the class III response was likely indicative of gas reservoirs. After careful consideration and much debate, the technical team recommended that Windjammer be the first prospect tested in the four-well program due to the multiple plays that could be tested with one wellbore and the large resource potential.

WINDJAMMER PROSPECT SUMMARY

Target Reservoirs

The primary target of Windjammer was an Oligocene turbidite fan section deformed into a toe thrusted-anticline by late Miocene compression (Figure 6). The stratigraphic control for Windjammer stemmed from a regional seismic correlation to the Mnazi Bay 1 well in Tanzania 70 km (43 mi) to the northwest. Mnazi Bay is located at the mouth of the Rovuma River on a land spit just north of the Mozambique border. The Oligocene through Plio-Pleistocene section at Mnazi Bay was shale dominated, with interbedded sands typically on the order of 5 to 15 m (16 to 49 ft) in thickness. The Miocene and Oligocene sands encountered by the Mnazi Bay 1 were good-quality reservoir rock with high porosities interpreted to be deposited as slope channels due to their limited extent, paleographic position, and thickness (RPS Energy, 2015). The depositional environment for the Oligocene at Windjammer was predicted to be submarine fan complexes at the toe of the slope out onto the basin floor. The Esso Mocimboa 1 drilled through the Oligocene section in a rotated growth fault that helped mark the shelf edge (Figure 7). Regional mapping of the growth faults and linked compressional thrusts was used by Van Mount, distinguished geologic advisor at Anadarko, to construct a structural restoration of the Palma and Lunique fold and thrust belts. As the Tertiary section slid down the slope created by the East Africa uplift, compressional faults formed at the dip change from

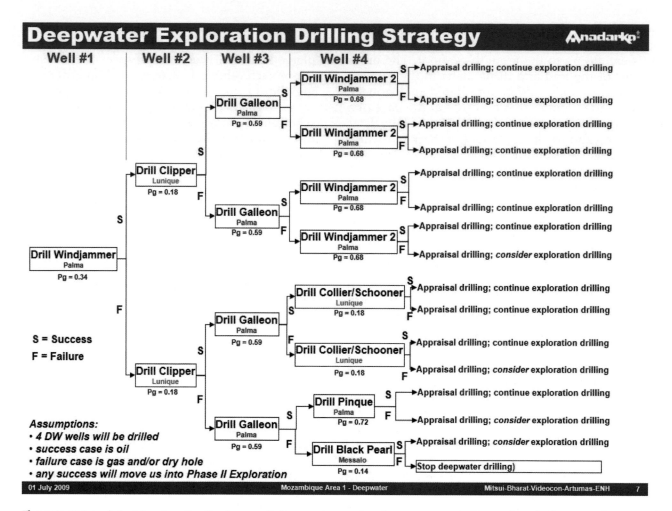

Figure 5. Original decision tree for the four-well deep-water exploration program. Collier replaced Clipper as the second well. Ironclad, which was not developed as the time, replaced Galleon as the third well. Windjammer 2 was renamed Barquentine 1. Galleon was repositioned and renamed Lagosta, and Pinque was renamed Camarão. After Barquentine, INP requested the prospect naming theme be changed from sailing ships to sea creatures. (Courtesy of Ryan Wilson; used with permission from Anadarko Petroleum, whose permission is required for further use.)

the paleo-slope to basin floor transition. The Oligocene rocks at Windjammer located at the leading edge of the Palma fold belt were interpreted to have been deposited near the toe of slope. A slice through the 3-D seismic data clearly showed fan and channel geometries typical of submarine fan deposition in plan view (Figure 8).

As the 3-D seismic data were processed into a prestack-depth-migrated (PSMD) volume under the direction of David Walraven, other members of Anadarko's Geophysical Technology group began creating several other volumes that were key to the success in Mozambique. Roger Reagan, a Distinguished Geophysical Advisor at Anadarko, developed a proprietary seismic attribute volume in which each trace is designed to emulate a gamma log from hypothetical wells. The resulting volume beautifully imaged sands

and depositional geometries ("RRA" volume). The RRA volume combined with the AVO volumes created by Distinguished Geophysical Advisor Stan Morris proved invaluable in the understanding of the reservoir rocks at Windjammer and the whole of Area 1. The same RRA and AVO signature of the Oligocene strata in the anticlinal closure was evident as the section was repeated below in the footwall block. From the RRA volume, the Oligocene section was mapped into two gross fan sequences. The sandy sections of each fan were estimated to range from 17 to 105 m (56 to 344 ft) in thickness at the well location (Figure 9). The Oligocene sands at Windjammer were expected to be both thicker, cleaner, and more widespread than those at Mnazi Bay. Even though these RRA and AVO volumes were uncalibrated prior to Windjammer, confidence in finding thick reservoir-quality rocks ran very high

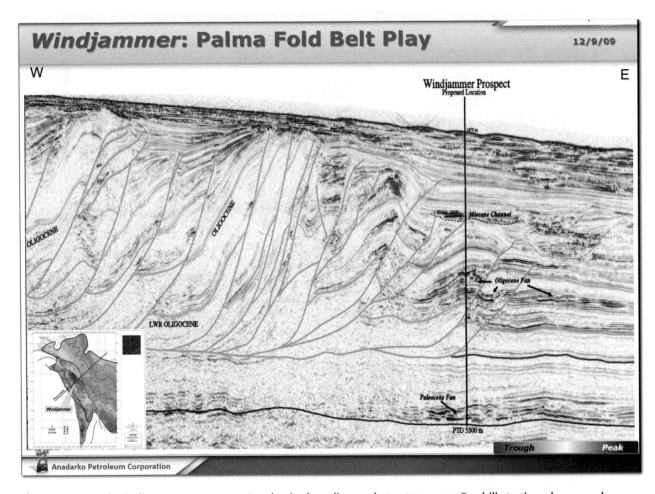

Figure 6. Original Windjammer prospect 3-D seismic show line and structure map. Predrill stratigraphy proved correct with the exception of the top Eocene being at the lime green instead of the interpreted purple horizon. The detachment for this portion of the Palma fold and thrust belt is along the middle Eocene marker (purple). Used with permission from Anadarko Petroleum, whose permission is required for further use.

among the exploration team. Confidence of the Oligocene sands containing hydrocarbons was also high as the offsetting fault blocks and downdip portions of the reservoir exhibited no AVO response, completely different from the Windjammer targets (Figure 10).

Windjammer had two secondary objectives in addition to the Oligocene hanging wall and footwall objectives, one Miocene in age and the other Paleocene. Above the anticlinal closure was a Miocene submarine channel complex that exhibited a class II AVO response. In order to drill a straight hole, Windjammer would penetrate the Miocene channel sand downdip from a class III AVO response in the same channel. The Miocene channel did not have significant resource potential but was important for seismic calibration and AVO analysis. The Windjammer prospect was proposed to a depth of 5500 m (18,045 ft), which allowed the well to test a Paleocene fan section as well as any

possible Tertiary source rocks at the stratigraphic level of the decollement and/or in late Cretaceous. The Paleocene fan was not well imaged, but a reasonable case could be made for a stratigraphic trap. At the time, little was known about the offshore stratigraphy and petroleum system; Windjammer was designed to test as much section and as many ideas as possible.

Source

The Rovuma delta contains active oil and gas seeps to the north and south of the Windjammer prospect. The presence of the Mnazi Bay gas field and apparent multiple direct hydrocarbon indicators (DHI) on the 3-D seismic data were evidence that an effective source was present within the delta and deep-water areas. However, the age, distribution, and properties

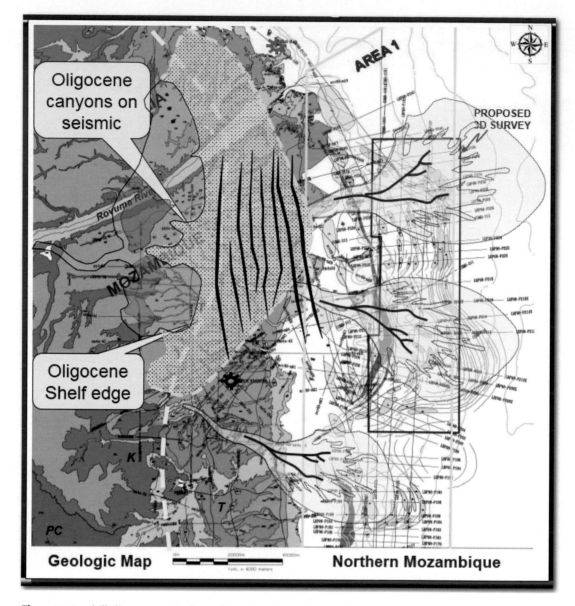

Figure 7. Predrill diagrammatic depositional environments for the Oligocene in the Rovuma Basin. Mocimboa-1 was interpreted to have been located at the Oligocene shelf edge. Using the modern shelf-to-basin floor as an analog, deep-water submarine fans were postulated in Area 1. Used with permission from Anadarko Petroleum, whose permission is required for further use.

of source rocks were highly uncertain. Likely potential source intervals ranged from the mid-Jurassic through the Eocene, and accordingly, a wide range of maturity scenarios were considered possible. One factor that was fairly clear on the seismic data was the age of the Windjammer toe thrust. Thinning across the crest of the Windjammer anticline in the Oligocene shale above the reservoir indicated that the structure began forming fairly soon after deposition. Folding and thrusting continued to middle Miocene. The structure is capped by a slightly deformed Miocene unconformity marking the end of major deformation.

The Palma fold belt continued to be deformed through the end of the Pliocene, but that later movement did not seem to greatly affect the Windjammer structure. So any hydrocarbons migrating after the Oligocene had a chance to be trapped in the Windjammer structure. Under the direction of Distinguished Geological Advisors Keith Mahon and Harry Dembicki (2011, personal communication), the Anadarko Geologic Technology team created models to predict when possible source rocks at various stratigraphic levels could have expelled oil and gas. The models were used to predict the fluid type likely to be trapped at

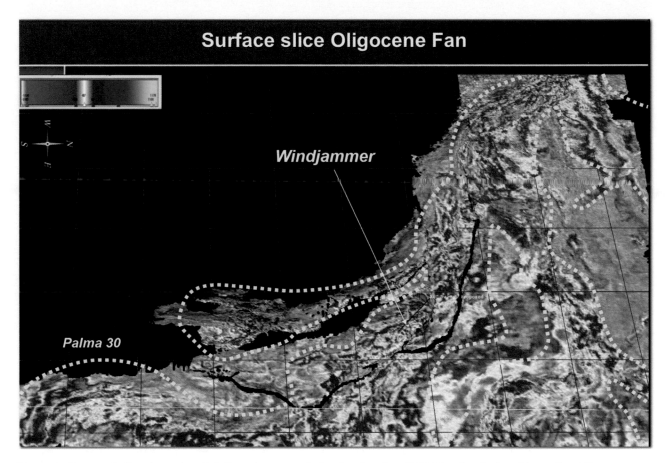

Figure 8. Flattened slice through 3-D full stack pre-stack depth migration (PSDM) seismic data illustrating Oligocene submarine fan geology. Note the lobe geometries composed of multiple channel meanders. Howard White (2012, personal communication) stated, "A submarine fan is generally many amalgamated channels." The Palma 30 "lead" eventually became the Lagosta prospect. Used with permission from Anadarko Petroleum, whose permission is required for further use.

Windjammer. Unfortunately, the models were unconstrained by hard data, so a variety of heat flows and possible stratigraphic locations for sources rocks were modeled, which generated multiple outcomes. The results of the models indicated for any source rock older than late Cretaceous that the hydrocarbon filling Windjammer would likely be gas. A late Cretaceous or Tertiary oil-prone source rock would be ideally suited to fill the structure with oil. Many of the analogous basins for the Rovuma contain key source rocks at the regional detachments associated with the faulting. Drilling Windjammer through this stratigraphic section and into the top of the Cretaceous was important to test for these possible source intervals.

Trap

The toe-thrusted anticline at Windjammer was well defined by high-quality 3-D PSDM seismic data.

However, much of the anticline was fault bounded, so for a large accumulation of hydrocarbons, the trap needed to include a fault seal in addition to a good top seal for the Oligocene sand section. The AVO response (classes II and IIp) was similar in both the footwall and hanging wall blocks, and a large stratigraphic trap was mapped based on the reservoir distribution from the RRA volume and the AVO response. The sandy sections appear to shale out to the north and west, where the RRA response vanished and become wet downdip to the northeast as the class II AVO response disappeared. However, the AVO response had only fair conformance to the structural contours at the downdip edges. The lack of good downdip conformance added risk to the upside resource but could also be explained by stratigraphic complexity. The team also recognized that another possibility was that the AVO response is driven by rock quality and/or thickness as opposed to hydrocarbons. A probabilistic assessment of the trap size yielded a wide range of possible outcomes

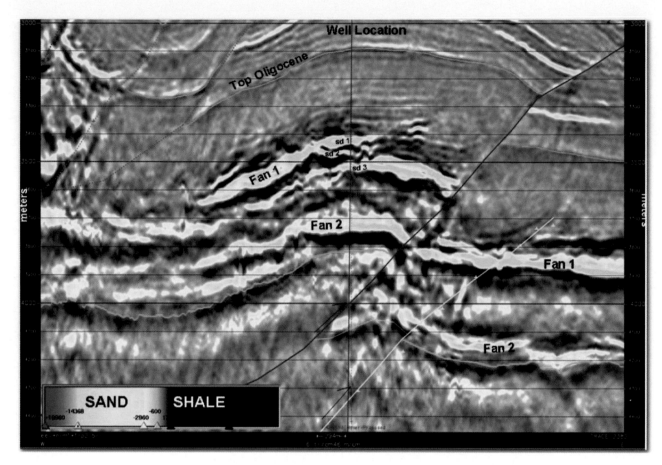

Figure 9. RRA volume seismic profile through the Windjammer location with excellent imaging of the proposed reservoir sections in the Oligocene. Used with permission from Anadarko Petroleum, whose permission is required for further use.

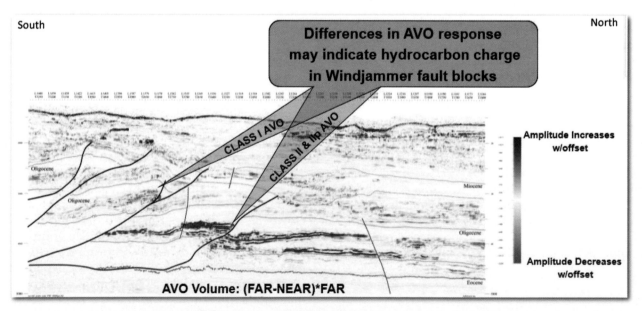

Figure 10. Predrill amplitude versus offset (AVO) volume illustrating class II AVO in the Windjammer and adjacent footwall block (dark blue). The RRA volume indicated reservoir facies in adjacent fault blocks to the south as well as downdip to the north, but note the lack of AVO. Used with permission from Anadarko Petroleum, whose permission is required for further use.

due to the overall uncertainty. The fault-bounded anticlinal trap was measured to be approximately 40 km² (10,000 acres), but the full AVO anomaly, including the footwall, extended to 105 km² (26,000 acres) in Area 1 (Figure 11).

Seal

The Oligocene sand section was covered by an extensive and thick (280 m [9189 ft]) shale package represented by a monotonous, relatively nonreflective seismic package. This shale was interpreted as a deepwater shale and expected to be an excellent top seal. As noted earlier, the technical team believed a fault seal was necessary to trap large volumes of oil or gas. The upper Oligocene fan (Oligocene Fan 1) section was mapped juxtaposed to the Oligocene shale across

the thrust fault, forming a good lithological barrier. The thick Oligocene shale also provided the material necessary for a shale gouge to form in the fault zone. The technical team utilized a PSDM tomographic velocity cube to aid in seal analysis. The tomo-velocity volume showed an abrupt velocity change across the key trapping fault, indicating a good fault seal was likely at that level (Figure 12). However, lower in the fault block, the lower Oligocene fan (Oligocene Fan 2) mapped juxtaposed to the Oligocene Fan 1 in the footwall, adding a risk of a leaky seal at the Fan 2 level in the toe-thrusted anticline. The footwall section of both fans required a both a fault seal against the thrust front as well as a lateral seal from a reservoir pinch out to form a valid trap. No rock properties were available for the Oligocene shale to aid in estimating seal integrity. Analogies from producing fields in similar depositional environments were the only risk reducers.

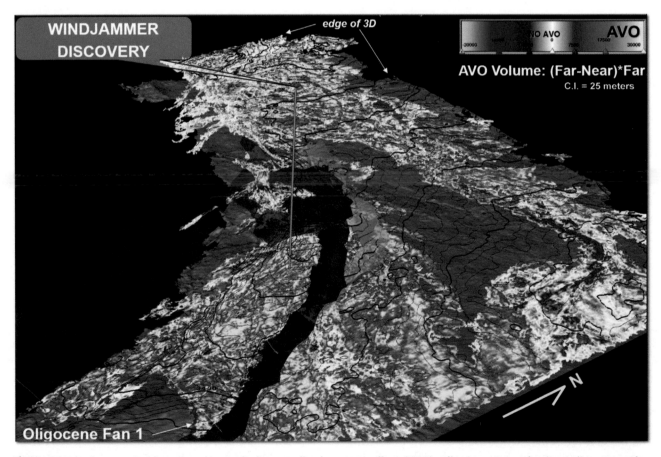

Figure 11. 3-D image of structure map overlaying amplitude versus offset (AVO) Oligocene Fan 1 horizon slice. Note that Windjammer was drilled in a fold-and-thrust anticline, but the AVO signature extended out from underneath the thrust into a wide area of the footwall block. The extent of the reservoir is constrained by the interconnected geo-anomaly generated from the RRA volume. The coloring on the anomaly is used to color the reservoir based on AVO response. Used with permission from Anadarko Petroleum, whose permission is required for further use.

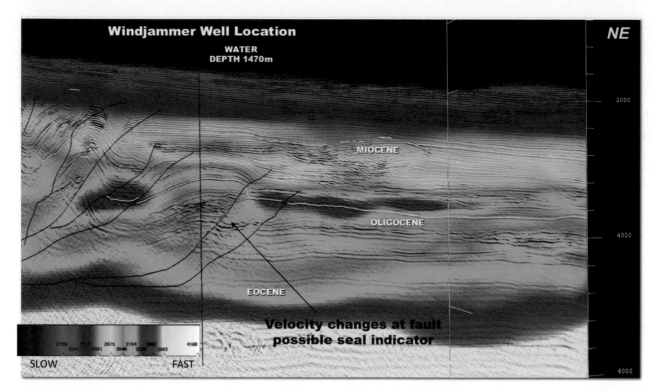

Figure 12. 3-D seismic profile with tomographic interval velocities overlying full stack pre-stack depth migration (PSDM) data. Note the color change across the thrust adjacent to the high reflectivity package of Oligocene strata. This change in velocity was indicative of a fault seal. Used with permission from Anadarko Petroleum, whose permission is required for further use.

Results

Windjammer 1 was spud on December 13, 2009, by the *Belford Dolphin* drill ship in 1466 m (4810 ft) of water about 32 km (20 mi) east of the small town of Palma (Figure 13). The early drilling of the well progressed quickly, passing through the Miocene channel secondary objective at 2609 m (8660 ft) without any indication of hydrocarbons. The depth of the sandy channel was within about 12 m (39 ft) of the predrill prognosis, giving the technical and drilling teams some confidence that the 3-D PSDM data were accurately imaging the subsurface. However, on December 22, as the bit dug ahead averaging 60 m (197 ft)/hr, the well began to flow on a connection, leading to a gas bubble in the riser and stuck drill pipe. The bit had topped into the primary objective Oligocene Fan 1 at 3257 m (10,686 ft), which was 163 m (535 ft) high to prognosis, and cut 15 m (49 ft) of high-quality reservoir before recognizing the target had been reached. The team had a bittersweet early Christmas present of finding hydrocarbons, though in the process lost the well. The team also learned a lesson about the 3-D PSDM data: uncalibrated seismic depth images still contain inherent risks of velocity variation and depth uncertainty.

The exploration well was respud as Windjammer 2 and drilled at a much more leisurely pace with a renewed casing depth planned above the adjusted top of the Oligocene turbidites. Unfortunately, problems cementing the 13 3/8 in. (33.9 cm) casing that ultimately parted led to sidetracking operations and more delays in reaching the primary objective. Windjammer 2 (BP1) drilled into Oligocene Fan 1 again on February 2, 2010. The reservoir package contained two fining upward packages overlying a blocky amalgamated sandstone. The stacking of these sands matched the Reagan RRA volume almost perfectly. The three sands in Oligocene Fan 1 had excellent gas shows throughout, top to bottom, and a gross thickness of 129 m (423 ft). No oil shows were noted, however (Figure 14). After another day and a half of drilling, the bit topped into the second Oligocene Fan 2 at 3525 m (11,565 ft). Oligocene Fan 2 was an 80 m (262 ft) thick and blocky sandstone with gas shows again, though the amount of gas and resistivity on the LWD logs fell off near the bottom, also without any oil shows (Figure 15). Once again, the RRA volume predicted this reservoir quite accurately.

As this well was a true wildcat, all felt it was time to stop drilling and run wireline logs to verify the fluid

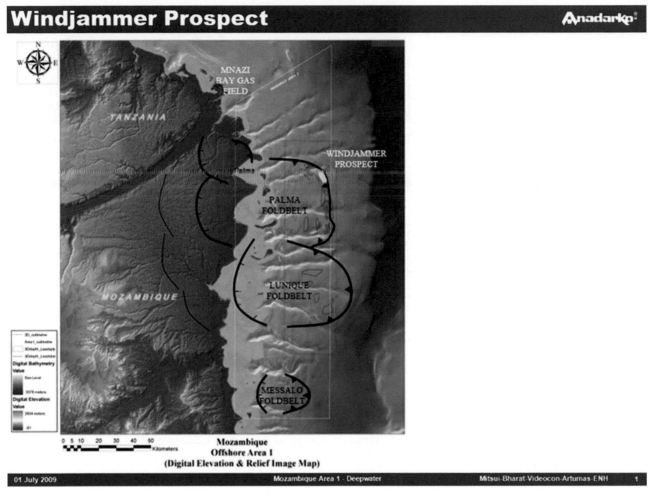

Figure 13. Location map from original Windjammer prospect well proposal (Windjammer photo and description from www.thepirateking.com).

contents of the primary targets. Led by Staff Petrophysicist Scott Birkhead, Senior Reservoir Engineering Advisor John Hagens, and Senior Staff Geologist Adam Heffernan, a comprehensive wellbore evaluation ensued. The three sands of Oligocene Fan 1 contained 86 m (282 ft) of net gas pay with an average porosity of 21% and a water saturation (Sw) of 25%. Using Schlumberger's Modular Formation Dynamics Tester (MDT), pressure gradient analysis and fluid samples confirmed these sands were all filled to base with dry gas. The gradient analysis also indicated pressure communication existed between the three sands. Visual inspection of the rotary cores showed fine- to very course–grained, clean sandstones. Logs indicated the volume of clay (Vclay) was only 13%. Oligocene Fan 2 logged 55 m (180 ft) of gas pay with 20% porosity and 27% Sw. MDT fluid recovery and pressures indicated a gas–water contact in the lower portion of the sand. The rotary cores from Fan 2 also looked to be excellent reservoir rock. The overall conclusion from the

evaluation was a great sandstone reservoir had been discovered that was filled with gas, not oil.

The intended total depth (TD) was still below the primary objectives, so the *Belford Dolphin* went back to drilling. As the Windjammer 2 (BP1) drilled out of the hanging wall, across the thrust-faulted zone and into the footwall, the technical team was thrilled to find another 21 m (69 ft) of thick sand filled to the base with gas (Figure 15). This sand was interpreted to be the lower portion of Oligocene Fan 2 repeated below the thrust. This sand proved to play a key role in the future success story of offshore Mozambique, effectively confirming that the gas accumulation extended beyond the simple anticline at Windjammer.

Windjammer 2 (BP1) continued to drill to a final TD of 5160 m (16,929 ft). The well encountered the final Paleocene fan objective at 4639 to 5102 m (15,220 to 16,739 ft). This sand was a thick amalgamated fan complex with porosities averaging 13% and a Sw of 26%. Petrophysical and MDT pressure and fluid

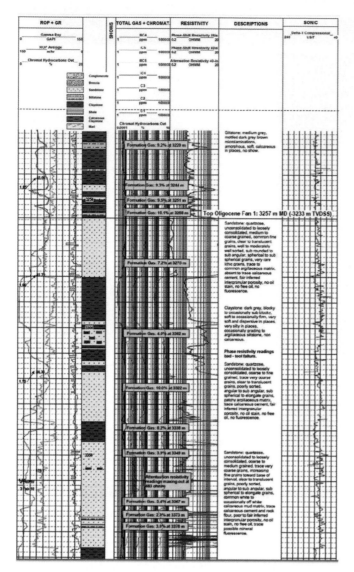

Figure 14. Lithology log through Oligocene Fan 1, Windjammer 2 (BP1).

recoveries indicated 23 m (75 ft) of gas pay overlying water-bearing sand. The lower porosities and permeabilities combined with the lack of full wireline coverage at the base of the hole left uncertainty as to the exact position of the water contact.

At the conclusion of Windjammer 2 (BP1), the final tally was 185 m (607 ft) of natural gas pay. The thick column of pay was exciting for the technical team, but gas was not the desired outcome. Prior to drilling, a gas discovery was viewed much like a dry hole. Gas analysis of the MDT samples indicated that the gas was thermogenic and likely derived from an overmature, oil-prone source rock (Dembicki). Even though the well drilled the stratigraphic equivalent to the detachment layer and through the Paleocene fan, no

potential source rocks were noted. The bottom hole temperature exceeded 150 °C (302 °F), making the temperature gradient at Windjammer similar to the onshore wells along the East African margin. One hypothesis prior to drilling was that the offshore might be cooler as distance from the modern East Africa rift increased; but this was not so. The technical team concluded the source rock was likely Jurassic in age, buried east of Windjammer currently in, or possibly below, the gas generation window. Migration likely began in the late Miocene and continued through the Pliocene along normal faulting associated with the Quirimbas graben, post-emplacement of the Palma fold and thrust belt. The Oligocene shale proved to be an excellent regional seal above the turbidites capable of trapping large columns of gas. The RRA volume developed by Reagan and massaged by Morris was confirmed to be an excellent indicator of reservoir rock. This volume would prove to be a key tool in the continued exploration and appraisal of Area 1.

FOLLOW-UP TO THE DISCOVERY

As Windjammer was being drilled, the portfolio of prospects continued to evolve. The gas discovery also validated the original strategy of testing prospects that looked different from Windjammer. Another significant change in strategy occurred when Law and Peffer negotiated with the Instituto Nacional de Petróleo Moçambique (INP) to convert the EPCC work program to six deep-water wells, eliminating the three shelf wells. After the change to the EPCC work program, six frontier exploration wells were scheduled to be drilled consecutively. The second well in the program was the Collier prospect. Collier was drilled in the Lunique fold belt to test an Oligocene sand package with class I AVO. In the hope of finding oil, the well tested the same stratigraphy as Windjammer, but with a completely different seismic response. As the well penetrated the target, the well encountered higher pore pressures than expected and flowed water. Controlling the flow led to lost returns as it appeared the pore pressure was very close to the fracture gradient at the reservoir level. The exploration team recommended plugging the well due to the drilling difficulties, water flow, and lack of apparent seal. The sand package was later determined to be Paleocene in age and was definitely not gas or oil.

The next prospect to test something different from the gas at Windjammer and the water at Collier was Ironclad (a replacement for the 2-D defined Black Pearl). Ironclad was a well-defined Cretaceous-aged stratigraphic trap with a fan-shaped geometry

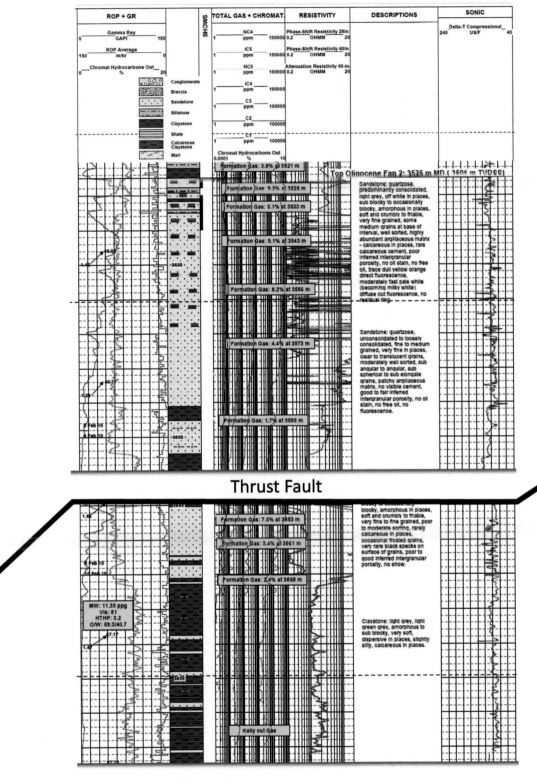

Figure 15. Lithology log through Oligocene Fan 2, Windjammer 2 (BP1). Upper portion is Oligocene Fan 2 in the hanging wall. Lower portion is Oligocene Fan 2 in footwall (entire section not displayed).

beautifully imaged on the 3-D RRA volume, but it also failed due to an apparent lack of seal. As the bit penetrated the objective sands, returns were lost, and the hole would not hold drilling mud of any density. The well eventually reached a TD of 5301 m (17,392 ft) drilling with seawater while still fighting lost returns. The very low fracture gradient of the Cretaceous sands prevented the trapping of any significant column of hydrocarbons. The reservoir also had low porosities and permeabilities but did contain the first oil shows of the campaign.

Armed with three wells for calibration, the exploration and technology teams began to feel quite confident that the AVO signature seen at Windjammer was in fact a direct hydrocarbon indicator (DHI). The fourth well in the program, Barquentine, would test the concept about 2.5 km (1.6 mi) northeast of Windjammer. The structural position at Oligocene Fan 1 was picked to test the integrity of the trap controlled by the stratigraphic pinch out as seen on the RRA volume. The DHI was readily mapped across a wide area in front of the Palma fold belt, not only in the Barquentine area, but also 28 km (17 mi) south of Windjammer, farther north to the edge of the existing 3-D survey in the Atum fan, even farther north on 2-D seismic data in the Golfinho fan. (A new 3-D survey was shot in 2011 over the Golfinho area and showed Oligocene Fan 1 extending 40 km [25 mi] northwest from the Windjammer discovery.) The thought was that a discovery at Barquentine would go a long way toward turning the gas "show" at Windjammer into a commercial discovery.

Barquentine 1 was spud in a water depth of 1542 m on April 21, 2010, and drilled to below the Paleocene fan at a TD of 5140 m (16,864 ft) (under the name Barquentine 1 (BP1) after stuck pipe and sidetrack). The well proved to be quite successful in the Oligocene with both Fan 1 and Fan 2 full to base with gas. The bases of both reservoirs were below the gas–water contact encountered by Windjammer 2 (BP1) in Oligocene Fan 2. The petrophysical analysis of Oligocene Fan 1 showed 23 m (75 ft) of high-quality reservoir rock with 20% average porosity and a Sw of 23%. MDT fluid recovery confirmed the reservoir was full to base, and the pressure gradient indicated separation from the thrusted Windjammer reservoirs. Recall that Oligocene Fan 2 in the Windjammer fault block was juxtaposed to Oligocene Fan 1 in the Barquentine fault block (Figure 9). Oligocene Fan 2 at Barquentine measured 71 m (233 ft) of pay and was also full to the base. Rock properties were also good with an average porosity of 16% and a Sw of 17%. MDT pressures from the Oligocene Fan 2 in Barquentine fell on the same gas gradient as the footwall section of Oligocene Fan 2

encountered at Windjammer. This revelation was significant and indicated a high probability of widespread, well-connected reservoirs capable of draining large areas, a necessity for commercial gas production in deep water. Barquentine 1 (BP1) also found gas in the Paleocene fan correlative to Windjammer with 28 m (92 ft) of gas on water, but with a different water contact.

The new Senior Staff Geophysicist on the technical team, Matt Morris, reevaluated the Galleon area and shifted the drilling location south to focus on Oligocene Fan 1 and a pair of Eocene targets. The new location, called Lagosta, was spud on October 26, 2010, and drilled to a TD of 4970 m (16,306 ft) in the Eocene. Lagosta 1 targeted Oligocene Fan 1 as seen in Windjammer plus two Eocene reservoirs not encountered in previous wells. The Oligocene Fan 1 section contained three very thick and blocky sands over a 329 m (1079 ft) gross interval with net reservoir-quality rock of 238 m (781 ft). The well encountered a water contact in the second sand resulting in 116 m (381 ft) of natural gas pay. Porosities averaged 20% over the reservoir with a Sw of 20%. The reservoir rock was interpreted as a set of amalgamated channel facies with fantastic reservoir quality containing 11% Vclay. MDT pressure analysis showed the three sands to be in static pressure communication with a clear water level at 3716 m subsea. The more surprising result from the MDT pressure gradient analysis was that the gas in the upper two sand packages fell along the same gas gradient as the three Oligocene Fan 1 sands at Windjammer 2 (BP1). Oligocene Fan 1 appeared to be in static pressure communication across the 24 km (15 mi) between the wells. The anticline drilled at Windjammer turned out to be a subsidiary structure in the overall truncation trap against the Palma fold and thrust belt. The gas column from the crest of the Windjammer fault block to the water contact in Lagosta 1 measured 520 m (1706 ft) (Figure 16). The gas gradient was offset from the Oligocene Fan 1 gradient measured at Barquentine 1 (BP1), indicating two separate reservoirs.

Below the Oligocene Fan 1 section, Lagosta encountered a 51 m (167 ft) Eocene sand filled to base with natural gas. This sand appeared to be slightly older than the Oligocene Fan 2 sands at Barquentine and Windjammer. The rock quality of the new reservoir was outstanding with porosities averaging 19% with a Sw of 11%. This new reservoir could be seen on the RRA volume extending 9 km (6 mi) to the north and to the east off Anadarko's 3-D data set. All three pay sands in the Oligocene and Eocene extended to the west and could be mapped truncating on the thrust front of the Palma fold belt. This footwall truncation combined with stratigraphic edges proved to be the

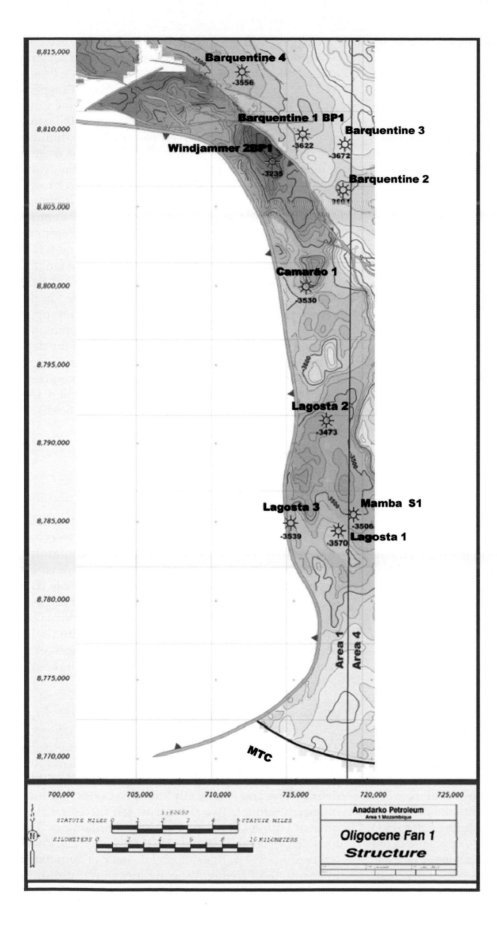

Figure 16. Structure map of top Oligocene Fan 1 for the Windjammer-Lagosta reservoir compartment in Area 1. Schlumberger's Modular Formation Dynamics Tester (MDT) pressures indicated a common gas gradient from Windjammer to Lagosta 1, indicating a column of 519 m (1703 ft) above the gas–water contact at 3716 m (12,192 ft) subsea. (Courtesy Dave Jones, used with permission from Anadarko Petroleum, whose permission is required for further use.)

primary trapping mechanism for all the key reservoirs in Area 1.

The lower Eocene target was a large fan-shaped stratigraphic trap that turned out to be tight and water bearing. The fan was primarily an interbedded sandy foraminiferal limestone with calcite-cemented sandstones that appeared to be a turbiditic flow from a carbonate-rich shelf environment. Lagosta was not in an ideal location to test the lower Eocene fan, as it was downdip more than 500 m (1640 ft) from the culmination of the trap.

The final well of the initial six-well exploration work program for Area 1 was called Tubarão. Tubarão 1 targeted an apparent stratigraphic trap in the equivalent of the Eocene pay zone found at Lagosta 1 and the updip portion of the carbonate-rich lower Eocene fan also penetrated at Lagosta 1. Tubarão 1 was also unique in that the well drilled through 3400 m (11,155 ft) of the Palma fold belt with the targeted reservoirs lying beneath the near horizontal detachment surface. The upper Eocene fan was well imaged on the RRA and AVO volumes, exhibiting a similar response to the gas reservoirs already discovered. The Ironclad reservoir had some indication of liquid oil for Cretaceous-aged rocks but was buried too deeply to preserve reservoir quality and lacked a seal. The Eocene-aged trap at Tubarão was older than the late Miocene traps at Windjammer, but not buried so deep as to lose reservoir quality. The hunt for oil at Tubarão once again proved elusive with the well finding 34 m (112 ft) of natural gas pay in a good reservoir with 15% porosity and a Sw of 25%. Later interpretation of 2-D data by Project Geophysical Advisor Fiona Kilbride concluded the Tubarão trap is likely a ramp in the detachment, causing a footwall trap that formed in the late Miocene similar to the other reservoirs in Area 1.

About a year after Lagosta 1, in late 2011, the Eni-led joint venture drilled the first well in Area 4 about 2 km northeast of Lagosta. The Mamba South-1 encountered 212 m (696 ft) of pay in the Lagosta reservoirs and was announced as the "largest operated discovery in Eni's exploration history" (Eni, 2011, p. 1–2). Eni went on to drill another five wells delineating the downdip portions of the Oligocene and Eocene reservoirs in Area 4. The Anadarko-led joint venture also continued to explore and appraise the Windjammer, Barquentine, and Lagosta Oligocene and Eocene reservoirs by drilling another 25 consecutive wells without a dry hole. The initial four-well exploratory work commitment in Area 1 ultimately led to the drilling of 51 consecutive deep-water wells (including sidetracks) before the *Belford Dolphin* departed Mozambique in the summer of 2015. The rig left behind a super-giant gas field containing world-class reservoirs poised to benefit the people of Mozambique for decades to come.

The gas field is so large that four names are currently used to describe it. The local sixth and seventh grade children from *Escola Unidade and Escola Primaria 16 de Junho* in Palma selected the name Prosperidade (Prosperity) for the Windjammer, Barquentine, and Lagosta reservoirs in Area 1. Mamba is the name given by Eni for the same reservoirs in Area 4 (unitization discussions are ongoing at the time of this writing between the two joint ventures). The Golfinho–Atum complex refers to the Oligocene Fan 1 and Fan 2 reservoirs north of Prosperidade in Area 1. The Golfinho–Atum reservoirs are stratigraphically equivalent to, and are trapped similarly to, those of the Prosperidade/Mamba complex, but they are in a separate pressure compartment. Finally, the Paleocene fan discovered at Windjammer is stratigraphically equivalent to the Orca discovery in Area 1 and is included in the overall field complex as that reservoir is also trapped by the footwall truncation of the Paleocene fan on a ramp in the Palma fold belt. The similarity of the depositional environments, gas composition, apparent timing of the hydrocarbon charge, and common trapping style against the Palma fold and thrust belt places all the reservoirs in the same super-giant gas field.

RESERVOIR DESCRIPTIONS

Oligocene Fan 1

Oligocene Fan 1 is the largest reservoir in the field, covering over 1175 km^2 (290,000 acres). The reservoir is composed of several submarine fans containing channel complexes, overbank lobes, mass transport deposits, and dilute turbidites based on whole core recovered at Windjammer, Barquentine, and Lagosta and seismic stratigraphy (Figure 17). Anadarko's Distinguished Geologic Advisor Howard White (2012, personal communication) describes the reservoir at Windjammer and Lagosta cores below (paraphrased).

Windjammer Core Summary

The Oligocene Fan 1 submarine sand complexes form an impressive stacking of gravelly to pebbly, sand-rich gravity flows along with intervals of sandy to dilute debris flows and chaotically slumped zones of dilute, muddy turbidites. Two submarine fan successions are present within Oligocene Fan 1 at Windjammer. The top Oligocene fan is 59 m (194 ft) thick, and the lower fan is 67 m (220 ft) thick. Each fan stack is dominated by sandy (and frequently conglomeratic) turbidites with zones of interruption via mass transport (chaotic

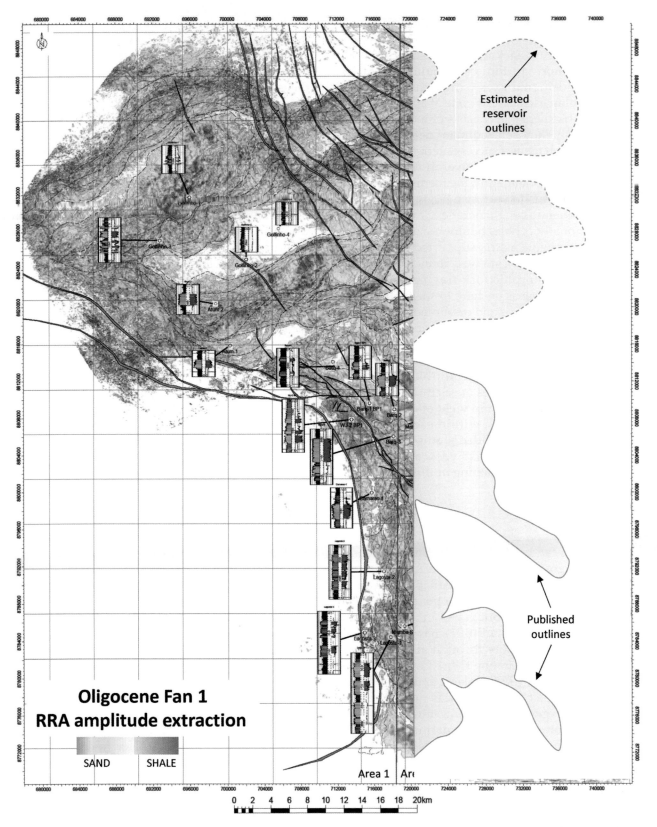

Figure 17. Amplitude extraction from RRA volume demonstrating full extent of Oligocene Fan 1. Note the channel and fan-shaped geometries. (Courtesy of Adam Heffernan; used with permission from Anadarko Petroleum, whose permission is required for further use. Reservoir outlines in Area 4 from published reports [ENI, 2014, p. 21] and estimated from trends in Area 1.)

slumps) consisting of debris flows and dilute turbiditic shales emplaced by gravity sliding into the Oligocene depocenter. Each fan stacking begins abruptly with conglomeratic sandy turbidites signaling dramatic shifting of depositional axes within the Oligocene depocenter. Within each fan is a zone of approximately 15 m (49 ft) in thickness that consists of mostly nonreservoir debris flows and soft sediment deformed shale beds. Capping each fan is a succession of thin-bedded, dilute turbidites signifying the overall retreat/abandonment of the fan. Dominantly, the medium- to thick-bedded sands are fine to very coarse grained, poorly sorted, and frequently conglomeratic. Granule to pebble and occasionally cobble/boulder-sized clasts are observed floating in the matrix-supported framework. Clast composition varies from well-rounded quartzite and igneous/metamorphic rock fragments derived from the provenance areas onshore to shelf- and deep-basin-derived shale rip-ups and disrupted muddy turbidites derived from slope canyon erosion just above the proximal to mid-submarine fan depocenter envisioned for the Oligocene reservoirs. Visual reservoir quality of the Oligocene sand-rich turbidites is good to excellent with minor patches of calcite cementation. Sand bed amalgamation should yield effective lateral and vertical communication within each reservoir, though the extent of the included slumps and debris flows is unknown. The dry gas hydrocarbon charge does not exhibit any visual staining or fluorescence.

Lagosta Core Summary

Oligocene Fan 1 can be divided into three fan complexes at the Lagosta location: (1) Fan A, the uppermost, is fully gas charged; (2) Fan B contains a gas–water contact; and (3) Fan C appears equally as sand rich as the other two but is wet in this location. The bypass wellbore, Lagosta 1 (BP1), recovered a total of 182.5 m (599 ft) total core through all three complexes and the shales separating them. Capped by and separated from Fan B by hemipelagic and heterolithic shales, Fan A can be characterized as thick- to thin-bedded, sand-rich gravity flows and minor interbedded shale and dilute turbidites. Submarine fan lobes in Fan A comprise an amalgamated 76 m (249 ft). Fan B is similarly sand rich and contains over 73 m (240 ft) of stacked fan lobe packages. Above Fan A, the top 9 m (30 ft) of the core consists of laminated to heterolithic shales with abundant thin, silty to very fine-grained turbidites. Fan A can be genetically divided into three depositional units, namely, (1) a basal, fan initiation succession of fining upward lobes—20 m (66 ft) thick; (2) fan growth facies with amalgamated, sand-rich

flow units—35 m (115 ft) thick; and (3) fan abandonment lobes—19 m (62 ft) thick—reflecting fan retreat from the Lagosta location. The massive medium to very coarse (and occasionally conglomeratic) sands of the growth facies represent the best reservoir quality observed. Oligocene Fan B spans 73.3 m (240 ft) below nearly 21 m (69 ft) of mass-transported (slumped) to hemipelagic (in-place) shale that occurs between Fans A and B. Fan B facies are similar to Fan A in regards to fan initiation, growth, and retreat segments. The fan initiation depositional packages reflect deposition on a relatively unstable substrate; the lower 46 m (151 ft) of the fan exhibits fine- to medium-grained turbidites with common dewatering structures and soft sediment deformation. The upper 28 m (92 ft) of Fan B consist of sand-rich flows that are medium to coarse grained, resulting in better sand quality. Very little (if any) abandonment/retreat heterolithic facies cap Fan B.

Anadarko drilled five wells into this portion of the Oligocene Fan 1—Windjammer, Camarão 1, and Lagosta 1, 2, and 3—plus the two bypassed wells for cores. The rock properties are outstanding, averaging 20% porosity, 23% Sw, and 6% Vclay while averaging 70 m (230 ft) of net gas pay. Even though the static pressures from Windjammer to Lagosta indicate a common reservoir, the fan complexes at Lagosta are younger than those at Windjammer based on cross-cutting relationships. The sediment input direction varies as well, although the direction of sediment input in the Windjammer area may be biased somewhat by the geometry and complications associated with the Palma fold belt. In general, the interpretation of the RRA volume indicates a sediment input from the west–northwest that turns and heads south outboard of the Palma fold belt. A second source of sediment input is likely present coming from the west near the Lagosta wells. Fault segments of Oligocene Fan 1 can be mapped within the Palma fold belt west of Lagosta (Figure 18). White's (2012, personal communication) interpretation of the amalgamated sands being well connected proved true with all six of these wells with multiple sands in each well all falling on the same gas gradient, indicating static pressure communication.

The common pressure gradient among the wells led Anadarko to conduct extended flow tests with pressure gauges in offset wells to test for reservoir continuity (Figure 19). This interference testing program deserves a technical paper in its own right, so just the highlights will be noted here. Lagosta 2 was an outstanding well with 163 m (535 ft) of pay in two lobes of Oligocene Fan 1 (Fans A and B). Two 7-day flow tests were conducted in Lagosta 2, one from Fan B averaging 105 MMCFGD and one from Fan A averaging 111 MMCFGD while monitoring the pressures in Lagosta 1 (BP1), 7100 m (23,294 ft) to

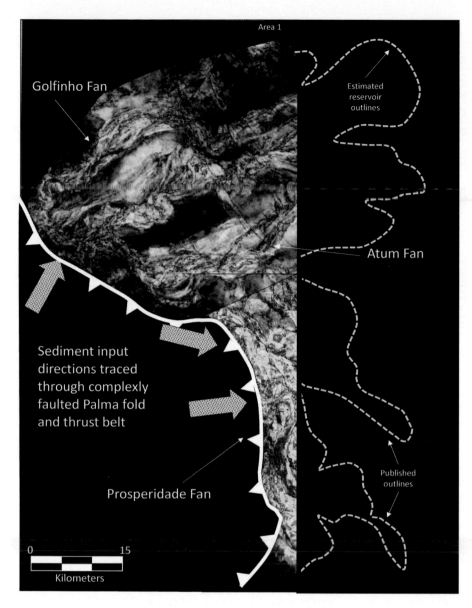

Figure 18. Seismic slice showing full extent of Oligocene Fan 1 outboard of the Palma fold-and-thrust belt. Stratigraphic features associated with submarine fan depositional environments are clearly illustrated. Sediment transport to the basin floor was likely through multiple slope canyons similar to the modern seafloor seen in Figure 13. Distance between the southeast and northeast stratigraphic edges is approximately 90 km (295 ft). (Modified image courtesy of Stan Morris, Glenn Rising, and Fiona Kilbride; used with permission from Anadarko Petroleum, whose permission is required for further use. Reservoir outlines in Area 4 from published reports [ENI, 2014, p. 21] and estimated from trends in Area 1.)

the south. The gauges in Lagosta 1 (BP1) were placed in both Fans A and B to test for vertical and lateral connectivity. The pressure response was conclusive, proving both lateral connectivity over 7100 m (23,294 ft) and vertical connectivity between sand lobes. Permeability was estimated to be over 520 millidarcys (md) in this, the best in the area of the field for Oligocene Fan 1. A similar set of gauges in Camarão 1, which was 8600 m (28,215 ft) to the north, did not record a pressure drop as a result of the flow test. An apparent baffle between Lagosta 2 and Camarão 1 leaked and equilibrated over geologic time but held fast during the real-time flow test.

Another core was taken at Barquentine 2 to help characterize that portion of Oligocene Fan 1. White's (2012, personal communication) summary is below (paraphrased).

The core in Oligocene Fan 1 recovered 56 m (184 ft) of the 58 m (190 ft) of reservoir sand present in the Oligocene submarine fan complex in the Barquentine-2 well. The fan consists of stacked, submarine fan lobe genetic units that, in total, constitute a single-sheet sand complex. Six lobe depositional units comprise Fan 1. Each lobe consists of fine- to medium- to coarse-grained, sand-rich turbidites exhibiting a modest admixture of very coarse to granular to small pebble-sized grains. Each of these lobes is inferred to begin as a medium- to coarse-grained, sand-rich turbidite that sharply overlies the unit below. The lobes vary from 5 to over 15 m (16 to over 49 ft) in thickness. Within the lobes of Fan 1 is a 36-m (118 ft) zone with abundant subvertical deformation bands (fractures in soft sand). Each band represents limited sand grain crushing and

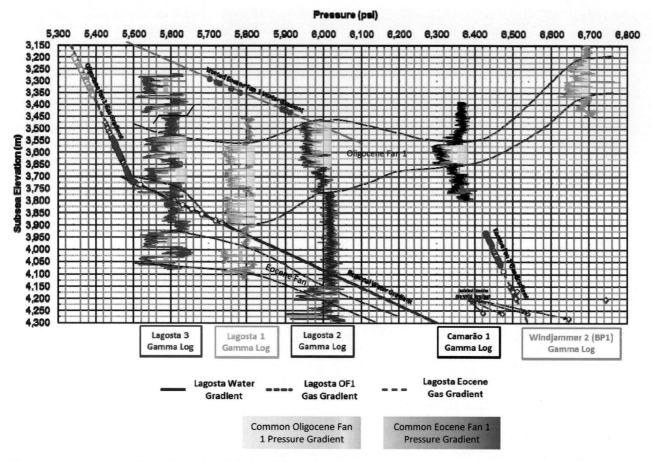

Figure 19. Pressure gradient plot, color-coded with log sections for the southern portion of Oligocene Fan 1. The Oligocene Fan 1 pressures from the gas leg of the reservoir from all five wells plot on a common gradient overlying a water leg. Extended flow test from Lagosta 2 confirmed that reservoir connectivity between Lagosta 1 and Lagosta 2 is 7100 m (23,294 ft) apart. Eocene pressures from Lagosta 1, 2, and 3 fall on a common gas gradient. Projecting the gas gradient to the regional water gradient would estimate a 650-m (2133-ft) gas column. Flow test from Lagosta 2 confirmed reservoir connectivity at Lagosta 1 at 7100 m (23,294 ft) apart. (Modified from John Hagens, unpublished Anadarko-owned figure.)

subsequent cementation, resulting in local permeability baffles within the reservoir. The extensive zone of deformation banding is likely proximal to a fault system through the Barquentine-2 location.

The rock properties from the four wells (Barquentine 1 [BP1], 2, 3, and 4) in the Barquentine portion of Oligocene Fan 1 are very similar to the same unit to the south, with 19.5% porosity, 26% Sw, and Vclay less than 8%. The fan complexes penetrated by the Barquentine wells are genetically related to Windjammer and Lagosta but are fault separated. However, the reservoir is thinner overall than the southern portion, even though Barquentine 3 contains 120 m (394 ft) of pay. The average net pay thickness over this area of the reservoir is 44 m (144 ft). Barquentine 3 also penetrated the gas–water contact at a different elevation than that at Lagosta 1, confirming the gradient analysis of the Barquentine area being separate from the southern wells. Anadarko conducted well testing operations in this reservoir compartment by flowing the Barquentine 1 (BP1) well while monitoring gauges in Barquentine 2 and Barquentine 3. These wells are 2800 and 4400 m (9186 and 14,436 ft), respectively, from Barquentine 1 (BP1), and both sets of gauges registered the pressure drop generated by the 5-day flow test of 90 MMCFGD, proving excellent reservoir connectivity. The flow test did pick up the baffle postulated by White (2012, personal communication) based on the deformation bands in the core, but it did not appear to be a significant barrier.

Oligocene Fan 1 continues north from Barquentine, encompassing the Atum fan and the Golfinho fan. These fan complexes are older than the Windjammer fans, with the northern channel complex being the oldest. Sediment input is from the west–southwest to the northeast (Figure 18). Although no whole core has been recovered in the Golfinho–Atum complex, rotary side-wall cores indicate the presence of facies similar to those of Oligocene Fan 1 farther south. Anadarko conducted extensive appraisal drilling and interference testing in the Golfinho–Atum complex as well. The entire productive area of the Golfinho–Atum complex lies in Area 1, and the joint venture drilled 15 wells to characterize the reservoir and resources. In general, the Oligocene Fan 1 is thinner and has slightly lower rock quality than at Prosperidade. The average thickness across the fan complexes is 46 m (151 ft) with an average porosity of 17.5%, a Sw of 23%, and a Vclay of 12%. This average thickness is bimodal based on depositional environments, thicker in the channel complexes and thinner in the unconfined lobe and splay deposits. The Atum and Golfinho fans appear to be in static reservoir communication based on MDT pressure gradients from the 15 wells (Figure 20). The pressure gradient indicates a

gas–water contact at a subsea elevation of 3730 m (12,238 ft), which was confirmed by wireline logs and samples in Atum 3. The proven gas column in Oligocene Fan 1 for the Golfinho–Atum complex is 770 m (2526 ft).

Although the pressure gradients indicated static pressure communication, the geometries of the sand bodies mapped on the RRA volume illustrated many possible baffles and barriers that might affect real-time production. Once again, an interference flow test program was set up with gauges in offset wells while flowing Golfinho 3 from a thick-channel belt facies. Monitoring gauges were placed in Atum 2 and Golfinho 1 during this phase of the flow testing. Atum 2 is located 9000 m (29,528 ft) from the flow test and required the pressure drop to follow complicated geology (Figure 21). Golfinho 1 was 5600 m (18,373 ft) from the test well but in a frontal splay facies. Golfinho 3 was flowed at 102 MMCFGD for 5 days, confirming

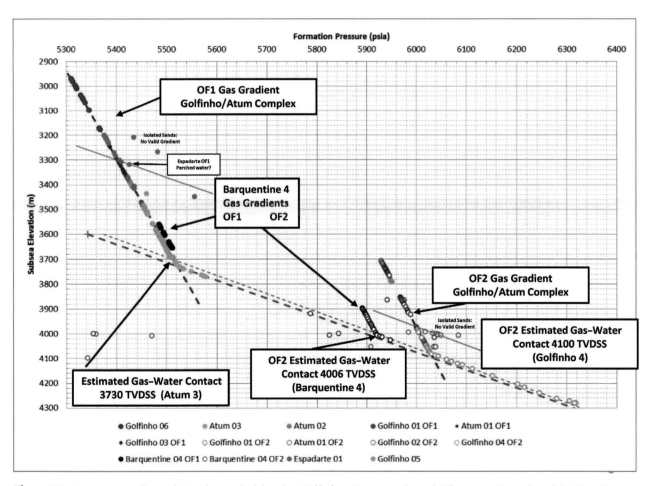

Figure 20. Pressure gradient plot, color-coded for the Golfinho–Atum portion of Oligocene Fans 1 and 2. Note the clear offset in each fan from the stratigraphic equivalent in Barquentine 4. The Golfinho–Atum complex has some stray sands that do not fall within the larger reservoirs and are indicated by the points not falling on the common gradients. (Modified from John Hagens, unpublished Anadarko-owned figure.)

excellent gas deliverability; however, the test also demonstrated that the facies boundaries acted as baffles and barriers to flow. Neither of the offset gauges recognized any pressure drop associated with the test. Overall, the Oligocene Fan 1 reservoir at Golfinho–Atum is thinner and contains less channel cutting and amalgamation than are present at Prosperidade.

Oligocene Fan 2 and Eocene

Oligocene Fan 2 and the Eocene fan are interpreted to be genetically related as both are deposited on a common seismically defined erosional surface. Three distinct reservoir areas of deposition can be readily mapped from the RRA volume: (1) the Eocene fan at Lagosta, (2) Oligocene Fan 2 in the Windjammer/Barquentine area, and (3) Oligocene Fan 2 in the Golfinho–Atum area (Figure 22).

The Eocene fan has been penetrated by three wells on Area 1 with a whole core recovered in Lagosta 1 (BP1). This fan extends from the footwall cutoff on Area 1 all the way to Quirimbas graben in the eastern side of Area 4 covering about 400 km² (99,000 acres) with the majority lying on Area 4 (Eni, 2014, p. 21). Lagosta 3 penetrated 93 m (305 ft) of this same fan in a thrusted hanging wall before encountering the gas-bearing fan package in the footwall block. Several other thrust-faulted sections of the Eocene fan can be mapped to the west–southwest, indicating the axis of sediment input. The reservoir parameters for the Eocene fan are good with an average porosity of 17.5%, a Sw of 24%, and a Vclay of 5.6%. Estimated average thickness for the reservoir is 50 m (164 ft) (Area 1). The geometries of the sand bodies in Area 1 indicate three meandering channels separated by fine-grained overbank deposits. The reservoir at Lagosta 1 is the cleanest and most amalgamated. White's (2012, personal

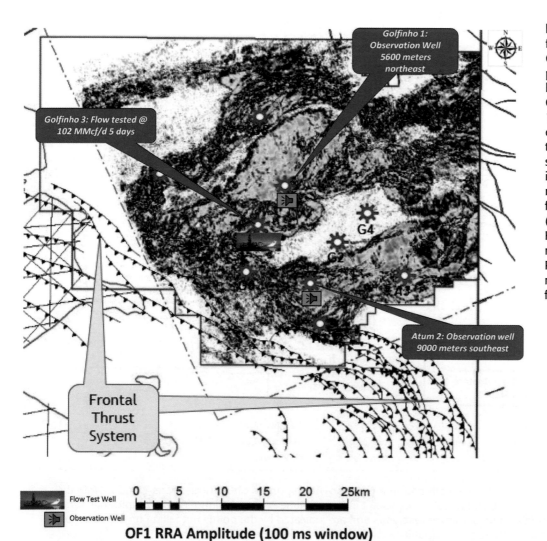

Figure 21. RRA display for Oligocene Fan 1 in Golfinho–Atum complex. Channel forms and lobes are clearly defined. Golfinho 3 flow averaged 102 MMCFGD from a channel belt facies. Neither Golfinho 1 in frontal splay facies nor Atum 2 in different channel belt recorded a pressure drop from the 5-day flow test. (Image courtesy Adam Heffernan; used with permission from Anadarko Petroleum, whose permission is required for further use.)

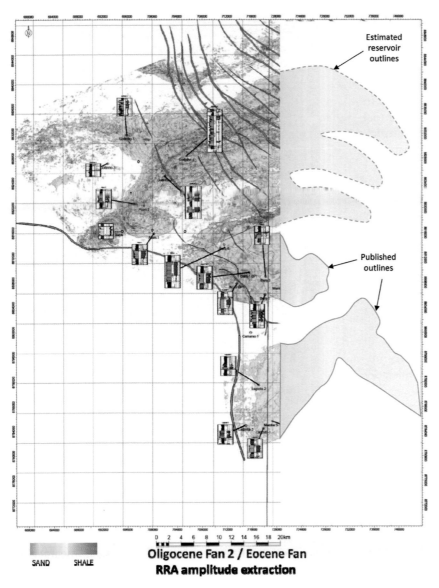

Estimated reservoir outlines

Published outlines

SAND   SHALE

0 2 4 6 8 10 12 14 16 18 20km

Oligocene Fan 2 / Eocene Fan
RRA amplitude extraction

Figure 22. Amplitude extraction showing areal extent of Oligocene Fan 2 and Eocene fan. The fan and channel complexes through the Golfinho 2 through 6, Atum, Windjammer, and Barquentine wells are Oligocene in age. The northernmost submarine fan through Golfinho 1 and the southernmost fan complex through the Lagosta wells are Eocene in age. Lagosta 3 confirmed that the lack of robust RRA response west of Lagosta 1 and 2 is due to poor imaging under the Palma fold and thrust belt. (Image from Adam Heffernan, unpublished Anadarko-owned figure. Reservoir outlines in Area 4 from published reports [ENI, 2014, p. 21] and estimated from trends in Area 1.)

communication) summary core description for the Lagosta Eocene whole core is below (paraphrased).

Lagosta-1 (BP1) captured 74 m (243 ft) of Eocene fan covering the complete reservoir section. Coring was initiated in hemipelagic mudstone/claystone above the Eocene sands. Four meters of sandy debris flow (with no reservoir potential) occur immediately above the upper sand package of the Eocene. Fifty-three meters of reservoir-quality sandstone are made up of two stacked, submarine fan sand packages. The upper submarine fan package is 18.2 m (60 ft) thick. Sands within the interval are dominated by coarse- to very coarse-grained sand with very minor amounts of granule to pebbly conglomeratic detritus. This detritus consists of both locally derived mudstone rip-ups and provenance-derived, rounded clasts of quartz, igneous, and metamorphic rock fragments. Reservoir quality is comparatively high

in the upper Eocene sand package with respect to the lower unit. The lower Eocene submarine fan package similarly consists of stacked lobe genetic units covering 35 m (115 ft). Similar to the upper Eocene package, the lower fan successions can be subdivided into fan initiation, growth, and retreat/abandonment facies. Fan growth, sand-rich turbidites comprise the best reservoir quality present in these fan complexes. Most of the sand-rich turbidite flows comprising the lower interval are medium grained with a subordinate percentage showing coarse to very coarse grain size. Very minor conglomeratic admixtures are observed. The lower fan succession rests on mass transport complex (MTC) shale and muddy debris flows. It is likely that the lowest 19 m (62 ft) is all MTC and occupies what may be reservoir accommodation space lateral to the slumped shale fill at base l in the Lagosta-1 location.

A flow test with offset pressure monitoring was also conducted in the Eocene fan from the Lagosta 2 well with pressure monitoring gauges in Lagosta 1 (BP1). Lagosta 2 flow averaged 101 MMCFGD for 7 days. Mapping the reservoir from the RRA volume showed three distinct channel complexes with Lagosta 2 in the northernmost and Lagosta 1 in the southernmost about 7100 m (23,294 ft) away. The middle complex has not yet been penetrated. The pressure drop was registered 4.5 weeks later on the gauges in Lagosta 1 (BP1) even though the seismic data suggested separation. The flow test confirmed high deliverability, lateral connectivity, and excellent permeability of the Eocene fan (Figure 23).

In Area 1, the Oligocene Fan 2 is penetrated in five wells in the Windjammer/Barquentine area with whole cores recovered from Windjammer 2 (BP3) and Barquentine 2. Oligocene Fan 2 in the Windjammer block is fault separated from Barquentine, but part of the same submarine fan complex and depositional environment. This fan rests on mass transport deposit similar to the Eocene fan. White (2012, personal communication) describes the Oligocene Fan 2 whole core in Windjammer 2 (BP3) below (paraphrased).

Oligocene Fan 2 consists dominantly of amalgamated sand-rich turbidites that exhibit increased conglomerate abundance toward the base of the succession. The single submarine fan depocenter exhibits several depositional features that are similar to the overlying Oligocene Fan 1 complex, yet with notable differences. The base of the fan rests upon chaotic muddy slumps and debris flows created by mass transport processes. The extent of the shale-MTC may be simply local to this part of the depocenter or extensively emplaced over a wide area of the Oligocene submarine setting. The first two genetic packages of the fan are two fining upward channels that begin abruptly with coarse- to very coarse-grained sand-rich turbidites. These sands are capped by very fine- to medium-grained, dilute turbidites separated by centimeter-thick mud/clay laminae, suggesting an off-axis to levee depositional setting. The main body of the fan spans 60 m (197 ft) of amalgamated, sand-rich flows that are conglomeratic in the lower 10 m (33 ft). This zone represents the initial fan lobe of the five stacked lobes comprising the sheet sand dominating the main body of the fan. Generally, each of these lobes exhibits a slight fining grain size; the majority of these beds contain a moderate to very minor admixture of granular-sized detrital grains. Minor debris flows and calcite-cemented sands occur within the fan complex. Capping the fan is a succession of thin-bedded, dilute sand turbidites gradually giving way to even

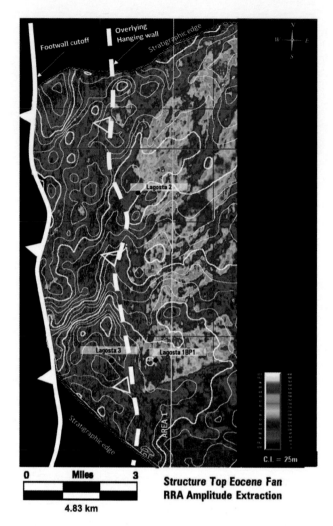

Figure 23. Eocene fan amplitude extraction from the RRA volume with the brighter colors indicating sand. The imaging dims in the area under the overlying hanging wall, but the sand continues to the footwall cutoff forming the updip trap. The extraction seems to indicate three separate channels, but interference testing between Lagosta 1 (BP1) and Lagosta 2 show pressure communication. (Modified image courtesy of Dave Jones; used with permisson from Anadarko Petroleum, whose permission is required for further use.)

more distal muddy turbidites marking the final fan abandonment.

Whole core was also recovered from Barquentine 2 in Oligocene Fan 2, which was 4800 m (15,748 ft) northeast of Windjammer 2 (BP3). White's (2012, personal communication) description of the Oligocene Fan 2 from Barquentine 2 is below (paraphrased).

Oligocene 2 is different from the other fans in Area 1 in that the basal conglomeratic sand beds that initiated fan deposition in this area overlie hemipelagic shales of abyssal plain deposition and not in disturbed shales incorporated into MTC deposits. The lower portion of

Fan 2 consists of a stacked succession of two to three lobe/channel sand packages and minor thin shale as well as very fine dilute turbidite beds. Sand-rich gravity flow beds comprise each depositional package. The upper portion of Fan 2 consists of two fan lobes to submarine channel succession sandwiched between lobe channel abandonment (shale) facies. The shale facies are very heterolithic with very abundant silt and very fine sand turbidites intercalated with laminated mudstone. Overall, the setting for these lobes or channel deposits is that of a more distal fan setting or, at least, is off-axis to the main focused lobe/channel deposition (as seen at Windjammer).

Barquentine 2 encountered the water contact defining the downdip limits of Oligocene Fan 2 and proving a gas column of 115 m (377 ft). The fan complex in the Windjammer/Barquentine area encompasses 145 km² (35,800 acres) and averages 41 m (135 ft) of net gas pay. Reservoir properties are good with an average porosity of 18%, a Sw of 28%, and a Vclay of 5%. Barquentine 2 and 3 were completed with pressure gauges to monitor the flow test in Barquentine 1 (BP1) (Figure 24). That well flowed at an average rate of 97 MMCFGD for 5 days. The gauges in both wells measured a clear pressure drop, demonstrating a reservoir connectivity of up to 4400 m (14,436 ft). The Oligocene Fan 2 package in Barquentine 3 was composed of two units separated by a shale sequence. Gauges placed in each of those units recorded the pressure drop from the flow test, indicating good vertical connectivity in the reservoir as well.

The northernmost reservoir compartment for Oligocene Fan 2 is in the Golfinho–Atum complex, encompasses 220 km² (54,340 acres), and is penetrated by 12 wells. The gas column is proven to be 450 m (1476 ft) from the highest known gas in Manta 1 to the gas–water contact in Golfinho 4. No whole core has been taken in this area, but the rotary cores suggest similar rock properties to the genetically related fans to the south. Average porosities are 15.8% with a Sw of 24.5% and Vclay of 10%. The reservoir can be quite thick with a maximum of 173 m (568 ft) in Golfinho 4 and an average pay thickness across the reservoir of about 50 m (164 ft). An extended flow test was conducted, which flowed an average of 103 MMCFGD for 7 days from Golfinho 2. Pressure-monitoring gauges were placed in Golfinho 1, located 9100 m (29,856) ft north of Golfinho 2; Golfinho 4, located 4800 m (15,748 ft) east of Golfinho 2; and Atum 2, located 5800 m (19,029 ft) southwest of Golfinho 2. The interference testing was successful along the channel axis of Oligocene Fan 2 between Golfinho 4 and Atum 2, a distance of 10,600 m (34,777 ft), indicating excellent reservoir continuity in that facies. The Golfinho 1 gauges were placed in a reservoir correlative to Oligocene Fan 2 but in a different channel complex that is actually slightly older in age, being Eocene. The channel complex of Atum 2, Golfinho 2, and Golfinho 4 scours into the older complex, but no real-time pressure wave was measured across the stratigraphic baffle (Figure 25).

Figure 24. Flow test at Barquentine 2 from the *Deepwater Millennium* drill ship. Barquentine 2 was the first well flowed in the testing program. Surface equipment on the drill ship initially limited the flow rates to 90 MMCFGD. Under the direction of Completions Engineering Manager Matt Marek, his team reworked the surface constraints raising the safe limits to over 100 MMCFGD. Actual production rates for the wells will be 150 to 250 MMCFGD.

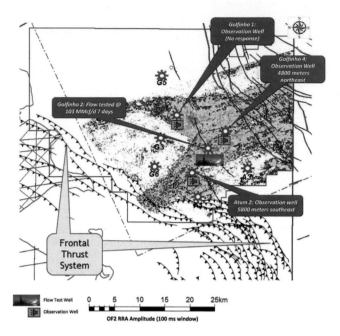

OF2 RRA Amplitude (100 ms window)

Figure 25. RRA display for Oligocene Fan 2 in the Golfinho–Atum complex. The channel complex through the Atum and Golfinho 2 and 4 wells can be seen truncating across the older Golfinho 1 canyon. Golfinho 2 flow tested at 103 MMCFGD, and the pressure response was clearly measured at Golfinho 4 and Atum 2. Atum 2 lies 10,600 m (34,777 ft) from Golfinho 4. (Image courtesy of Adam Heffernan; used with permission from Anadarko Petroleum, whose permission is required for further use.)

Paleocene

The final reservoir to be discussed as a result of the Windjammer discovery is the middle Paleocene fan seen both at Windjammer 2 (BP1) and Barquentine 1 (BP1). Both wells encountered a thick submarine fan complex with 23 and 33 m (75 and 108 ft) of pay, respectively, above high-water saturation reservoir rock containing residual gas but with separate gas–water contacts. Barquentine 4 was drilled structurally high to both Windjammer 2 (BP1) and Barquentine 1 (BP1) and encountered 100% water in the Paleocene fan. The Paleocene reservoir in the Windjammer-Barquentine area appeared to be composed of multiple small compartments of a breached reservoir. Kilbride and Senior Geologist Adam Majeski did an excellent job interpreting the trapping problems at Windjammer and Barquentine and proposed drilling farther west under the Palma fold belt where the reservoir is less faulted (although not very well imaged by seismic data). Away from the small fault blocks, the middle Paleocene fan formed a large gas-filled reservoir discovered by Orca 1, a well 11 km (7 mi) west of Windjammer. A step, or ramp upward, in the Palma detachment west of Orca sets up a footwall truncation of the reservoir, forming a trap similar to the Oligocene and Eocene reservoirs on Area 1. The core description of the Paleocene fan taken from Windjammer 2 (BP2) and described by White (2012, personal communication) below contains facies and depositional environments similar to the younger reservoirs.

The Paleocene cored interval within the Windjammer-2 (BP2) spanned an interval of 122 m (400 ft). The deep-water submarine fan setting received a high volume of Paleocene sediments entering the depocenter via sediment-laden gravity flows focused through steep-gradient slope conduits. The lower portion of the fan contains a boulder-sized calcareous clast possibly derived from an updip shelfal position. This composition along with quartz, igneous, metamorphic, and carbonate rock fragments occurs in the succession of a debris flow and conglomeratic grain flows that signify tectonic events in the source terrain. Given the overall submarine fan setting, multiple genetic depositional packages are present within the Paleocene-cored interval. The sand-rich packages of the lower portion of the fan complex depict a submarine sheet development consisting of channels to amalgamated sand-rich lobes. Capping the submarine sheet is an overall fan abandonment facies succession of finer-grained, thin-bedded turbidite cycles and ultimately distal mud-rich laminae marking the final abandonment of the Paleocene fan system in this area.

CONCLUSIONS

In the 1900s, Windjammers were the grandest of all merchant sailing ships, large with multiple masts to catch the wind and sail the oceans. In the early 2000s, the Windjammer gas discovery was one of the grandest finds in the history of deep-water exploration with multiple reservoirs holding vast quantities of natural gas. The discovery was the key to opening up a new gas province along the East African margin. Following the Windjammer discovery, joint ventures led by Anadarko and Eni have found over 190 tcf of gas in a stacked series of deep-water submarine fan complexes. The gas field is among the top five largest gas fields in the world. Also after Windjammer, other operators drilled north of the border, finding another 50 tcf of gas in the deep waters of Tanzania (Muhongo, 2014, p. 7). Anadarko was rewarded for taking a risk on frontier exploration in a relatively unexplored basin based on the belief that the geology was conducive for an active and robust petroleum system. The rewards for taking that risk were thick and expansive gas reservoirs covering hundreds of square kilometers rather than the originally expected multiple oil-filled anticlines . Extended flow tests proved the reservoirs were capable of very high, sustained flow rates with large drainage areas and excellent connectivity. The large and highly permeable reservoirs are ideally suited for the long-term gas production necessary for LNG exports. Mozambique and the operators are now challenged to recover the gas and develop one of the largest LNG projects in the world. The massive natural gas discoveries have the potential to elevate Mozambique to the world's third-largest exporter of natural gas. The project has the opportunity to be truly transformational for the country and people of Mozambique by providing employment, new infrastructure, and gas-supported projects while quintupling the country's current gross domestic product by 2035 (Standard Charter Bank, 2014).

ACKNOWLEDGMENTS

The author would like to thank the people and government of Mozambique for inviting Anadarko and our joint venture partners into their country to explore for oil and gas. Special thanks to INP, ENH, and MICOA for ensuring the smooth, timely approvals and support that allowed the joint venture to continuously drill for six and half years. An exploration project of this magnitude involved far too many people to name each one individually, but our success could not have been achieved without the diligent efforts of the Anadarko International Drilling, Well Site Operations, Logistics, Negotiations, Environmental Health and Safety, and Finance teams. The Anadarko staff and contractors in Mozambique performed superbly in an area far removed from normal oil field operating conditions. Furthermore, a project as dynamic as this exploration program would not have happened without the rapid concurrence and continuous support from our joint venture partners: ENH, Mitsui, Cove, Bharat, Videocon, PTTEP, ONGC, and Oil India. Thanks also to the Anadarko Development team headed by Scott Mowery, who spearheaded the ambitious and successful interference testing program. Finally, I would like to thank Scott Munsell, Anine Pedersen, Tom Griffith, and Lisa Fletcher for editing the final manuscript.

REFERENCES CITED

Agip, Reserve Estimate Mtwara-Mnazi Bay Structure, 1983, p. 13. Mozambique second round data package: unpublished, used by permission of INP.

Barber, P. M., 1997, Rovuma PSA & Option Area 1996 geotechnical activities report, v. 1: Mozambique second round data package, p. 1, unpublished, used by permission of INP.

Eni, 2011, Press release, October 20: accessed July 1, 2015, https://www.eni.com/en_IT/media/2011/10/eni-announces-a-giant-gas-discovery-offshore-mozambique.

Eni, 2014, 2013 Results and 2014–2017 strategy: p 21, accessed July 1, 2015, https://www.eni.com/enipedia/en_IT/financial-corporate-reporting/shareholders/2013-results-and-2014-2017-strategy.page?lnkfrm=serp.

Lonropet, S. A. R. L., 2000, Rovuma basin: Mozambique geological report: Mozambique second round data package, p. 44, unpublished, used by permission of INP.

Machete-Downs, C., 2007, East Africa exploration: Myths, myopia and misinformation?: Geo ExPro, October, p. 16–20, accessed July 1, 2015, http://assets.geoexpro.com/legacy-files/articles/East%20African%20Exploration-%20Myths,%20Myopia%20and%20Misinformation.pdf.

Muhongo, S., 2014, Interview in The Oil & Gas Year, Tanzania 2014, p. 7, accessed July 1, 2015, http://www.theoilandgasyear.com/content/uploads/2014/12/pre_TOGY_Tanzania_2014.pdf.

RPS Energy Canada Ltd., 2015, Mnazi Bay Field Reserves Assessment as at December 31, 2014, p. 3–3, accessed July 1, 2015, http://www.wentworthresources.com/pdf/RPS-March-2-2014-Reserves-FINAL.pdf.

Rusk & Bertange, 2003, The geology and geophysics of the Mozambique channel: Petromarex, accessed July 1, 2015, http://www.petromarex.com/projects/moz/Mozambique_Brochure.pdf.

Standard Charter Bank, 2014, Mozambique LNG: Macroeconomic Study, p. 128–130, accessed December 1, 2009, http://www.mzlng.com/content/documents/MZLNG/LNG/Development/2014-MozambiqueLNGReport-ENG.pdf.

ThePirateKing.com, accessed December 1, 2009, http://www.thepirateking.com/ships/ship_types.htm.

Jenkins, C. C., A. Duckett, B. A. Boyett, P. N. Glenton, A. A. Mills, M. C. Schapper, J. G. McPherson, and M. A. Williams, 2017, The Jansz-Io gas field, northwest shelf Australia: A giant stratigraphic trap, *in* R. K. Merrill and C. A. Sternbach, eds., Giant fields of the decade 2000–2010: AAPG Memoir 113, p. 305–326.

16

The Jansz-Io Gas Field, Northwest Shelf Australia: A Giant Stratigraphic Trap

C. C. Jenkins, A. Duckett, B. A. Boyett, P. N. Glenton, A. A. Mills, M. C. Schapper, and M. A. Williams

Esso Australia Pty Ltd., 12 Riverside Quay, Southbank, Victoria, Australia 3006 (e-mails: chris.c.jenkins@ exxonmobil.com, ashley.duckett@exxonmobil.com, barbara.a.boyett@exxonmobil.com, peter.n.glenton@ exxonmobil.com, andrew.a.mills@exxonmobil.com, m.c.schapper@exxonmobil.com, michael.a.williams@ exxonmobil.com)

J. G. McPherson

SED&RQ Pty Ltd., Melbourne, Victoria, Australia 3142 (e-mail: john.mcpherson@sednrq.com)

ABSTRACT

The Jansz-Io gas field is located in production licenses WA-36-L, WA-39-L, and WA-40-L within the Carnarvon Basin, northwest shelf, Australia. It is 70 km (43 mi) northwest of the Gorgon gas field, 140 km (87 mi) northwest of Barrow Island, and 250 km (155 mi) from Dampier on the northwest coast of Western Australia. Water depths vary from 1200 to 1400 m (3937 to 4593 ft) across the field.

The Jansz-Io gas field was discovered in 2000 by the Jansz-1 exploration well. A three-dimensional (3-D) seismic survey was acquired in 2004, and a further five wells were drilled between 2000 and 2009 to further delineate the field extent and size and characterize the resource to facilitate progress toward development.

The Jansz-Io hydrocarbon trap extends over 2000 km^2 (772 mi^2) with both structural (faulted anticline) and stratigraphic (reservoir pinch-out) components. The stratigraphic component of the trap is defined by the reservoir extent, which is limited by depositional downlap to the northwest, and erosional truncation by Upper Jurassic and Lower Cretaceous unconformities to the southeast.

The reservoir comprises muddy, bioturbated, predominantly very fine- to fine-grained sandstones deposited in a shallow-marine environment and is divided into two units. The upper wedge reservoir has 25 to 35% total porosity with 10 to 1000 md permeability, and the lower wedge reservoir has 15 to 25% porosity with 0.01 to 10 md permeability. Both reservoir units are expected to contribute gas during production.

The original gas in place (OGIP) for the Jansz-Io Oxfordian reservoir has a probabilistic range from 320 to 946 Gm^3 (11 to 33 tcf), with a P50 value of 632 Gm^3 (22 tcf). The ultimate recovered gas for the field will depend on both the development plan and the reservoir performance over field life. For the current 15-well development plan, the resource estimates range from 201 to 442 Gm^3 (7 to 16 tcf).

DOI:10.1306/13572012M1133708

The Jansz-Io gas field is a key part of the greater Gorgon liquified natural gas (LNG) project and will supply gas to the LNG plant that is being constructed on Barrow Island. The development concept includes subsea completions from three drill centers placed on the seafloor connected to a subsea production pipeline to carry gas to the LNG processing plant.

For the first stage of field development, 10 development wells were successfully drilled and completed during 2012 and 2014. The second drilling campaign is planned to commence after field start-up with the timing dependant on field performance.

INTRODUCTION

The Jansz-Io gas field is located in production licenses WA-36-L, WA-39-L, and WA-40-L within the offshore Carnarvon Basin of Western Australia. It is 70 km (43 mi) northwest of the Gorgon gas field, 140 km (87 mi) northwest of Barrow Island, and 250 km (155 mi) from Dampier on the northwest coast of Western Australia. Water depths vary from 1200 to 1400 m (3937 to 4593 ft) across the field (Figure 1).

The recent discovery of this giant gas field, in a basin considered to be mature from an exploration perspective, has challenged explorers to reconsider exploration strategies in mature basins. The Jansz-Io gas field has a number of geological features that distinguish it from more conventional gas fields in the Carnarvon Basin and, indeed, from many other producing fields around the world. Jansz-Io is a giant gas field in a structural/stratigraphic trap, with a large areal extent and variation across the field from distal lower-shoreface to offshore transition facies (Jenkins et al., 2008, preceding sentences with SPE permission).

The Jansz-Io hydrocarbon trap extends over 2000 km^2 (772 mi^2) with both structural (faulted anticline) and stratigraphic (reservoir pinch-out) components. The structural component of the trap is defined by a northwest–southeast trending faulted anticline (Figure 2). The stratigraphic

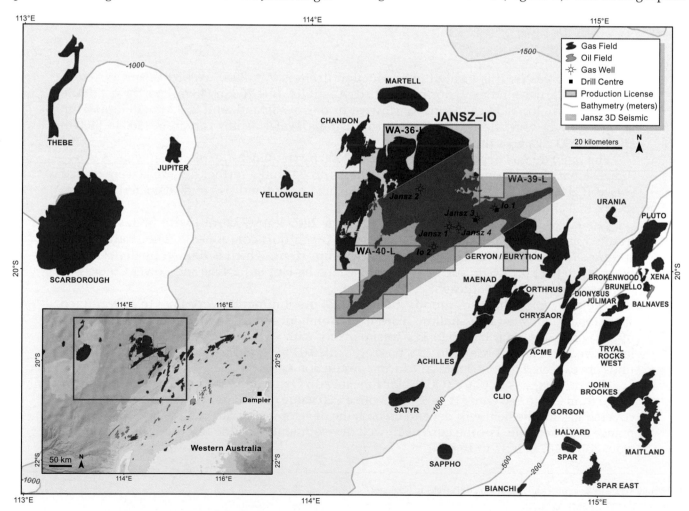

Figure 1. Jansz-Io gas field location. Includes data supplied by IHS, its affiliates and subsidiary companies, and its data partners. Copyright (2015), all rights reserved.

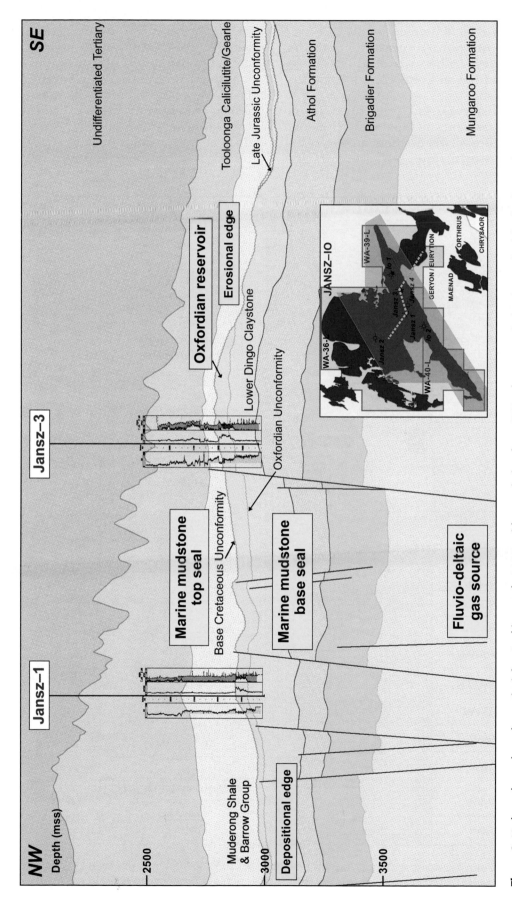

Figure 2. Hydrocarbon play schematic (after Jenkins et al., 2008, with permission from SPE, whose permission is required for further use).

component of the trap is defined by the reservoir extent, which is limited by depositional downlap to the northwest and erosional truncation by Upper Jurassic and Lower Cretaceous unconformities to the southeast.

The Jansz-Io reservoir is Upper Jurassic age (Oxfordian) and was deposited in a shallow-marine environment (Figure 3). While there are many hydrocarbon fields worldwide with reservoirs in a shallow-marine depositional setting, the difference between these fields and Jansz-Io is that the others usually contain hydrocarbons in high-quality, clean sandstones from upper-shoreface and lower-shoreface facies. By contrast, mud-rich offshore facies are the primary reservoir at Jansz-Io, whereas these deposits have low quality and typically have limited to no production in other fields (Jenkins et al., 2008, preceding sentences with SPE permission).

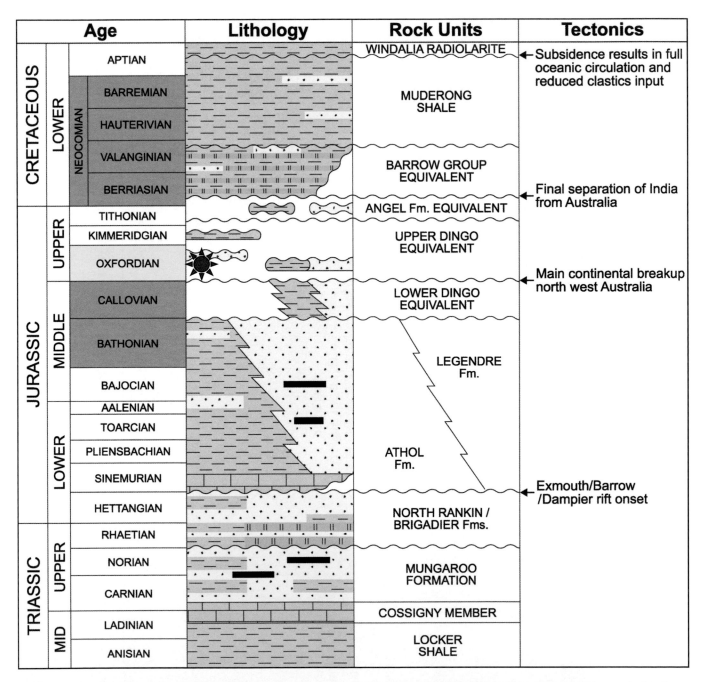

Figure 3. Carnarvon Basin Mesozoic stratigraphy (from Jenkins et al., 2008, with permission from SPE, whose permission is required for further use). The red gas symbol represents the stratigraphic interval for the Jansz-Io gas field.

The reservoir interval was first identified on 2-D seismic data with an apparent direct hydrocarbon indicator (DHI) response. This was confirmed after the discovery well was drilled and a high-quality 3-D survey was acquired. The reservoir unit is mappable on high-quality seismic data and is informally subdivided into the high-quality upper wedge and low-quality lower wedge reservoir units. The separation of these stratigraphic units is based on a seismically defined event designated the base of high permeability seismic marker (Figure 4). The top of porosity seismic marker defines the top of the upper wedge reservoir, and the Oxfordian unconformity marker defines the base of the lower wedge reservoir.

The marine mudstones of the Lower Cretaceous Barrow group and Middle Jurassic lower Dingo equivalent provide the top-seal and base-seal to the reservoir, respectively (Figure 2). The gas source is interpreted to be in the underlying deep gas-mature fluvial-deltaic section of the Upper Triassic Mungaroo Formation (Figure 3). The Jansz-Io gas composition exhibits a high methane content (89 to 94 mol%), with a low condensate yield of 25 m^3/Mm^3 (4.4 bbl /MMSCF) and a low CO_2 content (0.1 to 0.3 mol%).

The Jansz-Io play type contrasts with the nearby gas discoveries at Geryon-1, Urania-1, Orthrus-1, and Maenad-1A (Figure 1), which are fault-dependent structural traps, with gas-bearing sandstones in the fluvial-deltaic reservoir section (Figure 3) of the Mungaroo Formation (Korn et al., 2003).

Jansz-Io is a foundation field for the greater Gorgon LNG project; the other foundation field being Gorgon gas field located 70 km (43 mi) to the southeast. The project is a focus for development activity to meet an expanding global LNG market. The initial development at Jansz-Io has 10 high-angle wells drilled from two drill centers, DC-1 (five wells) located near Jansz-3 and DC-2 (five wells) located near Io-1 (Figure 5).

EXPLORATION HISTORY

The Jansz prospect was delineated with a 3 km × 1.5 km (1.9 × 0.9 mi) line spacing, 2-D seismic grid (Zeus survey), recorded during 1997, and the Jansz-1 discovery well was drilled in 2000 (Figure 1). A second well, Io-1, was drilled during 2001 some 10 km (6 mi) to the northeast of Jansz-1 and intersected the same Oxfordian gas reservoir updip of the discovery well (Jenkins et al., 2003).

The Zeus survey was reprocessed (in part) during 2001 and 2002, prior to the drilling of the Jansz-2 and Jansz-3 appraisal wells in 2002 and 2003, respectively.

The Jansz-2 appraisal well demonstrated the lateral extent of the Oxfordian gas reservoir albeit in a more distal depositional setting. The well also confirmed the use of seismic amplitude versus offset analyses to delineate the field edges (Figure 6). The gas sandstones generally exhibit a prominent far-offset, Class 3 amplitude anomaly according to the classification scheme of Rutherford and Williams (1989). The Jansz-3 appraisal well was located in the core area of the field near the crest of the Jansz-Io structure and produced gas to surface from the cased-hole production test (Figure 4), confirming reservoir deliverability.

The 2892 km^2 (1117 mi^2) Jansz 3-D seismic survey was acquired during 2004 over the core area of Jansz-Io and part of the northern extension of the field (Jansz-2 area), with pre-stack time-migrated processing completed during 2005 (Figure 1). The 2-D and 3-D interpretation has been fully integrated and provides seismic coverage of the Oxfordian gas reservoir. The quality of the 3-D image in the primary development area was improved by anisotropic pre-stack depth migration (APSDM), with a minicube processed during 2006, and the entire seismic volume was reprocessed in 2012.

The Io-2 appraisal well was drilled during 2006 and deepened the lowest known gas (LKG) for the field from −2883 meters subsea (mSS) (−9459 ftSS) in the Jansz-1 well to −2970 mSS (−9744 ftSS). The well indicated that compaction (caused by greater depth of burial) and diagenesis had affected the reservoir quality in the southwest part of the field.

The Jansz-4 appraisal well was drilled during 2009 to confirm the location of the third drill center for the development. The first two drill centers are located near the Jansz-3 and Io-1 appraisal wells. The Jansz-4 well confirmed high-quality gas-bearing sandstones in the upper wedge reservoir and flowed gas to surface during a cased-hole production test of this zone (Figure 4). Dual-packer wireline modular formation dynamics tester (MDT) tests were conducted in low-permeability sandstones of the lower wedge, confirming moveable gas in this zone.

Six exploration/appraisal wells were drilled in the Jansz-Io gas field prior to development, with 260 m (853 ft) of full-hole core cut within the reservoir. All of the wells have comprehensive wireline log suites, including vertical seismic profiling at Io-1, Io-2, Jansz-2, and Jansz-4 and magnetic resonance logs in all wells except Jansz-1.

For the first phase of the Jansz-Io development, 10 wells were successfully drilled at 80° through the reservoir and completed between 2012 and 2014. These wells were fully evaluated using logging while drilling (LWD) technology.

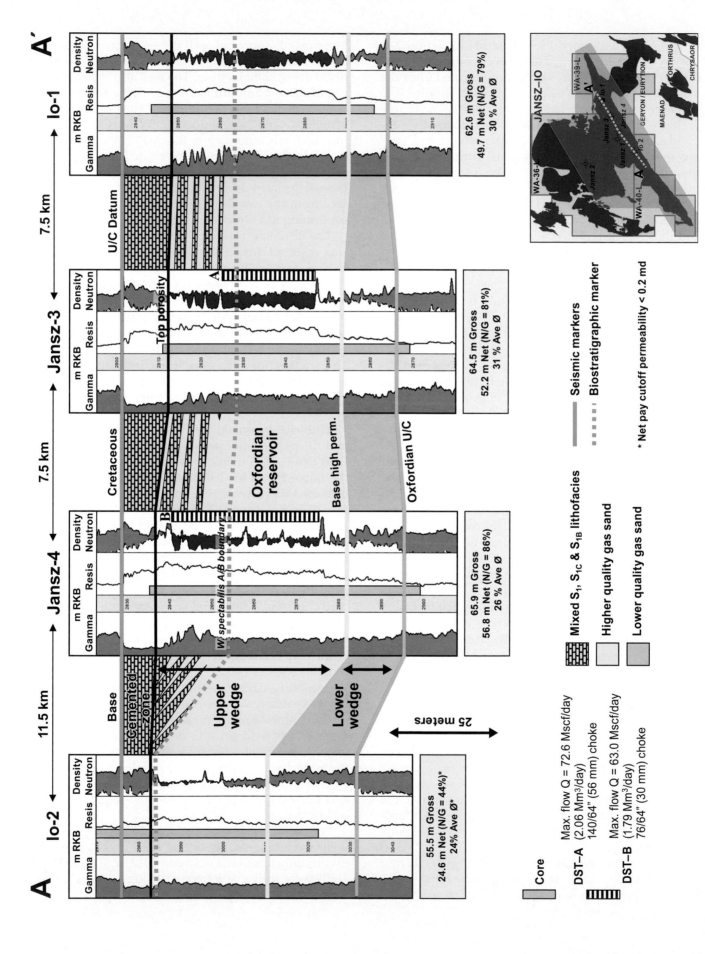

Figure 4. Stratigraphic cross section (after Jenkins et al., 2008, with permission from SPE, whose permission is required for further use). S_1 = medium grained sandstone; S_{1C} has calcite cement; and S_{1B} has berthierine clay.

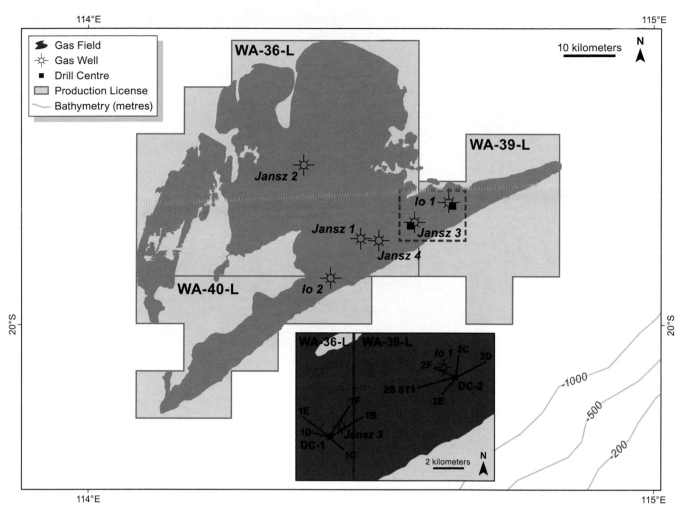

Figure 5. Exploration/delineation wells, drill centers DC-1 and DC-2 (black rectangles), and development well locations. A future drill centre (DC-3) is planned in the vicinity of the Jansz-4 well.

STRUCTURE

The depth structure map at the base-of-Cretaceous unconformity marker (Figure 4) is shown in Figure 7. The Jansz-Io structural feature is a northwest-southeast trending anticline. The Jansz-3 well is close to the structural crest of the field, and the Io-2 well is the most downdip well. The faults are extensional, were initiated by early Jurassic rifting of the Carnarvon Basin, and remained active until the early Cretaceous (Figure 3). The fault throws are up to 25 to 30 m (82 to 98 ft) at the base-of-Cretaceous unconformity marker with fault traces up to 4 km (2 mi) long.

The depth conversion issues at Jansz-Io are described in detail in Jenkins et al. (2008) and relate to the complex overburden, which consists of vertically stacked shelf-slope canyons filled with carbonates (high velocity) and lime-rich mudstones (low velocity). The composition of the sedimentary fill in the canyons varies spatially and temporally, and this causes distortion of seismic ray-paths, leading to artifacts in the seismic velocity field. The artifacts caused depth prognosis errors in the appraisal wells.

By using the depth conversion knowledge gained during the appraisal drilling program, and including an APSDM velocity field with the top of Muderong shale marker (Figure 3) as a geological constraint, a new velocity model was developed with the intent of minimizing depth conversion errors in the development wells. The velocity model proved to be robust, and the 10 development wells were drilled with minimal errors in depth prognosis and reservoir thickness prediction.

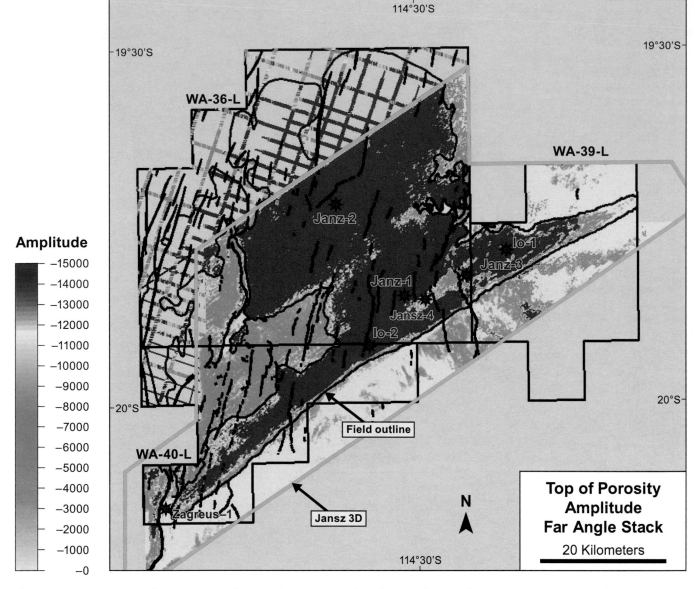

Figure 6. Seismic amplitude response at the top of porosity marker (from Jenkins et al., 2008, with permission from SPE, whose permission is required for further use).

RESERVOIR

The Upper Jurassic Jansz-Io gas-bearing sandstone can be correlated to the *W. spectabilis* dinoflagellate zone of Helby et al. (2004). The sandstone is part of the upper Dingo equivalent lithostratigraphic zone (Barber, 1988) (Figure 3). The reservoir comprises a shallow-marine sequence that prograded to the northwest during the Oxfordian. Erosion of this sequence by the Upper Jurassic and base-of-Cretaceous unconformities removed the coastal plain and most of the shoreface sections, leaving an erosional remnant of the distal lower-shoreface, offshore and open-shelf deposits. The 3-D seismic line (near-angle stack) that ties the Jansz-3 well is shown in Figure 8 with the polarity convention annotated. The base of high permeability marker is at the top of a progradational, parasequence set and dips at a low angle (less than 0.5°) to the northwest. The marker subcrops under the base-of-Cretaceous unconformity, to the southeast of the well. Mapping of the base of high permeability, top of porosity, and Oxfordian unconformity seismic markers has provided a framework for the reservoir. It has been informally subdivided into the upper wedge and lower wedge reservoir zones (Figure 4).

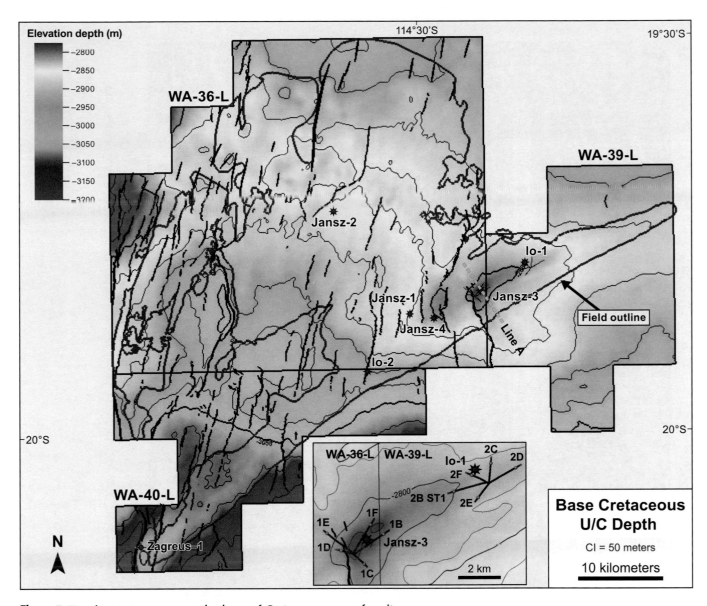

Figure 7. Depth structure map on the base-of-Cretaceous unconformity.

The upper wedge reservoir has a maximum thickness of 50 m (164 ft) and is the primary target for field development (Figure 9). The top of the upper wedge reservoir is defined by the time transgressive top of porosity marker that denotes the base of the pervasive, cemented sandstone zone (Figure 4). The lower wedge reservoir has a maximum thickness of 25 m (82 ft) and underlies the upper wedge reservoir in the core area of the field (Figure 10). A major part of the upper and lower wedge reservoirs has been removed by erosion at the Upper Jurassic and base-of-Cretaceous unconformities.

The primary development area of the field is defined by the 15 m (49 ft) isochore contour surrounding

the Jansz-1, Jansz-3, Jansz-4, Io-1, and Io-2 wells. A reservoir thickness greater than 15 m (49 ft) is generally resolvable on the Jansz 3-D seismic volume, and the seismic isochron can be scaled to an isochore using interval velocities (Figure 9). Outside the primary development area, the isochore is calculated using a detuning algorithm based on the product of seismic amplitude and apparent isochron (Jenkins et al., 2008). This area includes the Jansz-2 well and most of the northwest part of the field, and it typically has a thickness less than 15 m (49 ft).

The Oxfordian shoreline had a northeast–southwest orientation, with the Jansz-3, Jansz-4, Io-1, and Io-2 wells being in a more proximal depositional

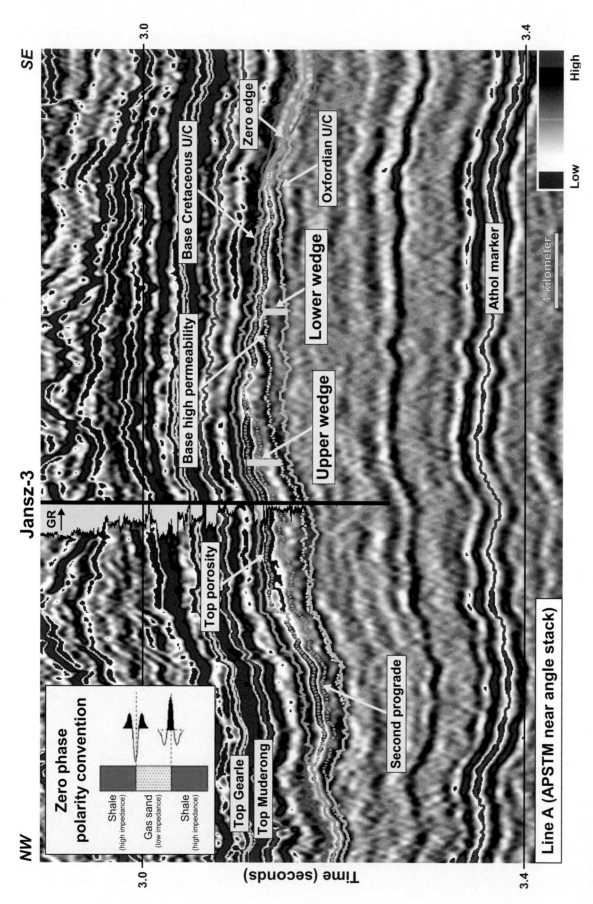

Figure 8. 3-D seismic cross line at the Jansz-3 well (from Jenkins et al., 2008, with permission from SPE, whose permission is required for further use). The line of section (Line A) is shown on the map in Figure 7.

314

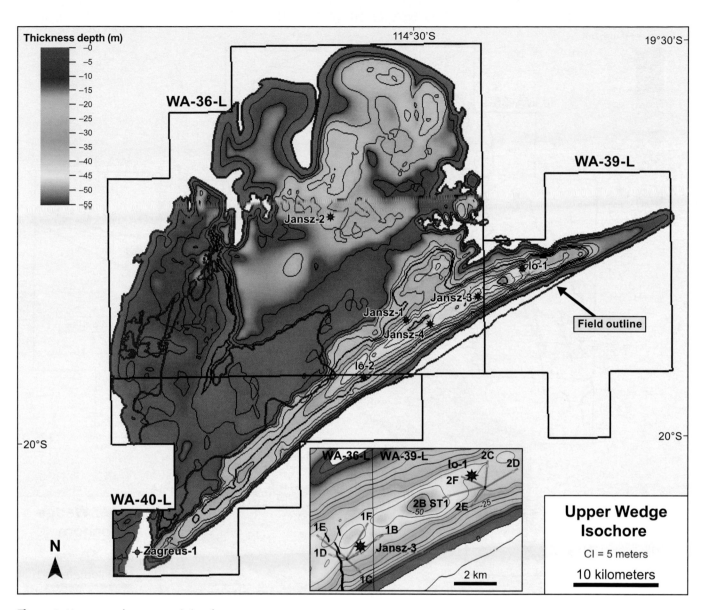

Figure 9. Upper wedge reservoir isochore.

setting than the Jansz-1 and Jansz-2 wells (Figure 11). The reservoir thins to the northwest beyond Jansz-2 and changes facies to siltstones and mudstones of the open shelf. The reservoir is composed of three primary lithofacies types as identified from core data. The highest quality reservoir and principal sands are designated lithofacies S_{42}, fine-grained sandstones with 10 to 25% clay, porosities greater than 25%, and permeabilities from 10 to 1000 md (Figure 12).

A secondary reservoir component is lithofacies S_{43}, very fine-grained sandstones with 20 to 60% clay content, porosities less than 25%, and permeabilities less than 10 md. A minor component includes poorly sorted, medium-grained sandstones of lithofacies S_1.

This lithofacies is commonly cemented and stratigraphically restricted to the top of the Io-1, Io-2, Jansz-3, and Jansz-4 reservoirs (Jenkins et al., 2008).

The lithofacies model has been further validated by the results of the development drilling program. The reservoir section at Drill Center-1 and Drill Center-2 is shown on the cross-sections in Figures 13 and 14, respectively, with the nearest offset well annotated. The log data were recorded by a single LWD tool string as the high-angle wells precluded the use of conventional wireline logging techniques. The depth prognosis, thickness estimates, and reservoir quality are within the predicted predrill range for the development wells.

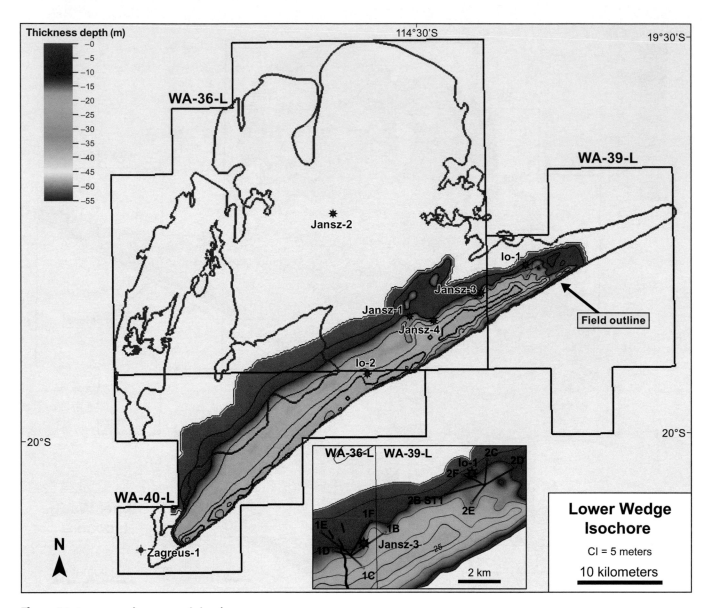

Figure 10. Lower wedge reservoir isochore.

FREE WATER LEVEL

The free water level (FWL) for Jansz-Io is interpreted from wireline MDT pressure data to be at the southwest end of the field at a depth of –3153 mSS (–10,344 ftSS), the aquifer being provided by the normally pressured fluvial-deltaic sandstones of the Mungaroo Formation (Figure 15). The Mungaroo Formation aquifer is juxtaposed with the Oxfordian reservoir across a major tectonic fault. The FWL for the field is more than 20 km (12 mi) from the development area, and water production in the development wells is considered unlikely. The LKG for the field is at –2970 mSS (–9744 ftSS) at the Io-2 well.

DEVELOPMENT OVERVIEW

The field development program includes subsea completions from three drill centers placed on the seafloor in the core development area of the field (Figure 5). A subsea production pipeline, hydrate inhibitor pipeline, and control umbilical connect the field to the LNG processing plant located on Barrow Island, some 140 km (87 mi) to the southeast of Jansz-Io.

Two drilling campaigns are planned. Ten wells were drilled in the first campaign (between 2012 and 2014), to be followed by five wells in the second campaign, the timing being dependent on field performance.

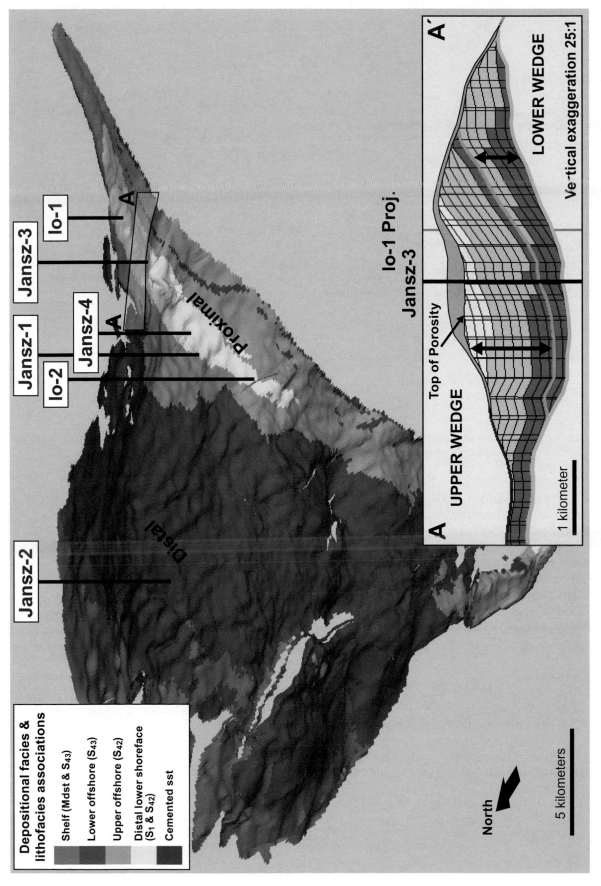

Figure 11. Depositional facies. The map is at the top of porosity and excludes the cemented sandstone (from Jenkins et al., 2008, with permission from SPE, whose permission is required for further use).

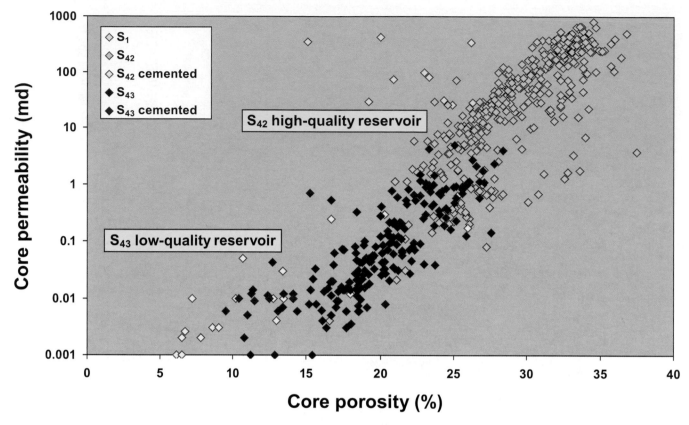

Figure 12. Lithofacies types and reservoir quality measured from core plugs analyzed at overburden conditions (from Jenkins et al., 2008, with permission from SPE, whose permission is required for further use).

The 15 big-bore wells are planned to be high angle (80°) to enhance reservoir productivity, and open-hole gravel pack completions are required for sand control in the Oxfordian reservoir.

Depletion drive is expected to be the primary mechanism for gas production due to limited connectivity with the Mungaroo Formation aquifer, and compression will be required to maximize the production plateau and extend field life up to 50 years.

RESOURCE SIZE

The results of a model-based uncertainty analysis (Jenkins et al., 2008) describe OGIP range, expressed as an exceedance probability plot, in Figure 16. The OGIP for the Jansz-Io Oxfordian reservoir has a probabilistic range from 320 to 946 Gm^3 (11 to 33 tcf), with a p50 value of 632 Gm^3 (22 tcf).

The ultimate recovered gas for the field will depend on both the development plan and reservoir performance. For the current 15-well development plan, the resource estimates range from 201 to 442 Gm^3 (7 to 16 tcf).

CONCLUSIONS

The Jansz-Io gas field is a large gas accumulation in a structural/stratigraphic trap that was discovered in the Carnarvon Basin in 2000, the basin being at a mature stage for large conventional structural hydrocarbon plays. The stratigraphic component of the Jansz-Io trap relates to a combination of erosion of the reservoir by regional unconformities associated with Upper Jurassic rifting and proximal-to-distal facies changes from sandstone to mudstone. The reservoir has been delineated using 2-D and 3-D seismic surveys to map the bounding surfaces with the edges of the field defined by a prominent seismic amplitude anomaly on far offset stacks.

The reservoir was deposited in a shallow-marine environment, but the upper-shoreface and most of the lower-shoreface section have been removed due to uplift and erosion during the Upper Jurassic, leaving the muddy sandstones of the distal lower-shoreface and offshore zones. Although these are lower quality facies, the shallow burial depth of the reservoir has preserved primary porosity and permeability in the muddy sandstones.

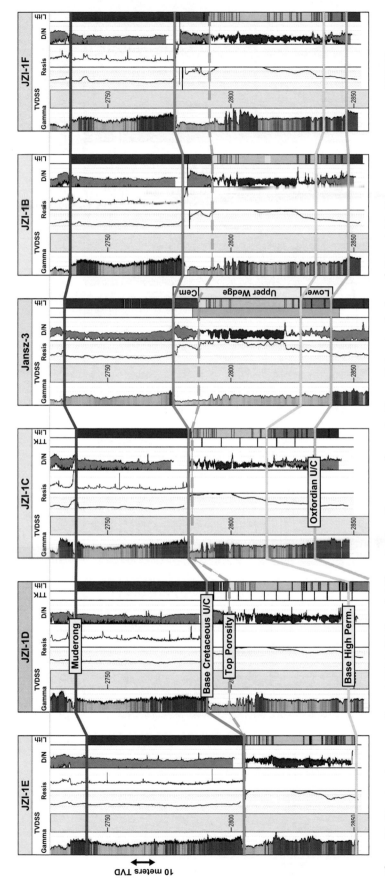

Figure 13. Structural cross section at DC-1. Well and drill center locations are shown in Figure 5. Log tracks from left to right: Gamma = gamma ray; TVDSS = true vertical depth from mean sea level datum; Resistivity; D/N = density/neutron; TTK = formation pressure; Cyan bar = core interval; Lith = lithology.

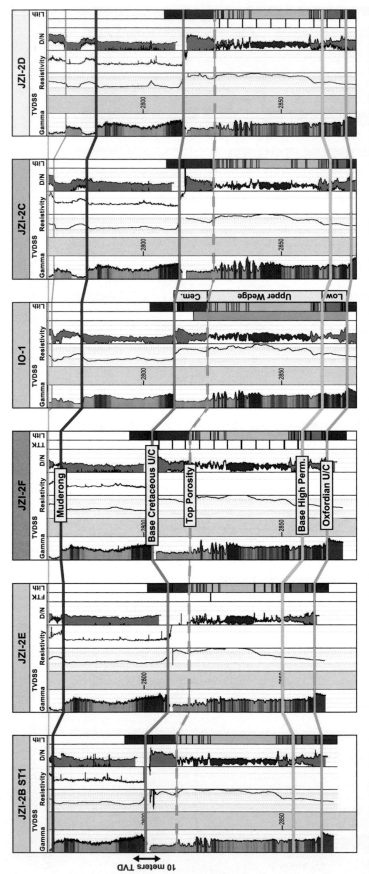

Figure 14. Structural cross section at DC-2. Well and drill center locations are shown in Figure 5. Log tracks from left to right: Gamma = gamma ray; TVDSS = true vertical depth from mean sea level datum; TTK = formation pressure; Resistivity, D/N = density/neutron; FTK = gas sample and formation pressure; Cyan bar = core interval; Lith = lithology.

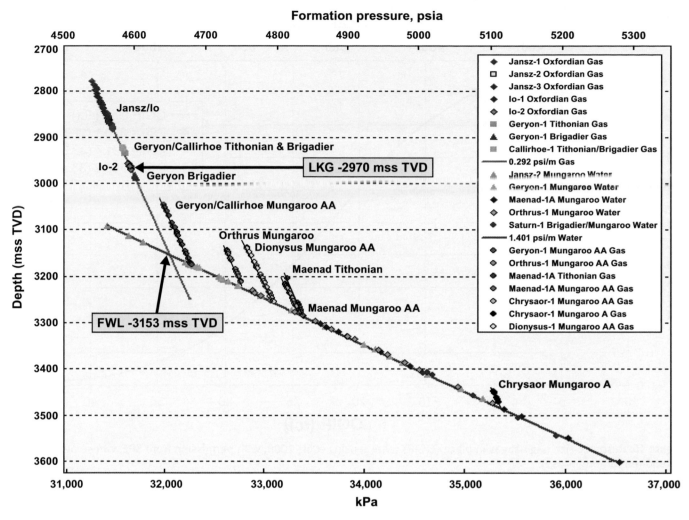

Figure 15. Jansz-Io fluid contacts. Depth is true vertical measured from mean sea level datum (from Jenkins et al., 2008, with permission from SPE, whose permission is required for further use).

The resource description and uncertainty analyses indicate the Jansz-Io gas field is a giant gas accumulation that will provide feedstock to produce LNG for the greater Gorgon LNG development. The first phase of the field development has been executed with 10 development wells successfully drilled at 75 to 80° through the reservoir. The wells have been completed with open-hole gravel packs and connected to the subsea in-field facilities and flowline.

ACKNOWLEDGMENTS

The authors wish to thank the Jansz-Io Unit in WA-36-L, WA39-L, and WA-40-L; ExxonMobil (25%), Chevron (47.333%), Shell (19.625%), BP (5.375%), Tokyo Gas (1%), Osaka Gas (1.25%), and Chubu Electric (0.417%) for permission to publish this chapter.

The views expressed in this chapter reflect those of the authors and are not necessarily the views of the respective unit participants. The authors acknowledge the Society of Petroleum Engineers (SPE) for permission to use some previously published figures and text (SPE copyright) in this manuscript. They especially thank Jane Quinn and Henryk Wojcik for their assistance with graphics work.

REFERENCES CITED

Barber, P., 1988, The Exmouth plateau deep water frontier: A case history, in P. Purcell, R. Purcell, eds., The North West Shelf Symposium Proceedings, PESA, p. 173–187.

Helby, R., R. Morgan, and A. Partridge, 2004, Updated Jurassic-early Cretaceous dinocyst zonation, NWS Australia: Geoscience Australia publication, accessed January 18, 2016, https://www.ga.gov.au/image_cache/GA5635.pdf.

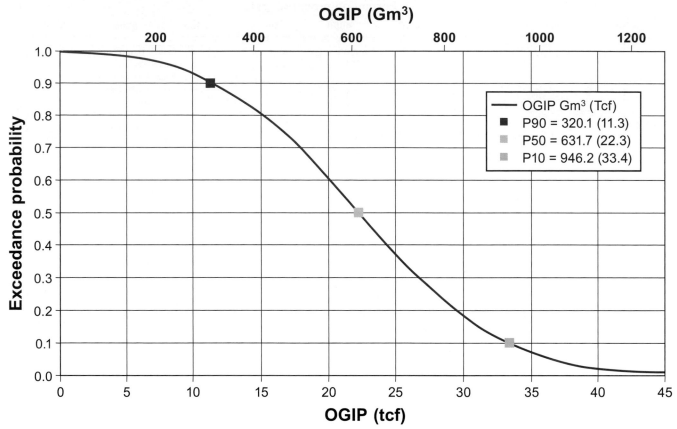

Figure 16. Resource size original gas in place (OGIP) (after Jenkins et al., 2008, with permission from SPE, whose permission is required for further use).

Jenkins, C. C., R. M. Chiquito, P. N. Glenton, A. A. Mills, J. McPherson, M. C. Schapper, and M. A. Williams, 2008, Reservoir definition at the Jansz/Io gas field, NW shelf, Australia: A case study of an integrated project from exploration to development: International Petroleum Technology Conference, Kuala Lumpur, Malaysia, Proceedings, IPTC-12461-PP, accessed January 18, 2016, https://www.onepetro.org/conferences/IPTC/08IPTC.

Jenkins, C., D. Maughan, J. Acton, A. Duckett, B. Korn, and R. Teakle, 2003, The Jansz gas field, Carnarvon basin, Australia: APPEA Journal, v. 43, no. 1, p. 303–324.

Korn, B., R. Teakle, D. Maughan, and P. Siffleet, 2003, The Geryon, Orthrus, Maenad and Urania gas fields, Carnarvon basin, Western Australia: APPEA Journal, v. 43, no. 1, p. 285–301.

Rutherford, S., and R. Williams, 1989, Amplitude versus offset variations in gas sands: Geophysics, v. 54, p. 680–688.